COUNTY REPORTS
To The
BOARD OF AGRICULTURE

THE REVIEW AND ABSTRACT

of the

COUNTY REPORTS

to the

BOARD OF AGRICULTURE

Vol. 3. Eastern Department

by

WILLIAM MARSHALL

DAVID & CHARLES REPRINTS

7153 4367 X

This edition first
published 1811

Printed in Great Britain by
Clarke, Doble & Brendon Ltd Plymouth
Published by David & Charles (Holdings) Limited
South Devon House Railway Station Newton Abbot

THE

REVIEW and ABSTRACT

OF THE

COUNTY REPORTS

TO THE

BOARD OF AGRICULTURE;

FROM THE SEVERAL

AGRICULTURAL DEPARTMENTS OF ENGLAND.

By Mr. MARSHALL.

~~~~~~~~~~~~~~~

IN FIVE VOLUMES.

~~~~~~~~~~~~~~~

VOLUME THE THIRD,

(Which was first Published, in 1811, and is now combined with the other
Volumes of the same Work;)

Comprizing those from the

EASTERN DEPARTMENT.

Which includes

LINCOLNSHIRE, SUFFOLK, AND
NORFOLK,   NORTHEAST ESSEX;

WITH THE MARSHES AND FENS OF

YORKSHIRE,   HUNTINGDONSHIRE,
NORTH LINCOLNSHIRE CAMBRIDGESHIRE,
SOUTH LINCOLNSHIRE, NORFOLK, AND
NORTHAMPTONSHIRE, SUFFOLK.

York:

Printed by Thomas Wilson & Sons,

FOR LONGMAN, HURST, REES, ORME, AND BROWN, LONDON; CONSTABLE,
AND CO. EDINBURGH; AND WILSON AND SONS, YORK.

1818.

THE

C O N T E N T S,

SYSTEMATICALLY ARRANGED.

Waters.

Drinking

October, 1811.

THE

EASTERN DEPARTMENT*

OF

ENGLAND.

In an INTRODUCTION to the NORTHERN DEPARTMENT
of England (recently published) I noticed, at some
length, the Origin and Progress of the Board of
Agriculture;—
Described the Plan and Execution of the *original*
Reports; also the Plan of the *reprinted* Reports;—
Defined the requisite *qualifications* of a *Reporter*;—
Explained my Plan of Reviewing them, by DEPART-
MENTS;—and sketched the Outlines and Characteristics
of the six *Agricultural* Departments, into which Eng-
land aptly separates.

The EASTERN DEPARTMENT is thus distinguished:—
'It is marked by its FENS and MARSHES; as well as by the
light SANDY quality of its UPLANDS : joint natural qualities that belong to no other extensive division of the
kingdom.

The

---

* In an Advertisement prefixed to the REVIEW of the REPORTS
from the WESTERN DEPARTMENT, I apprized my readers of the
sort of necessity which I was under of relinquishing my original
intention of pursuing the agricultural Departments of England,
geographically;—and I here copy the notice there given.
N. p. xxi. 'Of the twelve Counties, which come within the
MIDLAND DEPARTMENT, only six ' reprinted Reports,' as they
are falsely termed, (see pages 298 and 420 of this volume,) have
yet made their appearance; or, judging from those dilatory and
mysterious goings on, are likely soon to appear. I am, therefore,
constrained to relinquish the natural line of procedure—the
geographical order of succession—and to enter, next, on a REVIEW
of the REPORTS from the EASTERN DEPARTMENT.'

'The agricultural pursuits of this Department are directed, in a singular manner, to GRAZING,—to the fatting of cattle and sheep :—not only in the marshes and lower grounds ; but on the uplands; on which the TURNEP HUSBANDRY has long been, and until of later years exclusively, practised.'

Such is its general Characteristic. The few passages of cold lands, unfit for the turnep husbandry, to be found within the Outlines of the Department, are too inconsiderable to alter its general character.

This AGRICULTURAL DEPARTMENT of the kingdom includes a small portion of *Yorkshire* (namely the marshes and fens, that are situated at the southern base of the Vale of York, and which are inseparably united with lands of the same general nature, that are included within the political limits of Lincolnshire *)— nearly the whole of *Lincolnshire* † ;—the entire counties of *Norfolk* and *Suffolk :*—the northeastern part of *Essex,* —as far as the estuary and valley of the Blackwater‡;— the fens, marshes, and insulated upper grounds of *Cambridgeshire, Huntingdonshire* and *Northampton- shire;* which, uniting with similar lands in Lincoln- shire, Norfolk and Suffolk, compose one immense tract of waterformed lands, which, even to this day, are kept free from the waters that gave birth to them, by the art, industry, and incessant attentions of man ; the whole being preserved in the state of *land,* by ex- tensive systems of embankment and drainage. All the other

* From the Island of Axholm, which rises, prominently among these lands, they are viewed as in a map,—and as one naturally indivisible whole.

† The southwestern margin of Lincolnshire naturally and agriculturally assimilates with the Midland Counties ;—forms a part of the MIDLAND DEPARTMENT.

‡ ESSEX.—The more southern parts of Essex come, agriculturally considered, within the vortex of the metropolis ; and, by natural situation, belong to the SOUTHERN DEPARTMENT. While the NORTHEASTERN quarter,—whether in surface, soils, or manage- ment,—may well be considered as an extension of SUFFOLK. At the valley of Bocking, the comparatively flat, vale-like lands of Suffolk,—the Suffolk breed of cows,—and the Suffolk (other- wise Norfolk) breed of sheep,—may be said to prevail and termi- nate. Westward of that line, the surface breaks into hill and dale, —the longhorned breed of cows,—and mongrel sheep,—are seen ; and cold, summerfallowed lands take place.

other waterformed lands of the kingdom are as detached parts, when compared with this main body;—this widely spreading *natural District** ; which is, entirely, and most aptly, included in the EASTERN DEPARTMENT.

The REPORTS which relate, wholely or in part, to this Department, are the following; namely,

WEST RIDING of Yorkshire; by Brown and others.

LINCOLNSHIRE; by Stone; also by the Secretary of the Board.

NORTHAMPTONSHIRE; by Donaldson.

HUNTINGDONSHIRE; by Stone; also by Maxwell.

CAMBRIDGESHIRE; by Vancouver.

NORFOLK; by Kent; also by the Secretary.

SUFFOLK; by the Secretary.

ESSEX; by Greggs; also by Vancouver; also by Howlet and the Secretary.

* This one, and naturally indivisible, District (a well-sized County in extent) requires six *County Reports* to treat of it; and, eight or ten separate volumes to be studied, before the whole of the information, contained in the Reports to the Board of Agriculture concerning it, can be collected.

YORKSHIRE.

YORKSHIRE.

REGARDING the small portion of this County which inseparably belongs to the Agricultural Department of the kingdom, now under consideration, we find very little information, in the Reports to the Board of Agriculture. This little appears in the Report from the WEST RIDING.

What relates to the subject of ALLUVIATION, or "Warping," I inserted in the Review concerning the NORTHERN DEPARTMENT; it being a subject of too high importance to admit of delay, in bringing it before the Public; and I was not aware, at the time of publishing that volume, that I should so soon have occasion to speak of the EASTERN DEPARTMENT.—See note, p. 1.

The few notices relating to the NATURAL ECONOMY, and STATE of HUSBANDRY, of this recluse District, occur in the Reporter's Journal, in travelling between Doncaster and Snaith, by Hatfield and Thorne.

WEST RIDING REPORT.—Appendix, P. 37. "From Doncaster, eastward to Thorne, the land is capable of greater improvement than any we have seen in Yorkshire. There is a great deal of common field, superior in quality to most land: and there is, also, large tracts of waste. At Hatfield there are very large common fields, the rotation upon which is turneps, barley, clover, wheat, and barley; and one of the fields not ploughed; but kept in meadow grass."

"Betwixt Hatfield and Thorne, there are great quantities of waste land, and much under water. Upon the whole, the land we have seen this day stands in the greatest need of improvement; which cannot be done, without a previous division."

P. 38. "Left Thorne, and proceeded, northward, to Snaith. The greatest part of the land till we came within two miles of that place, is exceeding wet, and large

large tracts little better than in a state of nature*. The land, though wet and marshy, is generally rich strong soil. Ridges much straighter ploughed than is genetally the case over the West Riding; but kept by far too narrow and flat. As we approached Snaith, the soil turned as fine, as could be wished. Great quanrities of Turneps and those of good quality.

"Snaith is a small Market Town, situated upon the river Aire; not far from its conjunction with the Don. The land round the place is of exceeding rich quality."

In passing through this interesting District, from Gainsborough, by the way of Haxey and Epworth (in the Isle of Axholm) Sandtoft and Thorne to Howden (in a Journey of Observation that will be particularly mentioned) I took, among others, the following notices.

Gainsborough to Epworth.

14, *July*, 1810.

Cross the Trent, at Gainsborough (to avoid the ferry at Morton) and pass over a wide flat of rich meadows and grazing grounds.

Reach the rising grounds,—the *natural lands*, of Nottinghamshire;—charming upper grounds.—Pass through Beckingham and Walkeringham, and wind round, toward the Trent.

Reach the Trent, at Stockworth, (a river port) and cross the Bawtry canal; and the river Idle, highly embanked.

The elevation, here, is inconsiderable; the soil good; and the crops of wheat, flax, and potatoes large. All in a state of modern inclosure; with much grass land.

Enter a flat of still lower land. The soil blackish;—moor mixed with sand. The road across it somewhat raised; with a drain along the side of it.

Cross an embanked main drain, through swampy grounds.

Still

---

*Either this must be a mistake; or some extraordinary improvements have recently taken place; or the Reporters had viewed this passage in a very wet season.

Still low land and recent inclosure. Some sod burning. Much rye; and ley ground. The taller herbage of the latter—chiefly soft grass—Holcus lanatus.

Cross another embanked drain.

Approach the church and windmill of Haxey, on a bold rising ground;—the Isle of Axholm.

Pass a hamlet situated on the sandy flat; and a large farmstead; rising somewhat above the general level.

Pass through the large village of Haxey;—mount the proud height; and enter a wide-spreading common field of rich land,—heavily laden with *mixed crops!*—wheat, barley, beans, much flax, a little hemp, many potatoes, some clover, and some fallow.

Extraordinary fine crops! yet all of them standing, after much heavy rain! Quere, has the previous dry weather given peculiar firmness to the straw?

A wide-spread waterformed flat is seen, on the left,—toward Hatfield.

The soil of this quarter of the Island (the south west) is highly colored,—some parts approaching to redness,—uniformly fertile. The whole open; except around villages.

Cross a dip, and rise the fine eminence of Epworth, —situated near the center of the island, and overlooking, it may be said, the entire level of marsh and fen lands, that are incident to the Humber and its branches.

15, *July*, 1810.

Rode to the fens, on the east, or Trent, side of the island to see the operation of "Warping;"—of which, in its place.

EPWORTH to THORNE.

LEAVE Epworth (a small Market Town) by a gradual descent toward the west.

Skirt a common field of many crops (rich and beautiful,) surmounted by wind mills. The soil reddish; the crops large and clean; exemplary feudal husbandry.—Much flax and hemp observable.

Pass down a straggling street, a mile in length, and enter on a flat sandy passage, similar to that crossed at the south end of the island. All modern inclosure. The crops chiefly rye, potatoes, and *flax* (on this moory land!)

Cross

Cross a large embanked drain; accompanied by a catch-water sewer.

Still a dead-looking sandy soil. Yet meslin and flax.

Cross another drain; and appear to enter upon a somewhat higher ground. But still heavy sandy road : and the substratum (seen in a pit) a depth of sand.

Much lime in heaps, on fallow :—the first seen in travelling five hundred miles.

Some sheep and young cattle, in ley grounds;—the only stock observed, since entering the flat!

Still recent inclosure.

Continue to rise (if the eye does not deceive) a gentle ascent of sandy land.

Good rye. Quere, after limed fallow? And still large fields of flax!—and mostly good, for the season.

Pass Sandtoft Grove :—a house embosomed in trees.

Turn northward, on a raised drain-bank-road.

Still rye lands appear on the left. On the right, an extent of rushy pastures, very thinly stocked :—horses and a few sheep. The ground, apparently, has former-ly been under the plough.

Reach better land, and good wheat.

Cross the "Old Dun,"—highly embanked; and enter YORKSHIRE.

Turn, westward, on a good gravel road : that between Doncaster and Barton.

Now, charming crops of corn and flax.

Fields of rape, ripening.

Good short-horned cattle.

Still lime on fallow.

Heaps of bog-wood, on fallow ground; as stone heaps are seen on stony lands;—dug out of the sub-stratum (an ordinary sight in the fens of Cambridge-shire, &c.) see one fence made, and another making, with the larger roots, placed in close array :—a ragged, tolerable fence :—a proof, this, of the fenny nature of the land. Yet the substratum, here, would seem (from the slight views caught of it) to be of a brownish colour.—Quere, moory mold mixed with natural warp?

Charming crops of corn :—yet still water fences pre-vail; though marks of oldish modern inclosure are observable.

Still in an extended flat of rich soil, and good arable crops.

Many cattle seen on the left.

Still

Still pale, silt-like soil, highly fertile :—the wheat crops, here, are unable to stand.

Leave the high road; and turn north-west-ward, towards Thorne.

A field of beans :—the first from the Isle of Axholm. —Quere, is the whole flat covered with alluvion, natural warpe? The first, deposit *sand*,—the next, *silt*,—the farthest from the source, *silty clay?* But this by the way. Much study on the spot, examined as a whole, would be required to determine this interesting, though not very important point*.

Still among embanked drains; and doubtlessly still on water-formed lands.

A flag-path (for horses and foot passengers) by the side of the road again (an ordinary accompaniment through the Island of Axholm :) a proof of the strength and retentiveness of the soil.

Cross a canal; and pass a well herbaged common.

Old inclosure and hedge trees, about Thorne.

THORNE to HOWDEN.

(In continuation.)

Pass a common field, on the right.

Mount a raised road; and cross a well soiled, well herbaged, common pasture.

Touch on a bend of the river Don.

Now, a wider common,—stocked with horses, young cattle, and small, poled, white-faced sheep.

Enter between an extent of level inclosures, and hedge trees:—much fine timber.

Reach another wide common ; similar to the foregoing †.

Re-enter inclosures.—Still a sea-like flat; apparently, all waterformed. The soil, in appearance, natural warp:—very similar to the artificial warp examined below Epworth.

Recover, and keep, the immediate bank of the Don.
                                                    Heavy

---

* The NATURE of ALLUVION will be fully spoken of, in the course of this volume.

† These commons, probably, were covered with water, when the West Riding Reporters travelled this road. See the last note.

Heavy crops, on both sides of it.

Cross Newbridge, and the "Dutch River:" an extraordinary work. Mast vessels lying below the Bridge.

Still silt-like land :—level and fertile.

Pass Rawcliffe and its port, on the Aire.

Leave the river.

Still a rich flat of country :—old inclosure and hedge timber.

Much flax, at present, in this quarter.

Continue in a sea of rich flat land.

Now, rye ; quere, lighter soil?

Now beans, and a plot of cold woodland. Quere, *natural* ground (not waterformed) though the rise is barely perceptible ?

Pass Armin ;—another large village, and port, on the Aire.

Leave that river. Still a rich level country.

Extensive crops of potatoes seen, at present, in this passage.

A herd of good milk cows :—almost the only stock *observed,* in this stage ! unless, on the commons.

Cross the Ouse, at Booth Ferry.

Land on a still richer shore! The environs of Howden are not only rich, but almost beautiful (finely wooded, and a stately ruin;) though to the eye of the traveller, they are barely, if quite, out of the way of spring tides, and land floods.

GENERAL REMARKS.—The line of country travelled over, from the western bank of the Old Dun, to Howden, may, from present appearances, be fairly ranked among the most fertile passages of country in the island. In uniform productiveness, this year, (the commons and the plot above noticed excepted, a comparatively inconsiderable portion) as well as in surface, soil, and other circumstances, it much resembles the best lands of South Lincolnshire ;—in the neighbourhoods of Boston, Spalding, Long Sutton, and Wisbeach ; and, like those, the surface soil, at least, pretty evidently owes its existence to alluvion.

FURTHER information concerning the MUD-LANDS and MORASSES of NORTH LINCOLNSHIRE, &c. will be brought out, in abstracting the REPORTS to the BOARD, from that County.

LINCOLN-

LINCOLNSHIRE.

This County is strongly featured; and not inaptly resolves into Natural Districts.

Viewing it, geographically, the *first* that presents itself belongs to the waterformed lands (including the Island of Axholm) described aforegoing. These I will term the North Water-Lands * of the Eastern Department.

The *second* natural division of Lincolnshire, is the Trent-side District; which is formed of the cold vale lands, situated between the banks of the Trent and the Stone Hills, or uplands, that stretch *northward* from *Lincoln* toward the Humber; and which form the *third* natural division of the county.

The *fourth* I will denominate, the Vale of Raisin. It is composed of the vale lands that lie between the uplands, last mentioned, and the Chalk Hills, or "Wolds" of Lincolnshire; which reach from the banks of the Humber to the southern fens and marshes. These chalky Downs give the *fifth* division of the county.

The *sixth* is the Seacoast District,—situated between the Wolds and the British Ocean; and is composed, jointly, of vale and marsh lands†.

The

---

* The term Water-Lands may be deemed a solecism. But when it represents lands that have not only been formed by water, but are liable to be annihilated, and their place reoccupied, by the same element,—it surely is allowable as a technical term, to convey a joint idea of " Fens" and " Marshes,"—of *Mudlands*, and *Morasses ;*—than which, no two species of lands, are less alike ;—though, in most instances, they are so intimately blended, as not to be separable into distinct districts. Neither the term *Embanked Lands*,—*Drained Lands*,—nor even *Waterformed Lands*, (which I have hitherto used) would be equally *terse* and appropriate, for the purpose here required. *Lowlands* would be altogether indefinite and improper.

† This cannot be strictly termed a *natural* district, either in regard to *soil*, or *surface*. But the two descriptions of land which form it, being intimately united, and withal only narrow, it is, in

this

The *seventh* natural division of the lands of Lincolnshire lies on its southwestern skirts;—being, inseparably, a natural and agricultural portion of the MIDLAND
DEPARTMENT.

What was, formerly, " LINCOLN HEATH" (and still
bears that *name*, which, though now improper, I will
not change, as it is at present the popular appellation)
but which is become, in part at least, *an appropriated
waste!* next succeeds, as the *eighth* division.

The *ninth,*—the DISTRICT of SLEAFORD,—consists of
a line of vale lands, which lie between the " Heath,"
and the SOUTH WATERLANDS of Lincolnshire; which
form the *tenth,* and largest natural division of the
county; and which, uniting with the Waterlands of
Cambridgeshire, &c. contribute a principal share
toward the immense tract of waterformed lands,
spoken of in p. 2, aforegoing.

MY OWN KNOWLEDGE of Lincolnshire is less extensive, than it is of many other counties. It is, notwithstanding, I believe, sufficiently comprehensive to
enable me to separate its territory, (as aforegoing)
with the required degree of perspicuity, into UPLANDS,
VALE, and WATERFORMED LANDS *; and to convey to
my readers an adequate idea of the relative situation
of the several districts, or separate passages, that are
comprized within its limits.

My first view of the County took place, in 1782, in
travelling between Norfolk and Yorkshire;—by the
way of *Wisbeach, Spalding, Sleaford, Lincoln, Glanford
Bridge* and *Barton.*

My next, in 1791, was from *Barton,* by *Lincoln* and
Sleaford, to *Market Deeping.*

The southwestern margin has long been familiar to
me.

In June and July last, (1810) I took a JOURNEY of
EXAMINATION (several hundred miles in length, and
with due deliberation for the purpose intended) through
the EASTERN DEPARTMENT :—in order the more accurately to determine its NATURAL and AGRICULTURAL
OUTLINES :

this general view of the County, unnecessary to separate them,
especially, as, by *situation* and *occupancy,* they not inaptly form
one of its *agricultural* divisions.

* See my description, and sketch map, of the lands of YORK-
SHIRE,—in the RURAL ECONOMY of that County.

OUTLINES: and to assist me in separating it, with sufficient intelligence, into DISTRICTS:—as well as to enable me, by the help of written evidence, taken on the spot, to appreciate, with better judgement, the several REPORTS that have been given of it*.

My route, in going southward, through the *eastern* part of Lincolnshire, was *Barton, Caistor, Louth*, (from whence I made a short excursion into the *seacoast district,) Spilsby, Boston, Spalding, Long Sutton*, to *Wisbeach*. In returning, I entered the county at *Crowland*, and traced its *western* side, by *Deeping, Bourn, Folkingham, Sleaford, Lincoln, Spittal Inn*, (on the stoney uplands north of Lincoln,) *Gainsborough* and *Epworth*, to Thorne in Yorkshire.

See

* TRAVELLING INFORMATION.—In this, as in almost numberless other journies, taken with similar intentions (see WEST of ENGLAND for specimens) my practice has ever been to travel, in a carriage, with a blank tablet and pencil in hand ; to secure, *while under the eye*, the natural and agricultural facts that will ever present themselves to an experienced and inquisitive traveller : and, immediately at the end of each stage, with the face of the country, and its agricultural productions, still fresh, in the mind's eye, to bring to the recollection additional facts of minor importance, or of a more general and ordinary nature; so as not to be the immediate objects of the *pencil*,—by the help of a TABLET of RECOLLECTION, laid before me ;—namely, a methodized list of objects, more particularly to be attended to, in the given journey. My Tablet on this occasion was formed of the following particulars.

Boundaries of Department	Road Team
Natural Districts	Plow Team
Elevation	Implements
Surface	Manures
Climature	Tillage
Waters	Semination
Soils	Arable Crops
Substrata	Grass Lands
Appropriation	Grazing Grounds
Embankment	Orchards
Drainage	Horses
Inland Navigation	Cows
Roads	Rearing Cattle
Markets	Fatting Cattle
Woodlands	Sheep
Plantations	Rabbits
Farms	Swine
Fences and Gates	Poultry
Buildings	Decoys
Cottages	Bees
Occupiers	State of Husbandry
Labourers	Improvements

See an abridgement of part of these notices, afore-going.

Two distinct REPORTS of Lincolnshire have been sent into the BOARD of AGRICULTURE : the first by Mr. STONE ; the other, by the SECRETARY of the BOARD.

" GENERAL VIEW

OF THE

AGRICULTURE

OF THE

COUNTY OF LINCOLN,

WITH

OBSERVATIONS ON THE MEANS OF ITS IMPROVEMENT.

BY THOMAS STONE,

LAND-SURVEYOR, GRAY'S-INN, LONDON.

DRAWN UP FOR THE CONSIDERATION OF THE

BOARD OF AGRICULTURE AND INTERNAL IMPROVEMENT.

1794."

THIS is one of the ORIGINAL REPORTS (that have not yet been reprinted) which were delivered to the Board, presently after its establishment. These Reports were printed in octavo pages, on quarto paper,—of course, with wide margins—to receive " additional remarks and observations :"—a judicious plan, which, had it been followed up, and duly executed, would have been creditable to the Board, and beneficial to the Public *.

The

* These ORIGINAL REPORTS were mostly made, gratuitously; and were not intended for publication, *in the original form ;* but were distributed, gratis, to the members of the Board, and among gentlemen and others, in the several counties to which they particularly relate. Some remaining copies, however, were adver-tised (by GEORGE ROBINSON, the Bookseller) for sale. But few of them, I understood, were sold. Hence they may be said to be unknown to the public at large.

The

The REPORTER'S QUALIFICATIONS, for the part he undertook, is seen in the title page, above transcribed, and his performance does credit to his profession; in which Mr. STONE would seem to have had considerable practice, within, and in the neighbourhood of, the County of Lincoln.

With the subject of EMBANKMENT and DRAINAGE,— a subject of the first importance in that county,—Mr. S. is particularly conversant. On that of the APPROPRIATION of TERRITORY, he appears to have had considerable experience: and, on the GENERAL MANAGEMENT of LANDED PROPERTY, he, in the nature of his profession, possessed considerable information. But, out of his profession, we can seldom follow Mr. Stone, with safety. He possesses, it is true, that sort of *general* knowledge of AGRICULTURE which men of his profession necessarily imbibe; and who are naturally led by it to consider the *improvements* of which an Estate is capable, rather than to study, in detail, the *business* of *practical husbandry*. Mr. Stone, however, informs us, in a note, page 86, that he " was bred up a Farmer in the eastern part of Norfolk." If to these recommendations be added the circumstance of the late

The REVIEWING of these Reports has been deemed scarcely fair;—not by their Editor, only; but by a tribunal whose decisions are entitled to much higher consideration. It cannot, therefore, be improper to make a few remarks, on the subject, here.

Had I criticised these Reports, with any degree of *severity* or *minuteness*, I should, indeed, have been blameable. But I recollect not an instance in which this has been the case. I have, it is true, pointed out some absurdities, and many errors, that are capable of leading the inexperienced, who are in possession of those Reports, to acts of impropriety; and I may, moreover, have exposed to public view, the piles of rubbish of which *some* of those Reports, principally consist; and which certainly, ought not to have been *put into print*;—even though the cost and labour of printing them were to be paid for by the public.

Whatever merit or demerit I may have as a *criticiser* of the original Reports, I cannot believe that I am erring while I *extract* the useful information which many of them contain. The " Reprinted Reports" *may* be had by the public at large; but the unpublished ones *cannot*; although some which never have been, nor in much probability ever will be, brought before the public, are much more estimable than what are now selling under the *name* of " Reprinted Reports." DAVIS's WILTSHIRE,—WEDGE's CHESHIRE, and STONE's LINCOLNSHIRE, are sufficient evidences of this truth.

late Duke of Bedford's engaging Mr. S. as a principal acting manager of his Estates,—it were difficult to point out many of the Board's Reporters who have equal claim to public attention. And how unpardonable it would have been, in me, to have suffered his work to be lost to the Public.—See the last Note.

In a desultory introduction, of some length, as well as in different parts of the body of the work, it is pretty evident that the Reporter had a twofold view in writing it. The one, to furnish useful information, to the Board and the Public; the other, to set forth his own abilities, as a professional man*. And if his practice be equal to some of his recommendations, there can be few men more fit to be employed. I have rarely met with a man who appears, on paper, to possess in different instances, more comprehensive conceptions concerning the *outlines* of rural *improvement*, than Mr. Stone. I shall, therefore, more freely extract from his work whatever, I conceive, may lead to the improvement of Lincolnshire, or the kingdom at large;—lest his sentiments should, otherwise, be wholly lost to the Public.

As a Report of the *established practices* of *Lincolnshire*, it is very incomplete. The matter contained in it, altogether, is brief; and much of this consists of the Reporter's own *recommendations*. But no disparagement, this; provided they convey valuable suggestions. It is, moreover, to be remarked, that the Report under consideration, has evidently been a hasty performance. The language is, sometimes, scarcely intelligible, and, frequently, difficult to be understood.

It would seem to have been written from the Reporter's previous knowledge of the county; not from a general SURVEY of it, for the especial purposes of the Board.

The PLAN and ARRANGEMENT of the matter adduced is this. The COUNTY is divided into *four districts* †;
each

---

* This, however, was pardonable, if not commendable;—seeing how few men there are, who are capable of conducting the multifarious business, which is incident to the management of large landed properties, with any thing resembling strict propriety

† The REPORTER'S DISTRICTS.—" 1. Fen. 2. Strong loamy soils, not subject to be overflowed. 3. The Wolds, or light soils. 4. The marshes."

each of which is spoken of, separately,—as to particular points. In other matters, however, the county at large is brought forward, under different general divisions; under which a variety of topics are touched. But these circumstances do not invalidate the materials collected; they only render them tedious and irksome to be understood.

I shall, in this, as in every other instance, bring the whole of what may seem meet to be extracted, under one arrangement:—namely, that which I have invariably employed; and which may be seen in the table of contents, prefixed to this volume.

The number of pages one hundred and seven.
No Map.

SUBJECT THE FIRST.

NATURAL ECONOMY.

EXTENT.—The following is Mr. Stone's statement of the extent of the county; as well as of the present state of occupancy of its lands.

		Acres.
P. 12. " Inclosed marsh and fen land	-	473,000
Commons, wastes, and unembanked salt marshes	- - -	200,000
Common fields	- - -	268,000
Wood-land	- - - -	25,000
Inclosed upland	- - -	927,100
	Total	1,893,120"

Or about 3,000 square miles.

CLIMATURE.

P. 14. " The fens," (says the Reporter) " are situated on the south-east part of the county : the marshes extend along the sea-coast, from the mouth of the Humber, to Cross Keys Wash, the strong loamy soils on the south, south-east, and south-west, and part in the north-west, and skirting between the marshes, fens, and high lands, including that portion of mixed arable and pasture land called the middle marsh. The Wolds, or light soils, are chiefly north of Lincoln ; with a small portion on the south, extending to the Trent and Humber, on the north and north-east, and on the north-east and east to the marshes."—Thus confounding the " Wolds," or Chalk Downs, with the " Heaths" or Stoney Heights.

CLIMATURE.—P. 13. " The air and climate of this County, in point of salubrity, is, upon the highest part of it, equal to any in the kingdom. Upon the fenny and marshy parts, it has been very much improved of late years, since the drainage has been more attended to ; and at this time, the inhabitants of the County have no dread of their healths being impaired, in shifting their abodes, even at advanced periods of life, from the upper parts called the Wolds, to the lowest part of the fens and marshes. The time of harvest in the northern and eastern part of the County, lying open to the ocean, is a little delayed from that circumstance."

In a division of the work, entitled " Prejudice against the County,"—are the subjoined strictures, relating, in effect, to its climature. P. 10. " Estates have been sold in Lincolnshire, within a short distance of time, for half their real value. Gentlemen possessing landed property in this County, (and having Estates upon which they reside in others,) either from a prejudice against the district, generally imbibed upon an idea, that it is low, and subject to inundations, without minutely examining into the state and condition of their property, have for this, and various reasons, made their election to sell their property here, in order, perhaps, to purchase in another ; and, in one instance, it is said, that an Estate was sold in this County, not many years ago, for near £ 100,000 less than it was soon afterwards proved to be worth."

P. 18. (Fens) " The seed time is prolonged, on account of the general wetness of the land in the Spring, of course the harvest is on that account delayed, about 10 days longer than on the nearest high land."

WATERS.—P. 16. (Fens) " No part of the fens can possibly be watered as an improvement: in winter there is too much of that element, and in summer, the freshes from the highlands, will scarcely afford a sufficient quantity of water for the stock to drink ; and if more could be received down the rivers, to scour them out, and prevent their choaking up, it ought to be so used, as a primary object."

P. 66. (Fens) " This country, though low and subject to be overflowed in winter, very frequently suffers from
                                                        drought

drought in summer; as water is obtained with difficulty
in dry seasons, for the cattle depastured on the land."

SOILS and SUBSTRATA.—P. 12. " Every soil in the
united kingdom, may be found in this County, in considerable quantities, from the sharpest sand, and lightest
moor, to the strongest clay, in all its various mixture
and qualities.

" No County in England can boast such various gifts
of Nature, bestowed with so even an hand, that a general mixture of property and soils, if judiciously applied
in the letting, would operate upon the whole, in the
same ratio of advantage, with which such gifts are attended upon a well-cultivated farm; one and the same
district affording light loamy soils, for the production
of corn and green winter wood, whilst the neighbouring marsh affords excellent pasture for feeding cattle
and sheep in summer, advantages which, when laid
together, cannot be equalled in any degree by the
separate uses of either."

P. 30. (Vale Land) " Upon the banks of this river"
(the Trent) " there is some very fertile, inclosed,
strong, loamy soil, producing abundant crops of every
species of grain, pulse, potatoes, &c."

P. 23. (Fens) " Oak timber, holly, hazle, with the
appearance of leaves, nut shells, and faggots of the tops
of oak timber, set up in ridges, with the skeletons of
deer and other animals, have frequently been found
within three feet of the surface, by persons who have
made it their employment, with iron spikes, to search
into the soil for wood, which they afterwards dug out
to considerable advantage."—Remarks on this species
of soil will appear under the head *Sodburning*, ensuing.

SUBJECT THE SECOND.

POLITICAL ECONOMY.

APPROPRIATION.—It appears under the head
Extent, p. 16, aforegoing, that Mr. Stone's estimate of
common pasture lands, in 1794, was 200,000 acres, and
of *common field* lands 260,000 acres; in the County at
large.

The

The following are his notices relating to the existing *state* of Appropriation, in its several districts, *at that time* *.

P. 18. (Waterlands) " The fens are not yet completely inclosed. There are several considerable commons yet remaining open, but there is very little land in a state of common field.

" *Commons.* The principal commons, are the East and West Fens, and Wildmore fen.

" These commons are situated a few miles north of Boston, within the Manorial perambulation of the Soke of Bollingbrook, held under a lease from the Duchy of Lancaster, by Sir Joseph Banks, Bart, and contain together upwards of 40,000 acres, viz. West Fen 16,924 acres, 2 roods, 6 perches; East Fen 12,424 acres, 8 roods, 39 perches; and Wildmore Fen 10,661 acres, 2 roods, 25 perches. The number of towns within the Soke, having right of common in the West Fen, are 22; with falkage, turbary, fishing, and fowling. Eight towns of East Holland having similar rights with the Soke commoners of the West Fen, claim a right of pasturage only, upon the East Fen; which is accounted by the Soke commoners an intrusion, and will probably procrastinate the time of a division. Seventeen towns exercise a right of common on Wildmoor Fen, besides those towns which exercise a right of common on the other fens; so that it appears, that 47 towns claim a right of common on these fens."

P. 22. "The commons situated between the Welland and the Glenn, within the manors of East and West Deeping, which are held under a lease from the crown by his Grace the Duke of Ancaster. Those commons are said to contain upwards of 15,000 acres."

P. 30. There are " on the eastern side of the Trent, some thousands of acres of very valuable land in a state of common, extending along the Trent, from Stockworth towards Flixborough, which will well answer the purposes of draining and inclosing."

P. 42.

---

* I let these extracts and remarks remain as they stood, before I was aware that some alterations have taken place, in the state of Appropriation in Lincolnshire, since Mr. Stone's Report was written. They will serve, at least, as items of history, respecting those extraordinary passages of English *territory*,—the " Fens of Lincolnshire." Mr. S. appears to have been intimately acquainted with their existing states, at that time.

P 42. (Uplands) " There is but a small portion of this description of land in a state of common field, and what remains, is, for the most part, under contemplation of inclosure."

Obstacles to Appropriation.—P. 19. " The drainage of these commons," (East, West, and Wildmore Fens) " is very practicable, and which would have been doubtless some time since effected, together with a general inclosure of them; but, there are some reasons which have conspired to prevent the measure being adopted, and which may gradually wear away under proper explanations; and here I will endeavour to enumerate them :

" 1. That the respectable baronet just mentioned, who is deservedly considered the patron, and (if I may use the expression) the father of this country, has been, till lately, so much occupied by objects of a more distant nature; and of more general importance to the community, that, probably, he has not had time to turn his thoughts towards this measure, however interesting it may be, in which a deal of investigation and labour is involved, to remove the prejudices of the commoners against a measure, which though, in the opinion of impartial observers, it would be highly and abundantly to their advantage, they have not been able to perceive it; and the humanity of this gentleman's nature, would revolt at an idea of forcing upon them the execution of a measure, absolutely beneficial to their best and most essential interests, against their inclinations.

" 2. The adjustment of the claim of the 8 towns of East Holland, upon the East Fen, ought to be compromised, and settled before any application to parliament should be made.

" 3. The expence of an application to parliament, and obtaining acts for apportioning and dividing the commons belonging to 47 parishes; and the after-division of such apportionments, amongst the commoners of each respective parish, might probably involve the proprietors of the whole, in the enormous expence of 47 acts of parliament*; a very sufficient reason for the proprietors

_____

" * The general act for dividing these commons, by the usage of the house, would be charged as 47 acts, and pay the fees accordingly." This can never be. The parliament of England cannot have a usage half so irrational as this!

proprietors dreading the expence of the measure of inclosing the fens; and no indifferent proof of the necessity for a general act to promote the inclosure of all commons, common fields, common meadows, and waste lands, in the united kingdoms, under such regulations and restrictions, as the wisdom of the parliament may devise.

"A fourth reason may be, that an equitable mode of dividing the commons is not yet agreed upon."

"Lastly," (p. 21.) "The present scarcity of money in the country may so far affect some of the parties in this measure, that they may feel it necessary to defer an expensive inclosure till better times shall come."

The *disadvantages* of commonable lands, and the *benefits* to arise from their Appropriation.

1. Common Pastures.—P. 18. (Fens) "These commons" (East, West, and Wildmore Fens) " are under better regulations than any others in the fen country; which is probably owing to the directions of the respectable Baronet, a considerable part of whose estate is situated near to them : yet they are extremely wet and unprofitable in their present state, standing much in need of drainage, are generally overstocked, and dug up for turf and fuel. The cattle and sheep depastured upon them, are often very unhealthy, and of an inferiour sort, occasioned by the scantiness, as well as the bad quality, of their food, and the wetness of their lair.

"Geese, with which these commons are generally stocked, (from various causes, of a nature similar to those, which will be hereafter enumerated, with respect to Deeping Fens,) are often subject to be destroyed.

"It is not a constant practice with the commoners, to take all their cattle off the fens upon the approach of winter; but some of the worst of the neat cattle, with the horses; and particularly those upon Wildmore Fen, are left to abide the event of the winter season; and it seldom happens, that of the neat cattle many escape the effects of a severe winter. The horses are driven to such distress for food, that they eat up every remaining dead thistle, and are said to devour the hair off the manes and tails of each other, and also the dung of geese. A commoner, who farms his own estate in the vicinity of these commons. and pursues
a hope

a hope of gain from them, in the fullest extent, is eventually not in a much better state than the rack-renter, in a series of years; for when 2 or 3 successive flattering winters present themselves, he goes on adding to the number of his stock of cattle and geese; then comes a fatal season, in which most of them, by various diseases occasioned by a sudden and continued wetness, are swept away."

P. 22. (Deeping Fens) "They stand very much in need of inclosing and draining, as the cattle and sheep depastured thereon are very unhealthy. The occupiers frequently, in one season, lose 4-5ths of their stock. These commons are without stint, and almost every cottage within the manors has a common right belonging to it. Every kind of depredation is made upon this land, in cutting up the best of the turf for fuel; and the farmers in the neighbourhood having common rights, availing themselves of a fine season, turn on 7 or 800 sheep each, to ease their inclosed land, whilst the mere cottager cannot get a bite for a cow; but yet the cottager, in his turn, in a colourable way, takes the stock of a foreigner as his own, who occasionally turns on immense quantities of stock in good seasons.

" The cattle and sheep, which are constantly depastured on this common, are of a very unthrifty ill-shapen kind, from being frequently starved, and no attention paid to their breed.

" Geese are the only animals which are at any time thrifty; and these, frequently, when young, die of the cramp, or, when plucked, in consequence of the excessive bleakness and wetness of the commons. A goose pays annually from 1s. to 16d. by being 4 times plucked. These commons are the frequent resort of thieves, who convey the cattle into distant Counties for sale."

P. 29. (North Fens) " The commons in" (round) " the Isle of Axholm, surrounding some of the most fertile, strong, loamy, soils in the kingdom, may be here justly instanced. These commons and wastes contain upwards of 12,000 acres, which, divided and inclosed, would for the most part make very valuable land, being in considerable parts of a clayey bottom; but, in their present state, they are chiefly covered with water, and in summer throw forth the coarsest productions. the best parts, which are those nearest the inclosed

closed high lands, are constantly pared and burnt to produce vegetable ashes to be carried on them, in order to force repeated crops of white grain. The more remote parts of the common are dug up for fuel.

" On account of the general wetness of these commons, and their being constantly overstocked by the large occupiers of contiguous estates, or in such seasons as the depasturage is desirable in summer, to ease the inclosed land, the cattle and sheep necessarily depastured thereon at all seasons, being those of the cottagers, who are for the most part destitute of provision for them in winter, are always unthrifty, and subject to various diseases, which render them very unprofitable to the occupiers."

P. 47. (Marshes) " In contemplating the husbandry of this part of the marshes, I cannot pass over the parish of Long Sutton, without observing, that the former commons, belonging to this parish, about the inclosure of which so much opposition was made in both houses of parliament, have turned out productive to the parties interested, beyond all calculation of advantage, even of those who brought forward the bill : all animosities having subsided, the former contending parties sit down peaceably, enjoying the harvest of a well-fought field; the land producing immense quantities of corn, hemp, flax, woad, and every valuable production. And all this alteration, much for the benefit of the country, though so violently opposed, was carried into effect by the perseverance of one spirited proprietor, viz. Joshua Scrope, Esq. the Lord of the Manor, upon the petition to parliament, of the smallest majority of proprietors, ever known under similar circumstances.

" Farmers who took undue advantages of the commons, by hiring common-right houses, and, under colour of such rights, turning upon the commons 7 or 800 sheep in a season, and thereby eating up the poor cottagers rights, had address enough falsely to represent the case, and to prevail upon their landlords, and others in power, to support them in this violent opposition. This inclosure has been followed by that of the adjoining commons of Tydd; and some thousands of acres of common, in the parish of Whaplode, Holbeach, and Fleet, being in this neighbourhood, are now

now under notices for a bill of inclosure, to be supported by Lord Eardley, who is a lessee under the crown for considerable estates in one of these parishes."

2. Common Fields.--(Vale Lands) For evidence of their unprofitable state, see *Plan* of *Management*, ensuing.

P. 29. " Mixed with the common fields is a considerable quantity of commonable land, which suffers considerably for want of drainage, which is the frequent cause of the rot in sheep, and the dropsy, pheltrie, and various other disorders in neat cattle and horses."

P. 42. (Uplands) " The advantages here resulting from inclosures, have been chiefly the laying the land together; which, in a state of common field, was very much mixed and dispersed."

P. 43. (The same) " Inclosing has certainly decreased population in this country, for want of an introduction of the Drill, and other systematic husbandry; and from the lands being laid out in too large farms."

These I insert as unfledged popular ideas, which were attempted to be forced on the wing at the time this Report was written.

The *Business* of Appropriation.—1 Of Commons.—P. 31. (Fens) " A bill is intended to be brought into parliament, in the next session, for an inclosure and division of those commons," (belonging to the Isle of Axholm,) " and the preliminary popular mode seems to be on the eve of being settled, viz. to give to the lord of the soil* 1-20th part for that right; to the tythe owners, 1-10th; and 2-3ds of the residue to owners of common right houses and *toftsteads* (?), and the remaining third part to the owners of lands, having common right houses and toftsteads†.

" This mode of dividing the commons seems to be a compromise to prevent farther opposition, and not adopted altogether upon a principle of equity, because the owners of the land have certainly time immemorial occupied

" * Lord Carteret is lessee of the manors of Epworth cum Westwood, and Flaxey, under the Crown ; I had the honour of regulating the husbandry to be observed upon this estate."

† What an inequitous mode of procedure !

occupied the commons in a larger extent, and in proportion to the stock they kept in winter; whilst the mere cottagers, for want of provision for their cattle, in winter, as well as from the general unprofitableness of the situation and mode of occupancy, have kept a much less proportion of stock than the occupiers of messuages and lands."

2. Of Common Fields.—P. 43. (Uplands) "In every inclosure bill the commissioners are required to allot the lands to be inclosed, with due consideration to quality, quantity, and contiguity. Whether from mistaking the meaning of the latter word, or from paying too much regard to the situations of the farm-houses already erected, it commonly occurs, that the contiguity of the land to be allotted to each respective house and buildings, is more considered than the general connexion or contiguity of the allotments in a square manner, so that in those situations near a large village, the property is jumbled together in a degree unprofitable to all parties concerned; and 'e large proprietors are obliged to travel to their allotments; carried out, in parcels, to a considerable distance.

" Surely it would be more desirable for all parties interested, to have the distant parts of the parishes to be inclosed, considered, as to be detached in the first instance, and for suitable allowances to be settled by the commissioners, for the expence of new buildings in central situations, whilst the proprietors, whose estates are allotted to their houses and buildings in the villages, would have all their lands contiguous, at a rate proportioned to the advantages so to be derived. For the first great benefit resulting from an inclosure, is contiguity; and the more square the allotments are made, and the more central the buildings are placed, the more advantages are derived to the proprietors in every respect."

In page 21, Mr. Stone adverts to the *principles* of Appropriation. But I perceive nothing new in his strictures. They *agree*, as far as they go, with those previously laid down, in the RURAL ECONOMY of YORKSHIRE.

For the principles at large, and the groundwork of a GENERAL LAW of APPROPRIATION, see my TREATISE on LANDED PROPERTY.

POPULATION.

POPULATION.—(Uplands) See *Sizes of Farms*, ensuing.

PROVISIONS.—(Fens) P. 25. " The price of provisions is nearly the same as at all other places of equal distance from the metropolis : good mutton, pork, and beef, are nearly as dear as in London, deducting the value of the driving the animals thither; a more ordinary sort, not fit for the London market, is sold from 2¼d. to 3½d. and 4d. per pound.

" Bread, when purchased of the bakers, is nearly as dear as in London; and the poor have not the forecast to purchase corn, and to manufacture their own meal and bread, which might be readily accomplished. The price of provisions is not likely to decrease."

MANUFACTURES.—By the subjoined notices, it appears, that Lincolnshire is not, emphatically speaking, a *Manufacturing* County :—nor has it, I believe, any *Mines* in which its inhabitants are employed : nor has it any great extent of *Commerce* to boast of; as appears below. It may, therefore, be considered as almost purely *agricultural.*

P. 96. " This County has been remarkable for its manufacture of stuffs for ladies apparel, the spinning of which has been chiefly performed by their fair hands; this manufacture was promoted with great spirit by Lady Banks, and several ladies and gentlemen of extensive landed property, and unbounded philanthropy, during the American war, when long wool had no market; thus to induce the inhabitants, in some measure, to provide for themselves a remedy, for the then general decay of manufactures and commerce; and since the necessity for the measure, in a great degree, has been removed, an annual ball has been continued in the county, in commemoration of so laudable an undertaking, which is well attended by the nobility and gentry; where the native charms of ladies (if possible) receive an additional lustre, from the simple elegance of their dresses, chiefly composed of Lincolnshire stuffs.

" At Epworth, there is a manufacture of sackcloth, but it is not carried on very extensively; in many other parts of the County there are manufactures of coarse linen cloth, also malt-houses and breweries, and many other articles of common home consumption are made, but

but not of sufficient magnitude to deserve particular notice."

Commerce.—P. 95. " The principal ports in this County are Boston, and Gainsborough; whence corn, potatoes, oak and other timber, hemp, flax, woad, and other articles the produce of the County, are occasionally exported to the London, and other markets. The imports are chiefly coals, fir timber, &c. &c.

" The means of making such exports, and imports, may be said to be beneficial to agriculture, and have long given this County the superiority, in point of situation, to many other Counties, of which the inhabitants, from an indolence or supineness, commonly inspired by an abundance of natural gifts, have not availed themselves; now, the introduction of inland navigation, will put the inland Counties, for a series of years, at least, upon a footing with it; which will continue, until the vast beds of coals in them shall be exhausted, whilst our manufactures increase, or until improved agriculture shall so far increase, that the produce of the soil shall exceed the possible consumption of its inhabitants."

PUBLIC EMBANKMENT and DRAINAGE.—On this subject, as on that of Appropriation, (which are, in Lincolnshire, intimately connected,) we find a number of disjointed notices, scattered over the body of the Report. I will, here, endeavour to digest them, so as to bring the whole into the most intelligible form.

Notices respecting the *History*, and *present State* of Drainage, in Lincolnshire.

P. 11. (the County at large) " It is but since the American war, that a prejudice, which formerly prevailed amongst monied men, as to the precarious state of the drainage of this County, has in any degree been dispelled. In advancing money upon mortgage securities, this County formerly was particularly excepted, which is a circumstance well known to the conveyancers in London.

" A part of the County being low, and its drainage having for a series of years been neglected, a conclusion had been drawn by persons in remote situations, unacquainted with it, that the whole District is in winter a kind of duck pool. To have informed them that the two-thirds of it is high and dry land, requiring no extraordinary drainage, would gain as little credit

as

as the most extravagant assertion that could be devised."

P. 65. " I.1 the southern part of this County, called South Holland, a main cut, or drain, is now making, by authority of Parliament, from a place called Peter's Point, to Wheatmeer drain, near the hamlet of Peakhill. This cut will most certainly facilitate the drainage of this district. And another cut, intended to be made, (in a similar way to that of the Eau-Brink cut of the Ouse, in another district,) to confine the course of the Welland to a narrower channel, from a certain point below Spalding, to a more certain and deep outfall than the present, at Wyberton road, will most certainly tend to promote the drainage of Deeping Fen, and other low lands in this country. This appears to be part of a scheme suggested by Lord Chief Justice Popham, in the beginning of the last century, and afterwards touched upon by Sir Cornelius Vermuden. Colonel Dodson, and several other engineers of the last and present century; and it proves, that our ancestors have suffered these excellent plans to lie dormant for ages, as no new idea seems to have been now started upon these subjects, or any thing offered which had not been previously suggested or recommended by ancient engineers."

P. 26. (Deeping Fen) " The drainage of this part of the fens has been for a series of years very much neglected, and stands much in need of being better drained, which can be effected without a great exertion of genius."—And, in p. 49, we are informed that " the drainage of the manors of East and West Deeping, with their extensive commons, might, probably, be found, upon a proper survey, to be effected in the direction of the new cut, by proper tunnels laid for that purpose, under the river Welland, &c.* But those manors are held by his Grace the Duke of Ancaster, under a lease from the Crown, which is nearly expired; and, unless his Grace had a renewal of it, for a competent length of time, in which he might be at least repaid the expenses of such an undertaking, it is improbable that he should promote it.

" As

* I cannot speak with precision on this subject, not having been employed in any minute investigation, by levelling, &c."

" As we proceed northwards, the marshes stand very much in need of a better drainage, and for want of which the most profitable use of the land, in summer, is very much delayed; and in winter, almost denied."

P. 19. (East, West, and Wildmore Fens) Some notice, regarding the drainage of these fens, and the obstacles that stand in the way of it, appear under the head, *Appropriation*, p. 20, aforegoing.

P. 67. " An improved drainage of the northern, eastern, and western districts of the fens, may be accomplished in the most salutary way, whenever the inclosure of the east and west fen commons, and Wildmore fen, are accomplished by a general well-digested plan."

P. 49. (" Marshes") " An embankment, of many thousands of acres of salt marsh, fronting the parish of Gedney, and its vicinity, is carrying into effect, which will be of infinite advantage to the proprietors, and the community."—And, p. 51, " The sea certainly gains upon some parts of this coast, and retreats from other parts; and in the frontage of the parishes of Summercotes and Marsh Chapel, some thousand of acres of salt marshes may now be safely embanked from the sea."

Hints relating to the *business* of Embankment and Drainage.

1. Defects, on the present system.—P. 50. " The sea banks, according to the law of sewers, ought to be repaired and amended from time to time, by the occupiers of lands in the frontage towns; and whenever any banks are necessarily to be erected, the whole district is chargeable therewith; and it is customary to charge the expences by an acre-tax, and not according to the yearly value of the lands, which is certainly, in many instances, where the value of the lands vary, extremely oppressive. But it sometimes happens, that well-timed applications of a small expence, in the due repairing of parts of the banks, might be the means of supporting them for ages; but it is not always considered the interest of the occupiers of frontage towns, to repair the banks thereof, and they would rather, in some instances, when they become very bad by neglect, render new ones necessary, to the expence of which they would only contribute a proportionate share with an extensive district.

" It

" It is not a custom for gentlemen of extensive landed property, who are most interested, (Sir Joseph Banks, and a few other gentlemen, excepted,) to attend the meetings of commissioners of sewers, and to take the necessary views in this part of the country; and, therefore, the business of importance, in which the preservation and even salvation of a rich and fertile country is involved, is too frequently carried into execution, upon the votes of those gentlemen, who are not well versed either in the laws or customs which ought to be observed; nor possessed of that practical knowledge, which a decision upon objects of so much importance requires; for, however skilful the officers employed may be, it ought not only to be a satisfaction to them, that their judges understand their demerits, but a great share of the responsibility and ill-opinion of the country, even in cases of miscarriages that might occur, which no human foresight could prevent, would thereby be taken off their shoulders.

" A work of considerable importance, in the bank near Saltfleet, was lately blown up by a tide; which, in the first instance, recently cost the country from 1500 to 2000 l. and which is now to be replaced in a more skilful and substantial manner. More discernment in the commissioners, or in their agents, might probably have prevented, or rendered this expence unnecessary.

" It has, in some instances, been a practice, in erecting new banks, to retreat some way from the sites of the former bank, as if such retreat was giving a degree of ease to the pressure of the water. This measure ought not to be attempted, but in cases of extreme necessity.

" I should rather recommend the standing firm to the sites of the ancient banks, until the sea shall so far gain upon the shore, that the whole works must necessarily be abandoned, for new ones, in a more remote situation."

2. The Reporter's proposed improvements:—and, in the works of drainage we shall find him much *at home;* his *recommendations* being frequently entitled to attention.—P. 88. " I recommend, that the drainage of this very valuable tract of country, be taken, by act of parliament, out of the management of the commissioners of sewers, and divided into two, three, or more districts,

districts, as shall, upon investigation, be found necessary, for the better drainage and management thereof.
For the land-owners in each district, by ballot, or any
other more eligible mode, to delegate their interests
into the hands of three or more commissioners, well
skilled in the art of embanking and draining, subject to
their control, and removable for misconduct.

"To connect the embanking, and draining of each
district together, as if it was the property of one well-
regulated family; making each respective part of the
property contribute its share of expense, in proportion
to its share of advantages, to be derived from any improvements.

"If a plan of this kind were to be adopted, we
should not see the occupiers of a frontage town, letting their bank fall, from wilful neglect, in order, that
when it shall be condemned, the whole level may contribute to the expense of a new one; in which expense
their share would be less (as part of a large district)
than otherwise in doing their duty by upholding their
embankment, as occupiers of a frontage town. We
should not see the water held up by narrow passages,
and crooked rivulets, over-flowing large tracts of high
land, from the fear of letting it down upon works
below, incompetent to carry it to the sea. We should
not see some towns well drained, whilst others adjoining to them, equally capable, are overflowed. All
these evils may be speedily cured, and an immense
general saving had, by adopting a plan, similar to this
which I recommend; for, by connecting the embankment and draining of a whole country together, the
works will be constantly attended to, and well secured;
the water will be collected together, and carried off in
larger bodies to the sea, in the most advantageous
places, by which means it will have competent power
to scour out the outfalls.

"The number of goats (?) may be considerably decreased, and larger portions of fresh water may be
spared (if necessary) for the cattle in summer, than
at present, whilst almost every frontage town has a
goat, to which (in order to preserve any kind of effect) all the water that can possibly be collected must
be sent."

P. 49. "A great scheme of improvement, by means
of a cut, for the drainage of the lands in South Holland,

land, and parts adjacent, to a competent outfall in this district, is now carrying into effect.

"It is a matter of great public concern, that in every scheme of drainage, the interior parts of the country should be brought into the measure on the outset; for, by constructing works for drainage, nearest to the outfall, in the first instance, they are often found after-terwards to be incompetent to the general good; by reason of which, an after-expence is incurred, of which more than a moiety might have been saved in the first instance, as well as the general improvement of the country effected, instead of a partial one."

P. 66. "Notwishstanding the certain prospect of general good, which presents itself upon the adopting of the last-mentioned plan, it meets with opposition, from local circumstances connected with trade and commerce, which, it is hoped, will be accommodated between the parties before a bill is brought into parliament; otherwise, it cannot be supposed, that the good sense of the legislature will suffer objects, evidently short-sighted, and of a very inferior nature, to weigh against the general improvement of a very large tract of country, which, when improved by the means proposed, will, by the increase of every com-modity produced from the land, throw into the pockets of even the opposers of the measure, a very consider-able balance of gain, if even the existence of the ground of complaint should be admitted; yet, I must freely observe, that none of these plans seems to me to be sufficiently general and comprehensive. Before new outfalls are made, taxes imposed, and terms settled for watering intermediate estates, &c. &c. the whole country dependent upon, or likely to be affected by, any intended measure, should be invited to partake of the proposed advantage. And it should be pointed out to the parties, how their interests are likely to be affected; and a calculation and estimate should be made of the quantity of water likely to be brought down to the outfalls, upon a *general* scheme of im-provement, or who can answer for their being suffi-ciently capacious."

P. 67. "The retaining of the summer waters, or freshes, *in the main drains*, in order to scour out and cleanse the outfall at the sea, is absolutely necessary, or it would be in danger of being choaked up. This can

only

only be remedied by *confining the rivers to narrower channels*, shortening and straightening their direction to competent outfalls, and, in many instances, it would be a very dangerous practice to suffer the river-waters to be let out, and exhausted for the purposes of the occupiers.

" I should recommend to the landed interest, to examine carefully for springs of water upon their property, which would be a means of remedying the inconveniences each way, herein before pointed out, and which, I am inclined to think, may be easily brought to bear, at no very considerable expence, in wells and pumps. In the North Marshes I have lately promoted the searching for, and obtaining, the uses of inexhaustible springs of good fresh water; and, I lately saw, upon the sea bank at Theddlethorp, a spring of excellent fresh water."— For further remarks, see the head *Waters*, p. 17, aforegoing.

P. 21. " The drainage of these" (East, West, and Wildmore) "fens is not very difficult, and it will be attended with no greater expence than the land upon an inclosure can amply bear, without much inconvenience to the respective proprietors : but, as is the general case with all the low land which the sea has left, the lowest part of these fens is nearest the high land, and the greatest distance from the outfall; and these commons cannot be properly drained, without a catch-water drain under the high land, to take the *soke* and superfluous water, which would form a lodgement behind the commons, in a circuitous direction to the outfall."

P. 50. " The sewers and drains, which ought to be competent to conduct the water immediately from the high land to the outfall, at all times, as well as the outfalls themselves, are too much cramped or confined, and a false principle in drainage, by long custom, is established, viz. not to open or cut strait the sewers and drains nearest the high land, lest the water should come down too rapidly, and be forced over their banks, in its way to the outfall, where it cannot get away fast enough, to prevent the drowning of the intermediate lands."

The following suggestion is particularly worthy of attention.—P. 67. " Wherever engines are necessary to facilitate a drainage, I recommend the steam-engine, to accompany the wind-engines, in a considerable work; because, it too frequently happens, that a calm succeeds an abundant fall of rain, for a considerable length of time.

time. The steam-engine may be immediately set to work, at a time the most desirable, and when the expence of firing cannot be set in comparison with its advantages; and whilst the wind-engines remain useless, and those which will throw up one hundred hogsheads of water per minute, many feet, may be put up at any place near a navigation, for about 6 or 700 l."

P. 66. ". The imposition of taxes, by the acre, for any purposes of drainage whatever, are oppressive to individuals (when their amount becomes an object that will amply pay the expence of making distinctions by estimates, &c.), and will remain so as long as the qualities of land shall vary. I recommend all drainage-taxes to be laid according to the value of the respective improvements."

These several suggestions abound in good sense, and evince a more than ordinary compass of mind, and mature knowledge of the *general subject* to which they are applied. How far they are applicable to the *particular sites*, above spoken of, can be rightly judged of, by a deliberate survey, and length of study, of the given sites, only. They are of course, inserted, here, on Mr. Stone's authority. I have only to add that I have seldom employed a few hours more satisfactorily, than in endeavoring to place them, in such a manner as will render them most intelligible to those who have bestowed less attention, than I have, upon this important subject. See my TREATISE on LANDED PROPERTY, article *Embankment and Drainage;* together with the several sourses of information, there referred to.

The following remarks, concerning the *North-Waterlands,* or *Axholm Fens,* appear to be well entitled to attention.

P. 30. " The drainage of the commons of the Isle of Axholm will not be a very difficult undertaking, provided the outfall is made into the Trent, at a certain point, probably below Waterton. Hitherto the drains necessary to convey the water to the Trent from *Haitfield,* otherwise Hatfield, and the adjacent country on the Yorkshire side, have been carried over the isle commons into that river too high up, in the way of the Trent floods, which *override* the sluices and *goats,* and which operate at present as a bar to the improvement of the drainage of the commons; and lately, by authority of parliament, a canal has been made in a similar way across them.

" I am

" I am informed, that the isle commoners are empowered, by a clause in the act, to drain their commons
by means of tunnels, to be laid under this canal; but,
during the time all the improvements of the adjacent
County were completing, the isle commoners have been
unfortunately dormant, and have greatly delayed their
interest, in not draining their commons, by means of a
competent general cut, down to the best possible outfall
that could be obtained, which might have received, by
side cuts, all the water from Haitfield, and the Yorkshire
side; and which would serve to scour out, and deepen,
such general cut, not only in its progress to, but at the
outfall."

INLAND NAVIGATION.—For an instance of its utility
to the *Traffic* of a Country, or what I have termed the
INTERCOURSE of DISTRICTS,—see the head *Commerce*,
p. 27, aforegoing.

ROADS.—The subjoined observations, relating to the
roads of the lower lands of Lincolnshire, tho not of great
importance, may be useful as hints, in those and similar
situations.

P. 25. (Fens) " The roads are tolerably good in summer; but in winter, as the materials of which they are
composed are very soft (being chiefly of moory soil and
filth), they are then very often indifferent."

P. 52. (Marshes) "The roads on the South part of this district are, for the greatest part of the year, in a good state;
but, in the middle and North parts, they are nearly im-
passable in winter; in which season it is a practice to
attempt to mend them, as well as in other parts of the
County, which requires no comment."

P. 89. ("Improvement" of the same) " With regard
to the roads, I recommend that all carriages are confined
as much as possible to pass in dry weather, and that all
attempts to amend them are confined to that season.
Good materials for making roads, are obtained with
great difficulty and expence in this district. In proportion as such materials are weak, the more of them are
necessary, and, when applied, they might be more confined in width, than is the general practice, to be made
up in depth. Within a reasonable distance of the sea-
shore, materials may be had and fetched for the making
of the roads."

P. 96. (the County at large) " The roads of this
County may be considerably improved, by common attention to the searching for the best materials each district

trict affords; and to the using them in the summer
season. The present practice is more confined to the
winter, being a season when the farmers consider themselves most at leisure to prosecute such business, which
produces them the least immediate gain."

MARKETS.—*Surplus produce.*—P. 44. " Excellent constant markets for fat cattle, and sheep, are found in the
manufacturing towns of Yorkshire, whither they are, in
large quantities, driven."

Victualing Office.—The subjoined suggestion of Mr.
STONE, corresponds, in the main part, with that of Mr.
LEATHAM, in his Report of the East Riding of Yorkshire.
P. 90. " If a victualing-office were to be established
at Boston, for curing beef and pork for his Majesty's
service, it may be considered very expedient; because
near ten *per cent.* is lost in the expence of driving cattle,
&c. from the adjacent country to the London market;
and the cattle thereby heated, and rendered less desirable for the purposes required; from which circumstance, if the measure I have pointed out were to be
adopted, the business of slaughtering, and salting, might
here be carried on a month later in the season than at
Deptford."

Should such a public establishment be deemed eligible, it remains to be determined whether BOSTON or
HULL possesses greater advantages of situation.

SUBJECT THE THIRD.

RURAL ECONOMY.

DIVISION THE FIRST.

TENANTED ESTATES.

ESTATES.—*Sizes.*—P. 14. " The property in the Fens,
Marshes, and Woulds, is, in general, in the hands of
large proprietors; on the strong loamy soils, it is more
diffused among the yeomanry, and the occupations are
laid out in a similar way, proprietors of extensive landed
property, letting it, for the most part, in an equal ratio,
to be occupied in large parcels."

Tenures.—I insert the subjoined suggestion, respecting the copyhold tenure, without comment.

P. 95.

P. 95. " I recommend upon all inclosures and divisions of landed property, and in every other case where practicable, the enfranchisement of copyhold estates, from arbitrary fines, herriots, &c. For whilst the lord of a manor is entitled to two years improved value of them, upon the death of a copyhold tenant, or on the alienation of the property, particular cases every day occur, to prevent the tenants from expending their property in the improvement of them."

PURCHASE of ESTATES.—For an instance that shows how much the reputed value of lands may be influenced by fashion, or false conceptions, see the head *Climature*, p. 17, aforegoing.

IMPROVEMENT of ESTATES.—*Introducing* improvements.—The following desultory remarks are inserted, here, merely to convey Mr. Stone's opinion, concerning this highly important topic.

P. 96. " There are no societies instituted for the improvement of agriculture. The tenantry, who for the most part are occupiers from year to year, have no incitement to exertions of skill, they either want a certainty, or security (by means of leases), for being reimbursed the expence of any improvements, that might be considered practicable, or they (in general) are fearful of shewing any inclination towards improvement, lest a speculation should be made upon them, in an untimely, unqualified, and unjustifiable, advance of rent.

" The only means of exciting a general spirit for improvements, would be, by granting leases, under regulations, to enforce the most approved methods of agriculture, which are adopted with success upon soils of a similar nature; for gentlemen of extensive landed property, to shew the way, by undertaking the occupancy of parts of their estates under the best *practical systems* of Norfolk, Essex, Hertfordshire, &c. &c. and the choicest breeds of cattle and sheep, to be found in England, rejecting experiments for a time, or leaving it for the active zeal of Agricultural Societies."

Laying out Farms. (Uplands) P. 40. " The buildings upon the Would estates, are not placed in central spots; but the farm-houses are generally on the lowest situations."

And, in the Chapter " Improvement of the Woulds," &c. we find the following injudicious *recommendation*—P. 83. " It is extremely desirable, where consistent with central

central situations, that farm-houses should be placed
upon the *highest parts* of farms, because the most laborious part of the regular process upon a farm is drawing
out the manure from the fold-yards, which is easiest performed upon ground which slopes from them."

This erroneous dictation is noticed, here, not merely
to show the Reporter's want of thought and judgement,
in this particular; but to bring forward a striking instance (in addition to others adduced in the course of
my present undertaking) of a propensity, in men of
business, to fly to *extremes*.

There can be no precise rules laid down, concerning
the subject in view. The given circumstances of a farm
require to be consulted. But, as a general guide, we
may safely conclude, that, where farm lands are spread
over a slope, the farmstead, in common cases, ought to
be neither at the *summit* nor the *base* of it. There is
generally a point between them, where *shelter* and *water*
may be found; with a flattened or gently shelving site,
to receive the yards and buildings; and with lands fit
for *pasturing paddocks*, on the upper side of it, and for
mowing grounds, on the lower, to receive the washings
of the homestead. And it is to be recollected that, if
manure is to be carried, downward, from a homestall,
the crops are to be dragged upward, from the same lands;
and, this, at a busy season.

SODBURNING.—Mr. Stone is a declared enemy to this
practice; and, in this as in the last case, he flies to an
extremity. His strictures, therefore, are to be regarded
with caution. Indeed, after what has been adduced, on
this subject, in the NORTHERN and WESTERN DEPART-
MENTS,—little that is new, excellent, or even interesting, can reasonably be expected, in our literary travels
through the EASTERN: and, in truth, we find not much,
relating to it, in the Report under notice, other than
bold conclusions, drawn from doubtful premises.

P. 23 (Deeping Fen) " Upon the old ploughed land
in the neighbourhood of these commons, which have
been repeatedly pared and burnt, the ploughs frequently
take hold of wood, and the roots of trees, where they had
always uninterruptedly gone before, at equal depth from
the surface, during the memory of man; which is of
itself a sufficient proof, that paring and burning reduces
the soil; and such adjacent ploughed land, which was
considered higher than the commons, when first inclosed,
is now 18 inches lower, which is entirely occasioned by

                                              paring

paring and burning; for it cannot be presumed that the first cultivators of this country, since its drowning, would begin to plough the lowest part of it first; nor indeed could it be accomplished, by reason of the water, with which it remained overflowed."

From what is previously said of the soil, in this case (see p. 18, aforegoing) it pretty evidently appears, that it is chiefly composed of vegetable mold,—the production of the larger aquatic plants and mosses; which had, in process of time, overgrown the timber and faggot wood, there deposited: the ground being, in reality, a reclaimed turbary, or peat bog:—a species of soil which is doubtlessly capable of being greatly reduced by fire;— even as turf or peat is liable to be; and which is consumed, in a greater or less degree, according to its purity : ever leaving a portion of residue, or ashes, proportionably to the fossil matter it contains. Some part of the reduction of the soil under notice is, without doubt, owing to the " paring and burning" of its surface.

But this is not a good argument against sodburning, *in general.—Purely fossil soils* are incapable of being palpably reduced, by such an operation. And altho fossil ground, that is not in a perfect state of tillage, contains more or less of vegetable matter; yet even this small portion, I conceive, is not liable to be much more reduced, in bulk, by the imperfect combustion which takes place, or ought to take place, in the operation under notice, than it is by completely digesting it, through the means of tillage, diligently performed.

Hence, it appears to me, evidently, that the *vegetable soils* of the fens of Lincolnshire are liable to be lessened, and their surfaces lowered, not only by *sodburning* but by *tillage**. And when we consider the necessary pressure which is given by implements of tillage, and still more by carriages, together with the feet of heavy animals,—upon the spungey porous lands of the site now particularly under consideration, and this in a loose broken state, without a covering of sward to protect them,

---

* As well as by *drainage*. By this operation, alone, it has been observed, in different parts of the island, that the surface of a moist spungey morass, is liable to be lowered, one fourth, one third, or even a larger proportion, of its previous height, measured from the base on which it rests ;—according to the recentness of its growth, and the quantity of water it contained.

them,—there can be no cause of surprize at finding the
effect above stated. Instead of the timber and faggots
and stags horns being now *nearer* the surface than they
were before the sward was broken, and the loose porous
matter trodden and compressed into a comparatively
solid mass,—the surprize, in my mind, is, that their
more prominent parts have not, ere now, appeared *above*
it. I speak of the particular case under notice ; where
there must necessarily have been a great depth of vegetable mold, to have covered the surfaces of the
deposits spoken of, some five or six feet deep*.

Another, and only one more, of this Reporter's Remarks, on the operation under notice, appears to be
entitled to public attention. It is as follows :—P. 70.
" One of the principal arguments commonly used to
support the practice of paring and burning, is, that by
such means grubs and worms, with which this kind of
land is generally infested, are thereby destroyed.

" The case is not quite so bad, where burning is
practised, as this argument would lead to. The whole
of the soil not being burnt, and of course the whole of
the grubs, &c. worms, deposited therein, cannot be
destroyed ; besides, the sods undergo a process in being
dried before the burning commences, of course, during
that time, the insects may retreat into their natural
element, and shrink from the fire ; and, I am of opinion,
that if a heavy roller was to be used, by day, upon this
kind of land, at different seasons, whenever it is laid
down in grass, and at many other times, and a lighter
one by night; the insects which infest this kind of land,
would

---

* DEPOSITS in MORASSES.—Here the mind is spontaneously
induced to consider how those deposits were lodged in, or otherwise brought into, their present situations.

Admitting the above statement (p. 18) to be correct, it is evident
that the basis of these boggy lands was, heretofore, in a state of
woodland; and it is almost equally evident that its surface by
some unexpected event, was, in a manner instantaneously, covered
with water :—otherwise, the faggots would have been rescued, and
the animals would have escaped.

Had those woods risen behind an embankment of former times?
And did such embankment suddenly give way ? Or was the ground
they grew upon previously more elevated?—and was let fall, in
some convulsion of Nature, into its present situation ? If the precise degrees of elevation of these depressed lands, with respect to
the tide at high water, were ascertained,—probability might be the
more nearly approached.

This subject will recur, in reviewing the SECRETARY'S REPORT.

would very soon be more effectually destroyed, than they could possibly be by paring and burning:"—adding, p. 72.—" A heavy roller will be a better friend to the fen farmer, in the long run, than a thousand paring ploughs."

There is much good sense and propriety in Mr. Stone's recommendation of rolling the spungey lands of Lincolnshire, *while in a state of sward;*—and there is, in my opinion, equal good sense and propriety, in exposing the sward to the operation of fire, whenever there may be found occasion (should such an occasion occur) to *break them up*, for the purposes of *Aration*.

In performing that operation, however, it does not follow that, because a rough tough coat of sward ought to be exposed to the action of fire, that it should be continued to a degree of *calcination ;* but only so far as to loosen its texture, and destroy the vegetables and animalcules, together with the seeds and eggs, lodged therein. Should a few of the insects and grubs escape, alive, their pasture, if not their entire sustenance, will necessarily be destroyed.

For abundant strictures, on the subject of Sodburning, see the NORTHERN and WESTERN DEPARTMENTS.

IRRIGATION.—P. 42. "The improvement by means of flooding the land at pleasure, is not practised in this part of the country, nor are there many considerable spots upon which it could be brought to bear."—Most assuredly, in the *vallies*, and at the *feet*, of the *Wolds*, much land might be irrigated, with water of the first quality ;—with water similar to that by which such wonders are wrought, in the vallies, and at the feet, of the Chalk Hills of the southern Counties.

For a good reason, why the fens of Lincolnshire can seldom be watered. See the head, *Waters*, p. 17, aforegoing.

EXECUTIVE MANAGEMENT of Tenanted Estates.—On the improvement and management of landed property are found, in this Report, numerous remarks, suggestions, and recommendations of the Reporter.—Many of them are just; but few of them new: most of them having previously appeared in Public, under a more intelligible form.—Nevertheless, for reasons above given, I will preserve a few of them from oblivion; as there is not, I apprehend, much probability of *Stone's Lincolnshire* being " reprinted."

Managers of Estates.—P. 94. " I take the liberty of recom-

recommending to the Board of Agriculture, and to gentlemen of landed property in general, the measure of
promoting the education of young men for the offices of
surveyors and land-stewards, in the best cultivated
counties, by means of sending them to assist in the best
practical husbandry of Norfolk, Essex, Suffolk, and
Hertfordshire; and the breeding, feeding, and improvement of cattle and sheep, now so successfully practised
in Leicestershire. And, that all persons who shall in
future be disposed to practise as surveyors, should give
their names to the Board of Agriculture, stating their
pretensions, in order that they might undergo an examination, in a similar way as candidates for other professions; and, upon being appointed, to receive cer-
tificates for their qualifications. If a plan, similar to
this, were to be adopted, such men as had expended
their time and property in acquiring the fundamental
instructions for a competent knowledge of agriculture,
upon which subsequent experience have been grafted,
would have a fair prospect of success, from their exertions; and the interests of the community, as well as
that of individuals, would be essentially promoted."

No offence could possibly be given, were we to enquire, by whom the "Examinations" here suggested, were
proposed to be undertaken. Neither the President, the
Secretary, nor the Clerks in office, at that time (learned
as they might be in statistics and political arithmetic,)
had any pretensions to a sufficient knowledge of the
duties of estate agency, to judge of the due qualifications of an executive manager of tenanted estates.

I am here induced to say;—and, I fear, to gain a tolerably fair opportunity of saying it—has been the chief
motive toward making the above extract;—Had my
PROPOSAL for a RURAL INSTITUTE been adopted, ten
years ago, not only a PRACTICAL SEMINARY might now
have been completely established, but numbers of
CAPABLE MANAGERS have been, already, distributed over
the kingdom.

Tenancy.—P. 98. "There are but few estates, that
are so circumstanced, as not to admit of improvement;
few on which an occupier of abilities might not lay out
a considerable part of his property, for the sake of future
advantages to his landlord, as well as himself. On this
account it is reasonable, that he should be secured in his
expectations as far as human foresight will allow; and
this is most effectually done by a lease. Though a gentleman's

tleman's word may be as binding to him as his bond, his successor is not bound by it; therefore a farmer cannot be expected to lay out his money, which is often the dependence of a family of children, upon the uncertainty of an occupation from year to year. Such gentlemen as are determined not to grant leases at any rate, must be content to let their estates beneath their real value, and neglect many useful improvements, which would tend to their own, the tenants, and the public advantage."

P. 99. "Where an estate is let according to its fair value, a lease is as necessary to secure the landlord's interest in the premises as a tenant's. Where a farmer occupies land from year to year, particularly arable lands, if he is self-interested, indolent, or injudicious, a farm may almost imperceptibly become impoverished before any alarm is taken. Indeed such farms generally fall into the proprietor's hands in the most wretched condition. I have frequently heard gentlemen of landed property complain, that they are considerable losers by farming; and it may reasonably be accounted for, since the land usually comes into their hands in a reduced state, and in that case, let who will be occupier, two or three years rent must be sunk to restore it. *Rent is an annual sum paid by the tenant to the landlord, without diminishing the value of his property; and when the value of an estate is reduced, it cannot be called rent, but so much deducted from the real worth of the possession.* Proprietors of land, do not all of them consider this matter in a true light, and when they can advance the annual income of their estates, consider it as rent, whilst the property is suffering in an equal proportion to the annual sum received during the demise.

"In the course of my experience, I have had applications from the people to take farms consisting of arable and pasture, who have set out with a determination not to be bound by what I conceived to be the rules of good husbandry, but to do as they pleased with the premises during the intended demise; I always refused to treat upon such terms, well knowing the value of the land must be reduced. But, when such matters have been represented to a principal, who was not a judge in these things, he considered such denial as foregoing his interest, by refusing what appeared to him to be a great rent.

"There are particular situations where long leases are

are unnecessary and improper, especially when farms consist wholly of *rich pasture land, which will admit of no improvement**, or farms lying near to gentlemen's seats or parks, where a disagreeable neighbour, for a term of years, would be a great inconvenience."

On the *covenants* of leases, we find little to instruct, or interest (saving what relates to the system of cropping; and this is intimated rather than expressed) in this Report.

The following dictation conveys an unfavourable idea of the management of Estates in Lincolnshire.—P. 44. " Wherever the following custom prevails, it should be abolished, viz.

" For the incoming tenants to enter upon only the farm-houses, pastures, meadows, and fallows, at the time the tenancy, and the whole of the rent commences: the outgoing tenants taking the crops of grain, pulse, &c. in that year, and embarning them on the premises, and keeping possession of the barns and stack-yards until the Midsummer twelve month, after they cease to pay rent, in order to thrash out and carry away the corn. In other instances more barbarous, though more rare, it is customary for the outgoing tenants to sell all the last year's crop in the straw, at harvest, to the public, to be carried off the premises. Of course, the incoming tenant adheres to the custom of his entry, when it is his turn to quit, &c."

For mischiefs arising from a want of due regulations, respecting the " Breaking up of ancient pasture lands," —see the head Plan of Management, ensuing.

On the *time of entry, and removal,*—are the following loose Remarks, in p. 43. " The seed time and harvest here, fall later than in the more southern districts, not only on account of its being farther north, but from mismanagement in not getting the seed, or the Spring crops, sufficiently early into the ground, which is in many places delayed till May. And upon many estates here, and other parts of the County, this is the customary time for quitting, and entering upon farms, which is a bad practice, for if it is arable land, it is too late to put the spring seed in the ground; if it is meadow, clover, or

seeds

---

* Yet it will be seen that the Reporter is friendly to breaking up, and of course to deteriorating, lands in such a state of perfection.

seeds for mowing, it is too late to lay in the land for that purpose. If it is artificial grasses, or pasture, being fed off bare (for tenants, who are here going off, seldom leave any thing behind them) the interest of the incoming tenant is extremely delayed."

WOODLANDS.

ON Woodlands and Planting, I perceive nothing relating to the practice of Lincolnshire; or to its present state, in those particulars; excepting that (p. 25.) "but little wood is to be found in this part of the country," (the fens) " except the willows."

The Reporter's general remarks on those subjects are merely speculative, or emanate from works, previously published. The following recommendation, it is true, might, a century ago, have had its use : and lest some remnant of such irrational regulations, as are therein intimated, should still exist, I will transcribe the passage. It will, at least, serve as an item of the folly, or the iniquity, of former times.

P. 93. "I recommend that forest officers, stewards, agents, and woodmen, shall have regular fixed salaries, and that they shall not constantly have it in their power to take advantage of their own wrong-doing ; for, according to the present mode, pretty generally adopted in the falling and converting timber, it is customary for them to take part of the property in bark, topwood, &c. or poundage, as perquisites of office, upon the sale of it ; and therefore, whilst the quantity annually to be cut is limited, it is their interest not to cut down such trees as are mature or decaying, but otherwise the most trifling ones which would, according to the best mode of employing the land, pay most for standing longer, and which will consequently produce most bark, and top or lop-wood: and when gentlemen of landed property shall, from experience, feel the necessity, for giving more attention than at present, to the improvement of the agriculture to be adopted upon their estates, men of of skill and experience will be employed to superintend them, at such salaries as will not only make them respectable, but will place them above the temptation of abusing the trusts to be reposed in them."

SUBJECT THE THIRD.

AGRICULTURE.

FARMS.—*Sizes.*—For a general idea of the sizes of farms, in the County, at large,—see the head, *Sizes* of *Estates*, p. 36, aforegoing.

P. 40. (Uplands) " There are generally evident marks of a decrease of population, from the number of decayed farm-houses; whilst it appears, that in various situations, one or two opulent farmers, skim over some thousands of acres, formerly occupied by more inhabitants; and there cannot be a greater proof, that agriculture has not abundantly improved in this country, than the decrease of the number of its inhabitants."

Hence, Mr. Stone recommends,—p. 82. " The inclosing common-fields and waste-lands, and reducing the size of large farms, already inclosed, by dividing them, and building necessary farm-houses in centrical situations, not suffering any farm to exceed 800 acres. And in proportion as the soil is found to be good, to decrease the quantity of it in the hands of the respective occupiers."

Mr. S. proceeds to offer reasons for these recommendations. His opinion, drawn from them, however, is all that is requisite to be inserted, here.

P. 82. " I will venture to hazard an opinion, that farms, properly laid out, according to the nature of the respective soils of the yearly value of from 40 to £200 are the most desirable for the proprietors, and to the community."—And this I insert merely as Mr. Stone's opinion. I have, elsewhere, spoken my sentiments, fully, on this subject. See TREATISE on LANDED PROPERTY.

Cottage Cow Grounds.—All that I perceive, on this controversial topic, in the Report under review, is the subjoined intimation,—P. 25. (" Fens") " It is not an object of common concern with the landed interest, that the necessary labourers employed upon the respective

estates

estates should have provided for them comfortable habitations, and other accommodations, whereby they may keep cows, and produce necessary potatoes, and other roots for their families."

If there is any situation, in which farm laborers, *in general*, can keep cows, with strict propriety, it is in the fens and marshes of Lincolnshire &c. where the unhealthiness of the climature may demand such an indulgence;—to reconcile resident laborers to their situation; and where (grasslands abounding) no serious evil to the community at large, can arise from it.

Homesteads.—P. 26. ("Fens") "The farm-houses and buildings are generally very well adapted for the situation of the country, and generally well distributed." (?)

P. 35. (Vale Lands) "The farm buildings are not generally placed in central situations, and, for the most part, the farms are deficient of those conveniences, which are necessary in a due cultivation of the land."

For Remarks on the situation of Homesteads, see p. 38, aforegoing.

PLANS of MANAGEMENT of Farms; or the STATE of HUSBANDRY, in Lincolnshire.—On this fundamental topic, in agriculture, Mr. Stone has properly bestowed ample attention.

To endeavour to place under the most profitable arrangement, the several notices and remarks that are scattered over the body of the Report (chiefly owing to the many inapt subdivisions of it) I will first bring together what is said on the subject of COMMON-FIELD HUSBANDRY; as this will serve to show, in some sort, the progress of agriculture in the County :—and, then, to notice, under the respective districts, such particulars as I conceive to be of sufficient import for extraction,— belonging to its APPROPRIATED LANDS.

1. *Management* of *Common-field Lands.*—P. 26. (Vale Lands) "These descriptions of soils are about equal parts arable and pasture, and nearly in one-fourth common-field, in the management of which there is no precise or specific mode. In some parts of the country, the common-fields are divided in 4 parts, in others 3, in others 2, the whole being very much mixed, and dispersed. The mode of cropping in those fields, which are divided into 4 parts, is in the following rotine, or nearly so :

1 year

1 year fallow		fallow		fallow
2	wheat	or	barley	barley
3	beans		beans	or	clover
4	barley	or	wheat	wheat

" In those fields of 3 divisions, is the following rotine of cropping, or nearly so:

1 year fallow		fallow		fallow
2	wheat	or	barley	or	wheat
3	beans		beans	or	oats

" But the foregoing modes of cropping are not generally established, nor are the occupiers held to them by any particular rules.

" IN THOSE FIELDS WHICH ARE EQUALLY DIVIDED, it is the customary practice to fallow a moiety of one of the fields for wheat and barley, and to let the residue of intermixed lands lie the whole summer, which has, in the previous year, produced wheat or barley, without being ploughed or sowed with any grass, or other seeds, a very plentiful crop of thistles is generally produced. In settling the rents, and selling the land, under a specific mode of management, upon Colonel Manners' estate, who has some arable common field land in Allford, in 1790, I persuaded the occupiers to sow clover with their barley and wheat, for it was impossible to compel general adherence to any plan, which is not sanctioned by 4-5ths of the occupiers of a common field; that instead of a moiety of one field lying the whole succeeding summer, producing thistles only, clover might be had; this was practised for two years, but left off in 1783, and the reason assigned was, that in the previous winter the sheep had been destroyed by a general rot; and therefore the occupiers were disheartened, and did not think it worth while to sow clover. The thistles escape both mowing and hoeing; of course their seeds are plentifully distributed. The land thus producing thistles comes in rotine in the succeeding year, to be sowed with beans and oats. Hence it appears, that a moiety of the arable land produces wheat, barley, oats, and beans; the other moiety lies in a state of fallow, and producing thistles, as before described."

P. 30. " The common fields of Epworth, Belton, Flaxey, and Owston, within the isle," (of Axholm) " consist of a very fertile, strong, loam, the property in which is very much divided into many different small occupations. Potatoes, and every kind of grain, pulse, hemp, and

and flax, are indiscriminately and unsystematically cultivated. It is a common mode with the occupiers, to sow 5 or 6 successive exhausting crops (one of which is generally flax) without attempting to fallow the land, or throw any manure upon it.

" When it is reduced to a state of beggary and rubbish, it is well covered with manure, and hemp is sowed thereon, of which it generally produces a great crop; this smothers all other productions, and is the foundation of various other successive exhausting crops."

P. 53. (" General Remarks") " From the statements hereinbefore made, it must appear, that agriculture has not generally improved in this county of late years; but, I rather fear, has been on the decline : for if we refer to the usage of the common fields, and contemplate those which were originally divided into three parts, one field being annually fallowed, and in succession sowed in moieties, with wheat and barley; and the third season, or what is commonly called the breach-crop, being sowed in moieties of beans and oats. It is very evident, that these fields were first so arranged by our ancestors, with a direct view to a system of farming, and that system was the best that then could be devised."

P. 56. (The same) " If those gentlemen, whether proprietors or agents, who have any concern in the management of common fields, will examine into the present mode of occupancy of the different classes of them, as here stated, they will in most cases find them in a weak impoverished state; and that the original systematic farming of them, is either lost or laid aside, and that the agriculture of the common fields of this County, has rather declined than improved, in the present century."

2. *Management* of *Inclosures.*—P. 47. (" Marshes")— " The most considerable part of this land is in a state of pasture, and of a very good quality for feeding, or fatting, cattle and sheep; but not much used to breeding, for which purpose it is not well-adapted, nor could it be so profitably applied*.

" The Southern part is more used as arable land, than that towards the North, but no regular system of husbandry is pursued. Very little land is here let under lease, nor any precise rules for management observed ; but it is used in a manner similar to the fen, in respect to repeated crops of white grain, except that the destructive

" * The lambs would be drowned in the ditches, &c &c."

structive practice of paring and burning is more spa-
ringly pursued."

P. 48. (The same) " But whilst I contemplate the vast
advantage arising from the inclosure of the commons of
Long Sutton, I cannot but observe a considerable quantity of land in that lordship, which was originally gained
from the sea, and was, in the first instance, as productive
and valuable as the late inclosed commons, but which,
by a series of exhausting crops, and every species of
mismanagement, is reduced to a very low condition.
And, I fear, the late inclosed commons of Long Sutton
are under a similar treatment; and, unless the plough
be restrained, and a well-digested system of husbandry
adopted, we shall in the course of ten years, see this
amazing productive tract of land, in such a state, that it
will no longer bear exhausting crops of grain, laid down
for pasture, probably of but little more value to the individuals immediately interested, and to the community,
than it was in its state of common."—Yet we shall see,
by and by, the Reporter coming forward as an advocate
for converting lands, from the state of grass, to that of
arable.

P. 15. (" Fens")—" That part of the fens which is
used in the way of cultivation, is chiefly arable, and
occasionally laid down for pasture—when exhausted by
ploughing, with ray-grass and clover. Paring and burning is the great resource, and here it is practised in the
fullest extent.

" System of husbandry, or precise mode of management, according to the quality of the land (generally
speaking) there is none. Doubtless, in so vast an extent of country, there are occupiers who approach
nearer to perfection in their management than others;
but the general practice is, to begin with paring and
burning, as the foundation of their husbandry, to sow
cole, or rape-seed (which often stands for seed). Then
oats are sowed in succession, year after year, till the
powers of the land are nearly exhausted, or till it is
doubtful, whether the farmer shall, by a repetition of
croppings, be repaid for his seed and labour; and then,
such land is left to repair itself by rest, for many years.
Nor is it an universal practice to sow grass-seeds with
the last crop of grain, and if this process succeeds entirely to the wishes of the farmer, the sooner the land
acquires a great thickness of coarse productions, the
better; as then it will the sooner require paring and
burning,

burning, and yield a large quantity of vegetable ashes, a promising foundation for successive crops of oats, or white grain."

P. 16. (The same) " *Crops in the Fens.* Oats are the grain chiefly cultivated, with here and there wheat, beans, peas, and barley. Cole-seed and clover are the chief vegetable crops, but the latter is generally sown with bad or foul ray-grass, when the land is exhausted by repeated crops of white grain, so that the advantage to be derived by a fair separate use of it, is very rarely experienced."

P. 32. (Vale Lands) " The inclosed estates, which are chiefly in the hands of large proprietors, ant-hills, bushes, rushes, and water, occupy a very considerable part of the pasture land, which is not half so productive as it might be made, even if it was to be continued in a state of pasture ; a portion of this inclosed land is under the plough, probably such quantity may extend to one-fourth part, but few farmers have a sufficient quantity of ploughed land to enable them to go on systematically, in procuring green winter food, and artificial grasses, &c. if they were inclined to do so ; but the quantity of ploughed land is considered, by the proprietors and agents, as so much devoted to destruction ; and, upon this description of property, the tenants are under no restrictions, except as to the not ploughing up ancient pasture land. Upon tracing back the former usage of this property, it appears to have been the practice, as it is in the present day, for tenants to obtain permission from those into whose care the management of the property has been committed, to plough parcels of the pasture land from time to time, under assurances of laying land down again, for pasture, parcels of arable land, which have been heretofore under the plough; but as there has not been any stipulated proper mode, in which such land should be farmed, whilst it continued under the plough, or in what state it should be again laid down, the common practice has been, and now is, to raise successive crops of white grain, until its nature is not only exhausted, but filled with beggary and rubbish, and then it is sowed down with grass seeds to repair itself by rest ; and a common excuse for this procedure is the most absurd of all possible excuses, viz. "If grass " seeds had been sowed with the corn, when the land " has been lusty, or in a richer state, the seeds would " have been choaked by the luxuriance of the crop."

There

There surely cannot be a greater absurdity, than that
of exhausting the land with repeated crops, and thereby
making it poor and foul, at the very precise time when
it is to be seeded down, and when a foundation ought to
be laid for its heart and good condition for ages; and
this practice may be traced, in almost all the pasture
land which has been ploughed within the present century, so that it is not the natural face we are given commonly to behold, but a foul and disguising mask."—Yet
breaking up grass lands would seem to be a favourite
system of the Reporter.

P. 56. ("General Remark") "The agriculture in
the inclosures, according to the foregoing statements,
cannot have improved, whilst the occupiers have been
either under general restraints from applying the soil
to its right use, and thereby under insuperable bars to
cultivation, with respect to pasture land, which remains
in a state of nature; and whilst, with respect to the
arable, they have been at liberty to plough and sow
it without system, and without restraint. Yet, I must
freely admit, that by means of inclosing common fields
and waste lands, the science of agriculture advanced the
first step towards improvement, but there it has, generally speaking, remained, without making any additional progress."

P. 38. (Uplands) "This description of property was
formerly for the most part devoted to rabbits, the residue
as open common fields; but within the last century,
nearly the whole has been gradually inclosed, and
brought into tillage, and occupied as arable farms;
which are generally in the hands of large occupiers.
The tenants are rarely under leases, or bound by any
rules to enforce good management; and of course, the
interests of landlord and tenant are not defined, or in
any degree preserved from militating against each
other, by regular well-digested systems of farming, laid
down between landlord and tenant, in pursuit of the
best practical modes of husbandry, which have been
adopted upon soils of similar natures.

"On this account, we find the generality of the land
poor, weak, and foul; made so, by repeated crops of
white grain" (corn *) "and which procedure having been
long

---

* GRAIN CROPS naturally divide into those of *corn* and *pulse*,
which are well understood and long established terms. Beside,
"*white*

long continued, of course the means of producing the common manure to reinstate the land, have gradually decreased; and it is not an uncommon thing, to find very considerable tracts of land, by such means, reduced to a state much worse, than it was in when cultivation was first began, or when the inclosures were first made; and it is now considered, as only fit to be turned again to its original mode of occupancy, in rabbit-warrens; and which is, in many instances, adopted."

P. 46. (The same) "If it was not much more the design of this publication to state the general agriculture of the County, than the particular instances of good management, I could enumerate several proofs of it; but, as at least nine-tenths of the agriculture of this large tract of country, is barbarous in the extreme, I am certainly justifiable in representing such to be its general state, without giving offence, which is the furthest from my design."

3. *Proposed Improvements*, by the Reporter.—P. 73. (Vale Lands) " First, with regard to the inclosed land, I recommend that the soil shall be applied to its right use : that is to say, such parts of the pasture land, which are best adapted to the arable, shall be converted to such use, and such parts of the land, now arable, which might be better laid down for pasture, shall be so used.

" There is not a circumstance in agriculture so little understood, as the *application of soil to its right use.* And, independent of local circumstances, such as the vicinage of large towns, homesteads, or convenient spots near farm-yards, all light soils, and all thin stapled clayey land, are ill adapted for perpetual pasture ; as they are subject to be too suddenly affected by dry weather, to crack. and fly to pieces hastily, and thereby the roots of the plants are either destroyed, or very much checked, by being broken, or split to pieces, and the sun and air are let into the soil to dry them up, to the great detriment of the occupier.

" If I were to fix a criterion of the land which is best adapted to be laid down for perpetual pasture (independent of local circumstances,) it would be, that which has such a depth of soil, that no cracks, or fissures, in the

" *white* grain" cannot surely be well applied to *black* grain, or *red* grain, as that of oats.—This misnomer is not peculiar to Mr. Stone : or it would not have called forth these remarks, here.

the driest summers, are produced in it. I am confident that a very considerable portion of land in this County, now in a state of pasture, might be changed to arable, to the great advantage of both the proprietors and the occupiers.

"In particular situations, where it might be desirable to keep the land in a state of perpetual pasture, plough-ing it up, and cleaning it, by means of fallowing; and a well-chosen course of cropping, for five or six years, and then laying it down again with the best grasses, to be sowed with a first crop of grain, after a good fallow, and a green vegetable crop to be eaten off by sheep, would be a means of improvement, which is not calcula-ted upon in this County."

This might be deemed (not quite fairly though fashionably) an *Irish* mode of improvement :—" The best way to keep land in a state of perpetual pasture is to plough it up."—It is to be feared, however, that some Englishmen, instigated perhaps by necessity or avarice, have caught at this recommendation; to the injury of the permanent interest of themselves and their succes-sors.—Again,

P. 75. " I confess myself to have no prejudice for pasture land, as such, I am always inclined to apply the soil to the most immediate profitable uses it is capable of, consistently with the preservation and improvement of the inheritance in it; for, in proportion as the value of the land is diminished, by bad management, the rent is nominal, and a proprietor is receiving, as such, a part of his inheritance."

It would be difficult to produce a more ingenious argument, than this is, *against* the breaking up of pro-ductive grass lands :—an improvident expedient which bears no little resemblance, to that of ripping up the hen which laid golden eggs.

Nevertheless, this professional Reporter, whose recom-mendations are *not always* improper, but whose dictates may be liable, *in many instances,* to give the mind of an inexperienced practioner false and injurious impressions, —continues his strictures with the following specious, and *impressive* remarks.—P. 75. " All land subject to be overflowed by rivers, and in the vicinity of large towns, and in any other situations, where it has an ad-ditional value stamped upon it, for the conveniences it affords, ought to be continued in pasture (except small portions used as garden-ground;) but in more remote situations,

situations, it behoves every proprietor to apply his estate to the most profitable uses *. I am confident these opinions will meet with opposition from men, who are unacquainted with the most approved practical husbandry, and who, as agents or surveyors, know not how to apply the soils to their right use, nor how to lay down the regulating systems of agriculture, adapted to each soil, in order to preserve and improve the estates; for it is impossible, that mere measurers of land, or persons never having resided seven days in their whole lives in a well-cultivated country, and who have been constantly plodding in a district, where its agriculture is more than a century behind many other Counties, should be competent to a business of this nature; as reasonably might we expect an hedge carpenter, successfully to amend a Cremona fiddle."

This is too wide a field to enter upon, at large, here. Yet, seeing the mischiefs that have ensued, and may ensue, from false representations, wrong conceptions, or misunderstandings, in regard to this subject, it may be right to bestow upon it a few moments' attention.

Changing old arable lands to grass, and old pasture lands to arable; and, especially, changing *commonfield* lands of a nature suitable to permanent herbage, to a state of perennial grass, and rough ill-herbaged *commons* and unsuitably soiled *common meadows,* to a state of Aration,—I have formerly shown (in the instance of the Vale of Pickering, in YORKSHIRE) to be highly beneficial to proprietors and the community. But this is not a good precedent, nor furnishes any good argument, for *destroying,* during a length of years, *appropriated* MEADOWS, and rich GRAZING GROUNDS, that have been productive, as such, time immemorial; and that are, perhaps, rather increasing than diminishing in regard to their productiveness (a great extent of which lands there are in every Department of this kingdom)—under the theoretic idea of "cleansing" them,—by "fallowing" and a "course of cropping for five or six years."

The Reporter has furnished us, aforegoing, with ample proofs of the mischiefs which ensued from breaking up,
even

---

* This position is broad enough to cover *all situations.* But it is not the profit of a few crops, but of a long series of crops, and in the case in point, of a series of generations, that are to be consulted, and kept in view..

even the deep rich marsh lands of Lincolnshire. It would require ages, or centuries, probably, to bring these marshes to that state of rich grazing ground, in which they, now, would doubtlessly have been,—had they not been subjected to Aration.

To expect that tenants, in general, could be induced to lay down lands, so broken, in the manner most profitable to the proprietors, would be great imprudence; even were the Reporter, himself, to be placed over them.

On this important topic, viewed in a political light, it may be said,—while animal food continues to be considered as a necessary of life, a portion of territory is requisite to its production. And (notwithstanding what we have heard about "summer soiling") nothing is so proper, under the present circumstances of this country, as MARSH LANDS, and other GRAZING GROUNDS, for furnishing the community at large with the requisite supply. Whenever the entire island shall have been appropriated and improved, and be still found to be insufficient to the maintenance of its inhabitants, it may, then, be right policy to convert perennial grass lands to the purpose of producing grain crops. But till, then, (were it right for the public to interfere with private property) it would be wise to *prevent* their being broken up: unless in time of extreme scarcity. They are mines of more value, to this island, than those of the two Indies, added to all the garrisoned colonies in the Universe. They are treasures that may be drawn upon for the sustenance of its inhabitants, in cases where gold itself could be of no avail. They are the most secure granaries, for times of need :—storerooms, which no invader can plunder.—A nation rich in permanent grass lands may be said to be rich, indeed. And he is the truest patriot who preserves the greatest quantity of land, in that most valuable state.

WORK PEOPLE.—P. 24. (Fens) "The price of labour is not fixed to any precise rules: when labourers are required, and the farmer's occasions are pressing, the labourer exacts the utmost he can get: and, on the other hand, when the farmer's occasions are slack, the labourer's wages are proportionably low. No part of rural economy requires regulating more than this; but, on an average, the following statement is as near the price of labour as possible, viz. from the end of the harvest, till hay time begins, the hire of a labourer is

from

from 1s. to 1s. 2d. *per* day, and 1s. 6d. *per* day, from that time till the corn harvest begins; and during the time of harvest, from 2s. 6d. to 3s. *per* day."

WORKING ANIMALS.—P. 17. (Fens) " Brood mares of the black cart kind, are used instead of horses and oxen, which, from the ease with which the labour is performed by them, answer the purposes of agriculture equally well, and as they generally produce a foal every year, which sells for 10 or 12 pounds, they are undoubtedly profitable."

P. 42. (Uplands) " Oxen are used in a considerable portion of the labour, and are found to answer in point of advantage, to the occupiers."

IMPLEMENTS.—(" Fens") P. 17. " Low waggons are substituted for carts, the sides of which are made to take out, or fall down, as occasion shall require them, to deposit the contents, or receive their loads; and this mode of conveying the requisites upon a farm, may answer as well as carts. All the other implements are in the common way, and need no particular description *.

MANURES.—P. 16. (Fens) " The manures chiefly used in the fens are, the vegetable ashes arising from paring and burning, and common stable, or stable-yard, dung, which latter manure, till lately, was considered to be of no value by the fen-farmers, but rather an incumbrance; and I recollect an instance of its accumulating so much in a farm-yard here, that the farmer thought it more advisable, and did actually remove his barn further into his field, or home close, rather than carry out his dung upon his land. Since the land has become exhausted of late years, by repeated cropping it with oats, the manure is carried a little way into the fields, but the distant land gets none of it."

For the usage of the *sheep fold* in Lincolnshire, see the head *sheep*, ensuing.

TILLAGE.—P. 16. (Fens) " Fallowing is very rarely practised, paring and burning being its substitute."

SEMINATION.—P. 36. (Vale Lands) " No drilling, hoeing, or dibbling, is pursued in the common fields, but in some instances sheep are turned into the beans, to eat out a part of the weeds."—" Very small portions indeed, of inclosed land, are drilled and hoed, and I know but few instances where it has made any considerable progress."   POTATOES.

* These useful carriages, in soft sloughy roads, are seen in the Cambridge fens, also.

POTATOES.—P. 30. (Vale Lands) " Potatoes are here produced in great abundance, and of the best quality, and sent down the Trent, which bounds the eastern part of the isle, to the London market."

TURNEPS.—P. 39. (Upland) " Turnips are cultivated in this part of the country very extensively, but, for the most part, the fallows are ill-prepared for them, and they are very badly hoed, or not at all, by which neglect, from 20 s. to 3 l. per acre, in the value of them, is generally lost; and more, if we estimate the loss of the manure they would afford."

HEMP.—For its use in smothering weeds, see *plan* of *Management*, p. 49, aforegoing.

WOAD.—P. 16. (Fens) " At Brothertoft, or in its vicinity, near Boston, large quantities of woad are cultivated by Mr. Cartwright and Mr. Harrison, and with profit. The former of these gentlemen has erected some very convenient buildings, for manufacturing, or converting it to its right uses. The cultivation of this plant in a systematic manner, seems to be his intention, and being possessed of a considerable tract of land, he will be enabled to continue regular apportionments of it, for 4 or 5 years bearing woad, then to be laid down in pasture for 10 or 12 years, after which it comes round again for woad."

GRASS LANDS.—Here I must express my surprize, at the paucity, or nothingness, of information, relating to this subject; even in a first sketch, or " Original Report,"—of the husbandry of Lincolnshire. Whatever knowledge the Reporter might possess, concerning upland farming, and the winter and spring fatting of cattle, as practiced, in Norfolk, we may venture to conclude that he was deficient in practical knowledge of summer grazing; otherwise, he could not have *reported* the rural practices of Lincolnshire (nor even have *sketched* them) without speaking more fully of perennial grass lands and their management. The following extracts contain all that I find noticeable, on this subject.

P. 15. (" Fens") " Some parts of the fens are in a state of pasture, and now reserved from the plough by the respective proprietors; the best is stocked with fatting oxen and sheep, and the more ordinary with breeding stock."

For a hint respecting the rolling of fen lands, see *Sodburning*, p. 41, aforegoing.

Haying in the *Fens.*—P. 25. " Hay-making is very indifferently

indifferently performed, no particular attention being paid to it, as in the southern Counties; in fine weather it generally lies in the swath, if not a very thick crop, as the scythe left it, till it is considered to be half made, and then it is turned, and prepared for the stack; but, if it is a thick crop, it is in some places broken a little: the loss sustained in wet seasons, for want of attention to the hay crops, is very considerable. A similar want of attention appears in making and finishing the stacks, which are very rarely topped up, pulled, or thatched, in a proper manner to secure them."

Vale Lands.—P. 74. " It is not only an unsightly appearance, but a distressing circumstance to the renter of pasture land, of which, considerable portions (in many instances two-thirds of the fields,) are occupied by large ant-hills, producing sour, coarse, husky, sedge, or sword-grass, of no value, as it possesses no wholesome quality; and no animal in the creation will depasture upon it."

The Reporter speaks of different ways of removing so disgusting a sight; but I find nothing to be noticed, here; excepting a circumstance relating to the " gelding" of anthills (an operation he describes improperly) which may, in some cases, be worth attending to.

P. 75. " The latter practice" (gelding) " I have seen answer tolerably well, where the surface of the hills has produced a middling good herbage, and where it was an object with the occupier to continue the land in pasture, on account of some local considerations; but this process, when judiciously performed, was three years in being brought about upon a given spot; for apprehending that the best of the land would be over-burthened with dead earth, only each third ant-hill in a field was annually gelt, or thrown down."

The Reporter, however, recommends,—" In all cases where the hills cover a considerable part of the land, and their produce is bad, I recommend the ploughing it up, and converting it to tillage for one course of husbandry at least, that is to say, for five or six years*."

HORSES.—P. 62. " In the fens, the black-cart kind is chiefly bred, colt foals are sold off the mares, and sent into

* In a case of this sort, a proprietor may or may not (according to given circumstances) be right, in permitting his old grass lands to be broken up; and the best excuse that can be made for Mr. Stone is, that he had such lands as are above described, *principally* (he could not have them *wholely*) in view, when he wrote the preceding extracts.

into the high parts of Huntingdonshire, Cambridgeshire,
Bucks, Bedfordshire, &c. from 10 to 12 *l.* each; and
colts, rising two years old, from 18 to 20 *l.* each. In the
neighbourhood of Long Sutton, there is a breed of horses
for the saddle, remarkable for their bone, and activity;
sixteen miles an hour is the rate of their trotting, and
sixteen stone the accustomed weight they carry, in performing such exertions."

P. 63. " It is a practice, with many occupiers of grass
land, to purchase bay three year old colts, at the Yorkshire fairs, to keep them a year, or till they are four
years old, although, from the custom of drawing the
corner teeth, by which means the last teeth come up a
year before they otherwise would appear, and to a common observer, they appear to be five years old. They
are made fat, nicked, and sold, at Horncastle fair, to the
London dealers, at the customary prices, from 35 to 40 *l.*
each. They are then taken to London, where they undergo the exercise of the break, or carriage, for a month
or six weeks, and are sold from seventy to eighty guineas
each for gentlemen's carriages.

" Horses, thus young, being driven hard about the
pavement in London, and kept in hot stables, soon give
way in their feet, and they become foundered and useless; consequently a much larger quantity of these
animals are bred upon our land, than would otherwise be
necessary, if they were seasoned, and used for the purposes of agriculture, till they are six or seven years old."

CATTLE.—P. 57. " The *neat* cattle of this County are,
for the most part, of a large sort. The cows, when fat,
weigh from 8 to 9 hundred weight; the oxen from 10 to 12.

" They are generally large in the head, horns, bones,
and bellies; thick, short, and fleshy, in their necks and
quarters; narrow in their hips, plates, chines, and
bosoms; high in their rumps, and their shoulders not
well covered; their eyes small and sunk *. Those bred
in the common fields are, from 3 to 5 pounds *per* head,
of less value, at four years old, than those bred in inclosed parishes; and this difference may be attributed
to a neglect of shape more than size, and it may be fairly presumed, that the ill-shapen animal consumes as
much, if not more food, than those which are made with
more symmetry.

"But,

---

* For a sketch of the "ill-shapen," "neat" cattle of the *commons,*
see the head, *Appropriation,* p. 22, aforegoing.

" But, whilst I am stating this to be the description of the generality of the neat cattle of this County, I must, in justice to Mr. Tyndall's breed, at Ewerby, near Sleaford; and Mr. Hoyte's at Osbornby, near Folkingham, declare them to be the reverse of the foregoing description; and that for true symmetry of shape, lightness of bone and offals, great weight of carcase, and aptitude to become fat, they surpass every breed I have before seen in this County."

Dairy.—P. 57. " The pasture land of this County is not much used for dairies; and the art of making good cheese and butter is not generally understood.

" The reason given for this *delay* of the interest of the occupiers, is imputed to the general good quality of the land, which is said to be too rich to produce those articles in perfection, an inference drawn, I fear, from false premises, viz. that, upon poorer soils, those articles are generally good; whilst the contrary is here found. I should rather apprehend, that the same cause for the *delay* of improvement in this particular exists, which is found in most other respects, viz. that the general fertility of the land is, in the minds of the occupiers, considered to supersede the apparent necessity for personal exertion; whilst, upon poorer soils, the occupiers are, in a great degree, driven to supply the deficiencies of nature by industry.

" An evident want of cleanliness is too frequently discovered in the dairies, in not sufficiently, or frequently, shifting the cream, churning often enough, or properly scalding the vessels; and in making the dairies receptacles for meat, and various other family provisions; and it is frequently found, that the dairies and cellars are indiscriminately used for the same purposes, or placed too near each other, which must always tend to taint the milk and cream. In the construction of farm-houses, there is a general want of attention to the making of dairies in the north sides of them, or in situations out of the way of the farm-yards, and every effluvia which can tend to render them unsweet.

" The calves are, for the most part, weaned, and reared. The veal is generally of a very bad quality, not only on account of the coarseness of the animal, but also, from a total inattention to the pursuing of the best methods of confining, suckling, and lodging the animal in the most cleanly manner."

Of the *rearing* of cattle, we find no mention; except in the line, above transcribed, and a similar notice in, p. 25.

On

On the *fatting* or *grazing* of cattle, not a word!—in a report from a County which might be said to furnish the navy of England with beef.

SHEEP.—P. 58. " I now enter upon a subject which has been very generally discussed in this County, and which has produced much contention and emulation, between the disciples of Mr. Bakewell, and those gentlemen who have adhered to that sort of sheep, which have been most generally, of late years, bred in the County ; and the contending parties have now classed them severally under the Leicestershire and Lincolnshire sorts."

I perceive not, however, in Mr. Stone's strictures, a syllable to instruct, or even to interest, at this time, that part of the Public which possess any knowledge of the extraordinary improvements that have taken place, in the longwooled sheep of the Midland and Eastern Departments. And those who are unacquainted with its rise and progress, Mr. S's Report will lend but little assistance. As to the disputes, and caballistic feuds, to which these improvements have given rise, they are neither more nor less than the jealousies and bickerings of " *two of a trade.*"

In my register of the Rural Economy of the Midland Counties, I gave a circumstantial detail of the rise, the progress and, I believe I may say, the perfecting, of this extraordinary improvement :—and, moreover, pointed out the absurdity of attempting to establish any one particular breed of sheep ; showing, demonstrably, I trust, that not only the diversity of soils, but the varieties of manufactures, of this country, indispensibly require widely different breeds of sheep; and, in doing this, pointed out the requisite distinction, between the Lincolnshire and the Leicestershire breeds, as follows :— MIDLAND COUNTIES, Vol. I. p. 369. ' Viewing sheep, generally, and in their various capacities and intentions, as well national, as economical,—it appears, demonstrably, that, of the numerous breeds and varieties, at present in this island, some three, four, or five distinct breeds are indisputably and indispensibly necessary to its present state of prosperity.

' A very long-wooled sheep, as the Lincolnshire, or the old Teeswater,—for the richest grass lands, and for the finest worsted manufactures.

' A second, as the new Leicestershire, for less fertile grass lands, as well as for rich, inclosed, arable lands,— on which the fold is not used, and for the coarser wor-
steads,

steads, stockings, bays, coarse cloths, blankets, car-
pets, &c.

' A third, a middle wooled breed, as the Wiltshire,
the Norfolk, or the Southdown (of Sussex); or the
three; for well soiled arable lands, on which folding is
practised; and for cloths of the middle qualities.

' A fourth, a fine wooled sort, as the Ryland, for the
finest cloths.

' And a fifth, as the Shropshire, or a still more hardy
race for heathy mountains.'

In regard to Lincolnshire, nothing in human concerns
can be more obvious, in the present state of things, than
that, in strict propriety, it requires three distinct breeds
of sheep:—namely, the long established breed of the
County (if any incontaminate remains of it are now to
be found!!) for its rich marshes;—the improved Leicestershire,—or more accurately speaking the BAKEWELL
breed,—for its vale lands;—and the Norfolk, the Southdown, or some other folding breed (so long as folding
sheep shall be found requisite)—for the Wolds and
stoney heights—of that County. And, " woe be to
him," who shall attempt " to level all distinctions."

The sheep of the common fields of Lincolnshire (or
what might be termed the *native*, or established breed
of its upper grounds) are thus noticed by Mr. Stone.—
P. 62. " The sheep of the common-fields, I do not
bring into this account, from the circumstances of hardship, attending the scantiness of their food, the wetness
of their layer, the neglect of a proper choice in their
breed, their being over-heated, in being (when folded)
dogged to their confinement, where they are often too
much crowded; the scab, the rot, and every circumstance
attend them, which can delay their being profitable; so
that it may be reasonably concluded, that they are of
less value than those bred in inclosures, from 10 to 15s.
per head, and their fleeces are equally unproductive."

P. 29. " Folding sheep upon the fallows, in the common fields, is a pretty general practice in the south and
west part of the County; but on the north east, and east,
it is not much pursued."

On the *management* of sheep, in the *fens*, we find some
novel ideas. I insert them as the *opinions* of Lincolnshire fen and marsh farmers; or their *arguments* to
apologize for not raising fences.

P. 68. " It is asserted, by persons very conversant
with the open fens, and open marshes, that sheep will
thrive faster in exposed situations, than where they are
shaded

shaded from the sun in summer, and sheltered from the wind and weather in winter. This idea is drawn from an observation, which, in my mind, ought not to be conclusive upon the subject, which is, that when these animals, by any means are sheltered in bad weather, they lie quiet, and have no inclination to stir into the open parts to procure sustenance, and that they evidently, from this circumstance, decline in condition, whilst those in open situations, totally without shelter, never fail to seek for food, even in the snow, and keep themselves in much better condition than those which are sheltered. That, under the shade in summer, sheep will lie to be fly-blown rather than stir into the sun's influence to take their food."

Swine.—The following description being given, under the head, or division "Live Stock," is of course to be received as applying to this species of domestic animals, in the County, at large.—P. 64. "These animals are generally of a coarse, bony, long-legged, flat-sided sort, and much inferior, in point of make and shape, to the Berkshire, Wiltshire, and Hampshire kinds, not possessing the aptitude to become fat, which ought to be attended to, in the production of this, and every other animal for the use of man."

By the subjoined recommendation, we may estimate the extent of the REPORTER'S EXPERIENCE, in *practical agriculture*.—P. 87. "I recommend the cultivation of a few acres with carrots, parsnips, and potatoes, upon every farm, annually, as a means of feeding cattle and swine to great advantage. The latter animals are more valuable to a farmer than any other, for the following reasons: 1st. They yield a greater profit in a shorter time than any other animal; 2d. They are not subject to the losses and casualties which other animals are subject to; 3d. Their manure is more valuable than any other animal.

" I do not mean to be understood, that a farm ought to be wholly stocked with swine, but that a considerable number ought to be kept by every farmer; that is to say, upon a farm of 200 *l. per annum*, consisting of two-thirds under the plough, 100 head of swine might be annually produced, of the average value of 40s. kept or folded upon tares and clover by day, and brought into a fold-yard by night."

Poultry.—*Geese*.—Some notice respecting this numerous family of live stock, in Lincolnshire, may be seen under the head *Appropriation*, p. 22, aforegoing.

"GENERAL VIEW

OF THE

AGRICULTURE

OF THE

COUNTY OF LINCOLN,

DRAWN UP FOR THE CONSIDERATION OF THE

BOARD OF AGRICULTURE AND INTERNAL IMPROVEMENT.

BY THE

SECRETARY TO THE BOARD.

1799."

To speak of the QUALIFICATIONS of the Reporter, in this instance, might appear presumptuous and unnecessary. For, seeing the almost numberless volumes which this writer has published, on the subjects comprized in the Report under review,—it may well be admitted that the public are sufficiently acquainted with his qualifications for the undertaking.

All that is requisite, therefore, to be done, in this place, is to convey a general idea of its EXECUTION;—in order that the reader may more fully and clearly comprehend, and more accurately appreciate, what shall appear to me of sufficient consideration to be registered, here.

The MODE of SURVEY adopted, in this case is almost purely that of an enquiring tourist*. The information thus collected might well have been published under the title of a Tour in Lincolnshire, in which were noted down, not so much the cautiously drawn results of the deliberate examinations of the author, *on the spot;* as the remarks of others, *in conversation;*—many of them, no doubt, the bare assertions of guarded, or perchance designing men: —others, the mere opinions of the prejudiced; the incoherencies of the unintelligent; or, possibly, the extempore

---

* See the *Introduction* to the NORTHERN DEPARTMENT, page xl.

tempore answers of those who could scarcely have put the enquirer into the right road to the next market town.

Every man of experience and observation must be aware of how little is to be *depended upon*, in conversation :—even when the talkers have neither interest nor prejudice to induce them to deceive. I have, more than once, been led to say (somewhat in wrath, no doubt) that I would never believe another syllable I should hear in conversation ;—unless in that of a select confidential few.

The inaccuracies of conversation, among men in mixed company, I do not ascribe, so much, to premeditated intention,—as to the misconceptions that arise, the contradictions that goad, and the opposition, the self-pride, and wrong-headedness that ensue ;—and, most of all, to the foible of foibles, that of attempting in all companies and on all subjects and occasions, whether qualified, and prepared, or not,—" to cut a figure in conversation."

I have sat, week after week, several hours, among practical men, high in the rural profession, without hearing a sentence worth committing to paper. I have, moreover, had the honor of sitting, evening after evening with men of the very first class of amateurs, and of the very best general information, without receiving one new and useful idea, or even a suggestion, worthy of a minute desirous as I may have been, to profit by the occasion *.

But this, has not been, invariably the case. I can, however safely aver, I think, that not one assertion or opinion in a thousand, which I have heard, in ordinary conversation, on the subjects of Rural Economy, has appeared to me of sufficient value, to be entitled, even to a private memorandum ; much less, to public attention. As to what is, incidentally, picked up, by question-asking, in travelling, scarcely a word is to be believed ; unless it be corroborated, by other testimony, or by personal observation ; or some previous knowledge of the country travelled over †.

What serves to render this Report of Lincolnshire the less authentic, is the circumstance of the Reporter's withholding his own personal authority :—it being " easy to trace

---

* While, perhaps, the pencil of a ready writer filled many pages, if not books, with prompt assertions, and unsupported opinions.

† For a sketch of my own practice, in regard to question-asking, see the WESTERN DEPARTMENT (Worcestershire) p. 355.

race every article to its source."—His words are these :
—P. 40. (Section "Rent")—"In this article it would
conduce to clearness were the notes easily arranged under
the same heads as the acreable contents of the country,
respecting soil and situation; but much intelligence
having been procured from the same persons relative to
very different districts," (of course in general conversation) "to divide such articles would not only occasion
many repetitions, but the reader would lose the authority
in many cases; a point in such Reports as the present,
of the first consequence. My authority personally cannot
be what the reader wishes; but that of persons who,
from long residence and extent of knowledge, must be
acquainted with facts; stands in a very different predica-
ment—it is easy to trace every article to its source; a
satisfaction of much more consequence than an arrangement somewhat more agreeable."

Unfortunately, however, for the reader, not one tenth,
perhaps, of the articles of which the volume consists,
have any *name* to them :—and, of the names inserted, not
one in a hundred, if any one in the book, may be *known*
to many or most of its readers. And, unless where it
comes out, incidentally, in going through the volume, no
qualifications or pretensions, warranting the informants to
make assertions, or give opinions,—is furnished. The
most common *name*, and which would seem to prevail, in
every district of the County, is THEY. But we are not informed who the family of *they* are; nor what their qualifications, or pretensions. How, then, can it be "easy
to trace every article to its source?" In cases, where
real names are given, the Reporter is relieved from responsibility,—in the minds of those who *happen* to know
the qualifications which belong to the individuals bearing
such names. Had the qualifications of the several contributors been scrupulously declared, in a prefix to the
work, the author might with some degree of propriety,
have shifted the responsibility from his own to their
shoulders.

In going, repeatedly, over the volume, and appreciating the qualifications of the different informants, by
the internal evidence of their remarks, there are a few
who may impress the practical reader with a degree of
confidence. But most of those are either *professional* or
fashionable BREEDERS; and are of course, more or less
biassed by interest, or party spirit; and their sentiments
warped by controversy. There is one man whose information

mation is so uniformly good (except in a very few instances) that one might venture to rely on its authenticity and correctness, without any further evidence, or
the certificate of the Reporter.   This is " Mr. Parkinson
of Asgarby, agent of Sir Joseph Banks."

It is further required to mention an ANNOTATOR, whose
appending remarks not unfrequently recur.   They are
signed " *MS of the B.*"   And one, or more of them,
" *Mr. Craig,* (!) *MS of the B :*"—without any decypher-
ing, or any explanation, whatever, of this signature.
Are they notes that were written on the wide margins of
Mr. STONE'S REPORT?—A work that is not once mentioned, in that of the Secretary of the Board;—who, it
must be allowed, could scarcely be ignorant of its existence!—How disingenuous, or altogether mysterious,
is this.

The AUTHORSHIP of the Lincolnshire Report, by the
Secretary of the Board, or, in other words, its *language*
and *editorship,*—I should have been happy to have passed
over, unnoticed.   But the duty which belongs to the high
office, that I have assumed, calls on me, in this and every
other case, to perform it to the best of my ability ; and
" without favor or affection."   In the present instance, it
is peculiarly proper to speak to this particular; as it may
reasonably be expected, and doubtlessly is, by the public,
at large, and the generality of readers, that a Report
by the SECRETARY of the BOARD should be as a pattern or
example to the Board's Reporters, who might follow
him :—not only in the importance and purity of the
matter ; but in the clearness, terseness, and comprehen-
siveness, of the manner of communicating it to the
public.   But, instead of the Secretary's Report of Lincolnshire being the required pattern of excellence, in
those respects, it could scarcely be deemed severe to say
that, of all the performances the Board have sent to press,
the Lincolnshire Report, by its Secretary, bears the least
resemblance to such a pattern*.   The several articles,
collected, are, it is true, tolerably well brought within the
general heads, given out by the Board.   But in this may
be said to consist the whole of the *arrangement.*   No
                                                    subdivision,

* Yet, strange to be recorded, this very thing has been held out as
the *crack* Report of the Board !—See the *advertisement* prefixed to the
WESTERN DEPARTMENT, page xix.
    Was ever a literary work, since writing and printing were invented,
so *basely* conducted.

subdivision, whatever, is observed; excepting some slight attempts in the sections Woad and Sheep. Each general head is a perfect chaos (except as above excepted) without even an index to render this confusion the less confounded.

It may be urged (tho not fairly) that the Reporter's state of mind might well have been an excuse for this deficiency in manner. It might certainly have been appropriately brought in, as an apology for undertaking the tour; and, doubtlessly, serves to render the *matter*, collected, of less value, than it might have been, if gathered under more favorable circumstances *. But it cannot be a good excuse, for a want of accuracy, in language and arrangement. It could not be at all necessary that the crude collection should have been *hurried to the press*, in the chaotic state in which it was gathered together,—under the embarrassments pleaded,—let them have been what they might. If the Secretary, by reason of his *numerous* and *important* official duties, had not leisure to revise his memoranda, they surely ought to have been ' done into English," by some other hand †.

These

---

* In an introduction, the Reporter, after speaking, in terms the most grateful, of the flattering reception he met with, from all ranks, says—" The liberality of these gentlemen has laid a considerable responsibility on me; for if, with such advantages, and having nothing to complain of on their parts, I fail of giving a satisfactory Report, I can expect to receive only a well-founded condemnation. And here I have but two pleas, that can in the smallest degree extenuate such a failure: first, I was restricted in time, as my commission was only for seven weeks; my reception was, however, so flattering in every part of the county, that I extended it, without authority, to twelve; and could have remained longer there, but the usual time of the meetings of the Board prevented it. I had scarcely time to give a look at my own farm before I was obliged to attend in London. The fact is, that Lincolnshire is so very extensive, equalling the contents of two or three middling sized counties, that even twelve weeks I found too short a period for viewing every interesting part of it with sufficient attention.

" My second excuse is of a much more melancholy nature, and entirely personal. I made the Survey under a depression of mind resulting from the heaviest calamity to which the human heart is liable; a calamity in its nature irretrievable, that cuts off the prospects of hope here, and leaves the lacerated soul no balm but what it can derive from existence beyond the grave."

† In going through this volume, one is involuntarily led to conceive, that the tourist, on reaching town, delivered over his memorandum books to an index maker, or some other *literary artist*, to have

These remarks, most assuredly, have not arisen from
any uncharitableness, toward the author of this Report.
For altho it is a trite maxim that " two of a trade seldome agree ;"—this maxim is searsely applicable to that
writer and myself :—as, in our pursuits, we have ever
taken different routes.

The Secretary's leading object, it would seem (from
what I have formerly read of his writings *, as well as
from the Lincolnshire Report) has ever been that of
furnishing amateurs, with subjects of conversation ;—of
promoting agricultural knowledge, principally, with a
view toward amusement,—not in the field of practice, particularly, but in the drawing, or the club room ;—in fine,
that of gratifying farmers of *fashion* (no matter as to rank,
fortune, condition, or other circumstances in life)—who
are *at* all that is *new*,—*play* at any thing that is *in*, and
(the more adept) *up* to every thing that is *going* †.

Mine, on the other hand, from my earliest outset, as a
writer, has been,—not that of enabling the tyro to *talk*
about farming ; but that of endeavouring to direct him
into the way he should go, to become a proficient in
Practical Agriculture ;—to teach him the minutiæ of its
                                                    various

---

have their pencilled contents digested (in the sissar-and-paste manner)
agreeably to the formula of the Board ; and that they were sent to
the press, without revision, or correction. The intolerable task of
understanding those hasty memoranda arises not more from the want
of words to render them English, than from a wrong punctuation:
or a total want of points.

  * It may be right to mention, here, that I have not read a page (to
the best of my recollection) of this author's writings, on *English*
agriculture, during the last thirty years :—not, merely, from the sentiments I imbibed concerning them, on my re-entrance into the field
of agriculture ; but also lest I might catch, and afterward inadver-
tently publish as my own, any idea his works might contain ;—being
ever desirous to write, as much as possible, from my own experience
and observation ;—until I should enter upon the ever-intended RE-
VIEW of WRITTEN AGRICULTURE, which I am now prosecuting.
See the address prefixed to the RURAL ECONOMY of NORFOLK.

  † It will doubtlessly be said (and I do not say or mean otherwise)
that conversations of this sort may have their use. For although many
of the topics talked of may be frivolous as the fashions of dress, and
give place to others, as rapidly,—there may be some among them,
which, containing the seeds of improvement, may, by the warmth of
conversation, be *forced* into more general notice than they might
have attracted, in the open air of practice. And when men of experience and matured judgement assist at such conversations (as I have
repeatedly intimated) they may possibly remove a seedling plant,
thus nurtured, into the field of practice.

various branches; and, solicitously, to enable him to acquire, in the most ready and certain way,—PRACTICAL KNOWLEDGE, and the means of its IMPROVEMENT, from HIS OWN EXPERIENCE:—in other words, I have labored to instruct him how to think at his leisure, and act in the field.

In public agriculture, likewise, our views I believe, have been different. The Secretary's aim would seem to have been, chiefly, directed toward collecting fuel to add to an inordinate blaze of " national prosperity." Mine, to moderate the destructive flame, and to lay a broad and firm foundation, on which to ground the permanent welfare of the Country.

Before I close these prefatory remarks, it will not be irrelevant, to say,—that, whatever may have been the consideration, and the lines of conduct observed, by the several Reporters of the Board, while collecting their materials, and preparing their collections for the press (I speak generally)—I consider myself, in appreciating their performances,—not as an arbitrary judge, from whose decisions there is no appeal; but as one who is liable to be brought to account, before the first of earthly tribunals, —an ENLIGHTENED NATION. I therefore, know no *distinction* of *persons,* nor decide on the work of any one, without mature consideration. If I err, it is in judgement, not in design. In whatever instance my judgement may have failed, I shall be happy, indeed, to be favoured with an opportunity of correcting my error.

The number of pages, in the body of the work, 440,— in the appendix 15.

Two Maps, and twelve other engravings.

SUBJECT THE FIRST.

NATURAL ECONOMY.

EXTENT.—P. 1. " There is great difficulty in ascertaining, with any tolerable degree of accuracy, the extent of a County, when the maps of it are suspected to be inaccurate. I have no better source of information, than that of the last Survey by Mr. Armstrong; having employed a map engraver, on whom I could depend, for measuring that Map of the County of Lincoln, the result is,

" That

Square

" That the Wolds, as marked in the map annexed *Miles.*
to this Report, contain - - - - 367
The Heath north and south of Lincoln - - 185
The Lowland tracts - - - 1214
The remainder, or miscellaneous tract - - 1122

2888''

From this statement, it appears, that the Reporter separates the County into four descriptions of country ; and, prefixed to the work, is a map, colored according to those descriptions. It is, in reality, a pretty accurate division of the County, into upland, vale, and waterformed lands ; though not strictly so ; as will appear under the ensuing heads, *Soil,* &c.

SURFACE.—P. 2. " The discriminating features of the County of Lincoln are strongly marked by nature. Contiguous to the sea, in the southern part, there spreads a great extent of low land, much of which was once marsh and fen ; but now become, by the gradual exertions of above 150 years, one of the richest tracts in the kingdom ; these great works are not yet finished, but from the noble spirit which has animated this County, promise speedily to be effected. It is a region of fertility without beauty, in a climate not salubrious to the human constitution : advancing north on the sea coast, this rich tract becomes narrow, but reaches to the Humber, and there contracts to a mere edging of marsh land, cut off by the cliffs which rise on the Trent mouth, from a nearly similar tract, which fills all the part of the County on the left side of that great river."

CLIMATURE.—P. 5. " It is a curious circumstance, that immediately after the Witham drainage, the climate of the lowland district was rendered more aguish than before ; but upon the drains being completed, this effect disappeared, and it became much healthier than it had ever been. Still, however, the people are subject to inveterate agues occasionally. The north-east winds, in the spring, also are more sharp and prevalent than further inland."

P. 6. " There is an extraordinary circumstance in the north-west corner of the County. Agues were formerly commonly known upon the Trent and Humber side ; at present they are rare ; and nothing has been effected on the Lincoln side of the Humber, to which it can be attributed ;

attributed ; but there was a coincidence of time with the draining Wallin fen in Yorkshire, and this effect."

This, if well ascertained, serves to show, that, in the case noticed, it was the *foulness* of the *air*, alone, or principally,—and not the *dampness* of the *situation*,—which was unfriendly to human health :—and that the morbid effluvia were capable of being carried to a distance. Hence, the difference between living *in*, or *upon*, a marsh and *near* one,—would seem to be, that, in the former case, the inhabitants (during certain seasons, at least) *constantly* breathe foul air ; in the latter, *occasionally*, only, as the wind may set. And, further, that, as noxious effluvia, in the case noticed, were carried, some miles, it seems to follow that the margins of imperfectly drained fens and marshes are liable to their baleful influence,—to a similar distance ;—consequently, that the County of Lincoln, notwithstanding what Mr. Stone has said of it, and what is intimated in the subjoined extract, is much of it liable, more or less, to the pernicious influence of its fens and marshes.

P. 6. " Upon the whole there is nothing very peculiar in the climate of this County, or at least nothing noted which has come to my knowledge, though it was an inquiry I every where made. The most singular circumstance is, that the very general improvement which has taken place in it gradually, by the vast tracts which have been drained and cultivated, a work still going on, and which has rendered a district that extends many miles, incomparably more healthy than before."

WATERS.—The following notes are barely entitled to insertion here.—P. 15. " In the low districts the water is almost every where brackish.

" At Horbling there are very fine springs of water ; and at Billingborough, Mr. Fydel of Boston sends his cart seventeen miles for this water.

" On the Heath to the north of Spittal, there are brooks almost in every valley.

" At Haxey, in the Isle of Axholm, the water is uncommonly hard, impossible to wash with ; mixed with milk, it turns it in boiling to a curd ; the under-stratum an imperfect gypseous stone. They have here and there wells of better water.

" Upon the Wolds near Brocklesby they make artificial ponds for their sheep ; by a layer of clay of six inches, well beaten and trodden by sheep, &c. and then covered with flints, to keep the feet of cattle from piercing the clay   " In

" In the parishes of Tetney, Fulstow, and that vicinity, blow-wells, which are deep flowing pits of clear water, which flow in considerable streams; the depth said to be unfathomable; but Sir Joseph Banks found the bottom without difficulty at thirty feet. The same thing as at Bourne, where a spring turns a mill almost as soon as out of the earth, near the flat country, and from the chalk hills.

" There are sometimes in very dry seasons a want of water in the rich marshes of Skirbeck hundred, and about Boston; no springs or ponds are made for cattle which will fail: the *sock* or *soak* among the silt is sometimes brackish.

" In the sandy parishes that reach from Spilsby to Tattershal there is every where plenty of water, which breaks out of the hills in springs, and if not cut off, find their way into the fens below.

" Mr. Loft, at Marsh Chapel, bored for water, and with great success: it yields a constant stream from the depth of above 100 feet; runs equally every year, and in all seasons, enough for 100 head of cattle; but it is apt to silt up: to prevent which he tried a tin pipe, but it rusted and spoiled: has since put down a copper one to the depth of eighty-one feet.

" There is at Louth a spring, which always runs in summer, and never in winter."—No uncommon circumstance, in chalk-hill districts. See Treatise on Landed Property.

In the section, " Drainage," is a circumstantial account (much too diffusely reported, for insertion here) of a supply of water being procured, by Sir Joseph Banks, through the mean of boring, on the Elkington principle:—a successful expedient which is equally creditable to the professor and the pupil.

SOILS.—The *map*, above noticed, is entitled " Map of the *soil* of Lincolnshire."—Now this is such a palpable *error*, that whoever committed it must have done it through unpardonable negligence, or a less pardonable want of accuracy.—As a map of the *surface* of Lincolnshire, it has considerable merit, tho it is deficient, in this respect. The natural surface of the County,—that which was given to it, at the time of its formation,—is not sufficiently distinguished, from the flat morasses, and alluvious mudlands, which have, since, been formed:—two as distinct species of territory, as the surface of the earth exhibits.- The extended line of vale lands which lie at the

the eastern skirts of the Wolds,—are uniformly clad in the same yellow color which covers the widely spread fens, and southern marshes. Again, the Island of Axholm,—*original*, both in surface and soil, we find decked in the same garb with the fortuitous level of fen and marshy grounds, by which it is environed :—and, this, tho land and water are scarcely more different in *surface*.

In regard to upland and vale, the map under notice is sufficiently accurate, as a map of the *surface* of Lincolnshire.   And, in this respect, and in this only, it is valuable or useful ; unless so far as it serves to convey a general idea of the *substructures* of the different lands of Lincolnshire.   And it is an interesting fact, in the geology of the County, that these substructures, whether of chalk, of limestone, or of an earthy nature, are arranged in lines somewhat meridionally, or north-and-south :—a circumstance well noticed by the Reporter.

But to the *soils* of the uplands and vale lands, especially of the latter,—the *map* has no relation, whatever ; as will be seen in perusing the following extracts ; which I will arrange agreeably to the natural descriptions of lands into which the County most aptly separates ; conformably with the method pursued in reviewing Mr. Stone's Report.   They contain all that I conceive to be entitled to public attention, in the Reporter's section " Soil ;" in which, with various other notices of less value, they are miscellaneously inserted.

P. 7. (The County at large) " In attempting to give a general idea of the soil of this very extensive County, I must premise, that no one can be named which contains a greater variety ; for it may truly be said to include all the sorts of land that are to be found in the whole kingdom.   There are few exceptions, but granite, schistus, the white surface of the Hertfordshire chalks, and the pure blowing sand of Suffolk.   If soils are divided as they may be, relative to practice, into 1. clay, 2. sand, 3. loam, 4. chalk, 5. peat, they are all to be found in large districts, under many variations.   Harsh, churlish, tenacious, infertile clays.   Sands poor and of admirable fertility.   Loams of every possible description, and some that rival the best in the kingdom.   The calcareous class in chalk, limestone, and gypsum.   Peat of many sorts, from a wretched thin covering of bad sands, to the deep treasures of ponderous bog."

P. 8. (The same) " The variations of soil are nearly all longitudinal in the direction of north and south."

P. 14.

P. 14. (Fen) " The fen lands" (of west fen?) (" in the vicinity of Reevesby") consist of a heavy, deep, sandy loam, which makes very rich breeding pasture for sheep but not for feeding; another part of a rich soapy blue clay, and another of black peat, consisting of decayed vegetables, and when drained, is deemed by the inhabitants to be of all others proportioned to rent the best for arable."

P. 7. (Marsh) " On entering the County from Wisbeach to Long Sutton, every one must be struck with the richness of the soil. It is one of the finest tracts I have seen—a brown dark loam of admirable texture. The district continues, with some variation of peat near Spalding, quite to the sea at Freestone, beyond Boston."

P. 12. (The same) " In that part of the Marsh district, which I viewed at Humberstone, and to Tetney, the soil is a strong, fertile, clayey loam, but with much sand in it and mica; which looks as if the whole had been once an alluvion of the sea, resembling an argillaceous warp—no sand, no gravel, no chalk, no rock; with rain it is greasy, and with successive shunshine, hardens into brick. Nearly the same quality of land, but, with slight variations, holds all the way thence to the hilly lands near to Louth."

P. 11. (Marsh and Vale) " Between the boundary of the Wolds, (see the Map) and the sea, there is the tract called the Marsh and Middle Marsh; the former is a rich tract of salt marsh, the soil therefore well known; the latter is a line of strong soil, called *the Clays*, and it is stiff; but from Belesby towards Grimsby consists of a strong brown loam, much superior to a real clay."

P. 13. (The same) " From Louth to Saltfleet, Sutton, and then to Alford and Spilsby, a considerable tract of the Marsh and Middle Marsh is viewed. The soil of the Marsh is rich, adhesive, marine clay and loam; and the Middle Marsh resembles it; but is of inferior fertility."

Again:—" The hundred of Skirbeck is in general extremely various; in the part near Boston, and some other, the surface is a rich loam, upon clay first to some depth, and then the silt, which is found at a certain level in general; this silt is a porous sea sand, which has been deposited ages ago, becomes firm with rain, but is not fertile; near the sea there is a thin covering upon clay, and Mr. Linton has observed, that by ploughing into it no damage has been sustained; however, it is a general observation, that the soil is best where there is none near it. Near the fen there is an infertile very stiff blue clay upon

upon the surface ; grass almost always mown : the very richest pastures are a black mould, or mass of vegetable particles."

P. 9. (The same) " Between Gainsborough and Newark, for twenty-five miles, all is sand, with a flat marsh tract on the river, sometimes very narrow indeed ; whereas on the Nottinghamshire side, it spreads into wide commons. This is the case at Knaith. Behind the sand, which is good and in tillage, is a tract of cold wet clay. At Martin the sand is very rich, and lets at thirty shillings.

" The soil of the Isle of Axholm is among the finest in England ; they have black sandy loams ; they have warp land ; they have brown sands ; and they have rich loams, soapy and tenacious."

P. 10. (The same) " The finest estate I have seen of some time for soil, is the lordship of Wintringham ; it consists of three descriptions of land ; marsh, called here warp and *grove* ; strong loam under the bean husbandry ; and dry loam for turnips. All three are excellent. The marsh is a tract of alluvion of the Humber, deposited to the depth of six feet, and apparently as good at bottom as at top. The bean land is not a strong loam ; but a friable sandy loam, with clay enough in it to give it rather too adhesive a tenacity for turnips. The turnip land is a reddish, friable, rich loam, dry but putrid ; a finer soil can scarcely be seen, adapted to every crop that could be put into it.

" Various good soils through Whitton and Halton.

" Barton field, of 6000 acres, is a good turnip dry loam, on chalk of various depths, dry at bottom, yet moist enough on the surface from texture to fit it for all common crops, and does well both for sainfoin and wheat."

P. 8. (Vale Lands) " At Kirkby near Sleaford there is a tract of beautiful pasture land, dry enough for sheep, and rich enough for bullocks."

P. 13. (The same) " The sandy soil, which prevails from Spilsby to Revesby, extends very much in the following parishes."—These parishes are nearly forty in number. Among their *names* we find those of Spilsby, Tattershall and Market Raisin. From Spilsby to Tattershall is nearly fifteen miles : Spilsby to Raisin, twenty five miles. Hence, this uniform tract of sandy soil is of very considerable extent; and in a " Map of *Soils*," ought, surely, to have been distinguished.—Whereas, this tract of of sandy soil,—" The tract of beautiful pasture land," near Sleaford,—the line of sand between Gainsborough and Newark,—and the rich lands of Winteringham,—are all bedizened in the same bright red color.

How much more than ridiculous is it to hold this out as a map of *soils!*—When such a dazzling and deceptious device is prefixed to a Report by the Secretary of the Board, it cannot be too severely censured; as it is encoraging others of the Board's Reporters to be guilty of similar improprieties. In going through the Western Department, I found occasion to censure different maps of soils; as being imperfect and falacious. But no one of them equals, in deception, the "map of the soil of Lincolnshire;" by which, doubtlessly, the designer and dauber of the Glocestershire map hoped to be countenanced. Even the uplands; namely, the "Wolds" and "Heaths" of Lincolnshire,—tho they are distinguished by a degree of uniformity of substructure,—are not uniform, in soil; as appears by the subjoined extracts.

P. 11. (Wolds) " It would be loss of time to attempt many distinctions in the soils of the great tract of the Wolds; all I saw or heard of is, a sandy loam, on a chalk bottom; the quality very various, from poor sand, producing heath, *(erica vulgaris)* to rich, deep, fertile loams, that yield capital crops of barley and wheat, and some even beans."

P. 14. " The tract of Wold north of Louth, by Elkington, Ormsby, Wyham, Binbrook, Swinop, Thoresby, &c. exhibits a great variety of excellent soil, all calcareous, friable, sandy loams on a chalk bottom, dry enough to feed turnips where they grow, and much good enough for wheat. The red chalks are particularly good, being almost without exception excellent for turnips and barley. At Thoresby Warren the vales are red, and nettles are among the spontaneous growth. Nettles and rabbits together!!"—No uncommon sight:—the one being the cause, the other the effect!

P. 8. (Heath) " The reddish sands upon the heath, open field, arable at Blankney are excellent for barley."—Again, " The heath, now all inclosed, is a tract of high country, a sort of back bone to the whole, in which the soil is a good sandy loam, but with clay enough in it to be slippery with wet, and tenacious under bad management; but excellent turnip and barley land, on a bed of limestone, at various depths, from six inches to several feet, commonly nine inches to eighteen."

Beside

Beside the miscellaneous notices that are placed within the section " Soil," we find, in going through the volume, other passages that *relate* to the same subject. The following I have marked as being admissible, here.

P. 2. (The County) "The Heaths north and south of Lincoln and the Wolds, as marked in the map, are calcareous hills, which from their brows command many fine views over the lower regions : the rest of the County is not equally discriminated either by fertility or elevation, and, except certain spots more favoured by nature than the rest, do not exhibit a country that classes among the more beautiful features of the kingdom. Upon the whole, however, it is a better country than general ideas have permitted some to esteem it."

P. 116. (Fens) " On breaking up the rich commons of Long Sutton, the corn products have, for seven years, been very great; oats 10½ quarters, and wheat 5 qrs. which continue to be the crops at present.

" On the black peat land in Deeping Fen, Mr. Graves has had 8 and even 10 quarters of oats, after cole, on paring and burning : he sows six bushels. There is now a crop of barley in the Fen, estimated at 12 qrs. an acre.

" Corn in general upon the rich arable of Holland Fen, &c. of an inferior quality and price, which is of course occasioned by the extraordinary fertility giving such a luxuriance of straw."

P. 188. (Marshes) "The marshes near the sea, from Wrangle to Sutton, are part divided from the high country by the fens, and part by clay parishes, called middle marshes, which marsh is near the sea, a rich loam, on a silt or clay bottom; the part nearer the villages a very rich soapy clay, best adapted for feeding sheep and beasts ; with a smaller share of *ings*" (meadows) "for hay; nearer the middle marshes, cold wet clay."

This passage, if corrected, and fully worded, would convey valuable information, in a clear manner; and might have been noticed as a favorable specimen of the language and manner of this Report.

Substrata.—Besides what relates to subsoil, incidentally included in the foregoing extracts, on soils, we find (in the section " Soil") the following scattered sentences, on the lower strata.—P. 7. "In boring at the bottom of a well at Boston twenty-seven feet deep, they came very soon to a stratum of blue marl, colour of Westmoreland slate, which continued for upwards of one hundred and fifty yards, with exceptions only of a few inches, amounting

ing to not more, in the whole, than three feet."—P. 10.
" The under stratum at Haxey, Belton, &c. is, in many
places, an imperfect plaster stone."—See also the head
Waters, p. 73 aforegoing.

Nevertheless, in the same page with the last extract,
is the following round remark.—" Under the whole
country, generally speaking, stone is to be found at
various depths. No plaster."

P. 12. "In digging Grimsby haven, they cut twenty
feet deep in a bed of stiff, blue, clayey warp, with many
micaceous particles."—Same page. " The wold land
about Louth, to the west and south west, is good, very
generally a dry, friable, loamy sand, on a flinty loam, and
under that, chalk every where."

SUBJECT THE SECOND.

POLITICAL ECONOMY.

APPROPRIATION.—In this Report, as in that of Mr.
Stone, are found, in different sections of the volume, a
variety of materials collected, relating to this most important topic of Political Economy. I will in this, as in
the former instance, endeavour to class them, in the most
intelligible and useful form.

For the *history* and *present state* of Appropriation, in
Lincolnshire, the reader will do well to refer back to Mr.
Stone's account, p. 19, aforegoing. The Secretary is in a
manner silent on the subject. I find the two subjoined
passages, only, which relate especially to this topic.—
P. 79. "In the isle of Axholm, there is an immense inclosure on the point of beginning ; the act and survey having been passed, of no less than 12,000 of acres of commons, in the four parishes of Haxey, Hepworth, Belton,
and Owston."—P. 231. " Along the sea-coast of the hundred of Skirbeck, there are about 1000 acres of sea marsh
beyond the bank, covered by spring tides, capable of
being taken in to very great profit ; but not done, waiting
for an act to inclose the fens, in order then to take in the
marshes.

" Wrangle has a common of 1500 acres belonging to
itself ; and Leak, besides its right on East and West fens,
has

has one also of 450. The rest of the parishes in the hundred have a right, as they assert, on both East and West fens."—Other notices may be caught in the ensuing extracts. And see the History of *Drainage*, ensuing.

On the *Advantages* of appropriating commons and common fields, the Report, now under review, furnishes ample and valuable information.

P. 42. " The eleven parishes of Holland fen contain 22,000 acres, and let for about 27s. an acre, tithe free, but pay a drainage tax. Before the drainage and inclosure, it was worth not more that East, West, or Wildmore fens, at present, that is nothing at all."

P. 77. " There are few instances of the benefit of inclosing commons, greater than that of Long Sutton ; the act passed in 1788, by which near 4000 acres of common became *several* property ; the rent of it, before inclosing, was 1000*l.* a year, or 500 rights, which let the messuages at 40*s.* each more for the right ; the whole now lets from 30*s.* to 50*s.* an acre, and about half of it is ploughed. Before this act the old inclosures were subservient to the common, but now the common is subservient to those ; and, if all are included in the account, there is now more live stock kept than before, and of a much better kind ; though above 2000 acres have been ploughed up to yield an enormous produce.

" About Folkingham, many new as well as old parliamentary inclosures, of arable, open, common fields ; the improvements by which have been very great ; lands adapted to grass have been laid down ; and some better for the plough have been broken up. At Osbornby the rent of 10*s.* was raised to 17*s.* 6*d.* ; and several others, in an equal proportion."—Again—" The vast benefit of inclosing can, upon inferior soils, be rarely seen in a more advantageous light, than upon Lincoln Heath. I found a large range which formerly was covered with heath, gorse, &c. and yielding, in fact, little or no produce, converted, by inclosure, to profitable arable farms ; let, on an average, at 10*s.* an acre ; and a very extensive country, all studded with new farm houses, barns, offices, and every appearance of thriving industry ; nor is the extent small, for these heaths extend near seventy miles ; and the progress is so great in twenty years, that very little remains to do.*   " The

---

* Such, in truth, as I never beheld, until I travelled between Sleaford and Lincoln in 1810 ; when I saw hundreds of acres in the veriest

" The effect of these inclosures has been very great
for while rents have risen on the Heath from nothing, in
most instances, and next to nothing in the rest, to 8s. or
10s. an acre, the farmers are in much better circum
stances, a great produce is created, cattle and sheep in
creased, and the poor employed. The rectory of Na
venby, one of the Cliff towns, has become greater than
the total rent of the lordship was before."

P. 79. " I passed these commons" (of the Isle of
Axholm) " in various quarters, and rode purposely to view
some parts; they are in a wretched and unprofitable state
but valued, if inclosed, in the ideas of the islanders, at
10s. or 11s. an acre."

P. 82. " The parish" (of Barton on Humber) " inclu
ding every thing, may now be rented at, or worth 6000l.
a year; it was 2000l. and all the tenants better satisfied
than before."

P. 83. " By the acts for inclosing Barton, Barrow,
and Goxhill, no less than 17000 acres are rendered productive, to the infinite advantage of the community.

" I was told, before I got into the Clays, as they are
called, or Middle Marsh, that inclosing did not answer
that, however it had succeeded on the Wolds. When
I got to Humberston, I discovered the explanation: they
summer fallow for wheat, and then take beans, after inclosing, exactly as before. How then can it answer?
and old tracts of pasture are ploughed up in consequence
and not converted to a good system of tillage, but covered
with bean crops that never see a hoe. In passing from
thence to Tetney, Fulstow, Covenham, &c. I passed
through a large open field in the fallow year, which had
not, in September, received its first earth; but was
covered with thistles, passed their blossom, high enough
to hide a jackass; yet the dung was spread amongst them
as if the wheat would be sowed: and the soil thus horri-
bly neglected, a fine rich tenacious loam, not clay, as
greasy and soapy almost as a pure clay; but there is
much sand in it:—a soil well worth 30s. an acre, or
                                        upwards

veriest state of *waste* I ever saw land, whether appropriated or
unappropriated, in this kingdom. Half a dozen wild rabbits were all
the stock I observed upon them, with scarcely a blade or leaf of herbage
to keep even these alive:—doubtlessly thro the folly or madness of
the first occupiers (after appropriation) in converting them to
" arable farms," instead of *sheep walks* and *rabbit warrens*.

pwards, in rent, tithe, and rates. Who will be hardy
nough to hazard such a folly, as that any part of the
ime of Clays, I have seen or heard described, will not
nswer inclosing? Yet, such nonsense I have heard;
o wonder, in a country where landlords, stewards, far-
ners, are all five centuries behind in every idea relative
o strong land. They are awake and moving on turnip
and; but on bean soils, are still fast asleep.

"From Louth to Saltfleet, and from Sutton to Alford,
pen fields, with unploughed fallows, the 15th, &c. of
September; covered with thistles in beautiful luxuriance,
nd plenty of other rubbish."

P. 86. "For the following most important table, I am
bliged to Mr. Parkinson of Asgarby, steward to Sir
oseph Banks, &c. It is, in every respect, a very curious
aper, and shews the vast works, which have been carried
n successfully in this great county.

A STATE

"A STATE of certain IMPROVEMENTS by Inclosing and Draining.

Parishes.	A.	r.	p.	Improved value £	s.	d.	Old value £	s.	d.	Improvement £	s.	d.	Expenditure £	s.	d.	Interest at 5 per cent.	Net gain to the Owners.
Donnington	1728	0	0	681	5	0	380	0	0	301	5	0	1100	0	0		
Swaby	1555	1	24	738	5	6	310	14	0	427	11	6					
Belleau	649	1	14	323	8	0	274	0	0	49	8	0	1967	13	0		
N. Rauceby	3168	0	23	1129	16	6	352	0	0	777	16	6					
S. Ditto	2461	0	20	1010	18	7	347	0	0	663	18	7	3399	0	0		
Normanby	1718	3	20	1021	18	3	480	0	0	541	18	3					
Huttoft	3352	0	16	2356	2	0	1800	0	0	556	2	0	1820	0	0		
Hemswell	2581	2	20	1472	2	6	630	3	0	841	19	6	2300	0	0		
Legburn	2235	2	33	973	14	0	655	0	0	318	14	0	1874	0	0		
Canwick	2059	3	33	1437	3	1	672	12	0	764	13	0	1663	0	0		
Skindleby	1028	1	25	571	3	1	285	0	0	286	3	1	1722	0	0		
W. Enderby	798	0	0	526	4	8	340	0	0	186	4	8	800	0	0		
Anwick fields, &c.	954	0	0	708	19	0	385	3	0	323	16	0	848	10	7		
Greetham	1275	0	29	765	2	6	400	0	0	363	2	6	1510	0	0		
Hagg	2383	2	13	1806	17	0	1560	0	0	246	17	0	1348	0	0		
Kirton	4383	0	0	3864	3	7	1168	0	0	2696	3	7	2100	0	0		
Nettleton	3549	2	33	1523	17	9	460	0	0	1063	17	9	5267	16	9		
Osbornby	1451	2	0	1323	17	0	662	0	0	661	7	0	2425	0	0		
Scarthe	1186	2	0	876	15	0	452	0	0	424	15	0	2032	12	1		
Quarrington	1560	0	0	1268	8	0	627	0	0	641	8	0	1447	1	6		
Sleaford and Holdingham	2321	1	20	2191	2	0	918	0	0	1273	2	0	3569	0	0		
Dunsten heath and fields	1957	0	20	1037	1	3	641	0	0	396	1	3	1300	0	0		
Tattershall inclosure	4003	2	18	2168	13	11	1706	11	8	461	10	3	626	0	0		
Fens.—Ditto embankment	892	0	26	838	13	9	387	19	9	450	14	0	3630	0	0		
Anwick Fen	1097	0	0	703	16	0	54	17	0	648	19	0	4070	0	0		
The 9 embanked fens from Tattershall to Lincoln	19,418	1	34	15,534	8	0	1941	16	0	13,592	12	0	77,672	0	0		
Holland Fen, 11 towns	22,000	0	0	25,300	0	0	3600	0	0	21,700	0	0	50,600	0	0		

" There are other parishes, that I have been commissioner for, which I have not an account of, owing to my books being from home."

P. 88. " Mr. Ellison at Sudbrook remarked to me, that he is clear, if a register of offences at the sessions was kept, it would be found that a very large proportion originated with the inhabitants who lived on commons, and in uninclosed parishes."

P. 223. " Forty thousand acres in Sir Joseph Banks's fens would, if inclosed, let for 31s. 6d. according to the opinion of some; in that of others, for 26s. In East fen are 2000 acres of water; 32 parishes have right of common in these fens. At Brothertoft I crossed the ferry into Wildmore fen, and the little I saw of it was worth 40s.; but whole acres covered with thistles and nettles, four feet high and more. There are men that have vast numbers of geese, even to 1000 and more. Mr. Thacker of Langrike ferry has clipped 1200 sheep on Wildmore; and yet he assured me, that he would rather continue at his present rent, and pay the full value for whatever might be allotted to his farm on an inclosure, rather than have the common right for nothing. In 1793 it was estimated, that 40,000 sheep, or one per acre, rotted on the three fens. Nor is this the only evil, for the number stole is incredible: they are taken off by whole flocks. So wild a country nurses up a race of people as wild as the fen; and thus the morals and eternal welfare of numbers are hazarded or ruined for want of an inclosure.

" There may be five sheep an acre kept in summer on Wildmore and West fens, besides many horses, young cattle and geese; if there are any persons who profit, it is the people who keep geese. Some keep sheep in winter there, and suffer accordingly."

P. 225. "In discourse at Louth upon the characters of the poor, observations were made upon the consequences of great commons, in nursing up a mischievous race of people; and instanced, that on the very day we were talking, a gang of villains were brought to Louth gaol, from Coningsby, who had committed numberless outrages upon cattle and corn; laming, killing, cutting off tails, and wounding a variety of cattle, hogs, and sheep; and that many of them were commoners on the immense fens of East, West, and Wildmore."*   P. 239.

* These fens, I understand, have recently been partially or wholely appropriated. February 1811.

P. 239. " Matthew Allen of Brothertoft, before the inclosure and draining of Holland fen, paid 20s. rent for a cottage and croft. His stock on the fen was 400 sheep, 500 geese, 7 milch cows, 10 or 12 young horses, and 10 young beasts. Such a person, if ever one was heard of must have been injured by an inclosure; for never could be known a more perfect contrast between the rent and stock of a holding. He now rents about 50 acres of the inclosure at 25s. an acre; has a wife, five children, and two servants, and greatly prefers his present situation, not only for comfort, but profit also."—Can all this be accurate?

For the disadvantages of common fields, in regard to livestock,—see the head *Cattle* (breed of) ensuing.

On the *Business* of Appropriation, the following articles of information are entitled to attention.

P. 54. (Tithe) " In the new inclosures about Folkingham exonerated by giving land.—In Osbornby one-seventh of the whole. In some one-fifth of the arable, and one-ninth of the pasturage."

P. 79. " The expence, that is the commissioners' rate, for inclosing 5000 acres in Kirton, was about 7000l. including every public charge; roads came to near 1000l. of it."

P. 80. " Cottage rights are claims; but lands without a cottage have none."—How irrational and disgraceful is this, in a civilized, and in many respects enlightened, nation!

P. 80. " Barton Field is one of the greatest inclosures in England; the act passed in 1793. Before the inclosure, the quantities of land were supposed to be nearly," " 6240" acres.—" Of which " (p. 81.) "after deducting the roads, and the site of the town, there may be 6000 acres of land, used in pasturage and tillage.

" The assessments of the commissioners, under the inclosure act, amounted to about 13180l. to defray the expences of the act, fencing of tithe allotments, public and private roads, banks, jetties, cloughs, bridges, &c &c.

" The completing the public and private roads cost about 5000l. The Humber banks and jetties about 2000l. or rather more."—P. 82. " 150 acres were given to the vicar for his small tithes; and 900 were assigned for great tithe most conveniently for the impropriator."*

P. 274.

* It is proper to remark here, that the whole of the information, hitherto extracted, on the subject of Appropriation (excepting Mr. Parkinson's

P. 274. " The first irrigation I heard of in the County, was at Osbornby, by Mr. Hoyte, the lordship being inclosed by Act of Parliament in 1796, that very spirited improver took advantage of the capability of some of the lands to be irrigated, and advised the commissioners to award a power of taking water from a catch-water drain that was necessarily made, and offered to take for his own allotment, some lands reckoned of an inferior quality, because he perceived they would admit of this improvement."

There is so much liberality, good sense, and sound principles of business, in the subjoined remarks of Mr. ELMHURST, that I have singular satisfaction in registering them.

P. 84. " Upon the principles on which the commissioners of inclosures should conduct themselves, Mr. Elmhurst observes : ' Where the town happens to be situated in, or pretty near the centre of the lordship, the properties (upon the inclosure) may, with great propriety, be laid contiguous, or nearly so, to the farm houses; and as much in squares as the nature and shape, &c. of the fields will admit; but when otherwise, then the distant lands ought to be so laid out and allotted, as best to suit for occupation, as a farm or farms, on which houses, &c. may be built; having, as much as may be, an eye to water, and different sorts of land; but to have due consideration to the *whole* of the proprietors, (small as well as great so as not to injure any one, by making it *particularly* convenient to another or others. I acted as a commissioner a great many years; and was, at *one time*, concerned in *nine* different inclosures; and, from my first being in that business, (which is near twenty-eight years) I ever have attended first to what concerned the public, respecting the laying out, forming and making the roads, (at the expence of the proprietors) in the properest and most eligible situations, for the greatest conveniency of all who may travel, or do business upon them; for, I thought and said, that the legislature could never *intend* to place such power in any set of men, as commissioners, or delegate them

Parkinson's valuable contribution, and the articles in which the names of Mr. Ellison and Matthew Allan are mentioned) is registered on the sole authority of the Reporter Through what channels the several articles of information came to his knowledge (excepting those which rose to his own observation, in travelling) the reader can only surmise; notwithstanding what has been quoted aforegoing.

them with such extraordinary power (as they *then* seemed to *fancy* they had) by which they should or might injure the public.—And that *mode* I ever and always pursued, so long as I continued to act. Another observation I, at the first, made, and ever after put in practice, was this, *always* to begin to line out and allot for the *smallest* proprietor *first*, (whether rich or poor) in *every* parish, so as to make such allotment as proper and convenient for the occupation of such, or their tenant, (as that might be) to occupy; and so on, from the smallest to the greatest: for it is for the advantage of the greatest and most opulent proprietors, that a bill is presented and act passed; and at *their* requests,—and not the small ones; and, as the little ones would have no weight by opposition, *they must submit*, was it ever so disadvantageous to them; as it *very often* happens; and, therefore, there can be no *partiality* in defending *those*, who cannot help or defend themselves; and a *little* man may as well have *nothing* allotted to him, as to have it so *far off*, or so inconvenient for him, that it is not worth his having, as it would prevent his going to his daily labour; and, therefore, he *must* SELL *his* property to his rich and opulent adjoining neighbour; and *that*, in some measure, decreases population."

I have equal gratification in transcribing the liberal sentiments, and exemplary practice, of the late DUKE of ANCASTER, on this topic.

P. 89. " The Duke of Ancaster very justly remarks, that rents are usually raised much too soon upon inclosures taking place; the tenant is put to much inconvenience, and incurs, sometimes, a very large expence; to raise immediately is unjust; there ought to elapse three years before any increase takes place. His Grace, upon inclosing, has given his tenantry that indulgence."

Finally, on the subject of Appropriation, I cannot refrain from tendering my acknowledgements to the Secretary of the Board, for enabling me to add so many valuable materials concerning it, to my former collections :—the whole tending to evince the propriety of a PUBLIC MEASURE, which I have long been solicitous to promote :—not because I happened to be the first who urged it, in detail, to public attention (in the Rural Economy of YORKSHIRE, first published in 1788)—but from a clear conviction of its rectitude ; and the numerous advantages that would necessarily proceed from it.

For the *principles* of Appropriation, see as before referred to, p. 25.

POPULATION.

POPULATION.—In a section, bearing this title, we find en or twelve loosely or half printed pages of heterogeneus, desultory matter,—touching different topics.—The riter's principal intention would seem to have been that f ascertaining the effects of appropriating commonable ands, on the population of a country.— P. 421. " I wished procure, while in the County, the births and burials of nany parishes, but was unable to effect it; a few I was avoured with; some of which will shew in what manner nclosure has operated to diminish or increase the eople."

Nothing, however, is even attempted to be made out. ndeed, the bent of the article turns on the depreciation f money, and the consequent rise in the prices of farm roduce,—rather than on population. There is little, if ny thing, which even a topographical collector would ot have rejected. To me, the whole appears as waste aper; excepting a passage or two, relating to the rapid dvance of Agriculture, in Lincolnshire;—of which in the roper place.

PROVISIONS, and FUEL.—P. 403. " Boston; price of utton 6d.; beef 5½d.; butter 1s.; cheese 6d. Coals 7s. and in winter 30s. and 32s. per chaldron."—" The rent furnishes Gainsborough, &c. with some sorts of fish great plenty. Salmon, which rises to 46lb. at 1s. a ound; pike, up to 17lb. at 6d.; perch, to 5lb. at 6d.; nch, to 4lb. at 1s.; carp, to 10lb. at 1s.; eels plentiful; t carp and tench rare. Butter 10d per pound; the oor buy at 8½d.; and twenty years ago at 2½d. Wild cks 3s. to 3s. 6d. a brace; teal 1s. 6d. a couple; grey over 1s. 6d. Coals, 17s. for 48 bushels."

P. 412. "It is singular that the labouring poor, with the xtraordinary high price of labour at Norton, Kirton, &c. nsume very little meat, except the stoutest labourers at sk work, who earn 3s. a day; these have for dinner some eat in a pye; all consume a good many potatoes."

MANUFACTURES.—On this subject, we find nothing ticeable; excepting some astonishing facts (I take r granted) in the SPINNING of COMBED WOOL;—a topic hich is by no means foreign to a Report of *Lincoln-ire.*

P. 408. " A lee of woollen yarn measures in length ghty yards. A hank of ditto, by the custom of Norwich, nsists of seven lees.

24 hanks

Yards. Miles

24 hanks in the pound is esteemed good
    spinning in the schools   13,440   8

70 hanks in the pound is esteemed super-
    fine spinning at Norwich   39,200   22

150 hanks in the pound were spun in 1754,
    by Mary Powley of East Dereham in
    Norfolk ; and this was thought so ex-
    traordinary, that an account of it is
    entered on the registers of the Royal
    Society   84,000   48

300 hanks in the pound have already been
    spun by Miss Ives of Spalding; and
    though this young lady has carried
    the art of spinning combed wool to
    so great a degree of perfection, she
    does not despair of improving it still
    farther   168,000   95

" The manufacturers of Norwich, zealous to encourage
Miss Ives's ingenuity, are desirous of improving their
looms in such a manner as will enable them to weave her
delicate yarn.   Mr. Harvey of that place has already
manufactured some that is very fine ; and he is at present
engaged in weaving her finest sort into a shawl, the texture of which is expected to equal that of the very best
that have hitherto been brought from India."

POOR TAX.—Of the section, " Poor Rates," not a syllable merits extraction.   Not only is the rent, on which
the rates are calculated, nominal or uncertain ; but other
" Town Charges" are united with the poor rates.   Why
blot paper to so little purpose ? even the Reporter's conjectures, rising out of general information, are mostly, or
altogether, futile, with respect to the main subject of
enquiry.

In the section " Poor,"   " Major Cartwright,"—speaking
of the utility of *Provident Societies,*—makes the following
sensible remarks. P. 409. " But in touching on this subject, I had principally in view to point out a very material
defect, which runs very generally, I fear, through the
rules of such societies: it is the defect of not making any
provision for medical assistance when a member is ill.
He is allowed out of the box sick pay, merely for his
subsistence ; but how is that to cure him of his disease,
or obtain him the medical assistance of which he stands
in need ? He has the parish, it is true, to apply to ; but
in such cases, the poor man's application is seldom made
                                                        till

till he thinks himself dying, and even then seldom complied with so soon as the case requires."

To obviate this defect, Mr. C. after showing (what becomes self evident the moment it is suggested) the propriety and practicability of employing a medical man, in such a way, as to have an interest in keeping the members in health,—says p. 410. " It is on this principle, that I have drawn up a plan for the benefit of the poor of this township, and others in my employment; which is likewise open to such other poor as choose to become members of our society. Having met with an active surgeon, who accepts of such a subscription as we can raise, I hope the last hand will be put to the design in a few days."

TITHES.—In the section bearing this title, as in that of " Poor Rates," are seen a string of crude memoranda, in cramp language;—some of them totally void of intelligibility :—thus, p. 54, " About Sudbrook, compounded at 2s. or 2s. 6d. an acre."—A reader out of the County, and perhaps many in it, might say—Where is Sudbrook? What is its situation, and what its soil? Are its lands part of the rich mudbanks of the district of Boston? Or is it situated among the rabbit warrens of the Wolds, or the meagre sandy lands of the Heath?

The following ideas of Mr. Parkinson,—given, it would seem, in the Reporter's *own language!*—claim some attention.—P. 54. " Mr. Parkinson—the tithe of pasture is worth one-ninth of its improved rent, which he *proves*" (!) " thus; produce two lambs, on an average of twenty-one years, at 12s. or 24s., two ewe fleeces at 4s. or 8s.; in all 32s.; deduct for loss one-eighth, remains 28s.; the tenth of which 2s. 9½d.; deduct for gathering one-third, remains s. 11d.; call it 2s." (what is the rent?) " The tithe of meadow one-seventh, and one-eighth of inferior quality. That of rich grazing one-ninth of the rent. Of arable, the best one-fifth of the rent, and the inferior detached one-sixth and one-seventh, according to circumstances. Approves of the Bishop of Lincoln's tithe: for the present mode of taking it is such an impediment to improvements, that his corn rent is much better:* the rector often cannot cultivate or stock *it*," (what?) " and this prevents the necessity. Woods exempted, *because* from a very

* And this is all we hear of the Bishop of Lincoln taking tithe, by *corn rent!*

very ancient custom, all stand from twenty-one to twenty-three years. *

"*Mr. Parkinson's Estimate.*—Average tithes of the county is one-fifth; best arable one-sixth, inferior one-seventh; best meadow one-eighth, inferior one-ninth; pasture makes a mean of land 1 acre at 14s. the mean proportion one-sixth to 2s. 4d.

Do. 21s. per acre, do. one-sixth	-	3s.	6d.
Do. 28s. per acre, do. one-sixth,	-	4s.	8d.
Do. 35s. per acre, do. one-sixth,	-	5s.	10d.'

How are the last lines (quoted exactly as they stand in the original) to be read and understood ?

Substitution for Tithes.—P. 55. "I found throughout the county a very general desire that some law should pass for the commutation of tithe. The farmers here, with their brethren in every other part of the kingdom, consider this as one of the heaviest of obstacles to good husbandry."

And, speaking directly of "obstacles," we are informed p. 432. "In the hundred of Skirbeck, the chief obstacle is the height of tithes; and, as there thought, the unwillingness of landlords permitting grass land to be ploughed up, which would pay much more under the plough than in grazing. In all the parishes that have been inclosed here, the ancient lands have been exonerated of tithe, as well as the new inclosure, which has removed the former in many instances."

PUBLIC EMBANKMENT and DRAINAGE generally go hand in hand; and, in most great undertakings, are inseparable. This Reporter, however, has thought fit to separate the two subjects, so as to place them at some distance from each other; and has given drainage the foremost place; though it can seldome be availing, until banks be formed to prevent the water, to be carried off, at certain seasons,—from returning, at others; and most especially, when water is required to be raised, artificially it becomes essentially necessary, first to raise banks to throw it over. I shall, therefore, adhere to the same order of arrangement, in this, as in other cases.

EMBANKMENT.—It is on the *History* of embankment, in Lincolnshire, we are to look for satisfactory information

---

* This is no *reason* for their being exempt. The coppice woods of Devonshire are cut at a similar state of growth; yet some of them pay tithes *when they are reaped*.

in the volume under review. For what may well be termed engineership, the reader must revert to Mr. STONE's Report, p. 29, aforegoing.

P. 270. " Since 1630, ten thousand acres have been saved from the sea, in the parish of Long Sutton, and seven thousand acres more might now be taken in by altering the channel of the river.

" Holland Fen is a country that absolutely exists but by the security of its banks ; they are under commissioners, and very well attended to."

P. 271. " South Holland, grossly estimated at 100,000 acres within the old sea-dike bank, has long been an object of embankment. Ravenbank, the origin of which is quite unknown, appears to have been the third which had been formed for securing a small part of this tract from the sea, leading from Cowbit to Tidd St. Mary's. About six miles nearer to the sea is another bank, called the Old Sea-dike bank, which is unquestionably a Roman work. A very curious circumstance is, that a fifth bank, called the New Sea-dike bank, two miles nearer than the Roman, remains, but it is utterly unknown when or by whom it was made. The new bank mentioned above, takes in about two miles more in breadth. In taking the levels for making the new drain, it was found that the surface of the country. on coming to the Roman bank, suddenly rose six feet, being six feet higher on the sea side than on the land side, and then continues on that higher level, being the depth of warp, or silt, deposited by the sea since that bank was made. The estimated expence of the drain, 17,985 l. 8s. 6d. Sir Joseph Banks (from whom I receive this intelligence) has made this note on the back of Dugdale's map, in which no trace of the new sea-dike bank appears : ' Dugdale's History of Embankment and Draining was published in 1662, hence we may conclude, that the old sea-dike bank was then the outermost boundary of the inclosed marshes ; it appears by Hayward's map, published by Badeslade, that it was also so in 1605 ; notwithstanding the new sea-dike is said by Mr. Maxwell to have been made about 1640.' "—" An Act of Parliament passed in 1792, for embanking and draining certain salt marshes and low lands in Spalding, Moulton, Whaplode, Holbeach, and Gedney, containing in all about 5339 acres."—" Great tracts of valuable land remain yet to be taken in from the sea about North Somercots, and other places on that coast ; but I do not find that any experiments have been made

in

in Sir Hyde Page's method, of making hedges of gorse
fascines, and leaving the sand to accumulate of itself into a
bank. Mentioning this to Mr. Neve," (?) "he informed
me, that he had observed at least a hundred times, that
if a gorse bush, or any other impediment was by accident met with by the sea, it was sure to form a hillock
of sand."

It is now upward of twenty years since I detected the
practicability—that is to say, discovered the method—of
forming sea banks along a flat sandy shore, by the means of
double lines of faggots, and the sea reed, or marram plant
(arundo arinaria). See NORFOLK.—Min. 106:—first published, in 1787.

PUBLIC DRAINAGE*.—Its *History* in Lincolnshire.—
P, 225. " Every circumstance concerning so very large a
tract as the undrained fens, deserves attention. For the
following particulars, I am indebted to Sir Joseph Banks,
who knows more of them, perhaps, than any other person
in the County. The East and West fens were drained by
adventurers in the time of Charles I. some account of
whose undertakings may be seen in Dugdale's History of
Embanking and Draining; they were about that time
actually inclosed and cultivated. It is probable that the
undertakers and the king, to whom a share was allotted, had taken to themselves a larger portion of the fen
than the county thought just and reasonable; for in the
time of the great rebellion, a large mob, under pretence
of playing at foot-ball, levelled the whole of the inclosures,
burnt the corn and houses, destroyed the cattle, and killed
many of those who occupied the land. They proceeded
to destroy the works of drainage, so that the country was
again inundated as it formerly had been. After the
Restoration, the adventurers repaired their works, resumed
their lots of property, and began again to cultivate them;
but the country, who always considered themselves oppressed, by trespass upon the grounds, compelled the
adventurers to defend their rights by a course of law; in
which it was determined, that the original agreement was
not valid, and consequently the property of the whole
level was vested in its original proprietors. From this
                                                      time

* The section, " Drainage," is accompanied by " a Map of the
South Drainages of Lincolnshire,"—neatly engraven, and prettily
colored;—but in regard to its pretensions to accuracy; or by whom
it was drawn, or from whence taken;—no account appears.

time the drainage was carried on under the Court of Sewers, principally by means of the adventurers' drains; but the river Witham being neglected, and nearly silted up, they became so much oppressed, that application was made to Parliament in 1762, when an act passed, by which the present works have been made, which are probably sufficient to carry off the whole of the downfall waters; but till a catch-water drain is made to keep separate those that fall upon the hills, from those which fall upon the level, and a proper outfall provided, to carry the hill waters separately to sea, the expence of which will probably be equal, if not exceed that of the Witham drainage, the land can never be considered as safe winter land; neither can it be thought advisable to divide and inclose it. These fens, East consists of 12424 acres, one rood, one perch. The undertakers' drains left only 2000 acres under water; but I am credibly informed, that the outfall of Maudfoster, as that *goat* now lies, is capable of draining dry the deepest pits in that fen."

On the *Advantages* arising from Drainage, we meet with the following particulars.—P. 235. " Deeping Fen, which extends most of the 11 miles from that town to Spalding, is a very capital improvement by draining. Twenty years ago the lands sold for about 3 l. an acre; some was then let at 7s. or 8s. an acre; and a great deal was in such a state that nobody would rent it: now it is in general worth 20s. an acre, and sells at 20 l. an acre: 10,000 acres of it are taxable under commissioners, pay up to 20s. an acre; but so low as 2s.; average 4s. including poor-rates, and all tithe free. There are 5000 acres free land, but subject to poor-rates. The free land also sells from 15 to 20l. an acre; and more three or four years ago."

P. 239. " In that long reach of fen, which extends from Tattersal to Lincoln, a vast improvement by embanking and draining has been ten years effecting. The first act passed in 1787 or 1788; and, through a senseless opposition, an extent of a mile in breadth was left out, lest the waters should, in floods, be too much confined, and the other side of the river overflowed : better ideas, however, having taken place, a new act to take in to the river has passed. This is a vast work, which in the whole has drained, inclosed, and built, and cultivated, between 20 and 30 square miles of country (including the works now undertaking). Its produce before little, letting for not more than 1s. 6d. an acre; now, from 11s. to 17s. an acre.
" Mr.

" Mr. Chaplin had 300 acres of this, which were never
let for more than 10l. a year; now he could let it at
11s. or 12s. per acre; probably more. What an improvement over a country 12 or 14 miles long, and from 2 to 3
broad !"

P. 245. " Mr. Parkinson's table of the improvements in
Drainage, by acts in which he was a commissioner.

	Acres.	Improved value.	Old value.	Improvement.
Tattershall embankment - -	892	£. 838	£. 387	£. 450
Alnwick Fen -	1,097	703	54	648
The nine embanked fens to Lincoln	19,418	15,534	1,941	13,592
Holland Fen eleven towns - -	22,000	25,300	3,600	21,700
	43,407	42,375	5,982	36,390

On the *Business* of Drainage, the subjoined notices ma
have their use. P. 240. (Tattershall Fen) " It is subjec
to the tax of 1s. an acre to the Witham drainage; an
not exceeding 1s. 6d. to its own; but this is not mor
than 1s. Land here now sells at 25l. an acre. This va
work is effected by a moderate embankment, and th
erection of windmills for throwing out the superfluo
water The best of these, which cost 1000l. erecting
Mr. Chaplin of Blankney, who is a large proprietor her
and keeps 300 acres of fen in his own hands, as well
400 of upland, had the goodness to shew me, and ordere
to be set to work. The sails go seventy rounds, and
raises 60 tons of water every minute, when in full wor
The bucket wheel in the mills of Cambridgeshire a
perpendicular without the mill; this, which is calle
dritch, has it in a sloping direction, in an angle of abo
40 degrees, and within the mill. It raises water fo
feet. Two men are necessary in winter, working nig
and day."

P. 241. " In the north part of the County, the drainag
of the Ankholm is another great work, extending fro
Bishop Bridge to the Humber, in a curved line; but
an act passed about thirty years ago, was carried in
straight line through the level, for the purposes of drai
ing and navigation. Before the draining, it was wor

but from 1s. to 3s. 6d. per acre; now it is from 10s. to 30s. Much of it arable, and much in grass.

" The low lands that are taxed to the drainage amount to 17197 acres, the tax amounts to 2149 l. per annum, or 2s. 6d. an acre."

P. 272. " The Drainage of South Holland, 100,000 acres, is in its progress, and will also prove a work of immense consequence; and it deserves noting, that this business goes forward at present, because it is not effected by borrowing money on the credit of a tax, but the capital levied on the proprietors, who have now paid two instalments of 10s. an acre each.

" An Act passed in 1794, for improving the outfall of the river Welland, and better draining the low grounds, and discharging their waters into the sea. The plan of this undertaking is to cut an immense canal from the reservoir below Spalding, capable of carrying the whole waters of the river Welland, and issuing them into the Witham below Boston. It is expected that the consequence of this will be, not only the drainage of Deeping fen, and all the adjoining lands, as well as those in Kirton wapentake, through the middle of which the canal is intended to pass, but also that the present bed of the river Welland, and of the Fossdike wash, will shortly be converted into marsh land of the richest quality, there being a great disposition to warp up in that river; and so fully have the undertakers been convinced that this would be the case, that they have provided in the Act, for making a turnpike road across Fossdike wash, which they conclude will become perfectly dry. But in consequence of the scarcity of money arising from the war, they have not been able to raise the money; but it is hoped that the return of peace will remove this obstacle, and set this great work in full action."

General Remarks of the Reporter.—P. 246. " By the annexed Map of the Drainages in the south-east district of the County, united with the improvements on the Ancholm, and in Axholm, it will appear that there is not probably a County in the kingdom that has made equal exertions in this very important work of draining. The quantity of land thus added to the kingdom, has been great; fens of water, mud, wild fowl, frogs, and agues, have been converted to rich pasture and arable, worth from 20s. to 40s. an acre. Health improved, morals corrected, and the community enriched. These when carried to such an extent, are great works, and reflect the highest credit on the good sense and energy of the proprietors.

proprietors. Without going back to very remote periods
there cannot have been less than 150,000 acres drained
and improved, on an average, from 5s. an acre to 25s.; or
a rental created of 150,000 l. a year. But suppose it only
100,000 l. and that the profit on an average been received
during the period of thirty years; the rental has in that
time amounted to three millions, and the produce to near
ten ; and when, with the views of a political arithmetician,
we reflect on the circulation that has attended this creation of wealth through industry; the number of people
supported; the consumption of manufactures; the shipping employed; the taxes levied by the state; and all
the classes of the community benefited ; the magnitude
and importance of such works will be seen ; and the propriety well understood of giving all imaginable encouragement and facility to their execution."

The zealful Secretary then darts forth, on rapsodic
wing, into the region of politics :—Thus, p. 246. "These
are the results of that government, which so many living
and fattening under its protection wish to exchange or
hazard, for speculative legislation of a more popular cast.
Early in the days of republican France decrees issued for
draining marshes; I do not ask, what progress has been
made ? But I would demand, if any Drainages equal to
this have been executed in that kingdom during a century ? From Bourdeaux to Bayonne, in one of the finest
climates of Europe, nearly all is marsh. What French-
man has been so actuated by the blessings of republican
security, as to lay out one louis on that or any other marsh
or bog? These undertakings prove the reliance of a
people on the secure possession of what their industry
creates; and had it not been for common-rights, all
England would long ago have been cultivated and improved ; no cause preserves our wastes in their present
state, but the tenderness of government in touching private property." (!) "A farming traveller must examine this
country with a cold heart, who does not pray for the continuance of a system of legislation which has tended so
powerfully to adorn, improve, and cultivate the country
and to diffuse prosperity and happiness through the
whole society."

Unfortunately, however, for the prophetic powers of
the writer, England is now (November 1809) threatened
with famine ; while France is inundated with corn ; to the
great injury of its " spirited cultivators." This is on
the true principle of fanning the flame. See p. 71, aforegoing.—But a man who is basking in the sunshine of a
                                                                    government

government is in duty bound to applaud it. He must be an ingrate, indeed, who does not praise the bridge that carries him cleverly over the water.

CANALS.—In the section "Drainage," we have the following suggestion of the Reporter, respecting the *origin* of canals, in England.—P. 273. "The first navigable canal that was made in England, is in all probability that which was made from Lincoln to Torksey; it is evidently a part of the Cardike, an immense Roman work, which served to prevent the living waters from running down upon the fens, and skirting the whole of them from Peterborough to Lincoln, afforded a navigation of the utmost consequence to this fertile country."

The subjoined notices appear in the section "Canals." —P. 405. "There is an inland navigation from Boston, by Brothertoft farm on the Witham, cut to Lincoln, and then by the Fossdyke canal to the Trent, and thence to all parts of Yorkshire, Lancashire, &c. Rotherham having been, in good times for the manufacture, a great market for cattle and sheep, Mr. Cartwright executed a boat for taking sheep. It will carry eighty in two parcels, one in the hold, and the other on the deck; the latter secured by netting, supported by stancheons, The deck is of moveable hatches, covered with tarpawling to keep free of urine; to give air below, a line of hatches along the centre moveable; and the upper manger around that aperture. By this means they can be conveyed very commodiously, and saving the loss of 3s. a head by driving. See the annexed plate."

This is a simplex, well contrived mode of conveyance, which does credit to its inventor, and might, doubtlessly, be useful in other situations.

An engraving and explanation of it is given in the Appendix to this Report. But they convey little more than what may be caught in the above description.

P. 406. "At Sleaford, a new canal made from the Witham to Boston, finished in 1796, and has but lately begun to operate.

"Another, the Grantham canal, from Grantham, and goes into the Trent near Holm Pierepoint.

"The Ankholm cut extends, and is navigable from Bishop Bridge to the Humber, at Ferryby Sluice.

"Also from Horncastle to the river Witham at Dog Dyke near Tattershall; but not yet completed."

P. 407. "From Grantham to Nottingham, thirty-three miles, there is a very fine canal just completed, which cost

cost 100,000 l, and from which very great returns are expected. It passes near some fine beds of plaster, which will probably be productive; and lime is already brought in large quantities from Criche in Derbyshire."

ROADS.—It is rather extraordinary that any man travelling, for three months, in one County, for the avowed purpose of observing the existing state of its "Agriculture and internal improvement," should be in a manner unobservant of its roads. The following extract comprizes the entire contents of the section appropriated to this subject.

P. 405. " Upon its being proposed some time ago to make a turnpike to join the Spilsby road from Tattershall, the proposition was rejected, without throwing the expence by tolls on the public; and the issue shews, that without a very general public spirit, and proprietors being of ample fortune, or great spirit of exertion, such schemes rarely succeed : here the business has been well and effectually done through Revesby ; but I understood, that for a large extent of it the road is still much neglected.

" In the hundred of Skirbeck, to Boston, and thence to Wisbeach, they are generally made with silt, or old sea sand*, deposited under various parts of the country ages ago, and when moderately wet, are very good; but dreadfully dusty and heavy in dry weather; and also on a thaw they are like mortar.

" Take the County in general, and they must be esteemed below par."

In a section, headed, " RELIGION !" this Reporter of *local* practices, drags in the *general* subject of WORKING on SUNDAYS. On what principle of agriculture and internal improvement,—or to answer what private end or public purpose,—does not clearly appear.—Pure Christian *piety* could not be his motive. For he tells some merry stories about the clergy of Lincolnshire, without appearing to be in the least *moved* (unless to laughter) by their indecorousness.—They are much too ludicrous and light, and too derogatory of the clerical character, to be registered, here.—Those who have pleasure in seeing the established religion of their country degraded, may refer to pages 11, 21, and 437 of his Report.

His nonsensical insinuation, that, " in harvest, as much is,

---

* See the head Alluviation, ensuing ; for the probable origin of " Silt."

s, in many cases, gained by resting on a Sunday, as in others is lost by it,"—because,—" In a ticklish season, after some days of rain, the common error is carrying too soon ; at such times, being forced to lose a day is in fact a gain,"—is too pernicious in its tendency to excite laughter.—Are the husbandmen of England, taken in the mass, such dolts—such ignorant blockheads—as not to know their own interest! or when their corn is fit for carrying!—If it is an advantage to lose one day in a week, how much better (may we not say) it would be, on the *improving* plan of the Secretary of the Board of Agriculture,—to lose two or three.—Every man of *observation* must have seen valuable crops of corn, that were in perfectly high order, during the whole of a Sunday, lost to their owners and the community, by a rainy week succeeding. It surely cannot be otherwise than acceptable to the Giver of all things, to have his gifts preserved from spoil, on any day of the year.

SUBJECT THE THIRD.

RURAL ECONOMY.

DIVISION THE FIRST.

TENANTED ESTATES.

ESTATES.—*Sizes.*—In the subjoined extracts, will be perceived much appropriate Report.—P. 18. " In this immense County there are found, as in all such extensive districts, estates of every size : my list, without pretending to correctness, contains one of 25,000l. a year; one of 14,000l.; one of 11,000l. ; six of 10,000l. ; one of 8000l.; one of 7,500l.; two of 7000l. ; one of 6000l.; one of 4,500l.; one of 4000l.; seven of 3000l.; five of 2,500l. ; one of 2,100l. ; six of 2,000l. : but from the situation of these properties, not spreading into some large districts, I have reason to believe that the catalogue is very incomplete ; that it must be incorrect, the nature of such inquiries ensures to a certain degree

" Upon inclosing Kirton, it was found there were 146 proprietors in 5000 acres, two of them possessing 1500 acres.

On

" On the inclosure of Barton there were above 120 proprietors."

P. 20. "In the hundred of Skirbeck" (District of Boston) " property is very much divided, and freeholds numerous. In the parish of Frieston, containing above 3000 acres, there is not one plot of more than 48 acres together, belonging to one person ; some late purchases have raised it to 60 acres."

Tenures.—P. 21. "At Ferraby, Sir John Nelthorpe has a right to turn in horses on the common meadows saved for hay ; and it is preserved to the present time." (!)*

" Tenures in this country are much copyhold in the low country, but not much in the higher land; and a considerable quantity in church-leases; let some for three lives, and others for twenty-one years, renewable every seven : and many Crown lands let for years.

" Lord Exeter has property on the Lincoln side of Stamford, that seems held by some tenure of ancient custom among the farmers, resembling the *rundale* of Ireland. The tenants divide and plough up the commons, and then lay them down to become common again ; and shift the open fields from hand to hand in such a manner, that no man has the same land two years together; which has made such confusion, that were it not for ancient surveys it would now be impossible to ascertain the property."

In regard to commons, a similar custom has prevailed and indeed still prevails, in Devonshire and Cornwall And with respect to *common fields,* the same practice under the name of " Run-rig," formerly was common in the Highlands of Scotland; and, perhaps, in more remote times to Scotland in general. In the Highlands, it is understood, that this apparently irrational regulation was established in a sort of necessity, by the chieftains of clans, to prevent their vassals from claiming the lands which they were allowed to cultivate,—*as their own,* by the rights of constant and long occupancy. Something of a similar nature, it is probable from the above notice, may have prevailed, during the earlier periods of feuda lity, in England.

IMPROVEMENT of Estates.—*Alluviation*—" Warping."— This most extraordinary modern improvement is noticed at some length, in the Review of the Reports from the NORTHERN

* For a similar remain of barbarous times, see my GLOCESTER-SHIRE.

NORTHERN DEPARTMENT; in which it was discovered.
And an account of it is given in the Report from the
WEST RIDING of YORKSHIRE.

In that volume is inserted two valuable papers on the
subject:—one of them by Mr. DAY of Doncaster; the
other by the late LORD HAWKE. In these papers, not
only the practice, and the effects, of warping are de-
cribed; but some interesting particulars, relating to its
origin.

The effects of rich Alluvion deposited naturally, or fortuitously, on the banks of muddy rivers, must have been
observed, ever since rivers and men received existence.
All the waterformed mudlands, in the world, may be said
to owe their existence to such agency. But it remained
for modern times to conduct mud-laden waters, *artificially*,
away from the river, or estuary in which they are lodged,
and to spread them over exhausted lands; either as *manure*, or to provide low swampy grounds with a sufficient
depth of fertile *soil*; so as to raise them to the profitable
state of rich marsh lands.

In registering this practice, from the West Riding
Report, I classed it under the head *Manure*; under which
character, it, there, appeared. But, in the Lincolnshire
Report, now under consideration, we find it in the latter
character; namely that of creating *soil*, and, in effect,
forming MARSH LANDS. I therefore think it right to view
it, here, in that still more important light.

The Secretary of the Board has been laudably assiduous, in collecting information, on this subject. Such
parts of it as appear to me of public import, I will here
digest, under the following heads:—

1. The nature of this improvement.
2. Its history and present state.
3. The business or process of Alluviation.
4. Its beneficial effects.
5. The management of alluviated lands.

1. The theory, or nature, of Alluviation.—The following is this writer's account of it.—P. 276. " The water of
the tides that come up the Trent, Ouze, Dun, and other
rivers, which empty themselves into the great estuary of
the Humber, is muddy to an excess; insomuch, that in
summer if a cylindrical glass 12 or 15 inches long be filled
with it, it will presently deposite an inch, and sometimes
more, of what is called warp. Where it comes from, is a
dispute: the Humber, at its mouth, is clear water, and

no floods in the countries washed by the warp rivers bring
it; but on the contrary, do much mischief by spoiling the
warp.   In the very driest seasons, and longest droughts,
it is best and most plentiful."

The former part of this statement is concise, clear, and
satisfactory.   Why it should have been gratuitously covered with mystery, even as the surface of a fen is with
" warp," appears to me much more difficult to explain,
than the origin and operation of the latter.

In page 285, Mr. Nicholson of Rawcliff in Yorkshire
(notwithstanding what the Reporter has advanced at the
opening of his section) is said to be " certain that it does
not come from sea, or from the high country, but from
the Humber itself."   What I shall, therefore, more particularly attempt, here, will be to show—*how it came,
there.*

It belongs to the nature and operation of heavy rains,
to suspend, wear away and carry off, from elevated and
sloping surfaces, in general, the soils and earthy substrata
which lie in the way of the currents they produce; bearing the suspended particles down to the streams, brooks
and rivers, whose channels are most aptly situated to receive them; and the finer or more suspendable particles
are, in times of long continued rains, and consequent
floods, borne to the sea, or some other wide expanse of
water; in which the current of the river being lost, the
suspended matter falls to the bottom; the water, thereby,
recovering its transparency.

Even in *the state of nature*, considerable quantities of
earthy materials, lodged in a loose state, on the surface,
by worms, moles, and other inhabitants of the soil; as
well as in the tracks of wild animals, and the furrows and
deeper ravins, continually forming, or enlarging, in that
state,—were necessarily carried away by such means.

Those supplies, however, must ever have been inconsiderable,—compared with the quantities carried off, in like
manner, from the surface of a country, in *the state* of *cultivation;* most especially from the surfaces of retentive,
and slowly absorbent, lands, in the state of *tillage;*—as
every brook and rivulet, in clayey and strong loamy districts, sufficiently evince, in times of floods.

To apply these self evident truths, to the particular case
before us, we have only to conceive that, ever since the
wide extent of country which sends its surface waters to
the Humber, received its present form and texture,—certain portions of its soils and substrata have been necessarily

rily passing toward the estuary of that river (a receptacle of more than one hundred square miles in extent); and that some considerable share of the matter, thus and there deposited, remains, at this day, within its area.   But certainly not the whole of it:—for altho " the Humber at its mouth" (the mouth of its estuary) is, or may appear, " clear water,"—not only the waterformed marshes of Holderness, but probably those on the northeastern coast of Lincolnshire, have been formed from it*; as well as those on the banks of the Ouse, the Don, the Trent, and their various branches.

Having thus, I trust, satisfactorily shown " where it comes from,"—it would not be difficult to explain why the richest particles of the soils of a country, that have been agitated, by the rushing tide, or eager, of the Humber, twice a day, century after century, among saline or brackish water,—should be of a more fertilizing quality, than the more gross, crude, unlevigated, unsalined matters, forced down, by land floods.   But this is too obvious to need further explanation.

And why, " in the driest seasons and longest drought, it" (warp) " is best and most plentiful,"—is not less easily to be accounted for, than why the land floods should— " do much mischief, by spoiling the warp."

During high floods, not only is the water of the estuary deeper, but the weight of fresh water greater, so as to stem the tide, and thereby create a degree of stagnation, favorable to the repose of the prepared matter, deposited on its bed.   Hence, little if any thing more than the crude alluvion of the land floods can, at that time, be employed. And minor floods naturally operate to produce the same effect,—in proportion to the respective powers of their resistance.

On the contrary,—during long droughts, when the land waters are low, the estuary is comparatively shallow, and the tides have nothing to obstruct their impetuosity. They, of course, rush violently through the channel, and stir up the prepared mud, therein deposited;—scouring it, perhaps, to its very base:—thereby, giving the water the extraordinary degree of feculency, above reported.

On

---

* Does the comparative lightness of fresh water render it liable,— when forced out to the sea by continued floods,—to be thrown toward the coast? Or is the alluvion carried out, to the sea, and returned to the shore, by the tide; as are sand and gravel?—These marshes have doubtlessly been formed of rich alluvion.

On the *specific quality* of this highly prepared alluvion, I find nothing satisfactory, in the Report before me.
The Reporter defines it—" mud of a vast fertility; tho
containing not much besides sand; but a sand unique."—
He adds, p. 277, " Mr. Dalton of Knaith, sent some to
an eminent chemist; whose report was, that it contains
mucilage, and a very minute portion of saline matter; a
considerable one of calcareous earth; the residue is mica
and sand; the latter in far the largest quantity; both in
very fine particles. Here is no mention of any thing argillaceous; but from examining in the fields much warp,
I am clear there must be clay in some, from its caking
in small clods, and from its cleansing cloth of grease almost like fuller's earth. A considerable warp farmer
told me, that the stiffer warp was the best; but in general
it has the appearance of sand, and all glitters with the
micaceous particles."

Of its analytic, or component parts, there can be little
doubt: unless this vast elaboratory of the tide has decom-
posed and changed the nature of the original particles.
For these must necessarily have been collected from every
part (more or less according to its degree of inclination
and repellancy) of the extensive tract of country which
impels its running waters toward the Humber,—from the
highest mountain to the lowest vale lands.—Hence, it is
(or was) composed of the astringent infusions of the
moory earth of heaths,—the calcareous earths (whether
chemically or mechanically suspended) of chalk hills and
limestone heights,—and the argilaceous, siliceous, micaceous, and other earthy particles, carried off from vale
lands.

This heterogeneous aggregation of particles having
been, during centuries, agitated violently in waters of
different qualities,—whether or not they have been *chemically* changed,—have, doubtlessly, undergone a degree
of *mechanical* alteration:—especially, the grosser particles, as those of sand; which must necessarily have been
reduced in size, by agitation and reciprocal abrasion.—
Hence, probably, the " sand unique;" or, more techni-
cally, *silt*,—otherwise fine sand; namely, common sand
reduced, by attrition:—the probable origin of silts.

Not only the estuary of the Humber, but the southern
coast of Lincolnshire, abounds in alluvion.—P. 286. "They
have much warp on all the coast from Wisbeach to Boston, &c. and though a long succession of ages has formed
a large tract of warp country, called there *silt*, yet no
attempts

attempts that I have heard of, have been made to warp artificially there. How much the tides abound with warp may be learned from a remark of different application by Major Cartwright; he observes:

"' It is true, that immediately below the sea doors, the rivers warp up in dry seasons to a great height, with a muddy sand or silt, which the tides deposit. The Witham for instance, sometimes warps up 10 or 11 feet on the lower side of the sea doors at the grand sluice; but the first freshes in the fall of the year have always, hitherto, made an early breach, and soon swept this mud bank into the sea."

Whether some part of this "warp" has crept round, by the coast, from the Humber*; or whether it is wholely the produce of the several rivers of the Midland Counties. &c., that empty into the sea, between Boston and Lynn, must, perhaps, for ever be left to conjecture, only.

Having thus, I hope, rendered the origin and nature of alluvion sufficiently evident, we will pass on to

2. The history and present state of Alluviation, from the Humber and its branches.—On the rise of this valuable art, in Lincolnshire, we find no particulars.—In a Note, p. 282, we are told—" warping began,"—" within the line of the County of York."

By Mr. DAY's statement, in the West Riding Report, published in 1799 (see NORTHERN DEPARTMENT) it appears that Mr. RICHARD JENNINGS, a small farmer of Armin, near Howden, was the first person who tried the experiment of warping (with the desired success) then, about fifty years ago;—that is to say, about the MIDDLE of the EIGHTEENTH CENTURY; and that two *attempts* were made in that quarter, about ten years, afterward!!!†

How

---

* See the foregoing Note, p. 105.

† In my Tour of *Observation* (see p. 11, aforegoing)—one of the very few *enquiries* I made, was at Booth ferry, near Armin; where I incidentally asked if Richard Jennings the inventor of warping was still living.—I was answered, by the intelligent keeper of the inn, there, that one BARKER, a small farmer of RAWCLIFF, and not Jennings of Armin, was the first warper of land:—adding the following particulars relating to this most important event of modern times, in the History of English Agriculture.

This aspiring genius (for such the inventor of a new art must ever be) hurt himself, at the outset (as many others have done) by the prosecution of his scheme;—which he was, in consequence, on the point of giving up.—But laying his case before a friend, who advanced

How contrary to human reason, that a discovery of such magnitude, and so obvious to common sense, and ordinary understandings, should have remained a quarter of a century, in almost total neglect!—Mr. Day says—" I am not certain how long it is since warping came much into practice; but however it is not many years ago. I believe not more than 20 or 25 years, or thereabouts."—And the Secretary of the Board, speaking of this practice, in *Yorkshire*, says, p. 285,—" Mr. Walker, steward to Mr. Twistleden, *forty years ago* began this practice, but it dropped for twenty years, till Mr. Fareham, another steward, took it up; many hundreds of acres have been done."

But thus it not unfrequently happens:—valuable practices, like valuable books, come slowly and silently into notice : while light superficial performances in literature, and plausible schemes in practical economicks, catch, like other meteors, the immediate attention of the multitude.

The rapid progress of this improvement, since its intrinsic merits have raised it into notice, is seen in the subjoined extracts, from the Secretary's Report.

P. 284. " Lord Beverley has 6 or 7 sluices going; and has warped so far as 300 acres in one year."—" Provision is made for warping a great extent of country by a navigable canal, 40 feet bottom near the Trent, which is making at present from the Trent near Althorpe to Thorne, &c. by which extensive tracts will be done, 24,000 l. is expended; a branch to Crowle is marked out; and another from Thorne to the river Dun, these for navigation; but it is not by the canal that the warping is done, but by a soakage drain on each side of it, which drains the country, and at the same time is capable of admitting

vanced him fifty pounds, toward carrying it on, he was thereby enabled to compleat his grand design; by which he afterward made a little money; so as to be able to forward his children's progress in life. One of his sons is now in business at Hull.

Mr. Jennings of Armin,—my informant says—was not a small farmer, but a steward to some property, there;—*a professional man.* He was not the *first* who *practised* warping ; but the first, or one of the first, who *extended the practice.*—Mr. Day, it is probable, may have mistaken names.

But these things I notice, here, merely as *hearsays;* and solely for the purpose of exciting those who have made and are making fortunes, by the discovery, to ascertain who it was that made it, and to lose no time, in RAISING a MONUMENT to his MEMORY.

admitting the tides to deliver warp to the whole country for 12 miles, by cuts at right angles; and to sell warping on either side. The price talked of is from 4l. to 5l. an acre. And in case the drains should warp up at any time, provision of sluices is made to let water out of the canal into either, to scour them out clean."

3. The business of Alluviation.—For practical and intelligible information, on this subject, we must look into the papers of Lord Hawke, and Mr. Day, rather than into the Secretary's Report. Some general ideas, however, relating to the *outlines* of this improvement, may be discerned in the following notice.—P. 278. " The first warping works which I viewed were at Morton Ferry, where Mr. Harrison, who shewed me them, has a large concern in a very great undertaking, no less than to warp 4260 acres of commons, by means of an act of inclosure and drainage. They are attempting to warp 400 acres in one piece, which is to be sold to pay the expence of doing all the rest, and they have been offered 30s. an acre rent for it, when finished; a double sluice is erected to take the water from the Trent, which cost 1200l.; and a double canal, cut under the idea that the water should come in by one, and return by another; this apparently has created a great expence. They have used 15 tides over 200 acres, which has raised about 6 inches of warp in some places, but not uniform : and the opinion of the best informed persons is, that they must divide it into 50 acred pieces, and do one at a time. All this may be easily corrected, and the improvement will be amazingly great. The common is worth nothing as it has been hitherto fed."

The Reporter has inserted a Copy of the Plan and Estimate of this great undertaking,—by A. Bower and J. Dyson; dated, Gainsborough, 4th Jan. 1796. The total amount of the estimate, 4846l.

The subjoined maslet of heterogeneous matter may serve to furnish a few particulars of this improvement.—P. 284. " Mr. Nicholson at Rawcliff, takes the levels first ;—builds a sluice;—if a quarter of a mile or half a mile, 60 acres may be done the first year; the drier the season, the better. The clough or sluice 400l. 8 feet wide, and 5 feet or 6 high ; a drain 14 feet at bottom, and as much more at top; 30s. to 40s. an acre, of 28 yards; banks 4 to 8 feet high, and expence 7s. to 20s. an acre of 28 yards. Begin at Lady-day till Martinmas; but all depends on season; the depth will depend on circumstances :"—and the following

lowing loose memorandum, to convey *some idea* of the expence of warping, on a moderate scale.

P. 284. "A sluice for warping, 5 feet high, and 7 wide, will do for 50 acres per annum; and if the land lies near the river, for 70. Costs from 400 l. to 500 l."

4. The effects of Alluviation.—P. 281. "At Althorpe, Mr. Dalton is warping 300 acres, which will be converted from a very inferior state to 30s. an acre. At Knaith he manured a piece with it for turnips, on a sand soil; the rest of the field with dung; the warp equalled the dung.

" At Amcots, there are other undertakings of the same sort.

" At Gainsborough Mr. Smith shewed me a spot that was warped to the depth of *ten inches in eight hours.*"

P. 282. " Mr. Webster at Bankside*, has made so great an improvement by warping, that it merits particular attention. His farm of 212 acres is all warped; and to shew the immense importance of the improvement, it would be necessary only to mention, that he gave 11 l. an acre for the land, and would not now take 70 l. an acre; he thinks it worth 80 l. and some even 100 l. Not that it would sell so high at present; yet his whole expence of sluices, cuts, banks, &c. did not exceed 2500 l. or 12 l. per acre; from which, however, to continue the account, 1500 l. may be deducted, as a neighbour below him offers 5 l. an acre for the use of his sluice and main cut, to warp 300 acres, which will reduce Mr. Webster's expence to 1000 l. or about 5 l. an acre. Take it, however, at the highest, 12 l. and add 11 l. the purchase, together 23 l. an acre; if he can sell at 70 l. it is 59 l. per acre profit. This is prodigious; and sufficient to prove that warping exceeds all other improvements. He began only four years ago. He has warped to various depths, 18 inches, 2 feet, 2½ feet, &c. He has some that before warping was moor land, worth only 1s. 6d. an acre; now as good as the best. Some of it would let at 5 l. an acre for flax or potatoes; and the whole at 50s. He has 20 acres that he warped 3 feet deep, between the beginning of June, and the end of September; and 18 acres, part of which is 3½ feet deep. This

" * This is within the line of the county of York, as well as Rawcliff; but as warping began there, and has been very largely practiced, I thought it would contribute to rendering this account more satisfactory, and therefore viewed the works. No mention is made of it in the Reports of that county."

This is the worst year he has known for warping, by reason of wetness. He has applied it on stubbles in autumn
by way of manuring : for it should be noted, as a vast
advantage in this species of improvement, that it is renewable at any time ; were it possible to wear out by
cropping, or ill management, a few tides will at any time
restore it."

P. 283. " He" (Mr. Webster) " warped 12 acres of
wheat stubble, and sowed oats in April, which produced 12
quarters an acre. Then wheat, 36 bushels an acre. His
wheat is never less than 30."—" Warp, Mr. Webster
observes, brings weeds never seen here before, particularly mustard, cresses and wild cellery ; with plenty of
docks and thistles."

P. 285. " I viewed Mr. Nicholson's warped land with
much pleasure, and found his warp in some fields to have
been deposited from 2 feet deep at the bottom, gradually
shallowing up a slope to 5 or 6 inches to the top, forming
a level *. Mr. Harrad warping on the other side the
bank ; the tide was in the morning I viewed it, and a fish
pond and holes were filling up rapidly."

The following remarks are intelligible, and full of good
sense. P. 286. " *Note by a commissioner employed in
warping.*—Warp leaves one-eighth of an inch every tide,
on an average; and these layers do not mix in an uniform mass, but remain in leaves distinct.†

" ' If only one sluice, then only every other tide
can be used, as the water must run perfectly off, that the
surface may incrust, and if the canal is not empty, the
tide has not the effect. At Althorpe, Mr. Bower has
warped to the depth of 18 inches in a summer.

" ' Ten quarters an acre of oats, on raking in the seed
on warp ; the more salt in it the better ; but one fallow
in that case necessary, to lessen the effect, or it hurts
vegetation.' "—This well agrees with the sentiments of
other, or all, practical men, in regard to the operation of
salt as a manure. See WESTERN DEPARTMENT.

How incoherent, and inexplicit, is the information collected in this Report, with regard to the *depth* of *alluvion
deposited.*—In p. 276, " a cylinder, 12 or 15 inches long,
deposits an inch, and sometimes more."—In 285. " A kid-
ful of the thick water will deposit an inch, in a dry time."
—P. 281.

* This may seem to be an inconveniency of warping ; as it does
away all descent to carry off surface water.

† Slate rocks have doubtlessly originated in natural alluviation.

—P. 281. "Ten inches were deposited in eight hours."— But, lastly, we are told, by a man of experience, that " warp leaves, only, one eighth of an inch, each tide, on an average."

The quantity deposited (in a given time) must, necessarily, be as the quantity suspended; and this, as the degree of feculency and depth of the water when brought into a stagnant state. The degree of feculency may depend,—on the state of the river,—the state of the tide, and the consequent impetus of the eager *, to stir up, and carry forward, the alluvious matter that falls in its way,— the distance of the field of alluviation from the principal depôt, or repository of such matter,—and perhaps other minor circumstances.

It is not, however, the quantity, alone, that is to be regarded: the quality of the alluvion is, also, to be considered;—especially, for the purpose of manure, or wherewith to form the immediate surface soil.—Now, it seems equally clear, from reason, and from experience, that the quality of that which is lodged in the estuary, and doubtlessly more or less in the beds of the rivers that branch out of it,—is preferable to that which is brought down those rivers, by land floods. And it is almost equally obvious, to theory (we have I think no evidence on this head in practice) that the shorter the distance is, from the main lodgement of the prepared matter, the coarser will be its quality, and the further from it, the finer:—it being a general law of nature, with respect to bodies suspended in liquid lighter than themselves, that the heavier particles first subside. Thus, gravel and sand, suspended in agitated water, will ever subside, where the liquid becomes stagnant, or in a less agitated state, before the argilacious, or other earthy particles it may contain.

Those who have employed, or amused, themselves, with the process of ELUTRIATION, or " Washing over," well know this natural effect.

It is to be remarked, however, that, while the suspended matter is kept in a high degree of agitation, by the tide, whether in the estuary, or while impetuously rushing up the channels of its branches, the deposit may be inconsiderable ; so that it is the distance from the course of the tide, rather than from the principal repository, by which

* For a description of the " Boar," or Eager, of the Severn (I have not observed that of the Humber) see my GLOCESTERSHIRE.

which we are to measure and estimate the quality of the matter deposited. After the feculent water is taken out of the river or the estuary, the subsidence must in some degree commence; as the descent from thence to the field to be improved can seldome be great. Hence, the farther it is carried from the tide's way, the finer, the richer, the *stronger*, and more valuable will be its quality. —Thus, a *sand*, a *sandy loam*, a *clayey loam*, and a " *clay*," may be produced, by the same foul water.—See p. 8, aforegoing.

5. The Management of Warped Lands.—P. 284. " If a landlord warp, it should be deep at once; if a tenant, shallow, and repeat it; as good corn will grow at 6 inches as 6 feet; at 3 inches great crops; the stiffer the warp the better. Some seasons, sow corn the year after. Warp is cold, and if deep, takes time; a dry year best; great seeds." (?)

P. 286. " Mr. Wilson's idea of warping very just; to exhaust the low lands in favour of the hills, then to warp 6 inches deep, to exhaust that to make the hills; then to warp again; and by thus doing to keep the warp land in the highest order, and at the same time work a great improvement to all the higher grounds."

In regard to the cultivation and cropping of newly formed warped lands, nothing resembling a descriptive, readable account is to be found, in this Report. But a few more cramp, stump, disjointed, scattered crums of information may be picked out, of the general mass, and added to those which may have been discovered, in the above quotations.—Thus, p. 285. Mr. Nicholson of Rawcliff, in Yorkshire says, or is made to say—" it is full as good for grass as for tillage, and made capital grazing and by it; an acre will carry a good bullock, and some 2 sheep an acre; none in winter till after many years."—The same page—" Warp land has had crops of flax sold for 10l. an acre as it stands; and then they sow rape on good tillage."

P. 283. (Mr. Webster) " As to the crops he has had, they have been very great indeed; of potatoes from 80 to 130 tubs of 36 gallons, selling the round sorts at 3s. or 3s. 6d. a tub; and kidneys at 5s. to 8s. Twenty acres warped in 1794, could not be ploughed for oats in 1795, he therefore sowed the oats on the fresh warp, and scuffled in the seed by men drawing a scuffler; eight to draw, and one to hold; the whole crop was very great: but on 3 acres of it measured separately, they amounted to 14
                                                     quarters

quarters 1 sack per acre. I little thought of finding exactly the husbandry of the Nile in England. I had before heard of clover seed being sown in this manner on fresh warp, and succeeding greatly."

Concerning the courses of cropping, pursued on warp land, we find the following entries.—P. 285. (Mr. Nicholson) " Crops ought to be, beans 20 loads; wheat 10 or 12 loads; oats 10 quarters; never barley. After six years potatoes, and good flax :—He makes it worth 40 l. to 50 l. an acre.

    1. Oats.
    2. Wheat.
    3. Beans.
    4. Fallow.
    5. Wheat.
    6. Beans.
    7. Wheat.
    8. Beans, till it wants a fallow; it will

go four, five, six years without a fallow. Turnips bad; tread and daub too much. Has had it twelve or thirteen years without any manure."

P. 283. " Courses pursued on warp land.
    1. Beans.
    2. Wheat; and this the most profitable.

1. Potatoes.	4. Potatoes.
2. Wheat.	5. Wheat.
3. Beans.	

Also,

1. Beans.	3. Flax.
2. Wheat.	4. Wheat.

Flax, 40 to 50 stone per acre."

The following judicious remarks, in the section, " Embanking," may be applicable to warped lands. Marsh lands that are formed of similar materials, whether naturally or artificially, require, it is more than probable, a similar mode of treatment.—Winteringham is situated toward the upper end of the estuary of the Humber.

P. 270. " Upon taking in new tracts from the sea by embankment, it is always an object of consequence to know what should be done with the land. There is a new tract taken in by Act of Parliament at Wintringham, and some failures of crops makes it an interesting object. The second year after excluding the sea, they ploughed and sowed beans; but the crop so bad, being in some places for acres together absolutely destroyed, that the

manage-

management is plainly bad. The farmers, Mr. Peacock and Mr. Johnson, attributed it to the salt being too fresh and strong, and probably they are right; however, the spots in the field which were a little dry from inequality of surface, had beans, though bad, but the flat spaces none. From observations made in other places, I am inclined to think that the land should be pastured for three years after excluding the sea, after which, ploughing will succeed without hazard."

GENERAL OBSERVATIONS.

HAVING not, heretofore, had a favourable opportunity of studying the general subject of ALLUVIATION; and the present being the only one I shall probably have, while going through the Board's Reports,—I have thought it right to bestow some considerable share of time and attention, in analyzing it, and giving its several parts a degree of synthetical arrangement; and that sort of scientific existence of which every art is capable.

What I have to add to the remarks that have incidentally risen, in going through the West Riding and Lincolnshire Reports, is chiefly of a cautionary nature. And, for the want of further data, than those publications afford, little, I find, can be offered with sufficient confidence.

Unless we had the heights to which the tides rise above the lands to be alluviated, it might be indiscreet to censure those, who lavishly, it would seem, load them with *thick* coverings of mud.—Without any other evidence, however, than what is given by reason and common sense, we may assume that there are lands which lie very little beneath the top of the tide; and to deposit more, on these, than may be necessary to their fertility, must be an act of imprudence; as, thereby, a repetition of the process may be prevented. There are doubtlessly lands thus situated, which ought to be *manured*, rather than *soiled*, with Alluvion.

Further, I will venture to excite a degree of doubt, as to the INEXHAUSTABILITY of the repository of highly prepared matter under consideration. For altho the estuary of the Humber is a hundred square miles in extent, the more fertilizing Alluvion may be confined to a comparatively small space. And who ever has been in the habit of elutriating soils, or other earthy matters, is aware of how soon the more suspendible, may be separated from the grosser, parts.

It

It is possible, that, at very low water, examinations, approaching a sufficient degree of accuracy, might be instituted with effect. The extent of low lands, capable of receiving with profit, this species of improvement, might, with more certainty, be found.

Whether or not there is a sufficient quantity in store, to complete the first improvement, and enough, more, to keep up the fertility of the lands in perpetuity,—we may venture, I think, to suggest that the *quality*, at least, is liable to be impaired by this novel practice. The richer parts will assuredly be the first to reach the land:—a stimulus, this, to early Alluviation.

Admitting it to be possible, that the principal part of this prepared matter may be transferred, by this process, from the sea or an estuary to the lands on its margin, an improvement, highly favourable to NAVIGATION, would thereby, it is more than probable, be effected. And there may be situations in which Alluviation might be found eligible, solely to produce that end.

But enough, perhaps, of conjecture. I have, however, one suggestion to offer, which may be of great practical use to those who have lands capable of this extraordinary improvement, but which lie at a distance from the Humber. It is—not to set about a work of this nature, on a scale of any extent, until the existing works of the lowlands, in the neighbourhood of that river and its branches (lying within the compass of a few miles) have been duly examined.

Sodburning—After what has been brought forward, on this head, in reviewing Mr. Stone's Report, very little can be requisite to be added, in this place. There are, evidently, two *warm* parties, in Lincolnshire, respecting this operation:—a proof, in my mind, that, altho it may not be a new practice, there, it has not yet approached maturity. The two Reporters are, as to this subject, of opposite opinions; if not of adverse parties. A mediator may, therefore, be useful.

There are, in that County, two subjects, very distinct in situation, and differing, much, in their origins and specific qualities, that are equally and strikingly proper, for this practice:—namely, the *fen* lands (I mean whenever plowing them may be proper, to reclaim them from a state of nature, or of neglect) and the *heath* lands,—*when first broken up*. In those cases, " paring and burning,"
                                                            properly

properly performed, is so consonant with theory, and so fully demonstrated to be beneficial in practice, that, to my conception, no room is left for argument. But whether, or not, the operation can be *repeated*, with propriety, may depend on circumstances. Nothing but a degree of slovenliness can render repetition necessary. And the proprietors of Lincolnshire, who restrict their tenants to " one burning," have some reason on their side;—and much safety.

The Secretary of the Board has bestowed twelve pages, on this subject. I perceive in them very little, however, that could add to the value of this register. That he is a *strenuous* advocate *for* this practice is evinced, in the subjoined extracts.—P. 257. "At Stainton, rode through the beginning of some improvements by Mr. Otter (I regretted his absence) on the estate of Mr. Angerstein. It was with great pleasure I saw the effect of *paring and burning gorse land*, adjoining the warren of Thorseway, which had produced, even in this very wet season, so unfavourable to the operation, a fine crop of turnips. I was with my horse's hind legs in gorse, and his fore ones in turnips, worth 3 l. an acre; formed like enchantment in the short space of four months; and yet visionaries remain, who will plead against so admirable a mode of converting a desart to cultivation! By no other means upon earth could this have been effected."—P. 251. " Mr. Kershaw of Driby breaks up sainfoin by paring and burning. Upon 30 acres of worn out and old sainfoin, run to rough grass, he did it at a considerable expence, for he was forced to burn it in large heaps; he sowed oats, and got as fine a crop as ever seen; then cole and turnips, which were not great, succeeded by wheat, which was a very fine crop; laid down with this wheat, to white clover, trefoil, and ray grass, which turned out as fine as possible: before it was not worth more than 2s. to 5s. an acre; now very fine: a capital and vast improvement, which it was impossible to have effected without paring and burning. In all this account I use his own expressions; but I must add a word to the visionary enemies on mere theory to this admirable practice, to consider well the force of this instance, and indeed of hundreds I have given to the same purpose, before they determine to continue blindly to condemn a practice because some bad farmers will abuse it. Asking a party of farmers at Mr. Bourne's at Dalby, what was the greatest of improvements for poor land in

this

this country? *Oh! that is easily answered: paring and burning, and sainfoin.*"

As a further proof that the *natives* of Lincolnshire are determined supporters of the practice, I will gratify my readers with the sentiments of Mr. Elmhurst, near Horncastle (whose language, at least, is interesting) respecting this subject.—P. 253. "I will maintain it, even in the faces of any who seem to be such violent enemies to paring and burning, and who talk in such a glossed-up and theoretical style against it, that there is *no mode whatever* of treating and managing *such* land equal to this, either for quantity of *such proper* manure, cheapness to the occupier, so profitable, or so *good* for the land, as this noble quantity of calcined manure. What these gentlemen theorists may either say or think of *this, my declaration;* I neither know nor care; for it is all a true and *practical* narrative, and a real fact; and facts are stubborn things!"

On *fen* land, or other reclaimed *morass*, formed of vegetable mold, the following notice may serve as a useful caution.—Note, p. 248. " A material objection to paring and burning is, that in very dry seasons, when the moisture of the earth is very low, the fire catches the soil below, and causes what is called *pitting,* making great unsightly holes to the bottom of the moor, which with great difficulty are extinguished. About thirteen years ago, a large common at Chatteris in the Isle of Ely, was thus burnt up, 16 or 18 inches deep, to the very gravel. *MS. of the B.*"

By the subjoined passage, it would seem that the novel practice of spreading the ashes *over* the furrows of the first ploughing, instead of burying them *under* these,— had travelled out of Yorkshire, into Lincolnshire. P. 251. " On the Wolds near Louth, much practiced, and will do it on land that has not been down above five or six years. A good way of performing the operation has been to make the heaps in exact rows in the middle of the lands, to plough close to them when burnt, and then to spread the ashes on the surface of the ploughed land, in order to keep the ashes above, and not below the furrow."

At the close of his section, the Reporter comes to the following *resolutions,*—headed " General Result."—I insert them, here, not as they contain an idea that is new, or peculiarly interesting; but as they convey the *cooler*
thoughts

thoughts of the Secretary of the Board, concerning this truly interesting topic.

P. 258. " 1. It appears from these facts, that upon the various soils mentioned, this practice has succeeded to such a degree, as to justify the warmest approbation of the husbandry in the County of Lincoln.

" 2. That it has in several cases been attended with a general good effect, even with the incorrect course of crops.

" 3. That no instance has occurred in this examination, where land has been materially injured.

" 4. That where it has been attended with an ill effect, it has evidently arisen from injudicious management.

" 5. That by no other method can waste lands be so speedily, effectually, and profitably improved.

" 6. That the benefit results from the ashes; as if they are removed, the crops suffer greatly.

" 7. That the fire has not the effect of dissipating or destroying the fertility resulting from previous manuring; as the crop, after the operation, is proportioned to such previous fertility from manures."

Irrigation.—For an instance of setting out lands for this purpose, by commissioners of inclosure, see *Appropriation*, p. 87, aforegoing.

Drinking Pools.—For the eligible practice of treading the beaten clay, with sheep, see the head, Waters, p. 73, aforegoing.

EXECUTIVE MANAGEMENT of Estates.—*Assistant Managers.—Hayward.*—P. 19. " At Wintringham, Lord Carrington has a man employed, whose only business is to be constantly walking over every part of the estate in succession, in order to see if the fences are in order: if a post or a rail is wanting, and the quick exposed; he gives notice to the farmer, and attends again to see if the neglect is remedied. This, upon a tract of land large enough to bear the expence, is an excellent system."— A good regulation, well reported.

Business Rooms.—Those of Sir J. BANKS, at Revesby, are well contrived, and in exemplary keeping; as appears in the following description.—P. 20. " His office, of two rooms, is contained in the space of thirty feet by sixteen; there is a brick partition between, with an iron plated door, so that the room, in which a fire is always burning, might be burnt down without affecting the inner one; where he has 156 drawers of the size of an ordinary conveyance, the inside being thirteen inches wide by ten broad,

broad, and five and a half deep, all numbered. There is
a catalogue of names and subjects, and a list of every
paper in every drawer; so that whether the inquiry concerned a man, or a drainage, or an inclosure, or a farm,
or a wood, the request was scarcely named before a mass
of information was in a moment before me. Fixed tables
are before the windows (to the south), on which to spread
maps, plans, &c. commodiously, and these labelled, are
arranged against the wall. The first room contains desks,
tables, and bookcase, with measures, levels, &c. and a
wooden case, which when open forms a bookcase, and
joining in the centre by hinges, when closed forms a
package ready for a carrier's waggon, containing forty
folio paper cases in the form of books; a repository of
such papers as are wanted equally in town and country."

I have only to remark, that, at the time I wrote my
treatise on landed property, I had not the least knowledge
of the business rooms at Revesby; which in regard to
security from *fire*, are not equal to those recommended in
that Treatise.

Tenancy.—On this topic, the Report under review is
not satisfactory. The present practices of a few individuals are put down; the notices terminating with
the following remark.—P. 59. " Respecting the County
in general, the fact is that leases are very rare."

The Reporter is evidently a *leasean*; but, judging
from the sentiments he has delivered, in the Lincolnshire
Report, his knowledge of the subject is not sufficiently
profound, to entitle him even to speculate upon it; as
may be seen, pretty evidently, in the subjoined remarks,
on

Covenants.—P. 60. " As to covenants, a landlord would
not sign leases without consulting some person upon this
head, on whom he could well rely."

Rent.—This would seem to be another subject to which
the Reporter has not paid mature attention. He has
filled nearly a sheet of paper with memoranda, loose and
incoherent as sand, relating to the rents of lands in Lincolnshire;—generally, without describing their specific
qualities or situations, further than by the name of some
village, perhaps, which ninety-nine readers of a hundred
never before heard of, and, unless in a few instances,
without any authority given for the insertion of the respective rates of rents; notwithstanding what is discri-
minately advanced, in the exordium to this section:—
see p. 67, aforegoing.

Even

Even had the article contained what is here intimated, and had the soil and *natural* situation been, in every case, entered,—still the pages, thus filled, would have been waste paper.

It is well known to every man who is acquainted with the values of lands, in various parts of the kindom, that, not only in each county, but in each district, nay, in every parish, and every neighbourhood, there is a *peculiar*, yet *fair*, MARKET PRICE for its LANDS, as for their products. And, in each, the current value is, in general, sufficiently known, *on the spot;* not only to occupiers, but to professional land valuers. Where this does not happen to be the case, (a case that can rarely occur) an auction, or sealed bidding (which tho very improper, as a general mean of letting farms might be admissible in a case of this kind)—would ascertain the fact, not only sooner, but infinitely better, than a thousand volumes of crude, indefinite hearsays, collected *at a distance.*

The real rental value of farm lands depends on a multitude of circumstances; as I have elsewhere shown, at length.   See TREATISE on LANDED PROPERTY.—All *general* and *inexplicit* remarks, and observations, on the subject, must necessarily be useless to *Rural Economy.* How far the result of these enquiries (even admitting the individual statements to be correct) may be useful in *Political Arithmetic*, I will not, in this place, attempt to determine.   I will merely make a few remarks, on the probable accuracy of the final statement; which is all that I can prevail upon myself to find room for, here.— The previous statements, respecting the different districts, are little more than conjecture—are, in effect, the Reporter's own ideas of the matter ; and he had, previously, warned his readers, not to place confidence in his authority.

" RENTAL OF THE COUNTY.

Acres.

The Lowlands	- -	776,960 at 23s.	£. 893,504
The Wolds	- -	234,880 at 9s.	105,696
The Heath	- -	118,400 at 8s. 4d.	49,333
Miscellaneous	- -	718,080 at 14s.	502,656
		1,848,320 at 16s. 9¼d.	£. 1,551,189

" Thus

" Thus the average rent of the whole County appears
to be 16s. 9d. per acre.

" Uniting the information gained under this head, concerning the rise of rent, with that which appears in the
chapter of inclosures, there is some reason to believe this
rental to have been trebled in thirty years." P. 53.

Remarks.—In p. 46, we find the following entry, from
the most respectable authority, produced in the section.
—" At Brocklesby," (Lord Yarborough's) " by means of
the noble possessor of so large a tract of country, I made
inquiries into rents, and was informed that the average of
all the Wolds, as marked on the map, is about 5s. an
acre. That the line of what is called *the Clays*, between
the Wolds and the Marsh, is at 10s. 6d. to 12s."

For the other entries, respecting the Wolds, or the
" Clays," I find no other than the writer's own authority
—Thus, (the same page) " At Belesby, *inquiring rents
in general, found* that the Wolds vary from 2s. 6d. to 25s.
The Middle Marsh, as it is called, that is, the line of
clay, 20s."—What judgement can be drawn, from such
contradictory evidence?

It would be an inexcusable waste of time to dwell on
this head. I will therefore finally observe that, if the
answers to enquiries were received (in cases, where no
name or authority is given, which may be said to be common) from clever, keen, rack-renting proprietors, or from
pushing, dashing, *accommodating* land valuers,—the rents
set down are probably much too high. On the contrary,
if from cunning, shrewd, or *quizzing*, tenants, they are, in
equal probability, much too low.

Can the concluding intimation, that the aggregate rent
of Lincolnshire has been " trebled in thirty years," be
entitled to attention?

For a valuable suggestion, in regard to the fixing of
rents, on newly appropriated lands, see the head, *Appropriation*, p. 88, aforegoing.

Choice of *Tenants.*—P. 67. " Mr. Parkinson observes
that upon such a farm as is usual in Lincolnshire, to wit
part grass and part arable, so much should be the latter
that the fallow part shall raise turnips, rape, &c. to support the lamb hogs that the farmer breeds, and fatten the
two shears; upon such a farm for each 100l. a year he
should have a capital of 750l. Upon a farm of 300l. a
year, if a man has not above 2000l. he will soon want
money."

DIVISION THE SECOND.

WOODLANDS.

NATURAL WOODS.—P. 217. " The following is the system of Sir Joseph Banks's woods, which have been very carefully managed since 1727, in a rotation of twenty-three years The full grown oak timber is weeded out in proportion of one-fourth, in the woods of the best quality; and one-fifth upon the inferior land. The aquatics, such as willow, sallow, alder, are all cut clean every twenty-three years; the same with hazel, and all other brush. The ash, elm, &c. the full grown plants are cut, leaving a proportion of the best for the next crop. Of all sorts, leaving such as will pay for a second twenty-three years' growth : and the oak, upon a calculation of four successive growths, being ninety-two years when cut : and in some parts one hundred and fifteen years, or five growths; but of this very little; in general ninety-two. Produce per acre, on an average, 45 l. consisting of timber, bark, poles, and brush."

Mr. Parkinson's statement is as follows.—Same page.— " The common medium average of our wood books are about

	£.	s.	d.
" 20 oaks, average 22s. - - - - - - -	22	0	0
Bark about - - - - - - - - - -	11	0	0
Poles of ash, sallow, birch, &c. - - - -	10	6	8
Brush wood 3d. . - - - - - - - -	2	0	4
Total of an acre, cut once in 23 years - -	45	7	0"

With those data, the Reporter brings out the following conclusion.—P. 219. " The woods covering 805 acres*; if 45 l. 7s. be taken as a medium, the produe is 1 l. 19s. 5d. per acre per ann. from land, which being amongst the worst in the country, would not produce, in an arable farm, more than 10s. or 12s."

What an egregious error is this, to be made by an " Arithmetician," whose books abound with *calculations !*
—From

* Admitting this,—what follows? nothing.

—From the 1l. 19s. 5d, above set down, as the rent, per acre per annum, is to be deducted half the interest (or a fraction less) of that sum, during twenty three years; call it 40s:—the interest of which, at five per cent, is 2s. which multiplied by 23, gives 46s. the half of which is 23s. This being deducted from 40s. leaves 17s. the utmost rent paid by those woodlands, according to the above data :—that is to say, had those lands been let at 17s. an acre, as farm lands, and the rent had been received half yearly, and put out on simple interest, only, they would have paid, within a fraction, what they are now (or were in 1796) paying as woodland. Reckoning on compound interest or even common interest, on the interest received, placed out from time to time (which on large sums might be fairly reckoned) the estimated annual rent of the woodland would be brought much lower.

If we follow the Reporter in his calculations, we shall find him again in error. Having made what he would seem to have thought a discovery ;—namely, that if the whole of these woods were cut down and sold, the interest of the money arising from the sale would be a valuable consideration (a truth which must strike every man who bestows any thought on the subject, and which has been long, and often before the public *)—he proceeds, p. 219. "In *conversation* with Mr. Parkinson, the steward, *I found* that the whole produce of an acre at the time of cutting would vary from 150l. to 300l. in value. It is moderate to call it 200l."

Now, this only shows the slipperiness of "conversation," as a groundwork of reasoning, or calculation. Mr. Parkinson's statement,—*on paper*,—is that given above.

It is there plainly seen, that the timber and bark of one fourth of the whole is 33l. and of course the value of the whole of the timber trees, is 132l. †;—to which add the poles and brushwood—12l. 7s. 0d.—the amount of the entire growth will be 144l. 7s. 0d.

It is true, Mr. Parkinson mentions "that in woods, a 40 pole piece of 1 rood (?) *in some parts*, produces oak timber from 60 to 80 feet, value from 8 to 12l. and bark 6l. 18s. 0d, and we have some trees sold for 24l." But these,

---

* To consider the President of the Royal Society to be unacquainted with so almost obvious a fact, (tho his Steward might) was certainly not very civil.

† Supposing the whole of the bark to have been the produce of those trees.

these, probably, are in the *kept* woods, about the house, or have been elsewhere suffered to stand, by way of ornament; and altho some of such trees may have been taken down, it is not likely that Sir Joseph Banks would denudate his place, by clearing away the whole of the trees of this description.

Let us suppose that there are 105 acres of wood of that description, and 700 acres of convertible wood, to be made the most of, as a *crop*. Seven hundred multiplied by one hundred and forty four, would give 100,800 l. But only one twenty third part of it is worth 144 l. an acre. For what was cut the preceding year, is of course worth only (or very little more than) three fourths of the timber left upon the ground; namely 99, say 100 l.; and the other falls in proportion to the periods of felling. Hence, if we take the mean of the two estimates, we shall come sufficiently near the truth. 700 × 100 = 70,000 l.; which being added to 100,800, amounts to 170,800;—the half of which is 85,400 l.;—the real value (on the above data) of the 700 acres, at any given period of time, while kept under the present management. Whereas on the Reporter's estimate of 200 l. an acre, the value of these 700 acres amount to 140,000 l.

To those *errors* is *to be* added an *omission* in the general statement.—Inserted, in this article, (p. 218) is a list of the sums received from the " annual sale by wood and bark" of those woods, from the year 1757 to 1796:—the sums in 1757 being 478 l. 2s. 3d. for wood;—32 l. for bark; in 1796, for wood, 1772 l.; that for bark not being noted. But, in the foregoing statement, the bark is nearly one fourth of the whole. Let us, therefore call it, here, 400 l. together 2172 l. In 1786 the receipt for wood was 787 l. 15s. 8d.; and for bark, 106 l. together 894 l. Hence, beside the annual income, arising from the sales, there has been a progressive and rapid improvement, *in the value of the crop on the ground*.

Many of my readers will probably censure me, for entering thus widely into calculations, concerning the private property of an individual. But the Reporter has set the example; and his strictures are so determinedly inimical to the growth of timber, that I have thought it right to endeavour to bring them within the limits of truth. For altho he may, *himself*, think so lightly of his own authority, he may have *readers* who put more confidence in his works. How the Secretary of a public Board, professedly established to promote rural improvement.

improvement, could go far *beyond* the truth, to propagate
a system of management, that tends to the total destruction of the internal supply of timber,—even for domestic
purposes,—it were difficult to conceive.

What applies to the Woodlands of Revesby, is applicable to most of the Woodlands of the kingdom. It would
ill become the Secretary of such a Board to *drag forward,*
even the truth, on this *delicate* subject.

PLANTING.—On this subject is inserted, in the Report
under review, a valuable paper of Sir Cecil Wray ;—who
not being in the country at the time of the Secretary's
tour, favored him with written answers, to enquiries made

It may be right to premise (for I cannot bring myself to
believe that every man who may chance to read what I
am about to extract, is intimately acquainted with the
County of Lincoln and its numerous places) that Sir C
Wray's place, Summer Castle, is situated on one of the
bleakest and most barren parts of the stoney heights
north of Lincoln.

P. 213. " My plantations consist of 260 acres; and
have been made at such periods (from 1760 to 1794), and
in such proportions, that I can give no satisfactory answer
on that head :—They consist principally of Scotch firs:—
on my commencement as a planter, I planted oaks, ashes
beeches, elms, silver firs (in small quantities), spruce
larch, and Scotch fir.—My purpose was to follow up those
species of trees which throve best, as it was essentially
necessary for my comfort to clothe, as quick as possible
a situation in which I had not even a thorn or whin
growing.

" The larch, oaks, ash, and beech made no little progress during the first three years; and the Scotch fir go
on so well, that I planted for the ensuing ten years scarcely
any other sort; a thing I now repent of, as their value i
comparatively very small : but in size, I have this year
cut up several oaks not 6 inches round, planted with the
Scotch firs, many of which are from 4 to 6 feet.

" The silver fir has grown extremely well ; but (as i
is said) will in all probability be short lived ;—they are
however, my finest trees at present.

" The spruce fir also grows well and large; and man
of my beeches are as tall, though not so thick as the fir
they grow amongst ; but this respects only a few of them
as many do not thrive so well.

" Having some reasons to think better of my larches
I recommenced their propagation, about fifteen or sixtee
                                                    year

years ago ; and now have about 53 acres of them growing
completely well ; and, from the value of the wood, promise to pay twice as well, at least, as the Scotch.—Last
year, I sold some larches, which I thinned out of the
plantation at 5 l. per hundred ;—Scotch at the same age,
at 1 l. 10s. per ditto.

" I cut down every year a quantity of my oldest Scotch
firs to give room to the forest trees, and sell them at 8d.
per foot, or use them in buildings, for farm houses, barns,
&c. in which they answer very well ; also thin about 12 or
15 acres of the smaller sort, which I sell for rails, &c. to
the farmers in the neighbourhood, at 1 l. 1s. 1 l. 10s.
1 l. 15s. per hundred.—The whole profits arising annually
to me from my plantations, are from 150 l. to 200 l. clear
of all expences."

P. 215. " As to general observations, gentlemen differ
so much respecting their modes of planting and management of trees, that I can only give you my opinion : First,
that I would always plant each species of trees by itself ;
—at least, I would never plant Scotch firs intermixed
with others, on the idea that they are good nurses.   Plants
require very little shelter in winter ;—they suffer most in
summer ; and the Scotch fir soon becomes, from its
spreading branches, a bad neighbour.—Gentlemen say,
they would weed them out ; but they never do it in time
to prevent the mischief.

" Second, that I would never plant a tree older than
two years seedlings.

" Third, that I would never put so many on an acre as
the nurserymen persuade us to do : 2000 the very utmost ; 1200 full sufficient.

" Fourth, that I would always trim off the side branches,
this should be done when so small as to be cut off with
a knife ; when delayed till the bough is large, it makes an
ugly wound, is long in healing up, and if suffered to die
on the tree, makes a hole in the timber :—on the contrary, if cut off very soon, it grows over, and the wood
has no wound or knot in it.   I know this article is much
controverted."

I cannot refrain from saying, here, that I am peculiarly
gratified on finding a planter of such extensive experience, as Sir Cecil Wray, so perfectly agreeing with me
and the precepts I have long inculcated) concerning
these important matters.   And the subjoined observations
are a further proof of the good sense and experience, as
well as of the liberality, of this eminent English planter.

P. 216.

P. 216. " Having rather spoken against Scotch fir
give me leave to say a word in their favour.

" First, they grow fast; and the wood is of sufficient
use for farm houses, &c.

" Second, the poor people supply themselves with very
good fuel by gathering the fir-apples, and rotten wood;
you will sometimes see twenty children in my plantations
appleing, as they call it.

" Third, the green boughs keep deer completely well
in winter; and save much hay if given to sheep, particularly in snows: I have sometimes 3 or 400 sheep grazing
on them at once.

" Fourth, the boughs are of great use in ovens, fire-
wood, fencings, &c.—I sell 30l. every year."

But, says the Reporter, p. 216. " Of all the planters in
the County, Lord Yarborough takes the lead; for ten
years past he has planted 100 acres per annum, which he
is continuing in the same proportion; but designs soon
to lessen it, as the lands he had assigned for that purpose
will nearly be covered."

DIVISION THE THIRD.

AGRICULTURE.

FARMS.—*Sizes.*—Relating to this topic, we find in the
Report under consideration, a long string of loose memoranda. Whether they were made from repeated enquiries, on the spots noticed, or were put down, incidentally, in the Breakfast or Drawing Room, does not appear
There is no *name* (except one, I think) mentioned: of
course, no authority is given; as it cannot be " easy to
trace every article to its source." See p. 67, aforegoing.
—I will, therefore, content myself with inserting, here,
the general result of the Reporter's enquiries, in his
own words, and, of course, on his sole authority.—P. 39
" Upon the size of farms in general in Lincolnshire, it
may be very safely asserted, that they are moderate. The
number of large ones bears no sort of proportion to those
which are very small. And where both extremes are excluded, the size will be found much under what is common in many other Counties."

A few

A few other remarks, however, will appear, uuder the head, *Occupiers,* ensuing.

Plans of Farms.—(Fens and Marshes)—P. 182. " A great change has also taken place in the inhabitancy : within forty years, 4 four-wheeled carriages were kept by graziers in Theddlethorpe, (?) now deserted, few living any where in the marshes, without farms elsewhere ; by degrees the Wold farmers have gradually been getting the whole except some few small occupations.   These acts are remarkable, and they tend to contradict mate- rially an idea I have met with, common enough in the County, that this tract of marsh, which extends from the Humber to Long Sutton and Tidd, has not been much improved in rent except by inclosing.—We find, on the contrary, that it has been prodigiously improved ; without doubt by the generally operating causes of national pros- perity.   Wealth regularly increasing has raised the prices of products*, and in this County very greatly to its honour ; a subject that ought to be dwelt on longer here, but it is treated more expressly in another chapter, the poor have come in for a large, and perhaps an ample share ; for the price of labour throughout will surprise those who have been accustomed only to the more southerly Counties.   Under such a growing system of improvement, I must own I feel no regret at the loss of the carriages,—the people have changed place, but they are better employed."

This would seem to be the Reporter's opinion too hastily drawn.   For, in the next page, we find it, in some degree at least, contradicted, by a man who resides in the country, and whose knowledge of the Rural concerns of Lincolnshire appears to be superiorly accurate.

P. 184. " Mr. Parkinson of Revesby observes, that the
rich

---

* Would it not read better to say that " Paper money regularly increasing" in quantity, and of course decreasing in value, " has raised the prices of products."   But this would have ill served to brighten the delusive blaze of " National prosperity."

The Reporter gives, in the same page, a *curious* account of the advance of times."—P. 182. " Sixty or seventy years ago, Mr. Reeve's grandfather rented such marsh as would now let at 40s. for 3s. per acre ; and rarely went to pay to an old lady his rent, with- out the salutation, *I hope you are not coming to give up your land ?* The advance of times is seen in another circumstance : Mr. Welflet, lately dead, stocked a particular close at Saltfleetby with cows, bought at 19s. 6d. a head, and shearling wethers at 20s. the sheep costing more than the cows.   He was above eighty."

rich marshes were better managed, and in better orde
twenty years ago than they are at present; the Wol
farmers had not then got such possession of them, an
they were in the hands of resident graziers, who attende
much more to hobbing, which kept them fine, for nothin
hurts marsh land so much as letting it run coarse, fron
permitting the grass to get a head."

On the whole, are we to understand, that the fen an
marsh lands of Lincolnshire, in general, are occupied b
Wold or other upland farmers, as those of Norfolk an
Kent are? This is, surely, a very material point tha
should have been brought out and rendered prominentl
conspicuous, in a Report of Lincolnshire *.

Homesteads.—On " Buildings,"—(namely Seats, Farn
Houses, and Cottages) nearly a sheet of paper is rathe
unprofitably, if not unwarrantably, expended. Mr. Car
wright's paper, on stucco, is very ingenious; and migh
with propriety, have been inserted in a book of architec
ture. Mr. Hoyte's farm house, and out buildings are n
doubt convenient; and the plan and elevation neatl
executed; and may assist to embellish the book. Bi
I perceive nothing new or excellent; either in the plat
or the letter-press. In short I find not a line, in th
whole sheet, of sufficient importance to claim a right to
place in this Register. The following extract, howeve
may serve to convey some idea of the *materials* of far
house buildings, in Lincolnshire.

P. 34. " About Reevesby the farm houses built of lat
years, are of brick and tile; and for a farm of 100 l.
year, a dwelling will cost about 250 l.; the stables 50 l.; th
cart-house, cow-house, hogsties, &c. 50 l.; the barns wi
cost 80 l. and 50 l. The old buildings are of timbe
walle

* We need not stronger evidence to show that the Secretary
MODE of SURVEY was merely that of an ENQUIRING TOURIS
hunting after oral information, than the following gratuitous *confessio*
—P. 183. " It may appear whimsical, that one must go to t
Wolds for marsh intelligence; but so it is; the principal Wo
farmers have marsh land; and the facts can be got only where t
occupiers are to be found:"—Rather, surely, with the occupier,
the spot.—Judging from the "liberal spirit of communication," whi
the Reporter experienced, and the numbers that were " emulou
to contribute to his wants (as set forth in his introduction) the
could have been no difficulty in procuring an intelligent occupier
marsh lands, to ride over his grounds,—show his stock,—expla
the management of marsh lands, and the general Economy of t
marsh husbandry.—See the RURAL ECONOMY of NORFOLK,
Min. 118; for an instance of practice, in a like case.

walled with clay, called stud and mud, and covered with reed; some with wheat and rye straw, which when new, will cost one third less than brick and tile."

And the succeeding paragraph may afford an unprofitable subject of conversation. But neither materials, nor dimensions being furnished, it cannot be of any real utility.

Same page.—" Mr. Ellison, at Sudbrook, has built farm-houses complete; one cost 370 l. every thing included except leading, for a farm of 280 l. a year, being 478 acres. For another for 235 acres, 290 l."

Cottages.—P. 35. " In the low rich country they are commonly built of what is called *stud and mud;* the stud-pieces as large as a man's arm."

P. 36. " At Reevesby, &c. a brick cottage for two families will cost 80 guineas; and the smallest sort, for one family, will cost 50 l. Of stud and mud, one third less. There are many new cottages built, and especially in the new inclosed fens; sometimes land is leased on contract for building them."

P. 408. " Rent of a cottage with a garden 1 l. 11s. 6d. to 3 l. ; in common 1 l. 11s. 6d. to 2 l. 12s. 6d."

Cottage Cow Grounds.—I have already written and reviewed so much, on this (now stale) subject, that it is with some reluctance I can prevail upon myself to enter, again, upon it. But the Secretary of the Board, I believe, having been one of the principal promoters of the plan or providing farm labourers, in general, with cow grounds, and having in his Lincolnshire Report filled twelve pages, on the subject, it might seem to be a want of courage, to meet so powerful an antagonist, were I to flinch, in this instance, from the principles I have uniformly maintained respecting it.

I little expected, however, to meet, in a work of this writer, with evidence,—brought forward by the author himself, and arising immediately out of his own observation,—that completely establishes the impossibility of carrying this plan into any thing bordering on general effect. This evidence is given in the Secretary's best manner; and in the following few words.

P. 411. " In the new inclosure of Glentworth, on Lincoln Heath, I saw some large pieces under various crops, that were in a most slovenly and wretched condition, run out, and almost waste; and on enquiry found they were allotments to cottagers, who, each knowing his own piece, cultivated in severalty within a ring-fence; it is a strong
instance

instance to prove that their shares ought always to be given in grass; they are unequal to any other tillage than that of a garden."

One would scarcely think it possible, that any man,—who has seen so much,—written so much,—and talked so much,—and who must have thought, more or less, on rural subjects,—not to have been clearly convinced, by this occurrence, alone, of the entire impracticability of such a plan.

I have never condemned the plan of providing farm labourers with cow grounds, *altogether*; but have, on the contrary, always allowed its merits to extend so far as the environs of *residences* may reach.—In the preceding part of this volume, p. 47, I have willingly granted, that in a *fen country*, where grass land is plentiful, the climature unhealthy, and farm work-people scarce, it may be found *expedient* to indulge them with cow grounds;—in order to reconcile them to constant residence: their employers, of course, considering the inconveniences attending it, as a lesser evil*. And, in every district which *abounds* with perennial grass lands, as in grazing and dairy

---

* Where this expedient may be deemed advisable, the plan conveyed, in the subjoined extracts is, to my apprehension, evidently most eligible;—tho somewhat otherwise estimated, by the Reporter.—P. 410. "The management of Charles Chaplin, Esq. at Blankney and in the other lordships which he possesses, cannot be too much commended; he assigns in each a large pasture, sufficient to feed a cow for every cottager in the place; besides which he lets them a small croft for mowing hay, to keep their cow in winter."—P. 411. "At Kirton, in the new inclosure, there is in the vale 28 acres of grass in one close, and 22 in another; one for the cottagers' cows in summer and the other for hay; fifty in all; this is good, though not equal to every man having his own separate. None here find difficulty in getting cows, if they can but get land."

Nevertheless in p. 417, we are told, in unequivocal terms, that this is not uniformly the case;—nor, when they are gotten, do they always prove the source of that personal happiness, and those moral and political habits of which we have *heard* so much. One cannot but admire the Reporter's liberality, or his absence of mind, in giving them to the public.—"Mr. Ellison's bailiff informed me, that there are instances which shew, that the benefit of the practice depends much on the substance and management of the man; he had known that a family with a cow, &c. very poor, and in uncomfortable circumstances, and when they have had their cow no longer, to have been much better off; and this he attributes to their sometimes depending too much on their live stock, and neglecting their regular labour, getting bad habits from it."—Mr. E. or his Reporter, however, adds,—"It is quite contrary with the sober and industrious who are much more comfortable from having cows."

dairy Counties, such a plan is *practicable*. But I think we may safely assert that, in three fourths of the kingdom, it is at once *impolitic* and *impracticable*, or altogether *impossible*.

It is well known, to those who have superintended the management of Tenanted Estates, on a large scale, in different parts of the kingdom, that there are, comparatively, few estates within it, on which there is a sufficiency of grass lands to satisfy the eager cravings of farmers. Every acre that will lie, permanently, and profitably, in grass, is not only coveted by occupiers of arable lands; but, in the present state of agriculture, in the kingdom at large, is in a degree necessary to the most profitable management of those lands; whether the interest of the occupier, the owner, or the community, be considered*.

Were each cottager to have even three acres (too little, in a par of grass lands) allotted him, there would not be, I apprehend, in three fourths of the parishes or townships, in England, one acre left for the tenants of the arable lands. How irrational, then, or thoughtless, must have been those who have perseveringly recommended so impolitic, and impracticable a scheme.

OCCUPIERS.—On this subject, we meet with some interesting, readable, well reported information. In the chapter, " Property," are the subjoined remarks, on the minor yeomanry of the Isle of Axholm.—P. 17. " In respect of property, I know nothing more singular respecting it, than its great division in the isle of Axholm. In most of the towns there, for it is not quite general, there is much resemblance of some rich parts of France and Flanders. The inhabitants are collected in villages and hamlets; and almost every house you see, except very poor cottagers on the borders of commons, is inhabited by a farmer, the proprietor of his farm, of from four or five, and even fewer, to twenty, forty, and more acres, scattered about the open fields, and cultivated with all that minutiæ of care and anxiety, by the hands of the family, which are found abroad, in the countries mentioned. They are very poor, respecting money, but very happy respecting their mode of existence. Contrivance, mutual

---

* Do not we see, in Lincolnshire, in Norfolk, in Kent, and in Essex, arable farmers going many miles after grass lands? And the same is, more or less, observable, in almost every other County, in the kingdom.

mutual assistance, by barter and hire, enable them to
manage these little farms, though they break all the rules
of rural proportion. A man will keep a pair of horses
that has but three or four acres, by means of vast commons, and working for hire."

P. 19. "Laceby" (no matter where it lies) "is, I think
one of the prettiest villages in the County; containing
a great number of very well built houses, with much air
of comfort, and several of a more considerable appearance, and being on a slope of country, and very well
wooded, with a fine clear stream through it, the aspect is
on the whole very pleasing: I inquired the cause, and
found it inhabited by freeholders; each man lives on his
own."

Again.—" There is nothing in the state of property in
Lincolnshire that pleased me more than to find on the
Wolds, and especially about Louth, men possessed of
estates of three, four, five, and even six or seven hundred
a year, and yet remaining farmers, occupying other farms
hired, and some of them living merely on their own, but
keeping entirely to the manners and the appearance of
farmers; consequently thriving, independent, and
wealthy, and in consequence of all, as happy as their
personal merit, their moral virtue, and dependence on
and attention to, their religious duties permit them
to be."

In the chapter, " Occupancy," is the following flattering character of the superior and more enlightened
tenants of Lincolnshire.—P. 39. " As to the character of
the farmers who have occupations sufficiently large to be
met with at the most respectable ordinaries, or whose
exertions had occasioned their being named to me as
men proper to call upon, I can dispatch my account of
them in very few words; I have not seen a set more
liberal in any part of the kingdom. Industrious, active,
enlightened, free from all foolish and expensive show, or
pretence to emulate the gentry; they live comfortably
and hospitably, as good farmers ought to live; and in my
opinion are remarkably void of those rooted prejudice
which sometimes are reasonably objected to this race of
men. I met with many who had mounted their nags
and quitted their homes purposely to examine other parts
of the kingdom; had done it with enlarged views, and to
the benefit of their own cultivation."

PLAN of MANAGEMENT of Farms.— On this subject, that
forms the groundwork on which the whole business of
Agricultur

Agriculture rests, we look in vain, in the Report before
me, for any thing resembling an intelligent account of its
progress and present state;—either as to the general
outline of management; the proportion of grass and
arable lands, in Lincolnshire; or as to the objects kept
principally in view, by their occupiers.

It is true that on the "Course of Crops" pursued, or
occasionally, or accidentally, practised by *individuals*,—
we find more than twenty pages (loose ones it is true)
which impress one with an idea, while turning them over,
that each principal occupier has a course of his own ; or
perhaps two or three.

On the popular topic, at the time this Report was
written, of "Breaking up Grass Lands,"—that is to say,
of changing perennial herbage, for arable crops, we also
meet with a succession of pages : those two subjects
occupying more than two sheets of letterpress !

On the rapid advance of Agriculture, the following
craps have been picked up, in different parts of the
volume.—Speaking of the estate of Swinop (?) it is said,
under the head, " Population"—P. 424, " This estate,
which in 1728 let at 95 l. cottages included, would now
et at 12s. an acre round, tithe free, which, for sixteen
hundred acres, the measure then, is 960 l. supposing the
inclosure finished, which Mr. Allington has a power of
doing, and buildings for two farms raised."—Further, in
p. 425, " Mr. Allington keeps on this farm 1460 sheep,
which produce above 1000 l. In 1728 there were 420 on
it, which yielded from 60 to 70 l.; it was then nearly all
sheep-walk, but now a scene of cultivation."—And, in
p. 92, chapter " Arable Lands,"—the Reporter speaks of its
advancement, in modern times, from his own knowledge,
as follows.—" The management of arable land in Lincolnshire has never been celebrated; when I was in the
County upon a farming tour, near thirty years ago, I saw
ttle but what merited condemnation; and I entered it now
expecting to find it in a very backward state. There is
certainly much to disapprove in the management of wet
clay, but I was very agreeably disappointed in that expectation on most other soils."

The singular management of common field lands, which
is well described, in the subjoined extract, is I believe
peculiar to Lincolnshire. I do not recollect to have seen
. out of that County, and its environs.

P. 92. " In the vicinity of Market Deeping, the arable
common fields are ploughed up into broad arched lands,
                                                    as

as in the Midland Counties; but the furrows for three
four, or five yards wide, laid down to grass and mown for
hay, while the crowns of the ridges are under corn: this
management is excellent, and much superior to having
such miserable corn in these furrows, from wetness, as is
seen from Chattris towards Whittlesea to Peterborough
the centres of the lands being high, are dry and fit for
corn, and the furrows low, and do well for grass."

For an instance of the present state of *common field*
management, see the head, *Appropriation*, p. 82, aforegoing.

Succession of *Crops* on the *Inclosed Lands.*—In the
course of my Review of the Board's Reports, I have been
incidentally led to compare the almost endless courses
and rotations of crops, found in these Reports to the
admired *changes* of bell ringers. Judging from the
Lincolnshire Report and other works of its author, that
have formerly, fallen under my notice, this writer, alone
must be fast approaching the enviable " Bobmajor" of
those truly sublime musicians.

I am not, however, more astonished at hearing twenty
pages of changes rung, than at finding, in a cool deliberate conclusion, the most impracticable of courses indirectly recommended;—namely, that of *turnips, barley
clover, wheat;* which the Reporter says—p. 115.—Or
" Turnep Soils"—" is very well established; and that
improper deviations do not often occur."—And this, notwithstanding what his best informant, had previously told
him about it, in p. 133.—" Mr. Parkinson finds that his
land will not produce red clover in a four years course
more than two rounds; he then changes to 1 bushel ray
grass, 6lb. trefoil, and 6lb. of red clover for one round
and the next round 8lb. cow grass, and olb. of Dutch
clover."

I recollect that, while I was a *young* farmer, this beautifully simplex and *rational* rotation of crops pleased me
so well that I remember to have named it the UNIVER-
SAL COURSE;—not being, then, sufficiently aware of the
transitory nature of the cultivated variety of red clover
as a crop in mixed husbandry. But observing, during
my residence, in NORFOLK, that, even in the *six*-crop
rotation of that County, it would not succeed with sufficient certainty, more than a few rounds,—I was, of course
convinced of the impropriety of repeating, or attempting
to repeat, the clover crop, every *fourth* year. Yet the
Secretary of the Board emphatically terms this *four*-crop
course

course " The Norfolk Husbandry"!—P. 115. " The Norfolk husbandry of, 1. Turnips, 2. Barley, 3. Clover,
4. Wheat, is very well established ; and that improper
deviations do not often occur."—But more of this, in
going through the Reports to the Board, from NORFOLK.

Having, however, thought it right, to speak, above, in
terms of censure, on the practice of wasting paper, in
these scarce and dear times, with endless collections of
" course of crops," it may be proper, before I quit the
subject, in this place, to give my readers some account
of my motives for this conduct.

In what may be termed MODERN HUSBANDRY; (in contra-
distinction to the " feudal system")—namely that plan
of management, in which lands (perennial grass lands
excepted) are subjected, ALTERNATELY, to *arable crops*, and
temporary herbage;—a plan of management, which,
under existing circumstances, ought, I am clearly of
opinion, to prevail over the principal part of the wholely
appropriated lands of the kingdom;—there is little room
for choice, or even argument, as to the course or succession of crops.

The *duration* of the *herbage* will ever be *given*, in the
nature of the given land, and other given circumstances.
And the almost only point to be settled, with regard to
the *arable crops*, is whether one, or two, *corn* crops shall
intervene, between the herbage, and the fallow, or fallow
crop.

Near towns, or in other situations, where a sufficient
supply of dung, or other vegetable or animal manure, can
be purchased at a moderate price,—or in a country where
good marl abounds,—*two* corn crops may be found eligible. But in situations, in which neither of these advantages can be had,—more especially where lime is not
easily to be procured, or where it has been already long
in use ;—and, of course, where occupiers have little or no
other resource, with respect to manure, than in their own
internal supply, arising from the livestock they are able
to maintain,—*one* crop of corn, between the herbage and
the fallow crop (or eighteen months fallow wherever
such extra exertion may be requisite) will, I believe, in
general, be preferable ;—unless, it may be added, on
sound lands, of a superior quality.

These are, certainly, situations, and circumstances,
under which an alternacy of arable crops and herbage
may not be the most eligible plan of management :—as
in the immediate neighbourhood of a large town, or other
                                                    situation

situation in which a constant and adequate supply of
manure can be commanded ; and where a regular establishment of livestock is not necessary.   But, here, no
" course,"—no *regular rotation*, of crops being requisite,
it will generally be found most expedient to go by existing circumstances;—and to crop the lands according
to their respective states, as to tillage and manure,—the
state of the season,—and the prospect of markets for
particular crops.

In every situation, let a *novice*, or a *stranger* in it take
a ride round his neighbourhood, and learn what course is
taken by men who thrive on a soil, in a situation, and
under circumstances, similar to his own; and let him
pursue that, until, by experience on his own lands, he
finds that he can *improve it*.

Further, it may be right, while taking this general view
of the subject, to observe that, in bringing wild lands or
other neglected rough grounds, into a state of tillage fit for
the ALTERNATE HUSBANDRY,—different practices, or ex-
pedients, according to the particular states of such lands,
are required. But this department of the general management of farm lands has been spoken of, aforegoing, under
the head, *Sodburning*.

Those observations aptly lead us to another interesting
part of this Report from Lincolnshire ; in which (as has
been mentioned) we find lengthened strictures on bringing *profitable* grass lands, even those which are in the
highest degree of productiveness,—into the state of aration;
—under the general head of

" Breaking up Grass Lands."—In reviewing Mr. Stone's
Report, I considered it my duty as a Public Writer, to
show, in the strongest and clearest terms I was able, the
impolicy of such a procedure. (See p. 56, aforegoing.)
It was, perhaps, allowable in Mr. S. as a professional
man, to show his land-jobbing, and his avaricious, as well
as his necessitated, employers how they might make the
greatest *immediate* profit of their estates.—Well soiled
lands that have lain long, in a state of perennial *herbage*,
will ever throw out abundant crops of *corn*, during a
certain number of years,—more or less according to their
several intrinsic qualities, and the length of time they
may have lain in a state of herbage. This being a generally known truth among men of experience,—a shrewd
sensible tenant, " who knows what he is about," will,
when corn sells high, give an advance of rent, for the
privilege of breaking up such " old grass lands ;"—most
                                               especially

especially if his term in them be drawing toward its conclusion. And, as a further inducement toward obtaining this privilege, he will *promise* to lay them down, again, in a husbandlike manner—" and make them as good as ever."

This, however, may, without risk, be deemed *impracticable.* Even with all the covenants and restrictions that words can form, and all the care that a diligent manager can take,—there are many lands that would require a quarter or the half of a century, to raise them, again, to the same valuable state they were in, before the crime of breaking them up was committed. Many of the grazing grounds and meadow lands of the kingdom have received the benefit of centuries, to raise them to their present inestimable states.—Others have never been in any other state, since the time they were cleared, than that of profitable herbage.

These matters being duly considered, it appears, pretty evidently, to be bad policy, even in a *private* point of view, to break up perennial grass lands that have long lain in a productive state, and will long remain highly profitable, if not prevented by the improvident rapacity of their owners*.

The impolicy of such a measure, viewed in a *public* light, has been shown, aforegoing. To countenance it, unless in a case of extreme urgency, before the whole of the dormant, and in a manner useless, lands in the kingdom are brought into cultivation, would be the height of indiscretion in its government. Nevertheless, we here find the Secretary of a public Board, in a work addressed to that Board, and of course written for the guidance of government, countenancing, if not encoraging, that very measure.

P. 198. " No instance of breaking up grass land that I had heard of in Lincolnshire, proves the extraordinary fertility of that County more clearly than that at Wintringham, on the estate of Lord Carrington, who, upon the high price of corn, was willing to indulge his tenants with the leave which they desired, of ploughing 200 acres, and

---

* Be it remembered, however, that nothing herein contained is intended to militate against the reasonable request of a resident occupier of a grass land farm, to break up and keep in a state of aration, a *proper quantity* of it, to afford litter for his requisite *store* stock, during the winter months.

and for which they offered a compensation in rent; a great part of which, however, upon the sudden fall in the price of grain, which happened soon afterwards, his Lordship, I was informed, spontaneously remitted. Lord Carrington had requested Thomas Thompson, Esq. of Hull, who has the management of this estate, to meet me at Wintringham, and to give me every information in his power. Mr. Thompson was so obliging as to do this, in the most liberal manner; and assembling three or four of the most intelligent tenants, I wished to know from themselves, what their expectation of produce was, upon their own calculation, which had induced them to wish for this permission. I held the pen while they gave me, in answer to my inquiries, the following particulars."

In this plain tale, there is sufficient evidence to prove the countenance of the Reporter to the measure of breaking up grass lands of "extraordinary fertility."—For, had he been adverse to the measure, he would either have passed by the incident, without notice, or would have used it as a groundwork of argument, on which to show the impolicy of the measure;—instead of embracing it, as an opportunity of declaring the advantages which, under certain circumstances, may arise from it*.

Nor is this the only instance in which the Secretary of the Board has assisted in forwarding so baleful a design. He has, it is to be lamented, been instrumental in offering premiums—not directly for breaking up grass lands, but for the best mode of laying them down, again, after their having been broken up:—of course, as an encouragement of the ruinous measure under consideration.

In this instance, however, the Secretary, let us suppose, reluctantly acted, *officially:* and, by way of *atonement*, as it would seem, he has published the following notices, in his Lincolnshire Report.

P. 205. "Mr. Parkinson observes, that the less that is broken up the better, except in sandy or convertible, or weak, inferior, dry, open soils, where it is an improvement;

---

* It would be a dereliction of the principles I have adopted, not to intimate, that information,—*so begotten,*—cannot be admissible as good evidence. One really w uld almost as readily have held pen in hand, to take down the evidence of a culprit, concerning his own crime,—while a Crown Lawyer was listening.—Yet our Reporter, without apparent hesitation, has stained (filled I cannot put) nearly half a sheet of paper with *calculations!* and remarks, on "Facts"—*thus brought forth!*—A further evidence that the Secretary of the Board was "nothing loth" to the measure.

ment; on other land, better to leave the grass; but if permitted to plough as they like, they look only to virgin land, and will not pay a proper attention to the landlord's interest."

Again.—"Mr. Loft of Marsh Chapel, is of opinion, from considerable experience, that to plough grass which pays well is a bad system; yet much is done so. It is right only on land that is unprofitable, and which will be improved for grass by a course of tillage. Even on the Wolds some lands have been ploughed to great loss; the sheep walk at Wyham near Louth, was the largest and best in the whole county; and very bad management to plough it. The Rev. Mr. Allington coincides with this idea; and remarks, that the excellence of this walk was possibly owing to the good management long ago, when laid down, as some very large antient marl pits are on it, which marks attentive husbandry; and, as he observes, that for the last three or four years, the appearance seems that it will soon be of no better quality than the rest of the country. I crossed these walks, and may observe, that I found the country, from S. Elkington to Binbrook, in general more like a desart, than what such land should exhibit; extensive fields that had been ploughed up, and were over-run with thistles that had seeded, left in such a wild state that it was horrid to see it."

P. 209. "Mr. Harrison makes an observation which has a good deal of truth in it; he says, that good old grass should never be broken up, and strong clay arable never laid down; the former is sure to be mischievous to the landlord; and the latter to ruin the tenant."

Again.—"On good soils the mere age of grass is of evident consequence in this country; for on the slope of the heath, from Kirton to Glentworth, passing through several lordships, inclosed at very different periods, and laid down to grass at the time, there is a great difference between Hempswell, a new one, and Willoughton, thirty years; also between Willoughton and Bliborough, which may be seventy or eighty years; there is a rich luxuriance in the verdure not easily described, that mark a fertile pasturage, which nothing but age seems to give."

WORKPEOPLE.—P. 397. "At Spalding, in winter 10s. 6d. a week, summer 15s.; in harvest 7s. 8s.; and last year up to 10s. 6d. a day. Reaping 12s. to 20s. an acre.

"At Brothertoft, labour, in winter, 1s. 6d. the lowest; 10s. a week the average. Hay 12s. for a month. Harvest 5s. a day for 6 weeks, then winter price. Occasional
instances,

instances, when there is a scarcity of men, and corn ripens, up to 10s. 6d. a day; and all prices under; an acre of reaping 25s. by contract has been known. A head farmer's servant 16l. 16s.; common one 14l. 14s.; a hog boy 6l.; a dairy maid 5l. 5s.; a carpenter, wet and dry, 2s. 6d.; a mason 3s.; his labourer 2s.; beer to none of these prices. Thatching 3s. a square for houses; 6d. to 9d. a yard for stacks, running measure *."

Average Wages of the County †.—" Winter 10s. spring 10s. 9d. summer 13s. 6d. harvest 20s. women 6s. 9d. per week."—p. 402.

P. 413. "The women are very lazy; I have noted their indolence in spinning; Mr. Goulton's expression was, 'they do nothing but bring children, and eat cake;' nay the men milk their cows for them; but the men very sober and industrious."

WORKING ANIMALS.—The subjoined short notices, relating to this subject, gathered from different and distant parts of the volume before me, I insert miscellaneously;— they being too inconsiderable, and in too small a compass, to require to be synthetically digested.

P. 117. "Sowing barley, 8 bushels an acre, for mowing to soil horses, &c. with in the stable, a singular husbandry in Holland Fen, at three mowings an acre will support ten horses." Is this preferable to tares and barley?

P. 296. " At Bankside, Mr. Webster feeds his cows, and his team horses with steamed turnips and cut chaff, with great success."

P. 300.

" * In the Fens, from the end of harvest till Christmas, in dry autumns especially, the labourer earns, by ditching, &c. at least 2s. per day, nor is less than 18d. given to a day labourer. From the quantity of public works now carrying on from the war, the price of labour is on the increase. From Christmas to Lady-day from 1s. 3d. to 1s. 6d. is given; from thence to hay time 18d. from hay to harvest 2s.; and in harvest from 3s. 6d. to 7s. per day; but 4s. 6d. or 5s per day is the average price of a reaper for the last three years. This increase of the price of labour is owing in some measure to the scarcity of hands, but more still to the sudden ripening of the corn, which brought the harvest fit together in every part of the kingdom.

" The consequence of such high prices are very baneful; the workmen get drunk; work not above four days out of the six; dissipate their money, hurt their constitutions, contract indolent and vicious dispositions, and are lost to the community for at least one-third of their time in this important crisis. It is a pity but the legislature could interfere.—MS. of the B."

† The wages given in the " Fens," and those of the upper grounds ought, surely, to have been kept distinct.

P. 300. " Mr. Parkinson of Asgarby works oxen, and is very fond of them; I saw two and a horse draw home in a waggon, as good loads of corn as are common in Suffolk with three horses."

P. 377. "Oxen are no where worked in common; Mr. Cartwright has used, and approves them."

P. 378. "About Grantham many oxen have been worked, but all left off; once they were seen all the way from Grantham to Lincoln, now scarcely any; a pair of mares, and one man, will do as much work as four oxen, and two men."

How ill this last extract agrees with that from page 300? But the one was gathered from the practice of a man of accurate experience; the other, it is more than probable, from accidental enquiry;—possibly, from a stallion man, met with upon the road. The fact would seem to be, from the following entry, and other notices of a similar nature, that, in Lincolnshire, the business of husbandry is chiefly performed by brood mares. Its practice, therefore, is local; and cannot become general to the kingdom at large.

P. 379. " Horses are bred in the marshes about Salt-fleet, cart mares being chiefly kept; ten mares are found to one horse."

IMPLEMENTS.—On this head, I find not a syllable to extract. *Thrashing-mills* were, in 1799, fast coming into use. Some mention is made of the *wheel coulter* of Lincolnshire and other Fen Countries; but nothing explicit enough to convey an adequate idea of it, or its use, to those who have not seen it at work; and those who have, do not require any verbal description.

MANURES.—The tourist appears to have been more than ordinarily inquisitive to collect *information* on this head. The variety of manures, in use, in Lincolnshire, is uncommonly great. Yet, from this Report of them, tho it extends to ten or twelve pages, we find but little *useful knowledge*,—either practical or theoretical,—that will stand the test of extraction. It must not, however, be wholly passed, in silence.

Fish.—P. 259. " Sticklebacks in the East and West fens so numerous, that a man has made 4s. a day by selling them at a halfpenny a bushel. They come from the sea into Boston haven also, and the use of them, whenever to be had, immensely beneficial: they are the most powerful of all manures."

This

This is a curious fact, and valuable to those whose situations enable them to profit by it.

Lime does not appear, from this Report, to be either a popular, or a profitable, manure in Lincolnshire; even for corn crops; and would seem to be universally allowed, as of little or no use, to turnips.

Marl.—The information adduced, concerning this valuable species of manure, is very unsatisfactory; unpardonably so, as coming through the medium of a man of experiment:—thus

P. 261. " Mr. Dalton, at Knaith, has manured his sand there with blue marl; 60 four-horse loads an acre, which is attended with a very great improvement."

P. 262. " In the vicinity of Revesby there is a very commendable use made of white, blue, and red marl."— " Mr. Parkinson of Asgarby, steward to Sir Joseph Banks, has also marled a sandy farm largely, and with very great effect; he spreads 40 loads an acre. He shewed me a field of 36 acres under turnips, a small part of which, by a mistake of his men, was not marled; and the difference in the turnips is prodigious; where the manure was spread, a very fine crop; but in the spot not marled, they had almost entirely failed, and the land was covered with weeds.—I have rarely seen a difference in crop more striking. He has 6 or 7 quarters an acre of barley, which succeed turnips on marled land."

In this case, we are not told, even of what *color* the marl was; and, in neither, have we the slightest information, as to the *specific quality* of the fossil used. The public do not want to be told, at this day, that some marls are highly beneficial to some soils; or, in other words, that marl is, in some cases, a valuable manure.

Bones.—The West Yorkshire practice of collecting and grinding bones, for manure, appears to have been, in 1799, gaining a footing in Lincolnshire. See NORTHERN DEPARTMENT.

Blubber.—Mr. Grayburn at Barton, (p. 263)—" has tried whale blubber, and the effect great, but did not answer the expence."

Silt.—(Sleech or Sea Mud—see WESTERN DEPART.) has been used by Mr. Cartwright (in the neighbourhood of Boston) with advantage. In this case, it formed the base or substratum of the soil on which it was used.

Buckweet.—P. 265. " At Willoughby on the Wolds, for several years they sowed buckwheat to plough in for manure;

manure; and repeated it till conviction was gained
that it would do no good.   It was tried completely,
and given up."—But let not this notice of what *they*
say prevent others from making due experiments, with
this species of herbaceous melioration, on their own
lands.

About *long dung* and *short dung* we find a page filled
with unmeaning and contradictory notices.

Burnt straw!—P. 267.   "The most singular practice
which I ever met with in manuring, subsists on the Wolds,
it is that of spreading dry straw on the land, and burning
it.   At Lord Yarborough's I first heard of this custom.
His Lordship's tenant, Mr. Richardson, a very good and
intelligent farmer, gave me the account, having long
practiced it with success.   The quantity is about 5
tons an acre.   At Great Lumber he straw-burnt a piece
in the middle of a field preparing for turnips, and on each
side of it manured with 10 loads an acre of yard dung,
and the burned part was visibly superior in the crop.   In
another piece the same comparative trial was made in
1796, for turnips, which crop was much the best on the
burnt part; and now, in 1797, the barley is equally superior.   On another farm he had at Wold Newton he did it
for turnips, then barley, and laid with sainfoin ; and the
burnt straw was better in all those crops than yard dung.
Burning gorse in this manner returns great crops, but the
expence is too high.   He is clearly of opinion, that it is
the warmth from the fire that has the effect, and not the
ashes ; for the quantity is nothing, and would blow away
at one blast.   It is proper to observe, that they do not
value straw used in feeding cattle, at more than 4s. or 5s.
a ton."

P. 268.   "In discourse at Horncastle ordinary, on burning straw, the practice was much reprobated ; yet an instance was produced, that seemed to make in favour of it.
Mr. Elmhurst of Hazlethorpe burnt 12 acres of *cole-seed*
straw on eight acres of the twelve, and the effect was
very great, and seen even for 20 years ; he sowed wheat
on it, 4 bushels an acre, and had 5 qrs.; the 4 acres upon
which nothing was burnt much the better land, yet the
crops on the burnt part were by that made equal to the
rest.   But in another similar experiment for turnips, Mr.
Rancliff observed the result, and the effect, though good,
lasted only for one crop."

Thus, straw-burning, shall we say, ends in little more
than smoke.   The small quantity of ashes which **corn**
straw

straw must necessarily afford, may, like other ashes, be
beneficial to the first crop, *as far as they go*. But, quere,
does not this burning of straw smell much of a hoax ?—
set on foot, by the noble Lord first above mentioned ;—
in return for the good-humoured wish of the tourist, that
his Lordship might have a harmless somerset upon the
softest furze bush of his *hideous* fox covers!

The Reporter's " Remarks," at the close of his section,
" Manures," are not to be passed over, unnoticed.—
P. 269. " One considerable benefit of *examining* the agriculture of any district *on the spot*, is the opportunity it
affords of gleaning carefully in *conversation*. (!!) Many
able farmers make experiments without minuting them
on paper. If they were not drawn forth sometimes,
by conversing on very different subjects, the result would
die with the men who make them. But such circumstances are too valuable to be lost. What an immense
mass of information would be the result, if all such trials
and remarks were collected from one end of the kingdom
to the other.* *Experimental certainty* would be the
result, the cause of all apparent contradictions would be
cleared up, and one harmonious system extracted from
what at present seems confusion." (Oh fine !) "An effect
that never can flow from dissertations; it can arise from
nothing but *multiplied facts*."

These remarks are most unfortunately placed at the
close of that section. For, on examining the various
" Facts" it contains, I find but one that was *ascertained*—
" on the spot."—The rest are the *uncorroborated* " Facts"
of " Conversation ;" and, in estimating them as materials
of *science*, it matters not whether the conversations took
place, at a fair or market ordinary, at a great man's levee,
or on the King's highway. It were as well to *dissertate*
from the imagination, alone, as from confused heaps of
unauthenticated " Facts," collected in conversation. See
p. 66.

GENERAL REMARKS on FACTS, and the SCIENCE of
AGRICULTURE.

I CANNOT well expect to meet with a more favourable
opportunity, than that which here presents itself, of expressing my regret at the misapplication of the word *Fact*,
as it is here, and elsewhere, used; not solely by the
                                                    Secretary

---

* *This* is almost precisely what I said thirty years ago.

Secretary of the Board, but by many other writers ;—as if fashion were busily employed, in perverting its true meaning.

FACTS are *certainties, realities, truths.* What we barely hear, in conversation, is not a fact, a reality, a truth, until it be *ascertained.* If it be strongly *corroborated,* by other evidence, it may be *admitted* as truth; but unsupported, it is mere *hearsay :*—and of what value in *science,* are *multiplied hearsays?* they may serve to confuse and perplex :—but how can they aid in producing " experimental certainty"? How can *undigested hearsays,* such as are found in the volume under consideration, tend to " clear up contradictions," and produce " one harmonious system extracted from what, at present seems confusion"?

SCIENCE is certain knowledge. Every art, profession and subject of study has, or is capable of having, its correspondent science. Thus, we have the science of mathematics; the sciences of chemistry, botany, and the other branches of natural knowledge ; the science of language; the science of law; the science of medicine ; and have, or ought to have, the SCIENCE of AGRICULTURE.

Because an illiterate village " Doctor" can cure or relieve diseases,—a half literate " Lawyer" make deeds and testaments,—an ignorant field Preacher amuse the multitude, and an unlettered " Farmer" grow corn and breed cattle,—does it follow that law, physic, divinity and agriculture are equally incapable of being improved, by letters and science ! *

Useful science, however, cannot be framed of undigested hearsays,—of assertions, opinions, suggestions and crude conceptions, found floating in conversation,—nor even of a chaotic mass of well ascertained facts, realities, or truths ;—but of duly ORGANIZED FACTS,—ORGANIZED REALITIES,—ORGANIZED TRUTHS ; such as will render the whole, and every part, familiar to the human understanding;—easily to be studied, comprehended and referred to: —even as the systems, elements and institutes of other arts and professions.

It is far from my intention to intimate by those observations,

* Yet there are empiricks, in this art, who hold out that written agriculture is altogether useless !—Just as there are mountebanks, in physic and divinity, who decry, not only science, but learning in general.—The decline and fall of civilized nations, and the degeneracy of science must ever have been accelerated by such superficial charlatans.

tions, that hearsays are entirely unworthy of attention.
They may be false, or they may be true ; and may of
course be valuable, as SUGGESTIONS, or HINTS, that remain
to be *investigated*. Among the "multiplied facts"—the
myriads of hearsays, that must now be recorded in the
various works of this writer, doubtlessly are many valuable
hints, and suggestions, which, if duly *ascertained*, and
digested,—might become of real value; as *materials* of
agricultural science.*

TILLAGE.—Neither on the principles of tillage, nor on
its operations, generally, or abstractly considered, do we
find, in the Reporter's section, "Tillage,"—any thing
to be noticed, in this place. Under the head, *Barley*, a
few particulars will be mentioned.

SEMINATION.—*Drilling.*—From the particulars of information collected by the Secretary, this rural amusement was, in 1799, evidently *going out*, in Lincolnshire ;
so far, I mean, as relates to *corn* crops†. Of nine or ten
instances, mentioned, only one cultivator was then found
hardy enough to persist in its propriety; and in a note
(by "*M. S. of the B.*") p. 140, it is said "That the produce of the lands of Mr. John Cod have never compensated the expence of his management." The rest had
either entirely given it up, or were, then, declining it,
by degrees. The following are the Reporter's remarks,
at the close of his section.

P. 141. "Such are the facts I met with in this inquiry;
they confirm the general result through the kingdom.
Drilling is a practice which will be found to answer to a
certain extent; and with a certain degree of skill and
attention. But when a minute attention flags, and the
scale is much extended, then it is found that the conclusions drawn from one or two fields, were not applicable
                                                          to

* I do not mean to offend, in the least, the feelings of this writer,
when I suggest, that, if he is desirous the public should profit by the
" multiplied facts," which he has, during a length of years, been
drawing together,—it would seem to be full time, to set about the
digestion of them ; so as to put them into an intelligible form :—as it
is not probable that any other person will undertake the task. It is
not. indeed, fitting that any one, else, should enter upon it ; as no
one can judge of their several degrees of authenticity, so well as the
collector of them.

† Strange, that the Secretary of the Board should confound the
DRILLING of *corn* crops, with those of *pulse*, and *turneps!*

to a whole farm; that the necessary operations militate with other objects; and what was profit, becomes loss. Were all the men known who have tried this husbandry, and laid it aside, the advocates remaining would not figure by their number."

This was bold language at the time it was written. A few years further back, a man speaking out such bold truths, would have run the risk of being scoffed at, by farmers of fashion, and mobbed by drillmakers.

Dibbling, on the contrary, appeared to be, at that time, gaining ground.

HARVEST MANAGEMENT.—On this very important branch of husbandry, not a word is found in the volume under notice!—excepting what relates to "covering corn stacks;" for which valuable purpose we find, in the Appendix, a set of plates and explanations of a contrivance, by Mr. Cartwright.—But the more simplex expedient of two cart wheels and three poles, in use in the SOUTHERN COUNTIES, is much better adapted to common practice.

ARABLE CROPS, "commonly cultivated."—These (according to the silly arrangement of the Board, which the Secretary ought to have corrected, in his own Report) are spoken of in one and the same "*section;*"—and, in this instance, the *most* commonly cultivated, and *most* valuable, are treated of, *miscellaneously!*—altogether, the veriest olio that ever was served up to the public—*in print!*—wheat, barley, oats, beans—mixed up together in the same mess;—with some distinct remarks on beans, "seeds," rape, and turnips, by way of garnish.

In another section, entitled "Crops not commonly cultivated," we meet with some account of the culture of potatoes, in Lincolnshire, and a more satisfactory detail of the culture and manufacture of woad; with some less interesting hearsay information, respecting hemp, flax and sainfoin: also a few notes on cow grass, "Swedish turnips," parsley, cabbages, and carrots.

In examining this heterogeneous mass, I marked what seemed to me of sufficient import, to appear before the public eye; and I will here lay before my readers such particulars as, I conceive, are entitled to preservation, in this abstract.

Wheat, Barley, Oats, Beans.—On these four principal objects of the arable farm, as they are *jointly* spoken of, in the Report before me, there is only one line that requires to be inserted, here; namely, the "average" line of
a table,

a table, to show the quantity of seed sown, and the quantity of grain reaped, in different parts of the County.—But the natures or specific qualities of the several lands, under cultivation, being omitted, and their situations being no otherwise described, than by the *name* of a village, or an individual, the quality of whose lands can only be known in their respective neighbourhoods,—the table, itself, cannot be useful to the public.

The average quantities of *seed* sown, and *produce* reaped, according to that table, are as follows:—(p. 125.)

Wheat 3   bushels sown   28 bushels reaped
Barley 3¾ ....   34 ....
Oats 6   ....   52 ....
Beans 3¾ ....   30 ....

Other notices, relating to the quantities of produce, particularly in the Fens and Marshes, may be seen under the aforegoing heads—*Appropriation, Soils, Plan* of *Management* &c.; and the ensuing head, *Grassland.*

What, else, I have found in this volume, concerning arable crops, *separately* mentioned, and which is entitled to public notice, I will here select and arrange, in the manner observed on similar occasions.

WHEAT.—*Succession.*—The subjoined statements are truly interesting. If the incidents and experiments, therein set forth, were duly attended to, and the results accurately drawn, and faithfully reported, the information is highly valuable.

P. 97. " In Holland Fen, and particularly at Swineshead, if wheat is sown on a barley stubble, they get little. Mr. Stephenson has tried this; his predecessor had left a stubble field, of which the greater part had been oats, and a small piece barley. The whole field Mr. Stephenson sowed with wheat, and in the crop at harvest he observed a very great deficiency in the whole of that part which had followed the barley; insomuch that the very shape of the piece, which was remarkable, could be traced with the utmost exactness, by the failure of the wheat there, and *no where else.* Not knowing how this spot of land had been previously managed, he would not admit this as a proof, that barley was a worse crop than oats to precede wheat; although he had heard that upon fen land it was so. He therefore afterwards made the experiment, by sowing a small piece in a field with barley, of which the rest was oats; all the land being equally good, and prepared alike. The effect as before, in every respect;

respect; the barley piece producing only two quarters of wheat per acre, while the oat part yielded four and a half. Nor was the mere deficiency all the difference; for while the wheat after *oats* was *fine and healthy*, that which followed the *barley* was *diseased and blighted*, and required the sickle ten days sooner than the good corn. In 1793 the field adjoining his barn was sown with oats; while a small portion he sowed with barley, to mow for his cart horses. It was thrice mown, and produced a great burthen of green food. But this application of the barley made no difference in its effect on the crop of wheat which succeeded. After the *oats* it was extremely good; after the barley, the reverse. I am also informed, that in 1792 Mr. Moss of Swineshead experienced the like; and that his wheat after *barley* was *mildewed*, while his wheat after *oats*, in the same field, and with the same management, was very good."

Smut of Wheat.—P. 122. " Mr. Linton, in 1782, had some smutty wheat, for which he was offered 13s. a quarter, common wheat being 25s.; he washed it in repeated waters, and dried it in the sun, and in the autumn of the same year, sold it, wheat being advanced, at 39s.; he washed it in the month of June."

BARLEY.—*Soil Process.*—P. 93. "About Normanby, Burton, &c. they plough for barley but once, thinking that by so doing they preserve the manure left by eating off the turnips with sheep; this is general."

P. 120. "At Belesby they have a practice lately introduced, which is to baulk their turnip land on strongish soils, that is lap a furrow on unstirred land; then harrow down, and cross plough it clean."

Much more is said about ploughing, once, twice, thrice, or four times, for barley after turneps; but without mentioning the state of the soil, or the season!

For an evidence of the impropriety of sowing *wheat* after *barley*, see the foregoing extract, p. 150.

For the use of barley *herbage*, for feeding cart horses, see *Working Animals.*

OATS.—App. 455. " Major Cartwright sowed white oats the last week in December, 1797,—last week in January,—and the last week in February, 1798, all on one earth. As far as can judge from examination, the first sown the heaviest, most productive; and that of January equally superior to February, and February better than the common time of March."

BEANS.—*Succession.*—One instance is mentioned, in which

which beans and wheat were cultivated, alternately, for
a number of years. But the nature of the land not being
noticed, the information may be deemed useless.

Semination of Beans.—The valuable practice of *drilling
beans* was but slowly making its way into Lincolnshire, in
1799. The Reporter's general account of the bean culture, there, is as follows:—P. 130 "This article of beans,
in Lincolnshire, is so important, that I have been induced
to treat the article by itself, to shew how very few instances occurred of good management. As a general
fact, it is to be stated, that this crop is broad-cast, never
hoed, full of weeds, and wheat consequently not following them. In the wet open fields, fallow usually succeeds.
This management is so bad and unprofitable, compared
with a better system, that there is scarcely an object in
the husbandry of the County which wants more reforming."

TARES,—were not, in 1799, an object of culture,—
either for seed or herbage.

RAPE,—*Seed*, and *Herbage*.—The subjoined extract
contains all that is collected, on these particulars, in a
Lincolnshire Report, by the Secretary of the Board.—
P. 134. " Much cultivated in Deeping Fen on paring
and burning; and worth from 40s. to 3l. an acre, fed
with sheep.

" In Holland Fen it is now generally fed by sheep,
and is worth from 40s. to 50s. an acre; which space will
carry 10 sheep during twelve weeks; but it is of so feeding a nature, that numbers die on it.

" Two acres of land in Holland Fen has often produced
a last of rape seed, now worth 50 guineas; and seldom
worth less than 30 guineas.

" In the rape, which several considerable breeders about
Folkingham have been accustomed to buy in Holland
Fen, they have found that an acre will carry 10 sheep ten
weeks, and worth 6d. per head, per week.

" At Garthorpe in Axholm, rape seed 5 quarters.

" In the north-west angle of the County, Gainsborough to Barton, the farmers say, they had rather give
4½d. a week to feed sheep with rape, than 3d. for turnips.

" In the Marshes about Saltfleet, this is found a very
profitable crop for sheep; but one inconvenience attends
it, which occasions great expence or trouble, if not fed
off before hard weather comes; their fences being ditches,
these freezing, let the sheep of all the country together;
they smell cole to a great distance; so that a field of some
acres will be eaten up in a night: 500 and more have
                                                        thus

hus been known to get together;—the piece must be netted or hurdled round. When fed, they often seed it; but what is not fed yields much the better crop.

" Mr. Lofft, of Marsh Chapel, remarks, that there is a vast difference in cole; that which grows on fresh land, has the stalk as brittle as glass, and will fatten sheep beyond any other food; but what grows on old tillage and, the stalk is tough and wiry, and has little proof in t. An acre of cole will fatten more sheep than an acre of turnips; but turnips will keep more stock sheep than cole."

For the value of rape, as a nurse of young herbage, see he head *Cultivated Herbage,* ensuing.

For an ingenious and eligible method of getting rid of he *stubble* of *seed rape,* see the head, *Manure,* p. 145, foregoing.

HEMP.—Concerning this crop, we find some pages.— What relates to its *culture,* I will register, here. That which concerns the preparation, or *manufacture* of the rop, for sale, is not sufficiently *practical;* and as to the *calculations* of *profit,* I will let them occupy, in peace, heir native pages.

P. 157. " At Swineshead this crop is much cultivated; ormerly on the same spots year after year; but now they pread it over a farm accordingly as the soil suits, or the rice actuates; and on some lands that are foul, they sow : to clean. If the soil is weak they manure for it. Plough at Candlemas, again at Lady-day, and again the middle or the end of May; when they sow 3 bushels of eed; never weed, as it destroys all. At Old Lammas hey pull up, leaving the strongest for seed : they used to ake the female from the male, but that is left off."

P. 159. " The quality of the hemp is best from old emp lands, being worth 2s. a stone more than from other nds.

" At Haxey, sow it after wheat: plough before Christmas; some at Candlemas. Manure after the first ploughing; some turn it in, but not so good; a middling dressing, the shorter the better. Pigeon dung best; (added dung) a quarter or quarter and half per acre. Like to ave it best after wheat that follows clover. Plough gain between Candlemas and Lady-day. Plough three four times; sometimes roll and harrow much more the spring. Sow about the middle of May, 10 pecks chain acre. Weed out the largest weeds. Pull the
femble

femble or male hemp about the 20th of August, leave the
female till Michaelmas."

FLAX.—The same line of conduct is applicable to this,
as to the last, crop. The business of steeping, breaking,
swingling &c. is mostly done, I believe, by men who
follow it as a trade,—in flax-growing districts.

P. 161. " Much cultivated at Swineshead; grass land
fresh is preferred. Plough for it once, and harrow five
times; again with what they call an ox harrow, with a
batten set an edge under it, and drawn over to level and
pulverize; then sow 2 bushels an acre, Baltic seed a
10s. 6d. a bushel. Harrow two or three times. Pick the
broken sods, and lay in furrows. Very little weeding
Mr. Sumpter, of the Griffin, of this place, in 23 acres, ha
weeded only to the amount of eight men for one day
The beginning of August it is pulled by the day, an
costs 12s. an acre."

P. 163. " Most profit when seeded; for the crop i
from 12 to 15 bushels, at 10s. 6d.; but in that case, some
thing is to be deducted from the price of the crop, bu
not always, as it is the best flax that stands for seed
Getting the seed adds 20s. to the expence.

" At Haxey in Axholm, they often sow it upon swar
land; but more common on clover ley or wheat stubble
Plough between Christmas and Candlemas; three o
four harrowings, and rolling fine; if a fine mould, har
row in the seed on this one earth; if not, skim it wit
plough very thin to make it fine. Sow 2 strike an acre
plough it; skim it half in, and half on top, both ways
as opinion leads. Weed it carefully on their knees
Pull it the beginning of August for white line;—some
times leave it for seed, especially if a slender crop."

WOAD.—This plant (ISATIS *tinctoria*) is cultivated
—as are the two foregoing,—for the purpose of manufac
ture. From this is produced a common ingredient c
dying.—It is chiefly cultivated, in this, the Eastern De
partment of the kingdom. I have not observed it, else
where; unless, on a small scale, in Somersetshire. (Se
WEST. DEPART.)—In general appearance, it resemble
spinage and the garden orach. Its root leaves are the ob
ject of culture. These are gathered in a green succuler
state;—ground down to a pasty matter;—formed in
balls;—dried;—reground;—fermented;—and prepare
according to art, for the use of the dier, in producing th
blue color.

T

The Secretary of the Board has been particularly successful, in collecting information, concerning the culture and manufacture of this crop, in Lincolnshire;—principally, it would seem, through the favour of " Major Cartwright;" who is, or was at the time of the Secretary's tour, the most extensive cultivator of woad, perhaps, in the kingdom;—at Brothertoft, in the neighbourhood of Boston.

I shall, in this instance, as in the two former, confine my abstract to *culture*, only. The *manufacture* of woad to render it fit for market, being still more of a distinct art and mytery, than that of hemp or flax, and, altho the Reporter, on this occasion, attempted to treat the subject, analytically, he has not succeeded, so as to convey the entire process, to the mind of the inexperienced cultivator, in such a manner, as to enable him to set about, without other assistance, the manufacture of this very *limitted* crop in husbandry.

In p. 156, of this Report, we are informed that " it should not be imagined that it is an article, in which any man with skill, capital, and attention, can enter beneficially. The demand for this commodity is very limited ; so that probably besides Mr. C. and three other growers, there is not 50 tons per annum raised in the kingdom. Should a few other persons be added, without these declining business, and the quantity in the market increased considerably, the inevitable consequence would be a fall of price; and the profit, made at present, become loss."— Nevertheless the Reporter has bestowed upon it two well engraven plates; which, whether or not they may be conidered to embellish his book, certainly add to its bulk, and doubtlessly to its price.

Without meaning to be deficient in respect, toward the Secretary of the Board, one might venture to intimate that he is *not* a SYSTEMATIST. He will, therefore, I hope pardon me for arranging the particulars he has furnished us with, concerning the culture of woad, in the natural order of practice.

Succession.—P. 149. " Experience has proved, that the plant thrives best on fresh grass land; accordingly it has long been the common practice for the undertakers of this culture to hire grass land, with a permission to break it up and sow woad for a certain number of years; here for four years; in the more upland situation, for two. Sometimes for three, in the second rate soils of this country."

Soil.

Soil.—P. 149. "Woad being a tap-rooted plant, penetrating eight or nine inches, of a substantial size, is necessarily demands a deep soil; the best is a rich loam; a stiff clay is unfavourable. Here the *saline principle* of the soil is favourable to this plant, as well as to many others. Deep, fertile, *putrid saline*, (?) an alluvion of the sea, the richness of which on the dead maritime levels is every where great."

Tillage.—P. 149. "If the soil is dry enough to permit the grass should be ploughed early in February; if not later in that month. Great attention should be paid to ploughing it as carefully as possible to the depth of about 3 inches, with three horses in a plough, followed in the furrow by a man with a spade, so that if the turf is not turned over very flat, and well joined, it may be laid completely so by hand. This attention is necessary to prevent the grass rising in the seams; then the land is harrowed often to raise a depth of mould sufficient for the drill to work."

P. 150. "In very old grass full of roots, the harrowing is repeated even to twelve or fifteen times; and in case where the grass is rough and coarse with rushes, sedge &c. it is necessary to pare and burn it, if the land belong to the undertaker: and another reason for this practice is, that paring and burning destroys great numbers of the slug which produces the cock-chaffer, as well as the wire-worm which abounds here in the lighter soils very much; there are also many slugs of a smaller size, of a bluish-brown, about an inch long."

Semination.—P. 150. "The seed is so put in (after rolling about the middle of March, continuing till the middle of May, in portions, to vary the time of cropping), in equi-distant rows 8 or 9 inches asunder; if not loose enough, *it is sown broad-cast*, and the seed harrowed in. Quantity of seed per acre, 88 bushels (?) in husk. And the clods raked off into the sides of the furrows, and then rolled again to leave it smooth and neat."

Raising the *Crop.*—P. 150. "Being thus far done the field must be gripped very carefully, for whereve water stands, the woad is entirely destroyed. Upon the first coming up of the plant, attention must be paid to the turnip-fly, and also to frosts, as the plants are sometimes destroyed by both, in which case it must be sown again immediately. It is not unusual to sow the greatest part of a crop twice or thrice. Begin to weed about old May-day; this is a business that is executed wit

with much attention by men, women, and children, on
their knees, using short spuds with one hand, and drawing away the weeds with the other. It is done by contract per acre, for weeding and cropping in one bargain.
Weed twice before the first cropping, and once after;
which second weeding is given immediately after cropping, which, for the first, commonly begins the first week
in July here; in the upland countries in the centre of the
kingdom, (?) three weeks sooner, owing to the land
being warmer and forwarder."

Harvesting Woad.—P. 151. "Cropping is performed
by the same people: it is gathered by hand, grasping the
leaves of the plants, and taking them off with a twist: on
a rich soil and favourable season, it will be eight inches
high; in bad seasons shorter; 60 or 70 dozen of baskets
are spread in the field, ready to receive it, and for this
consumption there is a plantation of osiers, for occasionally providing this article. The old method was, to take
the crop from the field in very large carts, which were
packed to the mill, and shot down for spreading under
the grinding wheels. This was a slovenly operation, and
rarely kept free from dirt. Mr. Cartwright has improved
this part of the apparatus greatly, by substituting one-
horse carts, the bodies of which lift from the axis and
frame, and are discharged most conveniently."

This is done by hoisting up the *body* of the cart with
its lading (but without the wheels, axletree and shafts) by
the means of a crane and tackle, to a floor thrown over
the mill; which is, by this ingenious method, readily
ed:—a beautiful, simplex contrivance, which does credit
to whoever conceived and executed it.

P. 153. " The crop is regularly gathered twice, and in
favourable seasons a third is either wholly or partially
collected; this third makes an inferior woad, the first and
second only going into that of the prime quality."

P. 151. " The second crop is usually six weeks after
the first. Generally every day's cropping is weeded be-
ore night."

Aftermanagement of Woad.—P. 153. " The land is left
or winter in that state" (as it lay after the last gathering?)
well gripped, to keep it dry, ready for ploughing in the
spring, which is done as soon as it is in proper state, which
is rarely before the second week in March, when it is pre-
ared, sown, and finished in the same manner as in the
preceding year. A portion of every crop is however left,
in order to produce seed, the stems of which rise the
second

second year. Some growers gather it once for a crop ;
but as it is of an inferior quality, Mr. Cartwright has not
practiced it. One acre of seed will produce enough to
sow forty acres. The seed is less than that of the turnip,
but the husk is large.

" When sowing is very late, and the crop thin, it is a
practice to thicken it by making holes in the vacancies
with a triangular hoe, for children to drop seeds in ; and
this is done so late even as June."

The *effects* of *Woad* on *land.*—P. 156. " In regard to
any idea that may be entertained of a crop which returns
nothing to the soil, having an exhausting tendency, Mr. C
observes, that it is probably compensated by the thorough
cleaning it receives. On these rich soils he conceives it
to be a very beneficial culture, even in this respect
When these grass lands are broken up for corn, it has not
been unusual for the crops to be so luxuriant as to injure
themselves greatly. Any crop not fed on the ground will
deduct something; and it is beneficial to put one in which
shall do this more moderately than others, and at the
same time clean the land ; this must be an advantageous
mode of breaking up."—Provided, ought surely here to
have been added, a good market can be had for the pro
duce (see p. 155, aforegoing). Nevertheless, we find
Woad, more than once, spoken of, in general terms, a
a crop, for which *to break up grass lands.*

P. 197. " Joshua Scrope, Esq. at Long Sutton, upon the
inclosure of that common let 60 acres for woad for three
years, at 4l. per acre per annum net rent. After that h
took it into his own hands, and ploughed it for oats, get
ting 11 quarters an acre. Upon the oat stubble he sowe
wheat 5 quarters an acre, at 5l. a quarter; clover wa
sown with it, which was mown and fed, and sowed t
wheat again, 5 quarters an acre, and now would be let a
40s. an acre ; the land not being the least hurt, either b
the woad or the successive tillage.

" Some upon breaking up this common, sowed oats a
first, but they grew too rank.

" Others let it to flaxmen at 3l. or 4l. per acre; bu
they think that flax *draws* the land more than woac
No hemp.

" In Holland Fen woad is reckoned of all others th
most profitable way of breaking up, for the woad-plante
gives 4 or 5l. per acre per annum, for three years, fe
that crop, and then great ones of corn are taken."

P. 198. " Dr. Johnson of Spalding, let 300 acres
                                                    Moulte

Moulton Common, on the inclosure to a woad grower, at
May-day, 1797, at 5l. per acre per annum, for four years;
and four years more for three crops of oats, and a fallow,
at 30s. an acre, which oat rent, however, is much below
the value; he is *informed*, and believes that woad does no
harm to the land:"—an interesting fact; if such it is.

From those notices, it appears, that the ordinary ESTAB-
ISHED PRACTICE of cultivating and manufacturing woad,
in Lincolnshire, is carried on, by WOADMEN.—We are
not, however, informed of the particulars of *their* practice.
These migraters must necessarily have buildings upon,
or near the spots, on which they take up their temporary
residencies;—for mills, drying houses, couching rooms
&c.; and, in the fens and marshes at least, these buildings
must, of course, be of a *temporary* construction. Whether
the magnificent *stationary* establishment, at Brothertoft,—
employing twenty four mill horses, and of course a numerous body of workpeople) be unique, or whether there
are other establishments of a similar description, does not
appear in this Report.

Of *that* establishment, we have the following particulars.—P. 149. "The culture of this plant has been carried
to such perfection, on a very extensive scale, by J. Cart-
right, Esq. at Brothertoft farm, near Boston, that it will
be sufficient to explain his management. His father had
been largely in the old system by moveable colonies, but
as the trouble of that method of conducting the business
was considerable, his son attempted, and successfully, to
fix it to one spot. For this purpose it was necessary, first,
to secure a tract of land sufficiently large for affording a
certain number of acres annually in crop, for keeping
the buildings and machinery in work, so that the business
might go on with regularity. At Brothertoft he purchased such a tract."—This tract, we are informed, p. 154,
comprized " eleven hundred acres;" and the " buildings
and machinery are calculated for cropping 200 acres
every year."

POTATOES.—These are classed, in the Report under
review, among " crops not commonly cultivated."—We,
nevertheless, find five or six pages of *information* collected,
concerning them; which, if potatoes were a new crop in
England, and this the first Report of their culture, might
have been sufficiently interesting, for publication. But,
seeing the length of time they have been cultivated, in
this country, and after the volumes (it may be said) that
have been published, on their nature and cultivation, a
chaotic

chaotic mass of trivial "facts" (even admitting them to
be really such) surely, ought not to have been sent to the
press. In the few short notices that follow is comprized
all that appears to be, in any sort, worthy of preservation.

P. 142. " Potatoes have been largely cultivated about
Spalding, but have not answered for bullocks; one man
got to 200 acres; but was ruined, though the crops very
great."

P. 144. " About Folkingham they have increased very
much within three or four years; and much among the
cottagers. The effect very useful. But the principal
place for them is about Tattersal and Coningsby." But
of their management, there, we find no account.

P. 145. " At Haxey, in Axholm,"—" take up by pulling up the tops, which they throw aside. Plough out,
keeping the plough down under the potatoes; fixing
hands in divisions, 20 yards to a gatherer. Harrow th
new ridges, and pick again. Plough again in small furrows, when two or three pickers follow the ploughs, turning down the ridges; and harrow; then it is ready for
wheat."

Same page.—" Forty years ago, on Trent side, M
Durrand's father had hemp and flax every year; and, as
to barley and wheat, could not venture it so rank an
strong; but since potatoes, they have so much reduce
the fertility, that corn is common, and often not good
crops. The expression was, potatoes have quite killed
the land." This is highly interesting; and is not, I conceive, improbable.

CARROTS.—On this crop we find nothing new.—" M
Walker of Woolsthorpe has had carrots several yea
on his rich red sands; his crops have been large, and h
has a very high opinion of them for all sorts of stock."-
p. 174.

TURNEPS.—P. 135. " I was very much pleased with
viewing the turnips from Norton to Kirton, by the turnpike, and also by the Cliff-road: the quantity great, th
crops good and clean, and well hoed, with some few exceptions; it was a change from what I saw here twenty-
nine years ago, striking." And in page 138, the Report
breaks out, in fresh raptures at the change.—Now, I perceive nothing in it to excite astonishment:—a simil
change having taken place, in various parts of the kin,
dom, during that period of time. I have repeatedly e
pressed a degree of wonder that Lincolnshire shou
                                                    remai

remain, near a century, within sight of Norfolk, without perceiving the utility, and setting about the culture, of the turnip crop.—If we are to believe Mr. Stone, it is, even at this day, or was in 1794, behind nine tenths of the kingdom, in regard to the turnep husbandry. See p. 58, aforegoing.

Dunging for turnips.—By a notice in the section " Manuring," a rather unusual mode of dunging for turneps would seem to prevail, in the County of Lincoln.— I insert it, at length; tho the former part of it is not at all satisfactory; and the latter not always practicable.

P. 265. " Mr. Skipwith at Alesby, varies the common practice of manuring for turnips; which is to spread it towards the end of the year, and plough it in, which he thinks bad, as the wash of the winter carries it down below the plough, where much is lost. He ploughs first, and then spreads the dung, which he thinks answers better. Upon land not very dry, I should suppose this could only be done in a frost.

" He observes invariably, that where dung is carted for turnips to the land long before sowing, so as to give time for mixing with the soil by the plough, the crop much exceeds that which is spread before the last ploughing only."

On a very absorbent soil, this practice may frequently be eligible. But where there is the least repellancy, and especially where the soil requires to be laid up so as to shoot off surface water, such a method must be wasteful of manure.—Mr. Skipwith's soil not being given, we cannot judge of the propriety of *his* practice.

A *Disease* of Turneps.—P. 136. " At Belesby, they complain much of the distemper called *fingers and toes;* the root, instead of swelling, running into strings of that form, and rot, and come to nothing; it is common on all fresh land, and nothing they can do prevents it.

" At Alesby also, this distemper does much mischief on all land, but most on fresh broken up. Mr. Skipwith has known it ever since he was a farmer. Tried lime, but had no effect, in this respect; ashes he finds the best manure to prevent it; but not wholly."

P. 137. " About Louth they have been much plagued with fingers and toes; they assured me, that on cutting the roots, they find a worm in them about the eighth of an inch long, and the size of a large pin; worst on the richest land."

Under

Under the head " Manure," we are told that marl is a preventive of this disease. P. 261.

On BULBOUS RAPE—" Swedish Turneps."—I find nothing noticeable. It did not appear to be, at the time of making this Report, an established crop, in Lincolnshire. For the *herbage* of rape, see p. 152, aforegoing.

CABBAGES are grown by tupmen, for keeping up their rams; and for lambs, in frosty weather. The Reporter properly recommends them to the attention of the Lincolnshire husbandmen, " upon the rich lands of this County."—There can be little *rivalship* between cabbages and turneps :—the one being, in a general view of them, adapted to strong, the other, exclusively, to absorbent, lands.

On their culture, I perceive not a line that is proper for extraction.

CULTIVATED HERBAGE.—In the subsection, " Seeds," is little more than an unprofitable display of controversial notices, and vague opinions, about the eligibility and value of *raygrass*, as a species of cultivated herbage !— the mere wanderings of inexperience ;—a want of knowledge in the choice of the variety to be cultivated,—in the quantity of seed proper to be sown,—and in the quantity of stock requisite to render it most profitable, during early spring.—Strange, that the Secretary of the Board, instead of listening to such conversational crudities, and printing them ! should not have explained those essentials; or have recommended to his Lincolnshire friends a morning's ride, into the neighbouring County of Norfolk, in the early spring months ;—there, to be convinced of the value of raygrass.

The following remarks of the Reporter, on the raising of young herbage, under rape, I insert, with peculiar satisfaction, here. Speaking, generally, of the practices of Lincolnshire, in regard to " Seeds," the Reporter says, page 134,—" That of sowing grasses with rape, is new ; and is a thought that deserves attention. I heard it mentioned some years ago in conversation, as having been tried, and failed : but not seeing any reason for a want of success, I tried it myself, and it answered well. It is a management that gives full time for cleaning and preparing the land ; and for sowing at a season (July or August) probably the best, as new grass seeds are then to be had. Feeding the rape manures the seeds ; and, i done with a little attention relative to soil and weather would very rarely be injurious;—it is a system which should be adopted in other Counties."   Thi

This practice, I believe, originated in my proposals for the improvement of Dartmore (in the WEST of ENGLAND) first published, in May 1796.

SAINFOIN.—In a subsection, bearing this title, we find a string of desultory memoranda, *about* sainfoin. But the nature,—the specific quality, and texture,—of the given substratum, being seldom or never mentioned, no useful truths can be drawn from them ;—either as to culture or produce. The only particulars, noticeable, here, are the method of *breaking up* the worn-out leys, and the *effect* of sainfoin, on land.

Breaking up Sainfoin Leys.—From several notes, it appears that sodburning, so much in use in breaking up other grassy lands, is not employed on sainfoin leys.* See WEST. DEPART.—*Cotswold Hills*, on this topic.

Effects of Sainfoin on Land.—P. 168. " Mr. Parkinson of Asgarby disapproves of sainfoin ; because it makes land poor."—This is a new opinion, and can scarcely be well founded. Where the surface soil is good, and in high condition, it must necessarily be more or less ex-hausted ;—if not by the sainfoin,—by the undergrowth of herbage,—being uniformly carried off, for a series of years. But the sainfoin, itself, demonstrably feeds, principally, in the substratum ;—from which the valuable crops of this species of herbage are, no doubt, chiefly drawn :—as would sufficiently appear (were there no other evidences of it†) in what immediately follows the above extract :—p. 168. " On very barren heath, or Wold land, he thinks it is very useful ; as it makes a soil produce a crop of hay, which naturally would only feed rabbits by *har* grass :"—and what Mr. Parker says, in contradiction of Mr. Parkinson, affords farther evidence of the same fact.—P. 168. " Mr. Parker had 10 acres, and never had better crops than after it, in the course of turnips, barley, wheat ; and has never, for eight years, had less than 5 quarters of barley, and about 4 of wheat : a sure proof that no evil resulted from sainfoin, though there is a notion that it impoverishes, which Mr. Parker thinks idle ; not to speak of the manure which arises from great crops of hay."

Native Red Clover—" Cow Grass"—is highly spoken of, as being found, in different cases, to be much pre-ferable

* In one instance excepted. See head *Sodburning*, p. 117, afore-going.

† For other evidence, see my YORKSHIRE, article *Sainfoin*.

ferable to the ordinary variety of "broad clover"—doubt
lessly a *foreign* variety—which has long—perhaps to
long—been in cultivation.

Parsley!—This plant might, in 1799, be said to be
entering into the practice of Lincolnshire, as a species of
cultivated herbage. This Reporter has brought togethe
the following notices concerning it.—P. 170. "This
plant is cultivated as an artificial grass by Mr. Stephen
son of Swineshead, mixed with white clover; 14 lb. a
acre of the latter, and 2 lb. of the former. It lies thre
years; and the first supports from 6 to 10 sheep an acre
The second, it is manured; and keeps also from 6 to 1
an acre; the third, it carries from 7 to 11 an acre. Th
soil is the fertile loam of Holland Fen.

" About Folkingham, amongst the good farmers, the
have sown this plant with clover, 2 lb. an acre, at 8d.
pound; and every body that has tried, approves it fo
sheep, being healthy for them.

"Mr. Hesselden sows 2 lb. of parsley in his seeds; th
sheep are so fond of it, that they eat it down so close a
to kill the plant.

" The Rev. Mr. Allington of Swinhop has sown it fou
years; and Mr. Whalesby, his tenant, on this farm, sowe
it eight or ten years before, on the same farm. He ha
a great opinion of it, and means to have more in future
has not sown more than 2 lb. an acre, but designs more i
future, unless the price prevents him, it has increase
much in three years."

The *Sowthistle!*—For the forcing quality of thi
another new species of cultivated herbage, in fattin
sheep, see that head, ensuing.

In a distinct subsection, entitled, " Laying down t
Grass," some instances of practice in cultivating herbage
are found. They contain, however, nothing new, c
excellent. It may, nevertheless, be proper to inform m
readers how *they* are said to do those things, in Lincoln
shire. *

P. 20

---

* The Reporter opens this subsection with round assertions of *h
own.* But as he has cautioned us not to put confidence in wha
emanate from *himself,* I think it right to place them, here, in a note
—merely for the purpose of giving my readers an opportunity e
comparing his sentiments with those of a professional man, on th
same subject.

P. 206. " A tract of land called the New Marshes, which we
ploughed for several years after they were first embanked, and trea
ed much as Sutton commons now are, were immediately upon bein
la

P. 208. " In Holland Fen they sow white clover, rib grass, trefoil, and 8 bushels of hay seeds, and without corn, on which 14 sheep and 14 lambs have been summered the whole season through per acre, which is prodigious."

P. 209. " In Barton new inclosed field, I could not but admire Mr. Uppleby's new layed seeds, which were very thick and fine; he sows 16 lb. white clover, 4 lb. trefoil, and 8 bushels of hay seeds, which hay seeds cost 10s.; this expence is enormous, and carried further than necessary, however, the error is on the right side. The second and third years' grass were perfectly fine. The same gentleman has also laid 160 acres in Goxhill, fourteen years ago, with 14 lb. white clover, 4 lb. trefoil, and 1 bushel ray grass; it is now a very fine pasture. On part of it the soil is a strong churlish clay, fit for wheat and beans; yet the grass has taken well, and not declined; much crested dogs tail come naturally, which is a good sign.

" In all the Wold country near to Brocklesby, they have a common custom of laying to grass by sowing the seeds with rape; and they reckon it an excellent custom; indeed the best of all methods. What Lord Yarborough lays down in his park, &c. is done thus.*

" Mr Bourne of Dalby, lays down by sowing white clover, red clover, trefoil, ray grass, with turnip and cole, and finds it succeeds well.

" Best way, Mr. Parkinson says, is 12 lb. white clover, and a bushel of best ray grass; or better still, 3 bushels of finest hard hay seeds from Yorkshire†. He does not approve *Yorkshire white.*"   Holcus lanatus.

" The

aid down, and continue to be, the finest pastures for sheep feeding of any in the County. So also will those parts of Sutton common be, if properly laid down, where the under-stratum is of a clayey quality :—where it is all silt, as in most of the *old* marshes, all the fallowing, all the manuring, all the new theories on husbandry in the world, will not be able to make such land continue in a feeding capacity."

I wish the Secretary had explained to us how those lands can be " properly laid down," so as to produce the effects asserted. But it is probable he merely meant by those words to give due encouragement to " breaking up" such lands.

For Mr STONE's remarks, on those lands, together with my sentiments on the subject, see p. 50 and Sequel, aforegoing.

* The Reporter does not say how long *they* have been in this custom. See p. 162, aforegoing.

† Doubtlessly *raygrass* and perhaps a portion of *plantain.*

" The Rev. Mr. Allington has been anxious to lay
down with such seeds as will last in the ground ; but has
not hitherto found any thing better than white clover and
trefoil ; if with ray grass, not more than a peck an acre
of very clean seeds ; he has tried Yorkshire white, and
does not approve it."

PERENNIAL GRASS LANDS.—Of this fundamental subject
of Report, from the County of Lincoln, the Secretary of
the Board has not been unmindful. His active pencil
has accumulated matter sufficient to fill near forty pages ;
—to which his chapter, " Grass," is extended :—beside
others on the same subject,—directly or incidentally,—
which occur in different parts of his volume.—Several of
these items of information have been already noticed,
under the heads, *Appropriation*, *Plan* of *Management*,
&c.; as being most intimately, or inseparably, connected
with, and properly belonging to, those subjects.—The
remainder of what appears to me of sufficient moment, or
interest, to be registered, here, I will bring under the
following form of arrangement.

1. Fen.   4. Pasture Grounds.
2. Marsh.   5. Mowing Grounds.
3. Vale.

1. *Fen-land Grass.*—Of the nature of this species of
Land.—P. 223. (Chapter " Wastes") " I must consider
commons, however naturally rich in soil, as wastes, and
therefore class Spalding, Pinchbeck, and Cabbit commons
as such, to the amount of many thousand acres ; 15,000
acres from it were inclosed long ago, when in a state of
a forest, which the whole has been, as appears from the
black oaks dug up every where." *

P. 235. (Chapter " Improvement") " Through all
the fens of Lincolnshire we hear much of the *soak*, by
which expression is meant the subterranean water which
is found at various depths, usually but a very few feet
below the surface : this rises and sinks according to seasons, and is supposed, from its saline quality, to be the
sea water filtered through a stratum of silt : Major Cartwright in Holland Fen observes upon it,—

" ' The substratum of *silt* seems to be very general in
this neighbourhood, and not often, as I should suppose, at
any very considerable depth. It seems to be a conductor
of water in all directions ; so that when the main drain
o

* See N. p. 40, aforegoing.

of the country are full of water, the *soak* must lie high
in the land, even through the whole distances between
drain and drain. Hence it is obvious, that the lower
the land is situated, the later must be its seed time; and
I presume that many parts of the Fen must be incapable
of so complete a natural drainage in winter, as to bear
the plough at that season. Possibly the use of engines
in the form of windmills might be profitably extended
beyond the limits hitherto contemplated. I have not
heard of their being intended to do more than relieve the
surface from water; whereas they might perhaps be employed to advantage in keeping down the soak to a sufficient depth below the surface, to prevent the *chill*, and
to forward the spring seed time.' "

P. 237. (A further remark of Mr. Cartwright) " It has
been remarked of this district, although retaining its
ancient name of *Fen*, that upon the whole, it is liable to
suffer more in summer from *want of water*, than in winter
from a superabundance; for any thing in the nature
of a *flood*, to which the valleys in other parts of the kingdom are so much exposed, has been unknown in this
neighbourhood, ever since the grand system of drainage
took place. But I incline to think that the foregoing remark has been founded only in the *visible* want of water
for the *cattle*, when, upon a drought, the great drains become very shallow, and the *soak*, or water retained in the
earth, passes, in a great measure, off through the filtering
stratum of silt; at which time we must dig deep to find
the fluid in the form of *water*. But even in such seasons of drought, I conceive the earth, by means of its
saline quality, to attract and retain so much of the fluid,
in the form of *moisture*, as to be of the greatest use in
refreshing and feeding the roots of corn. Hence the
weighty crops of grain we get in very dry seasons, when
other soils through drought become comparatively barren.
Hence also the importance of correcting every top soil of
a stiff and too tenacious clay, with silt enough to render
it pervious to the moisture from below. A crop of barley
in the late droughty season, on the land above mentioned,
which I estimate at 7 quarters an acre, seems to confirm
this reasoning."

Those are sensible remarks. If water or strong moisture be lodged, immediately beneath the soil, it will ever,
through the mean of CELLULAR ATTRACTION, communicate
moisture to the soil itself, let its specific quality be what
it may;—even as water lodged at the bottom of a garden
pot,

pot, will pervade the entire mass of mold, which the pot may contain, and invigorate the plant that may be rooted in it,—in a manner similar to rain water falling on the surface. Hence in draining morasses (as I have else-where observed) it may be impolitic to drain them too dry.

P. 208. (Chapter "Grass") "The original maiden pasture of fen land does not wear so good a complexion, nor support so much stock, as after it has undergone a course of tillage. As this may be attributed in a great degree to bad grasses having possession of the soil, and some of them of an aquatic nature, favoured and estab-lished by former inundation and neglect of drainage; so it seems to be of consequence, to keep the land dry in future, that such grasses *may not return*."

From what we find in this, as well as in Mr. Stone's Report, the true "Fen" is a real *morass*,—formed by stagnant water and aquatic plants; with more or less alluvious materials; according to situation and other cir-cumstances:—of course, a species of land, widely differing from the true "Marsh;" which is altogether alluvious.

In Lincolnshire, there must necessarily (from the con-tiguity of the fens to the sea, or a wide estuary, and alluvious rivers, added to the natural flatness of the country, in the southern parts of the County) be many *intermediate lands*, which partake of the natures of those two distinct species.—Hence, unless we were sufficiently informed, as to the true nature of the lands spoken of, all information, that is grounded upon them, must be in a degree vague. The mere term "Marsh," or "Fen," is of course frequently defective, and may lead to error, instead of truth.

The "original, maiden" herbage of a mere morass is, in its nature, unfit to support much stock. The herbage of a mere morass, in a state of nature, is coarse, innutri-tious, and unpalatable to domestic animals. It requires a length of time, or a "course of tillage," to change the natural herbage of a mere fen, to a state of profitable pasturage.

But let not this truth be held out, as an apology for breaking up marsh and fen lands, indiscriminately; or even what are familiarly termed "Fens," that have been deeply covered, or intimately blended, with rich allu-vion, or natural warp.—Such intermediate, or *composite* lands partake more of "Marsh," than of "Fen."—And even marsh lands vary, essentially, in their natures, or specific qualities; as appears in the subjoined extracts.

2. *Marsh-*

2. *Marsh-land Grass.*—P. 206. " A tract of land called the New Marshes, which were ploughed for several years after they were first embanked, and treated much as Sutton commons now are, were immediately upon being laid down, and continue to be, the finest pastures for sheep feeding of any in the County. So also will those parts of Sutton common be, if properly laid down, where the under-stratum is of a clayey quality:—where it is all silt, as in most of the *old* marshes, all the fallowing, all the manuring, all the new theories on husbandry in the world, will not be able to make such land continue in a feeding capacity."

P. 179. " In the Marshes that are in the vicinity of Saltfleet and Sutton, there is some distinction, which it will be proper to note by parishes. In Northcots the quality is rather inferior, being chiefly for breeding. Marsh Chapel better; but still weak, and for breeding also. In Grainthorpe, a great deal very good grazing land. Conisholm low, swampy, and but little good. Skidbrook, a great deal very good. South Somercots the same; but 1000 acres of *ings*, or common meadow. The three Saltfleetby's, 5000 acres; and a great deal very strong and good for *feeding* beasts."

For an evidence of the want of *fences*, on the low grass lands of Lincolnshire, see the head, *Rape*, aforegoing. Also Mr. Stone on *Sheep*, p. 63, aforegoing.

3. *Vale-land Grass.*—On the natural qualities of these, we find but little intelligence, in the volume under review.—P. 190. " From Tealby on the edge of the Wolds to Wragby, there is a constant series of grass, with hardly any tillage; it is under sheep, and some breeding cattle, with mowing; and lets about 20s."

The following passage is not sufficiently intelligible.—P. 191. " From Sempringham down to Deeping, a line 2 or 3 miles broad of rich grazing land, made in a long course of time, by what has been brought out of the adjoining fens, worth, one with another, 20s.; applied to grazing sheep and beasts; though some in tillage."

4. *Pasture Grounds.*—The *dairy* is not, emphatically speaking, an object in Lincolnshire; and the *rearing* of cattle and sheep will be spoken of, under their respective heads,—I shall, therefore, in this place, consider its pasture lands, merely in the capacity of GRAZING GROUNDS; to which *this* Reporter has paid commendable attention.

His enquiries, however, would seem to have been directed toward the quality of those grounds,—to the quantity of stock they are capable of bearing,—rather than

to

to the art and mystery of grazing,—to the purchase, management, and disposal of grazing stock, in this most naturally grazing County.—As a matter of curiosity, and to convey additional information, respecting the nature of the *soils* of Lincolnshire, I will here insert some of the more wonderful accounts of the heavy loads of stock they are able to bear.

It was my wish to have analyzed the various entries on grazing, that are found in different parts of the volume, and to have digested them agreeably to the method I have observed on similar occasions. But many of them, I find, are of so miscellaneous a nature, and so reluctantly separable into elementary parts, that I must be content with inserting them, in the progressive order, in which they stand in the Report.

P. 174. ("Rich grazing Grounds") "These are the glory of Lincolnshire,* and demand a singular attention ; the soil is a rich loamy clay, some very stiff, but of uncommon fertility, as may be seen by various instances.

"Some of the grazing lands in Long Sutton, that were common, will carry five or six sheep an acre, and four bullocks to ten acres. Mr. Scrope there has four acres, which carry 45 sheep in summer, and must be *hobb'd* often to keep it down.

"On the grass lands in Deeping Fen, improved by paring and burning, (*?*) Mr. Graves keeps five sheep an acre from Lady-day to Michaelmas, and one and a half in winter ; and a bullock of 60 stone to two acres besides in summer.

"As a grazier, few men have been in a more extensive business, or practiced it with more success, than T. Fydell, Esq. M. P. at Boston. I was therefore particularly solicitous to procure information from a gentleman perfectly competent to give it. Several unfortunate circumstances prevented the interview I hoped for, but by letter afterwards, I received the following account of 20 acres of rich land near Boston, for the year 1796, and a more satisfactory one cannot be wished."

Mr. F. *begins* with a debtor-and-creditor account of the *profits* of grazing !—Now, what can be less certain than the profits of grazing ?—which depends, almost wholely, on seasons and unsettled prices,—added to the skill and foresight of individuals, in buying and selling.

The

---

* Yet see what is said on " Breaking up grass lands," aforegoing.

The more satisfactory part of Mr. Fydell's communication is the following.—P. 176. "The average weight of the beasts is 70 stone, being of the York or Lincoln breed; the sheep all Lincolns. The former are bought in April or May, and all gone by the 11th December; the sheep are bought in May; they are clipped twice, and sold fat in April or May following; that there is little difference in seasons; except that after a bad winter, the sheep are not ready for market so soon by a month, as they are after good winters. The loss in weight in driving to Smithfield, very little; the expence, beasts 15s. 9d. ; sheep 1s. 9½d. each.

"Mr. Fydell held for several years a piece of land in Skirbeck parish, which measured 21 acres, and kept, com. annis, from Lady-day to Michaelmas, 19 heavy beasts, and 100 sheep; and wintered 50 sheep.

"He now holds a pasture adjoining his garden at Boston of eight acres, which keeps in summer 10 oxen and 40 sheep; and winters thirty sheep."

P. 176. "The finest grazing Lands are at Boston, Alderchurch, Fosdyke, Sutterton, Kirton, Frampton, Wyberton, Skirwick; these will carry in summer a bullock to an acre and half, besides 4 sheep an acre; and 2 sheep an acre in winter.

"Rev. Mr. Berridge of Alderchurch, has near his house 40 acres of the rich grass, upon which the stock is, upon an average,   300 sheep,
                16 fatting bullocks,
                3 cows,
                4 horses;

and carries through the winter three sheep an acre. This land is valued at 40s. an acre. It is a vast stock. He favoured me with these particulars in the presence of a dozen neighbours, and called in his manager to confirm it; it wanted therefore no after-corrections.

"In the grazing lands at Swineshead, a beast an acre, of 40 to 70 stone, and two or three sheep; also two sheep an acre in winter.

"Mr. Tindall at Ewerby, which is on high land compared with Holland Fen, stocks a bullock to two and a half acres, and three sheep per acre, in summer; and two sheep an acre in winter.

"In the lordships of Horbling, Billingborough, Berthorp, Sempringham, Pointon, Dowsby, Dunsby, and Hackonby, there are extensive tracts of rich grazing land applied to fatting bullocks and sheep, carrying a bullock
to

to two acres, and three sheep per acre, in summer; and two sheep an acre in winter; which lands are generally rented at 30s. per acre."

P. 186. ("Hundred of Skirbeck"—Neighbourhood of Boston)—"The best kind of pasture is chiefly stocked with shearling wethers, bought at the spring markets at Boston, which, having yielded two fleeces of wool, are sold off easily in the next year; and by beasts in the summer, sold in autumn; some kept on farther in eddish, but all gone in the winter. The second best is chiefly fed by young beasts and hogs, kept on to shearlings: these are well kept, as their value materially depends on it; there are also some few breeding sheep on this division of the pasture. The third class is chiefly mown. But it is to be noted that all these particulars relate to an acre larger than statute measure, about 4¼ roods. The first division is stocked at the rate of 3 sheep per acre, winter and summer, with the overplus of some being bought in the spring, and not cleared from the land till some months later than the time at which they are bought. The beasts are in the proportion, on an average of 7 to 10 acres, from 54 to 100 stone. The second class winters about 5 sheep to 2 acres, with not less than 4 per acre in summer, with a few cows or young beasts; and on both these there will be some few horses, too uncertain to average. On the best land they are chiefly horses making up for sale; and on the second quality, horses employed in work or young ones; it is not usual to keep any horses in summer, except on the pastures. The produce of hay on the third may be about 35s. an acre; the eddish eaten by cattle from the other grounds, or by lamb hogs before they go to their winter keeping."—Here, we have something resembling considerate information.

P. 190. "Mr. Tennison of Lincoln, has 13 acres of marsh at Grimsby, that summer-feeds 14 bullocks; and carries 35 sheep the year through."

To convey a general idea of the great fertility of the grazing grounds of Lincolnshire, the Reporter has formed a table of the quantity of stock they carry,—according to the accounts he received, at the different places of enquiry. The "average" stands thus.—P. 192. "Sheep in summer per acre 3¾."—"Acres per bullock in summer, with the sheep, 1¾."—"Sheep in winter per acre 2."

On this average, the Reporter makes the following observations.—P. 192. "Considering the size of these sheep, which cannot be estimated at less than 24 lb. a quarter,

on

on an average; and that the bullocks rise from 50 to 100 stone (14 lb.) this rate of stocking is very great indeed : here are on every acre 360 lb. of mutton, and reckoning the bullocks at 42 stone, dead weight, there is also 336 lb. of beef; in all, 696 lb. of meat per acre in summer, besides the winter produce, which is immense. Let us, to simplify the account still more, suppose the whole mutton, and it amounts to $7\frac{1}{4}$ sheep per acre, of 24 lb. a quarter, for summer, besides 2 in winter. The wool is another great article, at $3\frac{3}{4}$ sheep per acre, and 9 lb. the fleece, each acre gives $43\frac{3}{4}$ lb. of wool. These products from such a considerable extent of country, are matchless."—Here, too, we have something to interest, if not to instruct.

P. 194. (" Feeding") " In the low land in Barton on the Humber, there was a horse-pasture and a sheep one contiguous, and upon the inclosure it was remarkable to observe the great difference between them; that had been under sheep so greatly superior.

" In the tract of marsh land on the sea coast they observe, that where most grass is left in autumn, there the herbage is the coarsest and worst next year; the remark was made at Louth, in answer to recommending eddish for spring feeding sheep, which would not do on rich marsh, though it might, they thought, on uplands. It also shews, that the Romney Marsh system of close feeding is right, and would answer as well in Lincolnshire.

" In the hundred of Skirbeck they like to have a tolerable head of grass in the spring, before turning in; and afterwards so to stock as to prevent its getting coarse by *running away*, so as to prevent the necessity of *hobbing*, which, however, must be done in a wet growing season.

" Mr. Parkinson observes, that the less sheep are changed the better; this remark, which I take to be very just, demands attention : it bears on the question of folding. Beasts are changed while *hobbing* is done; and the sooner it is hobbed the better; if cut while young, cattle will eat it."

Guessing, from what we can catch, in the close of the above extract, " hobbing"—a word repeatedly used— means mowing, or sweeping off, stale herbage, from the surfaces of pasture grounds.—Where *provincialisms* are employed, surely a *glossary* ought also to be employed, to explain them.

P. 207. (" Laying down to grass") " The great disadvantage these marshes are subject to, is, the want of fresh water for beasts.—Ponds or pits are obliged to be made

here

here to retain the fresh water; sometimes natural living springs are found, and the water perfectly fresh; but in very dry seasons these reservoirs are either exhausted, or so corrupted by the cattle running into them on hot days, that they cannot thrive; or they take to drinking the salt water, which is took in at the spring tides to make fences, which scours them, and causes a fever. In wet seasons, from certain saline qualities lurking in the herbage, the effect of which is the same as if they drank the salt water; and if not quickly removed to the old inclosures, or what is better,—some fen land, they speedily die. This inconvenience obliges the grazier to run his sheep thicker, in a wet season especially, than they can feed, or sometimes even thrive, turning crones, unless removed, and also much affected with the foot halt."

P. 432. (" Obstacles")—" A very singular nuisance in Deeping Fen, of late, has been mice ; which have multiplied to such a degree in the pastures as almost to starve the sheep. The land is alive with them. Mr. Greaves has, in a field of a few acres, killed eight or ten by his horse treading on them."—A circumstantial evidence, this, of the soundness of the soil, and the richness of the herbage.

5. *Hay Grounds.*—P. 195. " Mowing rich marsh lands cannot be done too tenderly. At Moulton, between Sutton and Spalding, they have greatly damaged their fine lands by overmowing; the same at Woplade.

" All land that will feed cattle, Mr. Parkinson observes, should be mown as little as possible; nothing pays worse than the scythe in Lincolnshire; it costs as much labour as a crop of corn, and more than in many counties, and is not of half the value.

" *Hay.*—In making hay it is observed here, as it has been in many other districts, that clover and sainfoin, and some other grasses, should be left in the swarth for some time, and when stirred, only turned; shaking out is found to be pernicious, not only in loss of leaf, but in exposing to damage. The same observation is found in fresh seeds.

" It is observed very generally in Holland Fen, that the hay, though upon land of 27s. an acre rent, is very bad, and will not fatten a bullock, or contribute to it, as is common in other countries. This must be owing to the bad management in making it: among other instances, it was mentioned to me, and I saw it myself, that they will leave the swarths, as they fall from the scythe, untouched so long that the grass under them is turned quite yellow.   " About

" About Folkingham they mow and leave in swarth, in the manner above described; turn it instead of shaking; the system is therefore the same.

" At Ewerby I remarked, that in making haycocks women were employed, who did the work with rakes; the consequence is, putting it together in lumps so imperfectly connected, or rather with such great interstices between them, that if rain comes it must do great damage; whereas, when made by men with forks, the bunch over the fork, it laps layer upon layer in a manner to shoot off rain. Every thing in haymaking that I have seen in Lincolnshire, is barbarous. About Grantham and Belton, hay made in the same manner; the grass bleached by the swarths.

" From Grantham to Lincoln, Gainsborough, Barton, every where in their hay some time after harvest began; at the latter place, carting hay Sept. 3d! this is too barbarous. About Grimsby, and to Alesby, much hay out, and some not on cock; colour hideous. (!) They defend themselves by saying, that the springs are so cold and backward after turnips are gone, that they are forced to feed all their mowing grounds late. I mentioned to Mr. Skipwith, kept eddish, but it did not make the impression so admirable a provision merits.

" From Louth to Saltfleet much hay out, Sept. 15th, and hundreds of loads between Sutton and Alford; indeed very little was cleared. In this tract I saw them drawing hay from all parts of a field to the center with horses and ropes, in order to form a stack without the trouble of carting; the frame for this work, a plate of which I inserted in my Northern Tour, is much superior.

" About Spilsby and Dalby, hay out the 18th of September, arising from want of labourers, not feeding in spring, fit to mow before it was done.

" Sept. 26th, hay out in the hundred of Skirbeck.

" Mr. Parkinson accounts for such lateness by observing, that the county is full of sheep, and they cannot spare the land early enough to have a forward crop of hay; not till the pasture land is increased enough to receive the sheep.

" Mr. Loft of Marsh Chapel defends the practice of being late in the hay; he is not convinced that May-day is not as good a time to save meadows in the Middle Marshes, as Lady-day; and asserts, that the *proof* of such hay in *feeding* cannot be exceeded, though bad for cows: and he remarked, that if marsh hay was *tedded* (strewed out), it would be good for nothing for bullocks; and further, that
                                                        some

some rain in making is beneficial; he would rather have six hours rain than none at all. Even with what I called execrable management and bad weather, the hay alone, without other food, will make bullocks very fat. Also, that the hay from the *ings*, at 10s. an acre rent, is much better for bullocks than that from rich grazing grounds."

I have inserted these remarks at length;—having had but few opportunities of presenting to my readers anything *new*, from this bulky Report.

LIVESTOCK.—The Secretary of the Board opens his thirteenth chapter, entitled " Live Stock," in the following manner.—P. 288. " Here we enter on the subject which has engrossed more attention in this county than perhaps any other; and one upon which opinions are more divided. Before I examine the county, I determined to keep my mind free from every bias, and to report the facts procured, and the ideas current, with as few comments as possible; concluding that the Board is solicitous to discover, not the opinions of a Reporter, but the practice of a county."

The conclusion of this passage would, perhaps, have run better, somewhat in this way:—not the opinion of a Reporter,—or of an individual casually met with in making a tour through a county; but the actually established practices of the higher class of experienced occupiers, in its several districts; agreeably to their respective situations and soils.

HORSES.—On this prominent object of Lincolnshire Husbandry, this Report of it is culpably deficient.— Under the section, " Horses," are a few pages filled with tour-book memoranda, on *breeding*;—also on *working* horses of different descriptions; also of working *oxen !*— thrown confusedly together.—A few of them may be worth transcribing.

P. 377. " Kept remarkably cheap in Deeping Fen, on rich commons in the summer, and in straw yard in winter Many never have any oats : cannot amount to 5*l*. a head; chiefly mares, and so nothing at all in fact.

" Every farmer in Holland Fen keeps mares for breeding, and the numbers are very great." " Mr. Thacker of Langrike Ferry, buys in Yorkshire at three years old in autumn, winters on straw, works a little in spring, and sells at Horncastle fair in August; one of the greatest fairs in the kingdom; a good judge makes money in this way."— " Mr. Cartwright has found that the common groundsel given plentifully to horses in the stable, will cure greasy heels." P. 379

P. 379. " About Normanby, Burton, &c. many bred, both for saddle and coach; sell at two, three, and four years old."—" Howden in Yorkshire is the fair, and one of the greatest in the kingdom; also many to Horncastle. Yearlings and two year olds, all to Howden.   Summer-gate, for a horse on the best marshes 3 $l.$ from May-day to Michaelmas."

P. 380. " Mr. Neve of North Sommercots, instead of giving his horses cooling opening physic, feeds them for three weeks or a month with oats, malted in sea water, and finds it highly conducive to their health."

N. P. 380. " The finest and best horses in the kingdom, chiefly of what are called the blood kind, are bred upon the Wolds; a greater attention is paid to that species of horse by the Wold graziers than even in Yorkshire or Durham, that formerly were so famous for their breed of hunting horses.   *MS. of the B.*"—This Mr. " MS. of the B" is a bold man.

For information respecting *Working Horses* see that head, aforegoing, p. 149.

CATTLE.—On this subject, we have a sheet of letter-press, filled, mostly, with pro-and-con opinions of *fashion-able* breeders, and bull-men, *by trade;* but containing some opinions and notices of practice, that wear a more profit-able appearance.

Unfortunately, however, for the feelings of *systematists,* not only are the various items of information thrown toge-her, without order or arrangement, but the first particular, which presents itself, is on *grazing!*—before the *breed,* the *breeding* or the *rearing,* has been touched upon. I cannot, however, persuade myself, in this instance, to fol-low so unnatural, irrational, inscientific, and unintelligent mode of proceeding.   And, fortunately, in this case, the more valuable parts of the materials collected, aptly enough resolve into elementary parts.—I therefore, place them, here, agreeably to the order of nature and practice.

1. *Breeds* of Cattle, in Lincolnshire.—Of what might uly be termed the *established* breed of the county,—the true Lincolnshire cattle,—such as we see (or saw at the time this Report was made) every market day, tied by the head to the rails, in Smithfield,—we find nothing border-ing on description; nor even an intimation that such a most-legged, square-buttocked breed of demi-elephants, with which the brave tars of old England may be said to be fed,—were bred, reared, and *fitted* for market, in Lin-colnshire.

It

It is true, this breed of cattle would, in a general trea‑
tise on the breeds of English cattle, be unworthy of no‑
tice;—unless as a base and monstrous breed, to be avoided
But, in a Report of " the Practice of a County," surely
this great enormous "fact" ought to have been fully, and
explicitly, brought forward.

The Reporter, however, has done (as it were by acci‑
dent) what appears, to my mind, much more estimable
than a minute description of the now prevailing breed of
the county;—by furnishing us with some (but very imper‑
fect) account of this breed, in its most debased state;—
namely, in the commonfield husbandry of this county;—
of course, with some idea of what was, heretofore, it is
probable, the prevailing breed of Lincolnshire.

P. 303. " Mr. Parker remarks, that there is little atten‑
tion paid to the breed of beasts in this country. In the
open field towns the breed is wretched: they all run to‑
gether on a pasture, without the least thought of selection.
At three years old, they are worth about 7 or 8 l.; and if
they would pay the same attention that is paid elsewhere,
instead of that they would be worth 12 or 13 l.; and all
this result is from being open and uninclosed; they will
breed four or five calves from a wretched cow before they
sell it, so that a great quantity of food is sadly misap‑
plied."

Of the modern *improved* breed of that county, we find
the following particulars.—P. 290. " Mr. Tyndall of
Ewerby, has been long celebrated for his breed of cattle
he found them many years ago upon his present farm
which he first occupied, and then purchased; I viewed
them with pleasure; for though he has in a very great
stock (breeding 40 to 50 calves every year,) many very
unequal, yet some are capital, and merit their reputation
The grand-daughter of the Two-pap cow; the daughter
of Bald-face; the Red-cow; the grand-daughter of the
old Blue; and the cow called Wide Hips; are all very
fine beasts: the last he thinks the best, and would sell at
no price; he would not sell the three former under 50 l.
each, valuing them equally. Apparently they have Durham
blood in them; but having been long here, and bred from
very old cows, they are called the true Lincoln breed, and
may be pure for what I know; supposing these breeds
are not originally the same, which there is great reason
to believe they are. These cows would any where be
esteemed well formed beasts: they are wide on the hips
and loin, have good quarters, clean light bones, thin horns
light

light dewlap, neat throats, and pretty full in the bosom, with middling spring of rib; and at the same time they shew good milk veins."

P. 291. " Several black and white cows of Mr. Tyndall's breed seem to class high for cleanness of leg, throat, and horns; very neat; with light offals."

P. 292. " Mr. Hoyte of Osbornby, is in the same breed as Mr. Tyndall, having had cattle from him; also in the dun French*."

P. 293. " Viewed Mr. Hough's cattle of Threckingham, amongst which there is nothing comes up to the dun breed, or French ones; in 1789 he killed an ox of this breed that weighed 116½ stone, at seven years old, and measured 2 feet 7 inches from the outside of one hip to the outside of the other; and he has now a three year old cream-coloured heifer of that breed, but with a small cross of the Alderney in her, which is remarkably wide, and feels vastly more kindly and mellow than any Lincoln beast I have yet handled. This dun breed of cattle was introduced above twenty years ago, by Sir Charles Buck from France; they were not originally larger than Alderneys, but they have improved here so much in size, that they are now nearly, if not quite, as large as the more common sorts of the country."

Admitting this to be the true state of the case, and without any admixture of Lincolnshire blood, the fact is interesting; as showing in a striking light, the effect of soil and management, and perhaps *climature*, on this species of domestic animals.

Regarding the controversial cabals of bullmen and others, about the superiority of " short horns" and " long horns," which fill no inconsiderable part of the section, " Cattle,"— I find nothing that is in the least entitled to insertion, here.— In the Reporter's opinion,—*the short horns have it.* His decision is as follows.

P. 303. " I have very little to observe upon the preceding notes · it is evident that the Lincoln breed of cattle, upon Lincoln pastures, are profitable; and it appears

---

" * In the vicinity of Folkingham, a dun coloured breed of beast has of late years been much attended to by several graziers, and though they may not equal Mr. Tyndall's, &c. in size, or symmetry of shape, yet their propensity to feed renders them a valuable acquisition to the grazier ; they are said to have been originally brought from the Isle of *Alderney* near the coast of France, by the late Sir Charles Buck, Bart. of Hanby-Grange.— *MS of the B.*"

pears evident, from the general colour of the comparison made with the long horned breed from Leicestershire that their own short horns are superior."

It is to be remarked, that, if " their own short horns" are superior to the improved long horns of the midland Counties (with which the comparison appears to have been made)—that is to say, if the very worst of the short horned breed be preferable to the very best of the long horned breed, how greatly superior must the " short horns" of Northumberland, Durham, and Yorkshire be, to the ordinary varieties of long horned cattle.—The *northern*, no the *eastern* department, is that in which to speak of short horned cattle. In that, most probably, they originated and in that they have, of late years, been raised to a high degree of excellence.

On the *size* of cattle, abstractly considered, we perceive a few incidental remarks, in the Report under review; and lest, in these *showing* times, the minds of well meaning practical men should be staggered with the immensity of *bulk*, and the honor and profit that have been bestowed on individuals of that description, I will here register a few of those remarks; tho somewhat contradictory.

P. 289. (Mr. Cartwright) " My observations upon stock have strongly persuaded me, that the preference so generally given to *great size* in feeding cattle, is a radical error and that magnitude becomes a defect instead of a perfection, much sooner than graziers are aware of. The perfections of the animal seem to lie in a healthy constitution ; a disposition to feed rapidly *at any age;* a capacity of fattening upon land *more or less rich by many degrees,* in proportion to the value of such land; light offal; the most delicate in grain and flavour; and most abundant meat on the most valuable parts. Although *shape* will be found essential to much of this merit, *great magnitude* can scarcely be supposed necessary to any of it."

P. 295. (Mr. Thorp)—" is of opinion, from very considerable experience, and speaking of grazing in general, both summer and winter, that middling sized beasts will pay better than large ones; for instance, two of 50 stone will answer better than one of 100; they do not take so much food to bring them to their weight; and will do on worse pasture "

P. 296. (Mr. Dalton)—" is of opinion, in relation to the size of fatting animals, that an ox of 80 or 85 stone will not eat more than one of 50, and his bailiff thinks he will not eat so much."

2. *Breed.*

2. *Breeding* and *rearing* cattle.—P. 292. " The system
of breeding pursued by Mr. Tyndall, is to keep all his
calves; they run with the cows all summer; but many
cows have two, and to let the other added have a fair
chance, as well as her own, they are coupled together till
the cow admits both equally; this leaves a few in milk for
a small dairy; for butter and cheese are no objects in this
country; cows seem to be kept chiefly for the sake of
breeding; and by this means the calves are pushed on for
size as the material object. In winter as well as summer,
all run in the pastures, only they have hay given occasionally, according to weather; and the cows straw in the
yards. Oxen sold fat generally at $4\frac{1}{2}$ years old; but they
pay well when kept to $5\frac{1}{2}$. His bulls leap at 5s. a cow."

P. 296. " About Normanby, Burton, &c. it is a great
breeding country: they wish some of their cows to calve
the latter end of the year, in October or November; then
they let them run with the cow all winter, in the fields
generally; but this is only in singular cases; and are fond
of autumn calves; but in general the calving time is in
spring; suck ten or twelve days, then weaned; what butter
they make goes to Hull; but in general breeding the
calves is the great object; dairy no where the first aim.
Suck a great while; by this means the dairy is sacrificed
to the breeding; when they wean, they do it with por-
ridge; they sell fat at six years old; heifers at three years
spayed."

P. 297. " Mr. Skipwith breeds many calves, and the
cows suckle 3 calves, kept in house, and even 5 to a cow;
buys calves for this purpose.

" Mr. Uppleby of Barrow rears many calves, some run
with the cows coupled together: and a cow will bring up
four in the summer: has known more. Others he brings
up by rearing at about six weeks, and gives first new, then
skim milk." What barbarous language!—And how inexplicit the information, it is intended to convey.—So extraordinary a practice ought to have been minutely explained. As it stands, it can only serve to raise doubts,
in the minds of many readers, as to its authenticity.

Same page.—" Mr. Lloyd of Belesby, has 100 head of
horned cattle in all, breeding 20 calves a year; he keeps
all his labourers' cows, and buys their calves, milking only
four or 5 himself. Sells at four years old fat; and spays
about half the heifers."

3. The *Dairy*, as I have said, is not an *object*, in Lincolnshire. The Reporter has therefore been, in a manner,
                                                silent,

silent, on this subject. The subjoined passages are all
that I have found concerning it.

P. 293. " Uncommon as dairies are in general, it is not
universal; Mr. Grundy of Heath Hall near Grantham, has
40 cows for making cheese, which he manufactures of various sorts, and with much success."—This, however, is in
the *midland*, rather than in the *eastern*, department.

P. 294. " The Rev. Dr. Ellis here informed me of a
Lincoln cow, that was in the possession of the Rev. Mr.
Hecket of Beckingham near Newark, that produced 19 lb.
of butter in one week; but at Leadenham 6, 7, or 8 lb. are
common for good ones."

P. 296. " At Haxey in the Isle of Axeholm, they have
an odd way of ladling the milk when it comes from the
cow, till it is cold, before they *set* it for cream. Experiments of comparison should be tried, to see if they are
right in this, or if wrong, in what degree. Mrs. Lambe,
I hope, will try it carefully."

How ill initiated, must this Reporter be, in the mysteries of the Dairy. No good dairywoman " sets" he
milk for cream, *in summer*, until it be reduced to a certain temperature. If it has not acquired the desired degree of coolness, before she is ready to place it in her
creaming utensils, (or before the cream is beginning to
rise) she of course lades it; to bring it down, more readily,
to that temperature;—as well as to prevent the cream
from separating, before the milk can be conveniently
" set," at the proper degree of coolness.

4. *Fatting* cattle, in Lincolnshire.—This, as might be
imagined, is chiefly *field* fatting, or " grazing;" altho, as
will be seen, some *stall* fatting is done: indeed, much
more (judging from this Report) than one could, priorly,
have imagined; especially in the waterland districts;—
where the great art of husbandry would seem to lie in
damping the too great fertility of the soil; rather than in
adding to it, by manures.

The following heterogeneous memoranda will serve to
give some idea (a very imperfect one it is true) of the
practice of the County, in this very important part of its
rural management.—It is with some reluctance, I think it
prudent to say, that I give them a place, in this register.

P. 288. " All round Spalding there are many good
bullocks grazed, and in Deeping Fen also; they give from
14 *l.* to 20 *l.* a head; keep them in winter in stable, on
cake at 9 *l.* per 1000; making no more than the manure.

" Lincoln oxen about Boston, 60 or 90 stone, 14 lb.
                                                    they

they are kept on some lands a bullock an acre, on others
2 to 3 acres: on others, 1 on 2 acres, all besides sheep.
A bullock and 6 sheep to 1½ acre not uncommon.

"About Swineshead, the grazing lands fed with bullocks and sheep; the former bought in at Boston fair, 4th
May; and at Lincoln, in April."

P. 296. "At Knaith, where the pasture is not of the
first quality, Mr. Dalton has fatted Teeswater beasts to
130 stone, at seven years old, and gave only half a ton of
cake to each. He prefers this breed to any other he has tried.
His beasts of 80 stone will be fat at five years from grass,
without any cake; and his regular return is seven a year,
at four years old."

P. 301. "Mr. Ellison at Sudbrook, buys in about 30
bullocks annually; from April to Midsummer puts to
grass till a fortnight after old Michaelmas; then puts them
part in stalls, and part remains in grass till near Christmas.
In the stalls, feeds with cake and hay; they eat about 2½
cakes a day, at 7 lb. each, and about half a ton of hay each
beast; and are up about 10 weeks, some 12."

P. 302. "Mr. Moody of Riseholm fats many beasts upon
oilcake, even as far as buying 100 tons of cake in a year.
He keeps them loose in a straw yard, and finds they do
well without any hay, giving straw only in addition; and
has sold beasts thus fed at 40 guineas."

This is to me a new practice. In an upland situation,
where straw is plentiful and hay not to be had, it may
answer. It has simplicity, at least, in its favor. The situation of Riseholm the reader is left to conjecture.

SHEEP.—If it was irksome to get through one sheet of
uninteresting, and, to the public, unprofitable, detail of
the conjectures, thinkings, opinions, and conversational
assertions of bull-breeders and their followers,—as to the
superiority of the short or the long horned breed of cattle,
—how much more intolerable must have been the labor of
wading through four sheets and a half! almost wholely
filled with similar details, about "*Lincoln*," and "*Leicester*," breeds of sheep,—at the particular juncture of time,
when the Board's Secretary happened to take his tour
through the county.

Such a detail, circulated in a periodical publication,
might have afforded conversation—have been food for
table talk—among fashionable breeders, for a few weeks,
or days, and have been thrown aside and forgotten, in as
many more. But it surely could not be suitable matter
to be entered on the Journals of a public Board,—as a
                                                    State

State Paper; as a document for a doomsday book!—A remark, this, by the way, which might be fairly applied to the major part of the volume under Review;—but most especially as it relates to livestock; on which we find little more than the gossipings of men of many minds, about the *strange breeds, crosses,* and *favorites* of the day :—with a croud of prices,—as variable as the wind,—and ephemeral opinions, which if carefully weighed, even while buzzing out their hour, would either be found *wanting,* or nearly balancing each other.

In reviewing Mr. Stone's Report, p. 62, I have spoken my sentiments, pretty fully, tho not in many words, concerning these controversial points,—so importunately, and officiously, pushed forward, by interested individuals :—as if the whole art and science of agriculture was dependent upon them!—were even the thousands of "facts," adduced by this Reporter, on the point now more particularly in view, mathematically demonstrated, they could be of little, if any, use to the public. On the contrary, they might be capable of doing irreparable injury to the community; —by inducing the breeders of Lincolnshire, and other *long*-wooled-sheep counties, to view the two breeds, indiscriminately; or without any other distinction than what is contained in their " *blood !*"—and thus, by contending about " flesh" and " fatting quality," *only,* the breeders of Lincolnshire may lose sight of, and thereby suffer to be deteriorated (for a length of time, or for ever!) the more essential produce of sheep—their WOOL.

I will, therefore, here repeat, the anathema which I extemporaneously pronounced, aforegoing.—Woe be to him who shall attempt to level all distinctions;—whether among wool-bearing animals, or among the animals that wear their fleeces, and require them to be of different qualities,—to correspond with the different conditions of society.

Regarding the general mass of information, relating to this controversial point, as it appears on the numerou pages of the Report under review, I have only to declare that I would as patiently listen to the speeches, arguments, disputes, and bickerings, of the candidates, and their partizans, at a contested election, as I would, *at that time,* have seriously attended to the speeches, arguments, disputes, and bickerings, of tupmen and their talking followers.—While the rage of contest lasts, whether about two rival breeds of cattle or sheep, or two rival candidate

for

for a seat in parliament,—not a syllable can be safely trusted.*

In registering the few particulars that appear to me to be entitled to the attention of the public, at the *present time*, and in *time to come*,—I will observe the principle of classification pursued, in the foregoing article, *Cattle*.

Previously, however, I will present my readers, with a concise, yet luminous, account of the GENERAL ECONOMY of the SHEEP HUSBANDRY, in the COUNTY of LINCOLN. It contains, in a few lines, more useful information—more *instruction*—than fifty pages of unconnected conversational " Facts."

P. 341. " Sir Joseph Banks, on the sheep system of this county, gave me a general hint (!) extremely to the purpose.

" As tups are always hired in Lincolnshire by the breeders, the lambs may be said to be purchased before they are born ; as a year's credit, however, is given on this occasion, they are not paid for till the actual value can be fairly estimated ; if, therefore, any one who has hired a tup at a considerable price, finds the lambs he has got not sufficiently above the ordinary sort to pay him the difference, with interest, he complains to the tup-man, who generally views the lambs with him, and makes a fair abatement, which is generally settled in the price of the hire of the next year's tup ; this regulates the price of letting, and makes the tup-men a most useful set of people. The great mass of breeders in Lincolnshire sell their heeder-lambs about old Michaelmas time, or a little after ;

---

* I had marked, for extraction, a sort of index, or LIST of VOTERS, *for* and *against* these two rival candidates. But unless the QUALIFICATIONS of those voters, and their several INTERESTS in the contest, had been fully and faithfully declared, it could have been of no real use, whatever to the public.—Indeed, the Reporter, himself, would seem to have been aware of this.

P. 364. " To draw this great variety of miscellaneous information into some degree of order, upon the heads which are most interesting, is not an easy task ; and I shall not attempt it, without cautioning the reader against passing over the minutes themselves, and looking only at the following extracts, which will contain merely the most prominent features of certain objects. When a question of comparison is so warmly agitated as that of the new Leicester, with the Lincoln breed of sheep in this county, the private interest, prejudice, and habits of mankind, are strongly in the way of pure and genuine authority. The careful reader, who examines with a view only to truth, cannot be too much on his guard."—Why, then, bestow so much time *unprofitably*;—I mean, as to the *public*.

after; a succession of fairs for that purpose are held in a village called Partney. These lambs are resold in the spring at Lincoln fair, under the name of hogs; at Midsummer their owners clip, and then winter them; the succeeding spring, they are carried to Boston, where, in a long succession of markets, they are sold to the graziers, with their wool on, under the name of shearlings, and immediately turned into the marsh to fatten; the graziers take their fleeces, and having wintered them, get the kindliest to Smithfield in the course of the succeeding spring; those that do not fat so easily, yield the grazier a fleece at Midsummer, and are got off the ground in the course of the next autumn."

1. BREED.—P. 334. "An observation I made was," (at Partney fair) "that in a very full fair for lambs, there was very little Leicester blood *clearly apparent.*"—Is not this circumstantial evidence, nearly amounting to a proof, (after what appears in the last extract) that the Leicestershire breed was, then, chiefly confined, in Lincolnshire, to a comparatively few fashionable breeders?

P. 337. " At Boothby, at the Rev. Mr. Wall's, I was on a sort of classic ground, for here were first reared that breed of true Lincoln sheep which afterwards became so famous in the County, under the names both of Mr. Wall (uncle to the present proprietor) and Mr. Chaplin, and which are now in the hands of Mr. Hyde of Tathwell; there are some very good tups here at present of the same breed."

In a sort of retrospect of the detail, about those rival breeds of sheep, the Reporter gives (with a degree of coyness) his opinion, on the matter.—P. 371. "A clear distinction is to be drawn between the rich south-eastern district and inferior soils; for upon the former the information is strong in favour of Lincoln.

" In general I should observe, that the new Leicester, are spreading very rapidly over the County; probably faster than they have done in any other, one or two only excepted, which may be attributed to the general goodness of the soil; for this breed makes a much more respectable figure than it has done in various trials made in countries inferior to it in soil; and the breed driving out the Lincoln so much as it has done in the poorer parts of this County, is a fact that unites with this circumstance. The true Lincoln is a larger sheep, and with a longer wool, and therefore demands better pasturage; where it finds such, *there* the old breed remains; subject, perhaps, to little more change than *fashion* may cause. Upon
inferior

inferior land the Leicester establishes itself; and upon
land still inferior in other Counties, experiments prove
unsuccessful for the same reason; that of the necessity of
having a smaller size and shorter wool."

Now, this is adopting the principles I laid down, in the
Rural Economy of the Midland Counties, in 1790; and
is, in substance, what I have said, aforegoing, p. 63; before, it is proper to say, I had read a line of the Secretary's
Report; and of course before I had seen the passage above
quoted.

How could the Secretary of the Board of Agriculture,
possessing those sentiments, not only listen to the silly arguments of contending tupmen, but take down, and
publish! their interested and mischievous effusions.—
Ought he not, rather, as the servant of the public, to have
endeavoured to counteract the evil tendency of their proceedings; and to have explained to the breeders of Lincolnshire, that the two breeds are both good in their kind;
that the best of the Leicestershire are proper for their
vale lands, or upper grounds, and the best of their own
long established breed, (if, after the operations of *fashion*,
as has been before intimated, a genuine remain of it be
left!!!) for their richer lower grounds; and to have urged
it, to the marshland farmers, in the most strenuous manner, to improve their own breed,—as a *distinct variety*,
that is *essential* to the perfection of the WOOLEN MANU-
FACTURE of this kingdom?*

But instead of pursuing this rational line of conduct, we
find the Secretary entering into the gossiping disputes of
tupmen; as a *warm friend* of the " Leicesters."—Take the
following as a favorable specimen of those entertaining
" discourses."

P. 321. " Calling on Mr. Edlington at Cadney to view
his Lincoln breed of sheep, having been often informed
that he held the new Leicester as a breed much inferior;
I was informed by a butcher who happened to be there,
that Mr. Euston at Manby near Brig, sold 40 two-shear
Lincolns of pure blood, in June, as soon as clipped, half
at 2*l*. 12*s*. 6*d*.; and the other twenty in August, 3*l*. each;
which was mentioned as a proof that the old Lincoln
would come to a great value at an early age. Mr. Edlington has bred his flock by hiring tups from the men
supposed to have the pure Lincoln blood, such as Mr.
Onnley

---

* More of this, under the head *Wool*, ensuing.

Onnley and Mr. Dun of Holdernesse, Mr. Preston by
Louth, Mr. Chaplin at Tathwell, and Mr. Johnson of
Kermond. He sells at two and at three shear; two shear
as soon as clipped as high as 50s. ; three shear, to 3l. 3s. ;
these prices for a few; but in general two shears at 42s,
with some three shears among them. For wool, he runs,
at an average, three to a tod ; some two, some three, and
a few four. He informed me, that Mr. Johnson at Kermond, kills at both Castor and Lincoln, and beats the new
Leicester in weight at the same age. He complains of
Mr. Bakewell buying of him the ugliest, worst Lincoln
tup he had at the time, and shewing it as a sight at Dish-
ley. This anecdote, however, proves that Mr. Bakewell
considered this as a good shop to get Lincoln blood *for*
his purpose. It cuts both ways; if it is said, that Mr.
Bakewell would go on such an errand, where he could
find the worst; then it may be replied, that if the worst
will do, what is here noted, what would the best come to ?
Having examined the tups, and adjourned to Mr. Edlington's tankard, and discoursing on the two breeds, he
dropped the observation, that if he bred for feeding only,
and let no tups, he would have *a little touch* of the Leicester.—How so, Sir, when Lincoln will come to such prices
at such an age?—*Why, they will feed a little bit quicker,*
and run a little bit thicker. If this is so, he is breeding
sheep to answer some purpose not well understood by
those who hire them. But I must suspect, from the countenance of some of his lambs, that he has, some how or
other, already got *a touch* of the Leicester."

2. *Breeding*.—Of the sizes of breeding flocks, we have
no direct account. In p. 318, stands the following insulated notice.

" Mr. Skipwith of Allerby tups 1400 ewes."

And in p. 330, we are informed, that the flock of Mr.
Brown of Dalby—"one of the most distinguished tup
breeders"—is 900 breeding ewes.

Other such notices might probably be *found*, if diligently
searched for.

Rams.—Great numbers, it would seem, are let.—In
p. 320, is this entry.—Itself an unsupported paragraph.

" Mr. Skipwith 1000 guineas this year, by rams."

Breeding Ewes.—P. 308. " In Holland Fen, generally
rear a lamb or something more to every ewe."

Management of Sheep.—The subjoined passage is worth
a series of pages, on either hand of it.—P. 310. (Mr
Tyndall) " This gentleman observed an article of management

nagement to me, which, though it may be well known here, is not generally so elsewhere; that in weaning lambs, they should not be drawn off from the sheep, but the sheep drawn off from them; by being left in the pasture they are more quiet, not apt to be equally disturbed, and generally do better."

The following practical hint is also worthy of a place, here.—Every shepherd of longwooled sheep ought to teach his dogs to perform this valuable service.—P. 329. "Much attention is necessary when heavy in wool, as the sheep are often found on their backs, and if not soon relieved, die. This is called *far wel tard*, or *lifting*, and they have dogs that will turn them. With Mr. Neve, in travelling to Alford, a dog of this sort *lifted* 21 sheep in the way."

For a suggestion that the less sheep are changed, the better,—see the head, *Grazing*, p. 173, aforegoing.

Shepherd's Perquisites.—The following regulation is grounded in wisdom.—P. 334. " Shepherd paid 12s. a week, a house, and 4 or 5 acres of land, and summering 2 cows; besides a few trifling perquisites, particularly 6d. allowed for every pair of lambs reared to Mayday. Many farmers allow the lambskins; but this, for obvious reasons, much better."

Diseases of Sheep.—The Secretary's industry has led him to put down (in different parts of his volume) several particulars relating to this highly important topic. But little, if any thing, useful is to be learnt from them.— What relates to the " respe," and the rot, alone, is entitled to notice, here.—And the information, even respecting the "respe," is somewhat contradictory.

P. 329. " The *respe*; probably the red water, not peculiar to sheep feeding on cole or turnips; for they have it on grass feeding in the spring, when thriving fast."

P. 374. " *Respe*—In hoggets; when dead, the flesh all rotten and putrid; it arises from being forced on cole."

P. 375. " In Holland Fen the *respe* is a fatal malady among sheep fed on cole; the loss has often amounted to 15 per cent. and particularly in very luxuriant crops, on fresh land; the best sheep die first. To prevent it, they drive them in the night, and some for a few hours in the middle of the day, to another field; Mr. Cartwright, after losing many, tried this, and lost no more. It is good, when this is not done, to *raise* them in the night; the shepherd goes into the field to disturb, and make them stale; the cole supposed to have a narcotic quality. All

sorts

sorts and ages subject to this distemper.   No losses but in cole ; the grass lands quite healthy.

"September 20th, 1796, observation by Mr. Gentle Brown of Lincoln, that putting a large lot of lambs upon cole, was told he should have great loss ; but by bleeding in the roof of the mouth before they went in, and once every three weeks afterwards, giving a large wine glass of strong salt and water, he escaped without losing a single lamb.   The cole was upon his fen land, which he described to be of a black peaty quality."

P. 376.   "The *respe* has also made considerable ravages ; Mr. Graburn has prevented it by giving, while on turnips, clover or sainfoin hay, which has prevented it ; turnips alone are too watery, and dry food is useful."

Same page.   "Mr. Hall from Yorkshire, has been informed, that antimony and brimstone in equal quantities, mixed up with treacle, is a preservative from the respe."

Quere, is this fatal disorder of a similar nature to the "Braxey" of Scotland,—the "Blackwater" of Yorkshire, the "Fellin" of Devonshire, and the "Blood" of other districts?

Rot.—Mr. Grayburn's discovery of live flukes, on water cresses, is not probable.—The subjoined remarks are entitled to more attention.

P. 329.   "The *rot ;* very little here; in rotten years, the sheep that feed on the salt marsh, over which the spring tides come, sell very high, in confidence that they are safe.   Upon this disorder it well deserves noting, that a shepherd, who when young was shepherd's boy to an old man who lived at Netlam near Lincoln, a place famous for the rot, told Mr. Neve, that he was persuaded sheep took the rot only of a morning before the dew was well off. At that time they folded, being open field; his master's shepherd kept his flock in fold always till the dew was gone, and with no other attention his sheep were kept sound, when all the neighbours lost their flocks."— Keeping sheep, in "cots," until the dew be gone off, has, probably, a similar effect.   See my GLOCESTERSHIRE.

Folding.—P. 374.   "This is dispatched in a few words. —I never saw a fold in the County, except in a few open fields near Stamford, nor heard of its having been practised, except in a trial made by Mr. Wright of Riseholm." —Without success.—" In the open fields near Stamford, there are yet some folds remaining ; but the sheep are miserably bad; in wool 8 or 9 to a tod."—What better could be expected, from *folding long wooled sheep !* either

upon

upon a fallow, or in a turnep field, in wet weather,—or during a thaw!

3. Fatting Sheep.—On this very interesting particular, in the Lincolnshire husbandry, we have nothing resembling a readable account.

Procuring Stock.—In this important part of the business of grazing, no explicit information (saving what is contained in the "hint," transcribed aforegoing, p. 185,) is discoverable;—excepting what is conveyed in the subjoined line.—P 337. "In the hundred of Skirbeck they breed two-thirds of what is fed in the district."

Materials of Fatting.—Beside the natural and abundant material of Lincolnshire, grass,—the following additions are in use.

Sowthistles.—P. 306. "Mr. Charles Trimmell of Bicker, killed a wether of 67 lb. a quarter, four years old; never had any cake, but was made up with sow-thistles for two or three months."—"He never ate any corn, oilcake, &c. but fed wholly upon grass and herbage; being turned, with many other sheep, into a field of clover, this sheep was observed first to search for all the sow thistles, and would eat no other food whilst any of them could be found in the part of the field that was hurdled off successively, a little at a time. A kind of hut was erected for him in the field to repose under in hot weather; and when the part that was hurdled off became bare of food, the shepherd, being guided by his propensity for sow thistles, gathered a quantity for him, at stated hours, three times a day, from 2 to 5 lb. at a meal."

Oil Cakes, at Turneps.—P. 317. "H. Dalton, Esq. at Knaith"—"has given wethers oil cake while on turnips, 1 lb. each *per diem*. They did well, and fed more profitably than they would have done on turnips alone.

"Whenever sheep have cake given them in this part of the County, it is in troughs in the turnip field."

Oil Cakes, at Grass.—P. 353. "Mr. Ellison of Sudbrook has practiced giving cake to sheep for eight years."—P. 354. "This time two years, he put 61 of his own bred hogs (new Leicester cross, one-third that blood) to cole about old Michaelmas, kept them till Christmas, then to grass which had been hained for them, giving cake as soon as to grass; kept them till the middle of February, and sold 60 at 3l. 15s. each, being only shearlings. They weighed upon an average 26 lb. a quarter; the fleece was worth 8s.; they tallowed well. Breaks the cake at first to the size of beans, afterwards of walnuts; but takes care the

the troughs are covered, as rain makes the cake pasty, and it is then wasted. The effect of feeding thus, to the land is very great indeed; he has advanced grass from 12s. an acre to be worth 27s. by six years' feeding in the manner and time abovementioned, 4 to an acre. The troughs are kept moving; best to do this every morning."

For rape, as an article of fatting for sheep, see that head, p. 152, aforegoing.

In the subjoined extract may be caught a general view of sheep grazing, in the rich lowland district of Boston.— P. 346. "Mr. Thomas Tannard of Frampton, near Boston, is one of the greatest graziers in Lincolnshire, he feeds above 100 oxen, and clips 1400 sheep; his growth is 600 tod of wool; but this year 1852 fleeces gave 768 tod; and his capital per acre may be estimated at 30l.; some years it will be less. His opinion is decidedly in favour of the true Lincoln sheep, which he sells at three-shear at 3l. 10s. and to 4l. a head. He has about three sheep per acre in summer and two in winter on his land. One superiority of the Lincoln breed which he remarked, was that they travel much better to London; and as to keeping more Leicesters than Lincolns on the same land, he observes that he has had both, and keeps as many of one as of the other."

Regarding the Reporter's retrospective remarks, on " Feeding," I have only to observe that, how far they may be interesting to the political arithmetician, it might be wrong to stop, here, to consider; but, respecting their value to the Rural Economist, this is the proper place to speak.

After listing a few " facts," in the shape of miscellaneous memoranda, the Reporter inserts a table, to show the progressively encreasing value of sheep, every six months,—from the time they are dropped, until they be sold,—(p. 373.)—The " increase by each 6 months" comes out thus :—the lambs, at six months old, are set down as being worth 17s.—The increase of value, the next six months,—a *winter half year*,—4s.—The next,—a *summer* half year,—4s —The next,—a *winter* half year,—14s. !— The next,—a *summer* half year,—2s. !—The last, a *winter* half year,—19s.—The sheep being, then, three years old.

To what purpose (I cannot refrain from asking) can such " facts," or a result drawn from "facts" so glaringly improbable, be applied, even by the " political arithmetician,"—either singly, or jointly with other simi-

lar

lar " facts,"—unless to deceive himself and his readers?
—and the inference drawn,—from the sum of information
gained in this tour,—for the guidance of the Rural
Economist,—has a still more harmful tendency.

P. 373 " It is sufficiently evident from this table, that
to keep breeding ewes, where the lambs will sell at 17s. is
more profitable than any other sheep system, supposing
the land be proper for the stock ; 7s. for the ewe's
fleece makes this 24s. per head for half the flock, the other
half producing ewe lambs, do not pay equally ; but let the
average be reduced to 20s. still it is far better than any
other system here noted, as, admitting the 19s. for the last
column, yet it is not to be attained without passing through
the periods which answer so much worse than any others ;
and though both ewe and lamb are to be well kept for six
months, yet the ewe is kept at a moderate expence the
other six ; whereas fatting sheep must be favoured in
food."

Lincolnshire, of all the counties of the kingdom, was
the last in which to propagate (directly or indirectly) such
impracticable doctrine.—Were the rich grazing lands of
that county, to be appropriated to the *breeding* of lambs,
—where would be found markets for them? and where
could they be *reared* and *fatted?* " O ! on cake and turneps."—Where could the cake be had? and where the
turneps,—after those of the upland turnep-soil districts
had been expended on, or reserved for, the *breeding
flocks?*

The *markets* for fat sheep, in Lincolnshire do not appear, in this Report ; unless in the " hint," aforemen-
tioned.

For an ingenious mode of conveying sheep to market,
by the means of *canals,* see that head, aforegoing.

WOOL.—P. 305. " It will not keep more than a year
without some damage."

P. 306. " Mr. Graves of Spalding has kept wool four
years, and lost nothing, neither by waste nor moth ; but
next the tiles. It will not do on a ground floor."

P. 313. " The following is a series of the prices of wool
per tod of 28 lb. sold from one farm near Folkingham in
this county, from A. D. 1758, to 1794.

Date.

Date.	Price.			Date.	Price.		
	£.	s.	d.		£.	s.	d.
1758	1	0	0	1777	0	18	6
1759	1	0	0	1778	0	14	6
1760	0	19	0	1779	0	12	0
1761	0	16	0	1780	0	12	6
1762	0	17	0	1781	0	12	0
1763	0	18	9	1782	0	11	0
1764	0	19	6	1783	0	14	0
1765	1	0	0	1784	0	15	6
1766	1	1	6	1785	0	13	0
1767	0	17	6	1786	0	16	6
1768	0	15	0	1787	0	17	0
1769	0	15	0	1788	0	17	0
1770	0	14	6	1789	0	18	6
1771	0	15	0	1790	0	18	6
1772	0	15	0	1791	1	0	0
1773	0	15	6	1792*	1	3	6
1774	0	18	0	1793	0	17	0
1775	0	17	6	1794	0	18	0"
1776	0	17	6				

P. 330. " It is observed in the Marsh, that nothin
makes wool grow so fast as feeding upon oilcake."

P. 346. " Mr. Thomas Tannard of Frampton, near Bos
ton, favoured me with some particulars of the progress
prices, which well deserve minuting.   He has a manuscrip
note of the year 1716, which runs thus.—' In the year 171
my father sold 366 tod of wool to John Aggs, at 22s. 9
per tod; and in 1717, 367 tods, at 27s. and one guine
over; and in 1718, 373 tods, at 27s. and a guinea.' "

In p. 366, a table of the weights of fleeces, as minute
in different parts of the County, is given; the average
which comes out as follows :—Of the Lincoln fleeces, 10 l
—of the Leicester fleeces, 7⅘ lb.—of the County, 9 lb.

Th

" * In this year the same sort of wool was sold as high as 27s. p
tod ; a price that wool of that description was never sold at since th
year 1728, when, by reason of a very extraordinary rot amongst th
sheep (in two preceding years), it was sold at 30s.   This informatio
I had from the late Mr. Metheringham of Spanby, county of Lincol
who died last summer at the great age of near 100 years, and retaine
his faculties in a wonderful degree to the last.

                                      Mr. Cragg, MS. of the B.

The Reporter observes, p. 367, " Upon the very remarkable *facts*, that the whole County carries a sheep and
half per acre, at 9 lb. per fleece, I may observe, that *if this
is true*, or *near the truth*, it is probably stocked far beyond
any other in the kingdom."—Here, I have only to remark,
we have the true modern perversion of the term " facts."
See p. 146, aforegoing.

The general remark that I have to make, on the wool of
Lincolnshire, relates to the encoragement which I conceive
ought to be given to it, as the material of the WORSTED
MANUFACTURE. In this Report, we have little or nothing
of its length of staple, or fineness of hair or pile :—the
weight of the fleece, and the price it bore, at the juncture
of time, when the tour in Lincolnshire happened to be undertaken (without any regard to its specific quality,)—is
what incessantly occurs, and fills up page, after page,
without any other apparent view, than as data wherewith
to calculate the grower's profit!

Commendable, and highly praise-worthy, have been the
efforts and perseverance that have been successfully employed, in promoting the growth of *fine wool*, for the manufacture of " superfine cloths,"—for the comfort and ornament of *men's* persons ;—and now would seem to be the
time, to pay a similar or more anxious attention, to the
ornament, comfort, and personal safety of the more amiable sex ;—a greater number of whom, it is probable, have
been sacrificed to foreign commerce, and a want of due
attention being paid to an indigenous material of manufacture, in England, than have ever been, in a similar
period of time, to the infatuate rites of India.—A fashion
for superfine stuffs has gone forth ; and now is the time,
if the sun of chivalry has not set, for every man, who has
it in his power, to encorage it, by the growth of combing
wool of the finest pile and staple ;—such as will bear
spinning to the extraordinary degree of fineness (if possible) mentioned, aforegoing, in the admirable and most
audible effort of MISS IVES,—see p. 89.

Lincolnshire is doubtlessly the scene in which this
greatly to be desired improvement can be most favorably
carried on. And no one can be so fit to plan, at least,
such an improvement, as he who has been the most instrumental in promoting the growth of FINE CARDING WOOL, in
England, and who possesses such ample means of promoting the growth of FINE COMBING WOOL, in Lincolnshire.

RABBITS.

RABBITS.—Relating to this minor species of livestock, the Secretary of the Board has furnished a succession of pages ; beside some scattered remarks, found under other heads. But as he appears to have entered the County, heavily burdened with prejudices against them (" Leicester sheep" being then the rage) the less regard is to be paid to his strictures. These prejudices are sufficiently apparent, in the subjoined extracts.—His calculations and remarks, concerning Mr. Holgait's practice and " conversation" (p. 394) are too *wild* for insertion, here.

P. 206. Speaking of the mischiefs occasioned by plowing up the old sheep walks of the Wolds (see plan of management, p. 141, aforegoing) he concludes his remarks, by adding,—" Warrens join in some places, which account for it partly ; they are rarely met with, without seeming to have an ill effect on the minds and conduct of all around."

P. 388. " Mr. Ansell was of *opinion*, that lately his warren lands would have paid him better had they been applied to the purpose of growing corn and grass seeds for keeping sheep. The rabbit produce he *supposed* to be from eight to ten shillings ; in some particular years they have paid from 15s. to 21s. an acre ; but to obtain any extraordinary profit, very great care must be taken in killing the many different kinds of vermin which depredate, and without the utmost vigilance will quite depopulate the warrens. A considerable expence also attends the necessity there is for night-watchers to protect them from the infinitely worse vermin, the poachers."

On the *nature* of rabbits, we find the following curious particulars.—P. 382. " A rabbit goes to buck the day she brings forth her young, as well known. She goes thirty one days with young, which are eleven days blind after being born, and eleven more before they appear above ground. She suckles them twice a day for about twenty-two days.

" A buck serves 100 does.

" Stock upon a good acre 200 couple.

" Winter food,—ash boughs, gorse, hay, turnips.

" From Louth to Castor, 18 miles ; 10 of it are warrens chiefly silvers ; rent 2s. to 3s. an acre.

" They plough a part every year for corn and turnips and laying down again with seeds, let down the fences for the rabbits to enter. Warrens are reckoned profitable, s that some fortunes have been made on them.

" In point of skins, those bred about Mayday undergo n
chang

change from their white colour, but from a *white rack* become a whole skin. Bred at Ladyday, become black. In June, white. In July, black. In November, white again; then in full season, as the carcasses are also. The skins ought to have those colours on the inside when dead."

A faint trait of the *history* of rabbit warrens, in Lincolnshire, may be caught in the following notice.—P. 225. " Forty years ago it was all warren for thirty miles from Spilsby to beyond Caistor; and by means of turnips and seeds, there are now at least twenty sheep kept to one there before."

Regarding the *present practice*, let the subjoined intelligent entry *(found* in the Chapter, " Wastes") suffice.— P. 224. " At Blankney and its vicinity Mr. Chaplin has 3 or 4000 acres of warrens let, at the highest, at 3*s.* 6*d.* an acre, some at 2*s.* ; the warreners have permission to plough part, keeping it in tillage for some crops, and then laying it down again for rabbits. In this management they inclose with walls, and pare and burn for turnips ; after which they sow barley, then turnips again, and a second crop of barley with seeds, for rabbits ; this system may extend to taking in, in this manner, fifty or sixty acres every year in 1000."

I have only to remark, in moderation of this writer's prejudices, against the species of farm stock under notice, that there are not many districts, or passages, of this kingdom that are well adapted to rabbit warrens, and that, to a large portion of these few,—rabbits are unknown in a state of warren.—Are rabbits, as an article of food, or their skins, as a material of manufacture, requisite to the present state of society, in this country ? If they are, let them be propagated on the particular lands to which they are best adapted.

For a circumstantial " printed" detail* of the general economy and management of rabbit warrens, and the rank which rabbits hold, or ought to hold, with sheep and cattle, as domestic animals,—see the Rural Economy of YORK-SHIRE, which was first printed, in 1788 ; but which would seem to have, unfortunately, escaped the notice, or the memory, of the Secretary of the Board.

On

---

* In p. 391. The Reporter speaks of rabbit warrens as a " branch of husbandry that is so little known to printed Agriculture."

On SWINE, not a line is worth preservation;—except that Mr. Fisher of Kirby, p. 381. "fattens his hogs on the same food as his bullocks, boiled lintseed mixed with barley meal, and finds it answers well."

POULTRY.—*Geese* may well rank among livestock, in Lincolnshire. And the goose husbandry being *really*, I believe, "little known to *printed Agriculture*," (excepting, perhaps, what I have noticed of it, in Somersetshire) I will here insert what the Secretary has collected concerning it.—P. 394. "Geese plucked five times a year; at Pinchbeck it is at Lady-day, Midsummer, Lammas, Michaelmas, and Martinmas. The feathers of a dead goose worth 6*d*. three giving a pound. But plucking alive does not yield more than 3*d*. a head per annum. Some wing them only every quarter, taking ten feathers from each goose, which sell at 5*s*. a thousand. Plucked geese pay in feathers 1*s*. a head in Wildmore Fen.

"Inquiring of Sir Joseph Banks's boatman on East Fen the *profits* of keeping geese on that watery desart, he gave me the following account of what he did himself:—his stock is eight score; and this year, which is not a good one, he reared 500; in a good year 700, eight the average brood: they sell this year at 2*s*. which is higher than ever has sold at 1*s*. Plucks four times, at 4*d*. each time (some folks five times), because he thinks more hurts the old ones. His expence in corn is from 20*l*. in fine winters to 50*l*. in bad ones. He plucks the young twice or thrice, and gets ten quills from each goose, at 6*d*. per 120."

PROFIT of FARMING.—No inconsiderable portion of the volume, under review, is taken up with *calculations of profit*.—Not however, of the annual profit made by the occupiers of the several farms, which the Reporter might happen to visit, or about which he might happen to converse; but of profit arising from particular articles of produce, whether arable crops or grazing stock.

This, certainly, has more reason and common sense in its favor, and is less liable to error, than are calculations on the general profits of farming,—as given out in the original instructions of the Board. See NORTHERN DEPARTMENT, for strictures on this topic.

But, even in making calculations on the profits of particular articles of farm produce, great caution is required to render them useful;—and not less, to prevent the mischiefs they are capable of producing;—by propagating in an *imposing* manner, FALSE INFORMATION.

Soun.

Sound principles are required to be previously laid down, and *strict method* to be used in applying them : otherwise, they become repulsive, if not impregnable, to examination, and unintelligible to any one, but the maker of them,—if not to himself.

In the volume under Review, we find no principles of calculation previously laid down *, nor any regular method observed. In some instances, it is true, *capital* is mentioned, and five per cent. upon it is added to the *expences*; and, in some, a few shillings are set down for "incidents;" but *what* incidents we are left to conjecture. In others, however, neither *capital, hazard, skill,* nor *industry,* enters specifically into these calculations.— Hence, had even the particulars of *rent,—taxes,* (not specified),—*labor,*—and *seed,*—been duly ascertained,—such calculations would, of course, still have been useless, if not mischievous.

I cannot refrain from intimating, here, that, had the time and industry, which these calculations must have cost the Reporter, been bestowed on considering, selecting, digesting, and revising, the exuberant matter, hastily, perhaps, committed to his travelling journals,—his volume might have been read with greater pleasure, and more instruction :—And, further, that, if, instead of the useless engravings, which it embraces, an intelligent Map of the County, describing the lines of country travelled over, and clearly pointing out the several places spoken of, and, moreover, showing whether they are situated on the hill, in the vale, or among the waterformed lands, of this variously soiled, variously surfaced, and variously climatured, County,—had been substituted, a large share of its present bulk and price, might, by these joint means, have been spared, and its intrinsic value greatly increased.

AT LENGTH,—much fatigued, I confess,—but not quite exhausted,—have I performed the most arduous and irksome task that has fallen to my lot, during the long course of my literary labors.—*How* I have performed it, I leave to others to decide. I have only to say—if I have not done it satisfactorily, the failure has not arisen from a want

* Except what is incidentally dropt in the section "Rent;" p. 47; where the Reporter says—"I think the fairest mode of calculating is to give the tenant 12 per cent. on a fair capital, and leave the rest to the landlord for the rent,"—A principle, however, which, I think, he as not applied.

want of time or attention bestowed upon it.—This single Report of Lincolnshire has cost me more patience and severe attention, than any two—than some half dozen—of the Board's Reports have required. And allow me, in perfect good humor, to add,—more, probably, than the author himself expended upon it.

For reasons, however, that I have repeatedly declared, I deem it an essential part of my engagement to the public, in executing the work I have undertaken, to examine, with more than common care, and decide on, with more than ordinary caution,—the Reports of men who are known to, and have acquired a *name* in, what is termed, the literary world.

HERE, it may be proper to prefer my own claim, and assert my OWN QUALIFICATIONS, more explicitly than I have hitherto done,—to fill the important office I have assumed:—an easy task, this, which I will perform, in as concise a manner as the nature of it will allow.

First, I was born in the field of Agriculture ; and was not only bred up among its various scenes, but initiated, in my earlier years, in its several operations.

Secondly. During my youth, I penetrated the labyrinths of science ; and acquired some considerable degree of proficiency, not only in the most useful, but in the one, which, more than any other, expands the intellect, and gives compass to the human mind :—And, moreover, rambled through the world of commerce ;—obtained a comprehensive view of its arts and mysteries ;—not in this island, only, but also in one, where it is conducted, if not with more uprightness, with more method and scientific accuracy, even than in the metropolis of the commercial world. And, thus, by viewing fresh scenery, experiencing a diversity of climates, and conversing with men collected together, from every country,—I acquired an additional stock of ideas, and a train of reflections arising from association and comparison, which I could not have gained on my native soil.

Thirdly. In early manhood, with a mind (I will presume to say) thus enlarged and supplied with general knowledge,—I RETURNED to the FIELD of AGRICULTURE;—commenced a constant residence, on a farm of many soils, and ample size ; and, day by day, season after season, and year after year, pursued, with uninterrupted and unremitted ardor, every branch, and every root, of PRACTICAL AGRICULTURE,—down to its very minutiæ;—cautiously
marked,

marked, and memorized, every success and miscarriage ; as a guide to future practice ;—brought the business of experiment, as well as the method of profiting, by the incidents of practice, to a degree of scientific certainty ;—revised the journals and methodized writings, so accumulated ;—and committed them to the press :—a thoughtful task, this, by which the principles, drawn from my own practice, were the more firmly fixed, in the science whose outlines I had thus defined.—See the MINUTES of AGRICULTURE ; also EXPERIMENTS of AGRICULTURE &c.,—first published, separately, in quarto ;—now united in two volumes, octavo.

Fourthly.—Having, by those means, acquired a radical and comprehensive view of the subject,—I formed a more extensive PLAN for PROMOTING AGRICULTURAL KNOWLEDGE ; by surveying, and registering,—agreeably to those outlines,—the ESTABLISHED PRACTICES of the superior classes of professional men, in the best cultivated parts of the kingdom ; with the more enlarged view of ascertaining the EXISTING PRACTICE of ENGLAND, at that time ; namely, toward the close of the eighteenth century.—See the INTRODUCTION to the NORTHERN DEPARTMENT.

This plan (with scarcely any alteration!) I have been prosecuting, during the last thirty years ;—regardless (let me declare) of my private interest ; otherwise than as it has been inseparably connected with my public design ;— and without the shadow of eventual advantage from it ; other than what might arise from the reflection of having done a public good:—added (I must confess) to the pardonable pride of being desirous to live long in the minds of those whom I have been solicitous to serve.

Fifthly.—In the prosecution of this plan, I have seen, and more or less examined, every interesting line of country in the island ;—whether in England, in Scotland, or in Wales. I have practiced, or immediately superintended the practice, not of Agriculture, only, but of the Management of Landed Property, likewise,—in seven different, and widely distant, parts of it —In six different and distant parts of England, I have been stationary,—*resident* —for a greater or shorter period of time,—with the view of making myself master of their several practices, in the various branches of Rural Economy :—not by casually conversing with professional men of the first class, but by living among them ; and, with much more solid advantage, by *studying their practices, on the spot :*—moreover, continuing to survey the District or Country round my
STATION,

STATION,—day after day, season after season, and, in most of them, year after year. I have, furthermore selected, at my leisure, such particulars of the information, thus collected, as appeared worthy of publication;—registered them, in a digested form;—revised them for publication; and twice corrected them, in the press;—together with, (in four of those instances,)—minutes that arose in my own practice, in those several situations.—See the ADVERTISEMENT, at the close of this volume.

Finally,—it may be useful, to those who are slow of conviction, or reluctant to be convinced,—to observe, that, if I am possessed of an ordinary portion of discrimination and judgement, I must necessarily know more (may I not be allowed to say much more) of the RURAL ECONOMY of ENGLAND, *aggregately considered*, than any other man.

Should the Reader pause, I would wish to ask him,—what *other* man has trodden nearly the same path,—or any path that bears resemblance to it,—viewed in its full extent? Can any other man with truth repeat what is above written, or any thing nearly resembling it,—*as his own*? *

What other man, therefore, can have so just a claim,—so legitimate a right,—so ample a qualification, to appreciate the works of others, on subjects relating to the Rural Economy of England, and, most particularly, to decide on those which relate to a general survey of its provincial practices; as he who formed the plan of it, and has, with the qualifications, above stated, been unremittingly pursuing it, during so lengthened a period of time?

It may be painful (to use a hacknied epithet); but it cannot fail to be, at the same time, useful to my present undertaking,—if not essential to the progressive advance of Agricultural Science,—to apprize the public of those truths.

THE

* Nor can any other man, in time to come, have the same motive, for dedicating a life to such a pursuit. The FOUNDATION is laid; and all that can be required, henceforward, will be to *improve* the SUPERSTRUCTURE, as the ESTABLISHED PRACTICES of the KINGDOM *shall be improved.*

THE WATERLANDS OF

NORTHAMPTONSHIRE,

AND

HUNTINGDONSHIRE.

THESE COUNTIES are noticeable, in the present volume, so far, only, as their FENS and MARSH LANDS extend *. And even these,—intimately uniting with, being in strictness parts of, those of LINCOLNSHIRE and CAMBRIDGESHIRE, —are the less entitled to especial notice, here.—It will be right, however, to preserve a few particulars, relating to them, which are found in the Reports from those Counties.

NORTHAMPTONSHIRE was reported by "JAMES DONALDSON of Dundee," in 1794.

HUNTINGDONSHIRE, by Mr. STONE (the Reporter of Lincolnshire); also, by GEORGE MAXWELL of Fletton, near Stilton;"—both in 1793.

Those three Reports are mere sketches, hastily sent in, presently after the appointment of the Board.

IN Mr. DONALDSON's NORTHAMPTONSHIRE, we find the following sensible remarks, on the APPROPRIATION of Fen Lands.

"The GREAT PETERBOROUGH FEN."—P. 30. "A tract of fine level land, containing between six and seven thousand acres, of a soil equal to any perhaps in the kingdom of Great Britain, and susceptible of the highest cultivation. It is situated between Peterborough and Crowland, towards the north-east bounds of the County, and is subject to the depasturage of the cattle, horses and sheep of 32 parishes or townships in the neighbourhood, which comprise what is commonly called the Soke of Peterborough.

* Their UPLANDS and UPPER GROUNDS belong to the MIDLAND DEPARTMENT.

borough. The farmers who live in the townships immediately adjoining, consider their right of commonage as of
no value to them ; and it may therefore be supposed, that
those who live at the distance of 8 or 10 miles cannot be
much benefited thereby. Indeed, considering the present
mode of management, it is impossible that any advantage
can arise to the persons having-right therein. That it is
a valuable tract of land, however, if under proper cultivation, is fully ascertained from the following circumstance. The annual expence of keeping the drains,
bridges, &c. in proper repair is considerable; and the
means adopted by those concerned, for raising a fund for
this purpose, is to let a certain number of acres to some
tenant in the neighbourhood for a course of corn cropping,
for 3 or 4 years, when it generally rents at from 3*l.* to 5*l.*
per acre. From this account, it may be safely stated, that
if these six or seven thousand acres were converted into
private property, and divided into farms of a proper size,
the whole might be rented on leases of moderate endu-
rance, at from 20*s.* to 30*s.* per acre ; and it may be further
observed, that the produce of these lands, under that system,
would exceed what they now yield, to the extent of many
thousand pounds a year, while the additional number of
hands which would be requisite for the cultivation of these
farms, could not be short of 1300 or 1400. The advantages,
therefore, both of a public and private nature, which must
necessarily result from a division of this common, are so
obvious, as to require no illustration."

These remarks are more or less applicable to unappropriated lands in general.

In Mr. STONE's HUNTINGDONSHIRE are found a
few particulars worthy of preservation.

Mr. S. estimates the EXTENT of FEN LANDS, entering
within the outline of HUNTINGDONSHIRE, at 44,000 acres,
p. 8.

The disgraceful STATE in which some of those lands were
suffered to remain (a blank in English territory!) in 1793,
is concisely, yet forcibly, conveyed by Mr. S. in p. 13.
" The Fen is generally unproductive, being constantly
either covered with water, or at least in too wet a state for
cultivation ; and considerable parts are very frequently
forfeited to the corporation of the Bedford Level, the tax
annually charged upon the land *for its drainage*, far exceeding any advantages the proprietors can derive from
the soil, in its present state, they rather prefer relinquish-

ing

ing their estates than to pay the taxes imposed upon them."

The following remarks, under the head, "Improvement of the Fen," will serve to give some general ideas respecting the DRAINAGE of the Lowlands of CAMBRIDGE &c.; as well as of the various interests that are connected with their Improvement.

P. 30. "A bill was brought into Parliament in the last sessions, for the purpose of altering the course of the river Ouze, from a place called Eau-brink, below St. German's Bridge, to the port of Lynn, as a means of improving the outfall of the river, and thereby to produce a better drainage of the adjacent country, and also of the Middle and South Levels of the Fens (the North Level being in a very improved state).

"The fenny part of Huntingdonshire, is in that division called the Middle Level; and, as I have before had occasion to remark, stands much in need of being drained.

"The promoters of the intended cut, have, for their object a nearer direction, from a given point of the river, to the sea; and thereby avoiding a circuitous passage over widely extended shallow sands. The water, from so expanded a course, is certainly the slower in its progress to the present out fall, and, consequently deposits in its course a considerable quantity of its impurities; which have, from a great length of time, tended to choak up the out-fall, to the prejudice of the navigation of the river, and the draining of the fens.

"The most zealous promoters of this plan, are those gentlemen, whose estates are situate nearest to the intended out-fall, whose immediate benefits are certain, and to the utmost of their wishes; others are less sanguine, whose estates are situated in the more interior parts of the fen. They are ready to admit, that the intended cut will be a fundamental point gained, towards effecting a competent drainage of the whole; but it stops short of the utmost benefit which they might derive from it, because a great system of interior drainage must be accomplished, before they can derive an equal benefit from the proposed measure.

"Persons interested in the navigation of the port of Lynn to the sea, are said to oppose this intended cut, upon the ground, that the rapidity with which the water will come from the high land, thus confined or circumscribed in its bounds, will not only increase the existing defects of the
harbour

harbour (there being sand-banks below the port of Lynn, which are immoveable, and, on that account, sediment will be there increased), but that it will endanger part of the town.

"Arguments supposed to be destructive of each other; for the same power which would endanger the town of Lynn, would not fail, in a proper direction, to clear its way, through no small impediments, to the sea; and it is an axiom in hydraulics, that where a proper fall of water is certain, confining any given body of it to narrower limits, will be the surest means of forcing, cleansing, and increasing its depth.

"It appears to me a fortunate circumstance (from whatever cause it might happen) that the intended bill did not pass into a law at the last sessions; as the time necessarily now given before it shall again be brought forward, may be a means of bringing all parties nearer together, and inducing them to unite, in framing a well-digested system, for promoting the general Drainage of the Middle and South Levels, by which measure, 300,000 acres may be improved, and indeed brought to the highest state of cultivation.

"The expences of carrying it into execution, will bear but a small proportion, to the advantages of advancing so neglected and rich a tract of land, to a state of fertility, producing hemp, flax, corn, and the means of breeding and feeding immense quantities of cattle and sheep, instead of fish and wild fowl, when the happy event shall take place."

Mr. MAXWELL, in his HUNTINGDONSHIRE, speaks more at large of its water-formed lands; which he divides into "FENS" and "SKIRTY LANDS."

Concerning the latter, we have the subjoined remarks. —P. 13. "We come now to speak of a kind of land, that appears peculiar to those counties which border on the fens; and this may very properly be considered, as an almost imperceptible link, in the great chain of Nature, holding together two distinct and different sorts of soil.— It is neither moor, clay, gravel, nor loom; but partaking of the properties of moor, and whatever soil is severed from the fens, (?) by that we are now speaking of. In the division of the fens into districts, for the purpose of draining them by engines, a great deal of this has been necessarily included within the banks, and is, generally speaking, rich, grazing land, the surface of which being considerably higher,

higher, than that of the fen, properly so called, it is out of the reach of floods, and is liable to be most damaged by being too much drained. But the generality of this land, is not included in the drainages above referred to; and this is precisely that sort of property, which is more annoyed than any other, by having the waters from the lower lands forced over its surface, by means of mechanical inventions, and which therefore, in its present state, is of little or no value.

" I presume there may be about 5000 acres of this sort of land in the county of Huntingdon."

Relating to the "FENS" of Huntingdonshire, Mr. Maxwell enters more into detail. The following are the particulars noticed.

Extent.—P. 8. " They consist of about 44,000 acres (including lakes), and form about one seventh part of what is called the Great Bedford Level, of which more than 50,000 acres are wholly unconnected with the county now under consideration, as they are drained by a different outfal, as I shall have occasion to notice hereafter."

Drainage.—P. 8. " Of these 44,000 acres, about eight or ten thousand may be called productive; but even these are kept, if kept at all, from inundation, at an expence which is equal to near one third part of the rent, and are at all times in a state of extreme hazard."

P. 11. "It may seem paradoxical, that the fens of Huntingdonshire, whose surface is comparatively high, should be worse drained than those which lie between them and the sea; the surface of which last is considerably lower; the natural supposition being, that water will inevitably fall from the higher to the lower level. But this is the case with all the fens that are upon the skirts of the high land, and proves only, that the general drainage, was executed upon principles fundamentally wrong. In truth, let what will be advanced to the contrary, there was not a proper outfal to the sea, at the time of the general undertaking, to drain the fens near a century and a half ago; and ingenious men employed themselves, not in obtaining an outfal, as they ought to have done, but in constructing large drains and high banks within the boundaries of the fens, expecting the water would force its own passage, in spite of every impediment, though the distance between the fen and the sea, was from 10 to 15 and 20 miles.

" This not proving to be the case, ingenuity was then set to work, to invent engines for the purpose of throwing the water out of the lands into the internal rivers. Still it did

did not find its way to the sea, but overtopped the banks, or broke them down by the weight of its pressure. To this moment, instead of resorting to the outfal, the engines have been increased in size, and the banks raised still higher, so that the water which, if there had been an outfal, would have found its way to the sea, and, if left to itself, would have rested on the lowest of the land, has been forced, in a retrograde motion, over the surface of the higher lands; and hence the deplorable state of the fens in Huntingdonshire. It is a state that every one must lament; whilst those who have constant intercourse with its inhabitants, must feelingly sympathize in their occasional distresses: for what can be more painful to a generous mind, than to see industrious families, with all their property and effects, at the mercy of the weather, and liable to be overflowed in windy weather, at every moment?"

P. 12. "The average rent of the fens in Huntingdonshire, is about 10s. per acre, subject to tithes, reckoning only upon the cultivated part, and excluding, therefore, about three fourths of the whole quantity, which may probably produce about one shilling or eighteen pence *per* acre on the average; but I know that very many acres yield no rent at all. The lowness of the rent, is to be accounted for, by the uncertain state of the drainage; and when it is considered, that the seed time depends entirely upon the weather, insomuch that I have known the land sowed as late as the middle of June; it must follow, that an improved drainage will necessarily bring about a great increase of rent, even in the cultivated parts; and more especially, as the advantage of applying a great part to the breeding of sheep and other cattle, is pretty well understood, and generally practised."*

Rent.

* In an "Appendix," Mr. Maxwell goes largely into the controversy mentioned, above, by Mr. Stone;—discussing, in a very ingenious and *argumentative* manner, the several points in dispute. But how far his arguments were, on the whole, well grounded can only be determined by those who are intimately acquainted with *all* the circumstances of the case. What a subject, this for a MINISTER of the HOME DEPARTMENT, to enquire into!—Yet this immensely valuable passage of territory, still remains, I understand, a disgrace to the Country! Alas! poor England's *self* ?

APRIL 1811.—The above note was written before I went over the Waterlands of the Eastern Department, or had bestowed upon them sufficient attention to enable me to form a proper judgement of their general

Rent.—See the last extract.

Farms and *Occupiers.*—See *Workpeople,* ensuing.

Plan of *Management.*—P. 8. "The precarious state of the fens, occasioned, from the time they were drained, the introduction of a mode of management that was barbarous in the extreme, for nothing was thought of, but getting as much as possible out of the land, and trusting to a general drowning for restoring its goodness; but now the mode of management commonly practised, is, first, to set apart some given proportion of the farm, which is held sacred from the plough; then, to have one third part of the remainder under the plough; and two thirds in grass; keeping the whole of that remainder in a succession of tillage and grass. That portion which is immediately under the plough, is divided either into three or four seasons for occupation, as follows:

" If into three—1st year—pare and burn, after six, seven, or eight years grass, and cole seed brushed in upon the first plowing, but little or none suffered to stand for a crop, it being fed off in the winter with sheep; and then generally after one plowing sowed the 2d year with oats, which are generally so rank, as to make it impracticable to have grass seeds, with them; 3d year, wheat, or oats, with seeds, to remain until it comes again into a succession for tillage. If three crops of corn are taken, oats are sowed, after the wheat, or wheat after the oats, and sometimes oats or barley, and the land is laid down as above.

" For this alteration of the fen system, the County is, in a great measure, indebted to the judgment and sagacity of the late Mr. John Wing; and the reader will be so good as to suspend his opinion of it, for the present.

" The grass-seeds formerly used, were the common red clover, with hay-seeds, or more commonly rye-grass; but white clover, called here Dutch clover, has been of late years introduced, and is much approved of, not only for its natural durability, but because it is found to bear drowning, which is not the case with common red clover."

Workpeople.—P. 12. "The cultivated part of the fens of Huntingdonshire, is comparatively so small, as to have little or no effect, on the price of labour, in other parts of the County, notwithstanding there are very few habitations

---

general Drainage. I have, since given them much thought, and shall convey my sentiments respecting them, in noticing GOOCH's CAMBRIDGESHIRE, ensuing.

tions for labourers within its limits; for the harvest generally comes in after the hurry of the high land harvest is
over; and a great part of what is really cultivated, is
held by farmers not resident in the fens, as appendages to
their high country farms, in the same parishes; and of
course so far as they are concerned, the business is carried
on by their constant labourers and own hired servants;
and the waggons, carts, and other implements, except
ploughs, are generally the same in both places."

Implements.—P. 12. " Those farmers who reside in
the fens, make use of no carts, but light waggons, which
are drawn by two mares abreast, with a pole, one side of
the waggon being made of loose boards," (or a sort of
open paling) "which are taken out, when it is wanted for
the carriage of dung; and this the driver commonly
spreads upon the land from the waggon, it either having
been first thrown into large heaps in the yard, or carried
into still larger heaps to some intermediate spot."

Tillage.—The following account of the plowmanship of
the Fens is satisfactory.—P. 10. " The fen men are the
most expert of any in the world at plowing, no such thing
as a driver being known, although they frequently plow
with three mares, which are always abreast, and guided by
a line; and it is incredible how fast the business proceeds.
The sort of plough for paring, was originally introduced
from Holland, and has only one handle; from the hinder
part of which projects a kind of crutch, horizontally disposed, and upon this the holder bears with his left hand,
walking upright. From the same handle, another crutch
projects at right angles with the former, but considerably
lower down; and this the holder uses occasionally with
his right hand, for the purpose either of keeping the
plough steady, or assisting to turn it at the lands-end.
Instead of a foot or wheel, to support the beam of the
plough, they use what is called a scaife, which is a circular plate of iron, turning constantly round, the edges of
which are steeled, and together with the edge of the share,
are kept as sharp as a penknife, by means of a file, which
the plowman carries with him for that purpose. This
they call the whole Dutch; they have likewise what they
call the three quarter Dutch, and the half Dutch plough,
differing from the former in the breadth and strength of
the share; and these two sorts are used for the seed-
furrow, as it is called, which means that plowing upon
which the seed is brushed in, if coleseed, and harrowed in,
if corn. The latter is used with a foot instead of a scaife,
and

and is equally adapted for plowing strong high land, on which it is frequently used upon the edges of the fens. A fen plowman has been known to win a considerable wager, by plowing an acre of high land, without a single balk, keeping his mares always in a trot, even at the land's ends, those being the two conditions of the bet; a proof, not only of his own expertness, but that his plough was constructed upon true principles of mechanicks. The common rate of plowing is about two statute acres with the paring plough, and about one acre and a half with the seed plough per day."

Livestock.—P. 9. "Sheep are bred in the cultivated parts of the fens of Huntingdonshire, and these are mostly of the Lincolnshire sort, and not the best of their kind. A few cows are kept for the dairy, the produce of which are generally reared; but these likewise are but ordinary; being a sort of mixture between the worst of the short-horned and long-horned kinds. Mares are used for all purposes of agriculture; and every farmer breeds from them as many as he can, selling the colts off at two years old, and as many of the fillies as can be spared, with proper attention to the filling up of his team, as the old ones wear off. Oxen are wholly inapplicable, for they could not walk upon the surface of the fen land without being bogged.

" It will be easily understood, that a farm thus managed, is pretty full of live stock; and it is a pleasure to observe, that every species has improved of late years." *

It is but justice to Mr. MAXWELL to remark—that, seeing the extensive knowledge which he evidently possessed of Huntingdonshire, and the judicious manner in which the sketch he has given of it is written,—it is much to be regretted that he did not enlarge his original Report, and that he should not have, afterward, been prevailed upon, by the Board, to have revised and completed it for publication.

SINCE this volume was put to the press, but, fortunately, before the foregoing particulars, respecting HUNTINGDON-SHIRE, were printed,—I received from my bookseller a third

---

* Nevertheless, in the ample view, I recently had of the Fens, a deficiency of livestock,—both in regard to quantity and quality,—was most noticeable.

third Report of that County, by R. PARKINSON *; from which I extract the following articles of information, —relating to its WATERLANDS.

PARKINSON's HUNTINGDONSHIRE †.

EXTENT.—This Reporter of Huntingdonshire has given a table of more than one hundred parishes;—showing the extent, or number of acres, in separate columns,—of *arable, meadow, pasture, commons, heaths, fen lands, waste, plantations,* ahd *woods,* lying in each;—measuring down to roods and perches!—Unfortunately, however, for my present purpose, the column headed "Fen Lands" comprehends, merely, the "unimproved Fens:"—p. 5. "The greater part of the Fens are under *the plough,* which it is proper here to mention, as it accounts for the small quantities denominated Fen-Land."—And in a "Map of the Soil of Huntingdonshire," prefixed to the volume, the same principle is observed;—"cultivated Fens, and best loams in the highlands, and woods," being uniformly of one and the same color.

Hence the aggregate quantity of the Waterlands which enter within the outline of Huntingdonshire, cannot be estimated from this Report.

DRAINING.—On this important subject, in a Waterland Country, we find lengthened remarks, in the Report under Review;—but not wholly *original.*

The Editor has inserted Mr. MAXWELL's paper, mentioned aforegoing. Also a paper of considerable length, by Mr. VANCOUVER, which will be noticed in the next article. Likewise, two communications, by Mr. SCOTT; whose remarks abound in the volume before me; and who appears to be well informed on matters relating to the watery region now particularly in view. He is, in one instance, designated "Mr. Scott of Chatteris."

Judging from his remarks, Mr. Scott would seem to be a professional man of some eminence. His first Paper is "On draining Whittlesea Mere."—P. 20. "When I examined

---

* April 1811. This Report, together with one from CAMBRIDGE-SHIRE, were announced as *published works,* in December 1809. Since which time, I have been making anxious enquiries after them; but without being able to receive any tidings of their existence, until the other day,—when I received them—*wet from the press!*

† This is a *third original;* but is printed in the octavo or "reprinted" form.

examined the depth of the mere in several places out of a boat, the water was not above eighteen inches, or two feet deep; and the person that rowed me about, who I think was a native of the house where the boats are kept, assured me that the mere was very little deeper of water in any part at that time.   As it is so very shallow, it might be made almost dry land, by only cutting the small river to convey the water of the Nene round the highland side to the drain that will convey it down to the forty feet river by Lynn to the sea.   This new little river also will catch all the other waters, that run from all the highlands into the mere.   And as there are seldom or never any springs in the low fens, it is probable there are very few, if any in this mere; a small-sized water engine therefore, at a moderate expense, will be quite sufficient to drain the whole.   And as the land is turf moor, the expense of cutting the little river, and all the draining and partitioning dikes, cannot be considerable, more especially as the turf will sell to great advantage.

"Whittlesea, and the other meres are now so much filled up with mud, and grown up with aquatic matter, that they are but of very little value as fisheries, either to the proprietors or the public.   And though they produce a little reed, which may bring a few pounds per annum to the proprietors, and are of some use to the public to thatch out-buildings with, yet as that exposes the villages, where they use it to thatch houses, &c. to such dreadful danger when a fire takes place, (as I have seen in many late fires), that upon the whole I think it would be good policy in the land owners to discourage thatching so much with reed or straw, either in towns or villages; especially where the houses and buildings stand near each other.

"That the draining of the meres would be of great service to many thousands of acres round about them, is undeniable; for the meres are dreadful nuisances to the low fen lands that lie round about them, because in the winter season they are kept always full of water by the rain and rivers, and mills, that work their water into them, and the waters that flow back up the rivers into them, when the rivers and sluices below them are silted up, and as they are situated in the high part of the fens, and surrounded with light porous fen-earth banks, that will let the waters through them almost as fast as a sieve.   Indeed so little will the fen-earth resist or stop water, that it is a proverb among the fen farmers, that the banks will let as much water soak back through the banks in a night,

as

as all the mills can throw into the river, even when the winds blow. And therefore, it must be self-evident, that those immense reservoirs, the meres, seated in the higher parts of the fens, must do almost incredible damage to all the circumjacent fen country. The new water-proof banks, would help them, but these go on slowly; as there are so many legal obstacles (!) to prevent their adoption.

"The drainage of the meres would also be of more service to the health of the inhabitants of this rich fertile soil, than any other measure that can possibly be adopted, for in their present state at some seasons, the meres are awful reservoirs of stagnated water, which poisons the circumambient air for many miles round about, and sickens and frequently destroys many of the inhabitants, especially such as are not natives. And the draining of these meres would be of immense advantage also to improve the drainage of all the countries, that drain through the outfall of Lynn; and the navigation of all the numerous places that navigate to and from that ancient port; because the fresh-water floods, the only natural efficient cause that can now effectually cleanse the rivers, would then flow down them with such great velocity, that they would sweep the sand and mud before them to deep water at sea; and thus amazingly cleanse all the rivers sea-ward, deeper and wider, and improve the outfall. A good outfall, all judicious engineers agree, and good authors, ancient and modern, that have written on fen drainage affirm, (see Dugsdale, Badslade, Lord Gorges, Armstrong, Bridgman, and Elstobb, Wattie, Maxwell, Vancouver, &c. &c.) is the chief and almost only thing wanting, effectually to drain the fertile fens, which lie many yards higher than low water mark at sea. And consequently if the outfalls were made good, the fens would drain themselves, and make this rich-soiled district the most valuable part of the kingdom.

"Whittlesea mere is a very large piece of water. Mr. Bodger states it to be only 1570 acres, which may be true concerning the space of water it contains; now it is almost filled with mud, and grown up with reeds and rushes, and aquatic rubbish. But Camden and Bowen say it is six miles long, and three broad; which I apprehend is a fact, according to its ancient and proper boundaries.

"As the necessary dikes also to part and drain the meres, will produce good turf, I am persuaded that the meres may be drained and enclosed for much less expense than most high country commons can be enclosed for. And
certainly

certainly fen-land, when well drained and enclosed, is of double or triple value, to most highland commons. The meres when drained would make excellent hemp land.

" Ramsey mere, Ugg mere, and the other meres may also be drained in a similar way, and will make most excellent land for hemp, or rich land for wheat, or any other grain for many years; and afterwards as fine grazing or mowing land as any in the island. The draining of the meres therefore is an object of the greatest importance to the proprietors, an agricultural acquisition of the first magnitude, and an improvement of unspeakable value to the whole nation."

A sketch and explanation of the mere accompanies those remarks. But the method of draining it is so obvious, and simplex, as not to require a diagram.

The outlet being sufficiently deepened to draw off the whole, or the principal part of the water, a straight main drain is proposed to be run through the middle of the site, lengthway; to receive the interior waters, and lay the land, or base of the mere, dry enough for the purposes of cultivation;—also, from that central receptacle, to cut a similar main drain, to convey them to the outlet;—and, on this discharging drain, to place a marsh mill,—doubtlessly, to free the area of the drained mere, the more effectually, from superfluous moisture.

Mr. Scott makes the following sensible remarks on DRAINING MILLS.—P. 23. " Here I will venture to observe, that water engines in this and in many other places would be much better worked with steam, than wind; because wind engines are dependant on the elements, and can only be worked when the wind blows; but steam water engines may be worked at any time. And as they may be worked in fen-drainage with turf, the expense of working a steam-water engine in the fens with turf can be but very little, where all the surrounding surface is fen-moor. Indeed all this expense might be more than defrayed, by grinding corn, when they are not wanted to drain the land. And especially as the grain and flour, might be conveyed to them and from them by water."

The other paper of Mr. Scott, on draining, is inserted in the Appendix to the volume under review.—It is well entitled to a place in this register.

P. 307. " There have been many enclosures in Huntingdonshire and other counties, that drain through the port of Lynn, within the space of eight or ten years past. And it was the opinion of many of the gentlemen that superintended

superintended the draining of the fens, and the inhabitants
of the fens in general, that these enclosures would cause
the waters to come so quickly and rapidly into the fen
rivers, that it would cause the banks to break; and that
ultimately these enclosures would ruin the fens: this opinion alarmed the inhabitants of the fens in general in a
very high degree, for several winters; but I assured them,
that if the first floods did not happen to be so large as to
break the banks, the highland waters coming into the fen
rivers quicker, and with more velocity than usual, would
greatly improve the drainage of the fens, as they would
scour the rivers; their weight also would grind them deeper,
improve the outfalls, and would drive the sands at the outfall to deep water at sea: consequently that these numerous enclosures would greatly improve the drainage. The
facts have happily turned out as I foresaw that they would,
for the drainage of the fens is greatly improved, and is
annually improving (in my judgment) in a very rapid degree; and the numerous enclosures in the adjacent highland counties, is the chief cause of this great improvement.
Indeed I have not a doubt but that these enclosures will
continue to improve the drainage of the fens, in a surprizing degree.

"As the large Whittlesea meer, as well as Ugg and Ramsey meers, are reservoirs that receive and hold the highland waters, and spoil the surrounding fens, and also
greatly prevent the highland waters from scowering and
grinding the fen rivers and outfalls; these meers therefore
ought to be drained, and the waters that run through them
confined to narrower channels, and then these meers
would be some of the very best lands in the fens. If the
meers were thus drained, the rich land that would be
gained, would in a very few years pay fifty per cent. to all
the proprietors, besides the advantages that the drainage
of these meers would prove to the fen rivers and outfall.
As there are also about a thousand acres of washes betwixt
Downham" (Bridge) "and Earith, left as reservoirs in
great floods, these nuisances to fen drainage operate the
same as the meers on the rivers and outfall, that is, causes
them to choak up fast with sand, mud, &c. therefore these
washes should be embanked. But to prevent this embankment of the washes from producing any dangerous
consequences, only one hundred acres more or less in a
year, might be embanked by way of experiment for a small
expense; and with sluices to let the water out, these washes
might be irrigated in the very best possible manner. If
the

the banks of the washes were made from two to four feet high, that would prove high enough to preserve them in general, either for grazing or for mowing. And in great floods, the washes would still continue to be as good reservoirs as they were before they were embanked at all, and small floods might be taken into the washes by sluices, and then such floods would irrigate or flood the washes in the very best manner. When the floods subsided, the water might be let off either by sluices, or cutting a few gutters through these counterbanks. These banks might be made very narrow, as well as low, and consequently for a small expense indeed, especially as there is plenty of materials for such banks in all these washes.

" If these little counterbanks were properly planted with oziers, they would soon become proof against any flood. And I have long laboured to recommend the planting of banks in the fens with willows, to be tried by the corporation of the Bedford level, and for a trial a few acres might be first embanked and planted in the washes, and the plan fully proved. Indeed I will try the plan at my own expense, if the Honourable Corporation of the Bedford level will grant me leave,—*Pro bono publico.* Farther to improve the rivers and outfalls, the Eau-brink cut should be completed.

" If these meers therefore were drained, and the washes embanked, the Eau-brink cut completed, the fens clayed, and the Bedford level irrigated, what might not be done under the auspices of the corporation? The fine fertile fens would not only prove by much the richest, largest, and most productive district in the British dominions, but I believe by much the best level of its size, on the surface of the whole globe."

Yet this same " Eaubrink Cut" (see p. 205, aforegoing) remains unexecuted!—The editor, at the close of Mr. MAXWELL's paper, inserts the subjoined notice —P. 203. " Respecting what has since been done in the furtherance of this certainly most desirable purpose, and to which the above most excellent remarks were so well adapted, I have been favoured with the following account from their very ingenious author, to whom the fen country was certainly much indebted, although it will be found by what follows, that the scheme there proposed has not been efficiently carried into execution. ' Nothing has been done towards a more complete drainage of the fens except obtaining a very expensive act of parliament, which cannot, as I understand,

derstand, be carried into effect without an additional tax; but not being a commissioner under that act, or any way concerned in its execution, I know very little of the detail of the business. March 31, 1807.'"

IMPROVING the Fen Lands.—On this subject, we find, in the Appendix, a valuable paper, by Mr. SCOTT.—The species of improvement spoken of is termed "Marling;"—that is to say, covering the vegetable mold of the fen lands, with the mud, or natural "warp," which gave rise to them :—a most obvious mean of improvement. See TREATISE on LANDED PROPERTY, Art. *Morass.*

The remarks contained in this paper are not uniformly eligible for insertion, here. I will select such, only, as appear to be proper for extraction.

P. 300. "The fen clay marl, lies under the fens in general near the surface, and is of a soft quality, and may be very easily worked, and even dug up in as large spades full as men can throw into any muck cart, tumbrel, or other carriage. And the marl in general that lies under almost all the fen-surface, is of a very rich soapy nature."

P. 301. "It may indeed be fully demonstrated by undisputed facts, that fen marl will improve fen land, both for grass and grain. There are many deep dikes and drains, in most fen parishes, where the clay marl has been thrown out of the bottoms, and is now well mixed with the fen soil. Where the land is consolidated by being mixed with this clay marl, and where such banks are grazed or mown, the finer grasses flourish to astonishment, beyond what they do on the fen soil unmixed; and whenever such banks are ploughed and sown with any sort of grain, the grain is always heavier, and the crops do not fall so soon down to the ground, but stand up much better; and the crops of all sorts of wheat, oats, beans, and hemp, and artificial seeds on such banks are always better than any of the other parts of the land.

"Where there is plenty of rich marl on the premises, and it is laid bare in the bottoms of the dikes, as is a general case in most fen parishes, an excellent plan of marling in the fens would be, for one or two men with spades called casting tools, to go into the dikes, and to cast the clay marl out of the bottoms of the dikes, upon the land intended to be marled; and one man at the dike sides to cast the marl over the land as far as he can, which with a casting tool may be thrown to a great distance; and the remainder, when frost sets in or in summer, or after hay harvest,

harvest, to be carried about with carts, and spread over the land ; and thus much fen land might be marled, without spoiling a foot of land, and for only about half the expense that land can be marled for in any other district.

" Where a good watering pond is much wanted, as is the case in almost all the fens, a marl pit might be made in the most convenient corner of the land ; and as much marl got out of it as is wanted, and thus a permanent watering place might be made, and the land manured at the same time. If the dikes were deepened also, by getting the marl out of the bottoms, it would greatly improve the drainage of the land, and prevent the stock from running through them when nearly dry, at which time the stock are more frequently lost in the dikes, than when the dikes have plenty of water in them ; for when they have much water in them, sheep or other stock will seldom go into them ; and if one slipped in by any accident when there was plenty of water, the cattle would seldom be smothered in the mud, &c. as they could easily swim in plenty of water, to the watering places where they could get out.

" Such deep dikes and deep watering places would also make most valuable and excellent fisheries, and provide plenty of wholesome water for stock all the year ; which would prove an unspeakable advantage to every fen estate."

Mr. Scott very properly recommends the mud to be laid on a firm surface.   Not on a fallow, or broken ground. But " on grass, either while it is grazed, or as soon as it is mown."

From the strenuous manner in which Mr. S. urges this species of improvement, one is led to conceive that there are strong prejudices against it ! But the experiment is so easily tried, that no fen farmer, who is gifted with common sense, and who shall hear of Mr. Scott's proposal, can, one would willingly hope, delay to make it.

SODBURNING.—This is another species of improvement of fen lands, for which Mr. Scott is an advocate.—P. 305. " Paring and burning, or ploughing and burning, when practised in a careless manner, and permitted to burn deep holes in the moor, has injured some fen lands.   But as this is solely the effect of setting the heaps on fire, when the land is too dry, or neglecting to spread the ashes properly, it is no defect of the system, but entirely the result of mismanagement.   Indeed after fen, or other low
lands,

lands, are well cleaned and laid down with artificial seeds
if the land be burned too frequently, for instance, every
five or six years, or is ploughed too deep for burning
namely, three or four inches, it is bad husbandry.

"But notwithstanding these abuses of burning, it is my
unbiassed opinion, after more than twenty years mature
reflection on the effects of ploughing and burning in the
Bedford level, (where it is practised more I believe than
in any district, of equal dimensions in the whole world,
that it is the very best branch of agriculture that can possibly be adopted on all old swarded low lands, as an introduction for ploughing them to sow with cole seed; and
that such old swards need not be ploughed very thin, no
indeed is it practicable to plough the land thin the first
time."

A FEN FARM YARD.—P. 41. " Mr. Scott observes" (says
the Editor) " that in the fen-farms in general, and alway
where they have but only a few small agricultural offices
they make a well contrived large farm-yard; with a watering place or two in it, all round the east, north, and wes
sides, and sometimes round the whole of the farm-yard
except where the buildings stand. The wall is often made
of cole-seed straw, is about six, eight or ten feet broad a
the bottom; and they carry the straw wall up six or eigh
feet high, tapering narrower till it comes to the top. This
makes a very warm fence, and will endure many year
with now and then a little fresh cole-seed straw or stubble
laid on the top; and as there is plenty of such straw in
the fens, it is of very little value for any other purpose
Such farm-yards are frequently parted into two or three
partitions, so that the farmer can put his horses in one
part, his young stock in another, and his hogs in that par
that is next to the barn-doors."

GENERAL MANAGEMENT of Fen Lands.—P. 115. " I
regard to fen lands, the following rotation was adopte
with success by John Ilett Esq. of Somersham fen, and i
now practiced by several fen farmers.

" First year plough and burn and sow cole-seed, to be
eaten on the ground; second year oats, and sometime
the third also, then fallow for cole-seed, and the rubbis
burned; then cole-seed eaten on the ground; then a cro
of oats, afterwards a crop of wheat, to be laid down with
clover and other artificial seeds several years. The produce is very extraordinary every crop, and also when it i
laid down.

                                              " Th

" The rotation, however, which Mr. Scott, of Chatteris, recommends, is, first year plough and burn, and sow cole-seed, which should be eaten on the ground; except a little carted off for bullocks, hogs, &c.; second year, oats; third year, beans; fourth year, wheat; fifth year, fallowed for cole-seed; which should be eaten by sheep, bullocks, and hogs, chiefly on the ground; sixth year laid down at spring, with ten lbs. of red clover, and ten lbs. of white clover, and about a peck of the best hay-seeds, or rye-grass; with a small portion of parsley seeds, and a few other seeds also, then lie two or three years in grass."

HAYMAKING—(" as drawn up by Mr. Scott")—P. 158.
" The hay in the fens is commonly cut a few weeks later than the hay on the highlands and best meadows; chiefly because the fen lands are grazed later in the spring; and there are also great quantities of hay mown in the fens, and when the fens are properly managed and irrigated, or clayed, the greatest part, indeed almost all of them, will be grazed and mown, and the fens will then be the finest district for grazing and mowing in the British empire, if not in the world. They lie sufficiently near the metropolis, if the navigation from Cambridge to London were made, to send all their produce, hay itself not excepted.

" The fen-hay is made in a very easy and cheap man-ner: after the grass is mown, it lies in the swarth just as mown, several days, more or fewer, according to the dry-ing state of the weather; then it is turned over, and lies several days more, till supposed to be sufficiently dried; and then it is put into moderate sized cocks, and stands till carried, and this is all that is done to it in tolerably good hay harvests. This custom was first introduced, be-cause the fens produce great crops of hay, and the farmers were poor, and willing to get it in the cheapest manner; and the open, unshaded state of the fen lands renders art less necessary to shake the grass and hay about, than in the highland closes, surrounded with hedges and buildings, or trees or mountains. And as the hay made in this cheap artless manner appears to grow and feed the stock, as well as hay shaken and turned about ever so much, and espe-cially as it is so much cheaper, the richest farmers, and even the fen gentlemen on their own lands, continue to make their hay in this easy cheap mode.

" Indeed after many years observation, although I have formerly written against this mode of hay-making, I now
believe

believe that when hay is dried gently, without being too
much exposed to the burning rays of the sun, that it retains more of its valuable juices; that it is much more
nutritious, and palatable to cattle, and much better than
when over fiercely dried in the modern mode of shaking
it much about, and turning it frequently over.

" In the highland parts of this county, the hay is stacked
very well, and in much the same manner as in other
counties; but in the fenny district, the hay is frequently
put up in round stacks, and the roofs, well raked down,
but seldom thatched; this wasteful practice is continued, chiefly owing to the great abundance of hay in the
fens."

TH

THE WATERLANDS

OF

CAMBRIDGESHIRE.

THIS COUNTY, as the two last, claims consideration, here, on account of its water-formed lands, alone. But, in this instance, they occupy not less, I apprehend, than half the extent of the County, at large. They are consequently entitled to every attention.

MY OWN KNOWLEDGE of the morasses and mudlands of Cambridgeshire has principally arisen in pursuing the journey noticed, aforegoing, p. 11.—Their northern extreme I saw in passing, southward; and, in returning, I had an extensive view of the main levels (of Cambridgeshire, Huntingdonshire and Northamptonshire) in crossing them, by the route of Cambridge, Ely, Chatteris, Whittlesea, Thorney, Crowland, Deeping.—Formerly, I spent some days, on the north part of the Isle of Ely (proper) and, thence, passed toward Newmarket; thereby gaining a general idea,—not only of the Cambridgeshire Fens, in that quarter, but saw something of those which are fortuitously included in the Counties of Norfolk and Suffolk.

The BOARD of AGRICULTURE have not, hitherto, afforded the public the most desirable means of information, respecting this extraordinary passage of English *territory*;—as such it can be strictly termed.

The only Report, that has yet come to light, is the *riginal* one (which has not been "reprinted," and of course never *published)* by Mr. VANCOUVER.

" GENERAL

"GENERAL VIEW

OF THE

AGRICULTURE

IN THE

COUNTY OF CAMBRIDGE;

WITH

OBSERVATIONS ON THE MEANS OF ITS IMPROVEMENT.

By CHARLES VANCOUVER.

1794."

OF Mr. VANCOUVER'S QUALIFICATIONS as a Reporter of *Rural Affairs*, I have no other knowledge than what I have gathered from the evidence afforded by his Work;—which furnishes abundant proofs of the Author's spirit and indefatigable industry; and many of his acquaintance with rural pursuits.

Mr. Vancouver's MODE of SURVEY is amply and explicitly set forth, in his " Introduction."—" On receiving from Sir John Sinclair, about the latter end of the month of September last, the Request of the Board of Agriculture, to draw up an Account of the present State of the Stock, and Husbandry, of the County of Cambridge; with the means of their Improvement; and from the Board, printed Lists of Queries, in which are included, 'Whether proper attention is paid to the draining of land, particularly the fenny part of it; and if there are any obstacles to improvements; and in what manner they can best be removed:' and having some years ago become acquainted, that a considerable portion of the county of Cambridge, had long laboured under the most pressing inconveniences, from its imperfect drainage: I thought it prudent, as the season of the year was now far advanced, to direct my attention in the first instance, to the present state and condition, together with the means used for the improvement of the low grounds, and fenny parts, of this county.

" On the first day of October last I commenced my Survey, and found that a measure of the greatest importance
to

o the fenny part of the county, (but which did not meet he concurrence of all the parties interested,) was then in contemplation, and likely to be brought under the consideration of the then ensuing Parliament. Under this circumstance, and reflecting on the probable consequences, that might attend any experiment in which such a diversity of interests appeared to be involved : I considered it my indispensible duty to the public in this important enquiry, to be minutely attentive, and conform in the strictst manner to the requisitions abovementioned. My particular observations were of course directed to the prominent, and leading features, of the great level of the fens; he means at present employed, not only for their internal district drainage, but that of the external and general ne; under the immediate direction of the corporation of he Bedford Level, and how far the proposed measure, of iverting the course of the river Ouze, from its present channel, between Eau-brink, and the Haven of Lynn, ould embrace all the objects so fondly anticipated, by ie promoters of that measure.

" The intersection of this country by the rivers, public des, and private drains, render the communication, even i the summer months, between one village and another, xtremely difficult; and information respecting a neighbouring township from this extreme want of intercourse, not to be acquired by any conversation, with the most telligent persons in the adjoining parish. The variety interests that are awakened by the means proposed, for ie general relief of the fens, the more elevated parts of hich, may be considered as islands and want little assistance; the skirty lands, and the passage of the water, to hat is injudiciously deemed its natural and proper outfal; gether with the injurious effects, apprehended to the avigation, of the several rivers, passing through the level the fens; all conspired to impress my mind, with the solute necessity, of a thorough and minute investigation, this long neglected, though valuable country. For the tter investigation whereof I determined to put difficulty t of the question, and that I might perform the task had engaged in, to the utmost of my abilities; I not ly visited every parish in the county, and traced the esent, and original watercourses, from the foot of the ghland country to their respective outfals, thereby ascertaining the general inclination of the country to seaward, m the antient and voluntary courses of its waters, but chored in the entrance of the Lynn, and Wisbeach
channels,

channels, at the low watermark of the ocean ; for the purpose of ascertaining the effect, which the sea waters have, on the descent of the land waters; to their only outfal. the low watermark at sea. In prosecuting these enquiries, I have to lament the shortness of the days, in addition to the earnest desire I had, of transmitting this part of my Report to the Board, (which was done, at the conclusion of the month of January last,) (?) did not permit me, to establish all the various and necessary facts, and to draw such inferences and conclusions from them, as under less pressing circumstances, with regard to time, I should have thought indispensibly requisite to so material a part of the survey.

" The very important information I acquired, of the face of this valuable country; of its structure, and general inclination to seaward ; of the original course of its waters ; its present mode of draining, and state of husbandry; together with the general opinion I was enabled to collect, by patiently walking over the whole of the fenny part of the county, and daily conversing with the resident inhabitants, as to the advantages likely to result from any proposed measure of improvement, tempted me, to pursue the same mode of travelling through, and visiting the several districts, and villages, of the upper part of the county, although the inconvenience of riding from place to place, or having the care of a horse, ended with my survey of the Fens.

" As I cannot but be aware that the importance and use, which these surveys, will be of hereafter, must be in proportion to the information they impart, of the detail observed, in the farming, grazing, breeding, and dairy business ; of the different counties of the kingdom : I very much regret the time allotted, for the finishing of this enquiry, will not permit my revisiting, those parts of the county, wherein I discover, the minutes taken on the spot, to be deficient in the full information I so much wish to communicate, or where, from the absence of the most intelligent persons, I have been able to acquire but little information."

This was a truly spirited and arduous undertaking ; which few men could have prosecuted, with equal ability, in so short a space of time, and at so unfavourable a season.—If Mr. V. instead of spending a month or two, at one particular season of the year, had remained a year or two in the Fens of Cambridgeshire, and the adjoining Counties,—thus examining them, at every season,—something

thing really entitled to a place, in "a modern Doomsday Book," might have been produced.—Under the disadvantages stated, much valuable information has been collected.

THIS Report, though of considerable bulk, is stitched up, in the pamphlet manner. The number of pages 219.

A valuable *Sketch Map*,—not merely of Cambridgeshire, but properly including the Fen Lands of the Counties of Northampton, Huntingdon, Norfolk and Suffolk;—which are inseparable parts—the natural margins—of those of Cambridgeshire,—is prefixed to the Volume *.

IN ABSTRACTING the useful matter, which relates to the "Fens," or waterformed lands,—and which constitutes by far the most valuable part of the Report,—I will first go through the PAROCHIAL SURVEYS; and select, more particularly, what concerns

| The Extent, | The State of Appropriation, and |
| The Soils, &c. | The State of Drainage, |

of each parish.—And, then, systematize, as in other cases, the items of GENERAL INFORMATION that are scattered through the Volume.

PAROCHIAL SURVEYS.

Mr. VANCOUVER'S ROUTE through the County was irregular. The "*Fen*," and the *upland* parishes are, in his own account of them, *intermixed*; the former are, of course, not readily to be detected, by a stranger, in a Map of the County.—I shall, therefore, for the conveniency of my readers, arrange such of the parishes, situated wholly or partially within the water-formed division, as have given rise, in Mr. V's survey and account of them, to materials of information which I have deemed proper for extraction— *geographically*: that is to say, agreeably to their respective situations, on the ordinary Maps of the County. From several of the fen parishes, no information was obtained, and, from others, none that requires to be transcribed into this register.

TID

* Also *prefixed* to the Volume is a "Sketch of a Proposal to make an actual Survey, and publish an accurate Map, of the County of Cambridge, by Charles Vancouver,"—with a brief explanation of the proposed plan.

TID ST. GILES'S (a marshland parish, at the northern extremity of the County).—P. 163. "The highland lying around and near the village, may be described a strong loam, or clay, of a very good staple, lying upon a gault, and proper for the culture of wheat, oats, beans, and cole seed ; contains about one thousand acres, and is rented on an average, at twenty shillings per acre. The soil in the marshes, is an hungry silt, with little or no variation, from the bed upon which it lies, proper in a less exhausted condition to permanent pasture, but has been too long improperly employed in the culture of wheat, barley, and oats ; it contains about four hundred acres, and is rented at eight shillings per acre. The fen answering the general description of such land, amounts to about two thousand acres, and is rented at ten shillings per acre."

The rent of the largest farm 250l. a year.

NEWTON- (the same).—P. 162. "The inside or highland agrees in general with the description of that in Leverington ;" (see below) "it contains about twelve hundred acres, and is rented, on an average, at twenty-two shillings per acre. The marshes also correspond with those in that parish ; they contain about five hundred and sixty acres, and are rented at fifteen shillings per acre. The fen amounts to about nine hundred acres, is rented at twelve shillings per acre, and agrees in description likewise with that in Leverington. About one-third of the highland and marshes are under tillage, and about two-thirds of the fen."

The rent of the largest farm 550l.

LEVERINGTON (the same).—P. 161. "The upland of this parish, is a deep, brown, under clay, or loam, lying upon a clay; the marshes are a loamy silt, of a gentle nature, and easily to be managed, lying upon a silt, or sea sand. The fen land is composed of vegetable matter, or loose black mould, upon a turf moor, resting upon a *bears muck*,* and a clay. The upland is proper for the culture of wheat, beans, barley, clover, cole seed, and permanent pasture, and is rented at twenty-five shillings per acre. The marshes have been too long injudiciously employed in the cultivation of wheat and oats, and being now much exhausted

* The want of a GLOSSARY of PROVINCIAL TERMS (which a few minutes might have supplied, they being few in number) is the most striking defect of this Report. What is *Bear's Muck!* Is it the remain of decayed Brushwood?

exhausted of their original richness, are not valued at more than sixteen shillings per acre: clover and turnips have been tried with tolerable success upon these lands; but the produce will never be obtained from them, that they would have yielded, had they been suffered to have rested under pasture at an earlier day. The third description is employed under the common fen husbandry, and valued at twelve shillings per acre."

LEVERINGTON PARSON DROVE (the same).—P. 184. " The more elevated parts of the inside highland, consist of a strong loam, upon a silt, and the lower parts of a mild silty loam, lying upon a silt also, taken together, the whole may be advantageously employed in the culture of wheat, beans, oats, hemp, flax, cole seed, and turnips; but it is unquestionable most proper for the culture of grass and permanent pasture; it contains about nine hundred acres, and is rented at twenty-four shillings per acre, on an average. Another description of inside land, consists of a clay, with a mixture of vegetable matter, or fen mould, of a good depth, lying upon a buttery clay or gault;* this contains about nine hundred acres, but in its present state of drainage, is not valued at more than fourteen shillings per acre; is proper for the culture of wheat, oats, and cole seed. The fen land of the first quality, consists of a vegetable matter, or moor, mixed with an hazel-coloured loam, or tender sea clay, of a rich deep staple, upon a silty clay, and proper for the culture of wheat, oats, and cole seed; contains about eight hundred and fifty acres, and is readily rented at twenty shillings per acre. The fen of the second quality, consists of moor, or fen mould casually mixed with clay, from off the road hams, or small hills, which are intermixed through this level, and rising from the bed of the fen; of this there are about five hundred acres, but from the uncertainty of its drainage, is not valued at more than fourteen shillings per acre."

P. 186. " The intermixture of property in the fen, and inside districts is much against an effectual drainage of those lands. An improvement to the drainage of the low lands in the inside might be made, by additional mills, properly placed."

The largest farm 400 l. a year.

WISBEACH

---

* Here, we have some resemblance of a definition of the term GAULT.—In another instance it is denominated Gault or " blue clay."

WISBEACH ST. MARY (the same).—P. 186. "It is much
to be regretted, that the information obtained here, is by
no means so full or satisfactory as could be wished, being
unfortunately suspected to be in the interests of the rector,
I was not only received coolly, but treated with great
jealousy and distrust. Such information as I was able to
obtain, and such observations as I was enabled to make,
are as follow: The inside high land of the first quality,
lying between the Murrow banks and Wisbich St. Peters,
and binding north westwardly upon Leverington Parson
Drove, is an open, loamy soil, very similar in its nature,
to that described in the preceding parish; it amounts to
about three thousand acres, and is rented at twenty shillings per acre. The low land within the same district,
consists of a fen mould, mixed with and lying upon a
clay; is at present adapted to the culture of wheat, oats,
barley-big, and cole seed, but from the uncertainty of its
drainage, is not valued at more than twelve shillings per
acre."

ELM (the same).—P. 154. "East of the village, taking
the church for the centre, the highland may be described,
a silty, tender loam, lying upon a loam, and proper for the
culture of hemp, flax, wheat, oats, beans, clover, and turnips after flax; it contains about one thousand acres, and
is rented at twenty shillings per acre. South-west and
north of the village, is a clayey loam, mixed with a small
portion of infinitely fine sea sand or silt, and vegetable
matter, of a manageable nature, well stapled, and lying
upon a clay, proper for the culture of hemp, flax, cole
seed, wheat, oats, clover, cabbage, colewort, and carrots;
of this there are about twenty-two hundred acres, which
are also rented at twenty shillings per acre. The fen land
in this parish amounts to about seven thousand acres; the
soil or surface of which, is composed of black, putrid,
vegetable matter, lying upon a substratum at different
depths of turf moor, and *bear's muck*, (?) which finally
rests upon a clay, the natural and antient surface of the
country; * this fen land is proper for the culture of cole
seed, oats, wheat, clover, and rye grass, and is rented at
fifteen shillings the acre."

Rent of the largest farm 700l.

OUTWELL.

---

* Rather say—the alluvion deposited, previously to the growth of
the " Turf Moor," or Morass; and out of which it grew.

OUTWELL (the same).—P. 160. "The highland in this parish, answers to the same description of that given of Upwell;" (below) "it amounts to about seven hundred acres, and is rented at twenty-five shillings per acre. The nature of the fen land also is similar to the adjoining fens of the preceding parish ; of this there are about six hundred acres, and in their present inundated condition, are not estimated higher than two shillings and sixpence per acre."

Rent of the largest 200l.

UPWELL (the same).—P. 158. "The highland, consists of a strong silty loam, of a good staple, proper for the culture of wheat, hemp, flax, and potatoes, and permanent pastures; this amounts to about two thousand acres, and is rented at twenty-five shillings per acre.* The soil, or surface of the fen, is a silt mixed with vegetable matter, or fen mould, lying upon a turf moor,† under which, in many places, is found a bear's muck; though the soil, or super-stratum, is sometimes found upon a clay, proper for the culture of wheat, barley-big, oats, cole seed, and were the fen in a proper drained state, it might be advantageously employed in the culture of artificial grasses; it contains about fifteen thousand acres, which are valued at six shillings per acre ; but under a proper drainage, would readily rent at fourteen shillings per acre."

The largest farm 300l. at will.

P. 160. "The defective drainage of the fens, is imputed to the want of a better outfal, for the fen waters through the Haven of Lynn to the sea."

THORNEY (a fen parish, on the border of Northamptonshire).—P. 187. "The highland consists of an ash-coloured, tender clay, of a good staple, lying upon a gault and gravel, and proper for the culture of permanent pasture, or grazing ground; it contains about six hundred acres, and is rented at twenty-five shillings per acre.

"The fen of the first quality, is composed of completely putrified vegetable matter, with the natural clay, upon which it rests, forming together, a deep, strong, black earth, proper for grazing ground, in which it is at present chiefly and judiciously employed ; of this there are about three thousand acres, which on an average are rented at eighteen shillings per acre. That of the second quality is

---

* Doubtlessly, pure alluvion.
† The true composite soil, spoken of, aforegoing, p. 168.

is a fen mould, or moor, from fourteen to twenty-four inches deep, lying upon a gault and gravel, and proper for the culture of wheat, oats, cole seed, and temporary pasture; it contains about six thousand acres, and is rented at sixteen shillings per acre. The third class of fen land, consists of fen mould, upon a turf moor, under which it bears much of various depths, which finally rests upon a clay; this class of fen is proper for the culture of oats, cole seed, and temporary pasture; it amounts to about eight thousand acres, and is rented on an average at eleven shillings per acre."

Rents of farms 25 to 400l. at will.

P. 189. "The annual draining tax for the internal drainage of this parish, is about one shilling per acre."

WHITTLESEA (the same).—P. 190. "The field lying north eastwardly of the village, and adjoining thereto, (called Barsonby field) consists of a brown friable mould, of a good staple, lying upon a clay, and gravel, proper for the culture of wheat, barley, peas, clover, and turnips, and with the meadow land annexed to it, contains about four hundred acres, which taken together, are rented at sixteen shillings per acre. The second, or lattice high field; binding southwardly upon the foregoing, and adjoining the village upon the south-east, consists of a mixed brown earth, and gravelly loam, of a tolerable staple, lying upon a clay and gravel, may be employed to advantage in the same manner with the last described; it contains about four hundred acres, and is rented at fourteen shillings per acre. The churchfield adjoining the village, answers to this last description, and is applicable to the culture of the same crops; it contains about four hundred and fifty acres, and is rented at fourteen shillings per acre. The fourth field adjoining the above, and binding westwardly upon the village, answers to the description of the first field, and contains about three hundred acres. The King's delph-land extending southwardly from Whittlesea-dyke, is found to be a fen mould, incorporated with clay; proceeding thence south eastwardly, the clay is gradually lost in an unmixed mass of fen mould, upon a turf moor, and bears muck; this is appropriated to the culture of wheat, oats, barley, cole seed, and clover, and contains about twelve hundred acres, which are rented at sixteen shillings per acre.

"The pastures in severalty, called black birch reach grounds, bind south eastwardly, upon the N. W. side of the King's delph lands; they contain about twelve hundred

dred acres, and are rented at eighteen shillings per acre. The soil of the fen, consists of putrid, vegetable matter, upon a turf moor, under which is bear's muck of different depths; it amounts to about seventeen thousand acres; and in its present deplorable state of drainage, is not estimated at more than five shillings per acre. The wash-lands amount to about three thousand acres, lying between the north and south banks of Moreton's Leam; but being subject to frequent overflowings, even in the summer season, from the highland freshes, is not valued at more than three shillings per acre."

Rent not mentioned. Tenancy at will.

P. 191. "The miserable condition of these fens, in consequence of the deplorable state of the drainage, preclude any comparison at present with those of Thorney."

CHATTERIS, (a central fen parish).—P. 151. "There are about one hundred and fifty acres east of the village, which are rented at twenty shillings per acre; the soil a deep, brown, compact, clayey loam, lying upon a gault, proper for the culture of wheat, barley, beans, and clover. South of, and adjoining the town, is a common field, containing about two hundred acres, and rented at twenty shillings per acre, the soil of which, consists of a strong, brown clay, of a good staple, lying upon a red clay; the lower parts of this field are much injured by lying near the springs, but is nevertheless proper for the culture of wheat, beans, black oats, and clover. North-west of the village, the soil is of an open, warm, and gravelly nature, lying upon a clay mixed with gravel, proper for the culture of wheat, barley, clover, and turnips; of this there are one hundred and fifty acres, rented at sixteen shillings per acre.

"The enclosed pastures partake of the same variety of soil with that of the open fields, they contain about two hundred acres, and are rented at twenty-five shillings per acre; there are about three hundred acres of highland common, which in severalty would be richly worth the same rent as the enclosed pastures.

"The fen-land common contains about three thousand five hundred acres, which in severalty would readily let for fifteen shillings per acre; there are about one thousand five hundred acres of this last-mentioned common, now under cultivation by the authority of parliament, and the remainder, will, at the option of the proprietors of common rights, come in regular rotation for breaking up; five hundred acres of this fen common are at present under tillage, and two hundred acres still under
pasture,

pasture, but subject to the regulations of the same act. There are about seven thousand acres of fen land in severalty, and under cultivation, valued, free of the draining tax, at ten shillings per acre."

P. 153. "A provision was made in the act before mentioned, for cleansing and scouring the highland drains; in consequence of which, the open fields are very well drained; and under the cover of the same authority, the fen lands and low grounds, are so well drained, as to render them tolerably certain summer grounds."

LITTLEPORT &c. (a fen parish bordering on Norfolk).— P. 140. "East of the village, and immediately adjoining it, are about fifty acres of strong, rich, deep, black land, proper for the culture of hemp and potatoes, which are readily rented at forty-five shillings per acre. Thence extending south eastwardly, are about one hundred acres of a warm, sandy loam, of a good staple, lying upon a clay and sand; westwardly of the village, are three other fields, containing about one hundred acres each, the soil of which, consists of a black and brown mould, of an irregular depth, lying upon a clay, and sand. The whole is proper for the culture of every species of grain, pulse, and green crops, and is rented at an average, at fourteen shillings per acre.

"The enclosed pastures of the best quality, lie in and near the village; these contain about one hundred acres, and are rented at twenty-five shillings per acre. The quantity of fen in this parish, amounts to six thousand two hundred and thirty-five acres, which being rendered extremely precarious, from the very bad state of the drainage, under its present cultivation, is not rented at more than six shillings per acre, but were it improved to the full extent, would be amply worth double its present rent. The driest and best part of it, is appropriated to the culture of wheat, oats, turnips, cole seed, and bare cole, all of which, in a favourable season, are found to answer extremely well."

The largest farm 950 acres.

DOWNHAM, (a fenside parish, at the northwest extreme of the Isle of Ely).—P. 143. "The enclosed pastures of the first quality, comprehend about four hundred and eighty acres, and are valued at twenty-five shillings per acre. The lands skirting upon the fens amount to about one thousand acres, and are valued at twelve shillings per acre on an average. The fen includes five thousand seven hundred and forty-four acres, two thousand acres of which, have been much injured by the cutting of turf, and are not

not valued at more than one shilling per acre. The remainder of it, is appropriated to the growth of fen fodder, except a small part under the common fen husbandry, which is estimated at six shillings per acre; and five hundred acres in a very uncertain state, from the frequent overflowings of the fen, lying north of the old Bedford river, and adjoining Manea, are rented at five shillings per acre. There are besides about one thousand acres, lying in the Hundred Foot Wash Way, which are rented at eight shillings per acre."

The largest farm 300*l.* on lease of 16 years.

ELY *, (an upland parish toward the center of the Isle). —P. 138. " The town is bounded on the north, by very rich pasture lands, variable in their soil, and lying upon a gravel, clay, and gault; in this direction, we find the beautiful villa of New-Barnes, and extending thence northwardly, the hamlet of Churcham. The pastures of the first quality, in this quarter, may contain about twelve hundred acres, and are rented at twenty-eight shillings per acre. The lands skirting upon the fens, may be appropriated as before, but the fens below, and bearing eastwardly are miserable indeed."

The largest farm 500*l.*; at will.

P. 139. " The fen contains about six thousand acres, including the skirty lands, which together are valued at three shillings per acre. To this may be added about five hundred acres of common, appropriated to the purpose of digging turf, and mowing sedge, and fen fodder."

MEPAL, (a fenside parish, on the western skirt of the Isle of Ely—proper). P. 144. " The arable land in this parish lying in an open common field, south-east of the village, contains about one hundred acres, and is rented at nine shillings per acre; it consists of a strong, close clay, of a fair staple, lying upon a gault, and is proper for the culture of wheat, peas, beans, barley, and clover.
There

---

* The ISLE of ELY.—This, like the Isle of Axholm (see p. 6, aforegoing) is, *in reality,* HIGH LAND.—These two islets, doubtlessly, received their present names, while they were begirt with water.

The Isle of Ely is greater, both in extent and elevation, than that of Axholm. The village of Haddenham is seated on a bold promontory that rises a hundred feet or more (I speak from the eye, in passing it) above the level of the fens which it overlooks.—The surface of the island is beautifully varied; and the soil, in general, of a fertile nature, tho varying in specific quality. Were the common fields, which still occupy its lands wholly appropriated, and inclosed, it might be rendered one of the most valuable plots of country, in the island, at large.

There are about two hundred acres of highland pastures in severalty, rented at fifteen shillings per acre, and about forty acres of land lying in the wash between the Old and New Bedford Rivers, rented at ten shillings per acre. The Highland and Wash Common contains about one hundred and fifty acres, and a Fen Common, containing about one hundred and thirteen acres, had formerly by digging of turf, been much injured, but is now completely reclaimed, and under a fine crop of coleseed, the winter food of which has been eagerly purchased at forty-five shillings per acre. Previous to this fen being drained, and the turf bars levelled, it was not valued at more than one shilling per acre. The other fen common, is a mow fen, and depastured only from Lammas to Christmas. The fen land in severalty amounts to about six hundred and eighty acres, and is rented at ten shillings per acre."

The largest farm 100*l*.

SUTTON—(upon the Island of Ely)—P. 145. "The arable high land lies in four distinct open fields, north eastwardly of the village, the soil of which, is a brown earth, of a good staple, upon a reddish clay, or brick earth; a tough, thin clay, upon a gault; and a small part of a mixed nature upon a gravel; the whole of these contain about seven hundred acres, which are rented at ten shillings and six-pence per acre, and their respective parts might be usefully employed in the culture of wheat, barley, beans, peas, clover, and turnips, upon two furrow work. The improved pastures lying in and near the village, contain about fifty acres, and are rented at twenty shillings per acre; those of the second quality, some of which are rough, and abounding with ant's-hills, contain about one hundred and fifty acres, and are rented at twelve shillings per acre. The lands skirting upon the fens, amount to about fifty acres, and are estimated at fourteen shillings per acre. The fen of the first quality amounts to about two thousand acres, rented at ten shillings; and there are about eleven hundred of the second, or inferior quality, which are rented at five shillings per acre. This fen drains partly into the old Ouze, and Hundred Foot rivers, and partly into the old Bedford river, the latter of which is best drained."

The largest farm 280*l*.; at will.

HADDINGHAM (upon the Island).—This, like Sutton, is an upland parish, in a state of common field; but, being bordered by the fen lands, has had a portion of them laid to it;—as have the other parishes of the Isle.

P. 148.

P. 148. " The inferior pastures, or those skirting upon the fen, contain about two hundred and eighty acres, and are rented at ten shillings per acre. The fen land amounts to about two thousand acres, and in its present state, is valued at seven shillings per acre."

The largest farm 400*l.*; at will.

WILBURTON (also a common field parish on the island) —P. 149. " The improved pastures which lie in and near the village, contain about one hundred acres, and are rented at twenty shillings per acre. The fen at present, though at a very considerable expence, is tolerably well drained; it contains about eleven hundred acres, and is rented at ten shillings per acre."

The largest farm, 250*l.*; on lease for 20 years.

STREATHAM (on the eastern skirt of the Isle)—P. 150. " East of the village are about one hundred acres of enclosed pastures, the soil of which, consists of a strong, deep, black mould, lying upon a gault, and rented at twenty shillings the acre. The village on the south is bounded by the fen. West and adjoining the town, are two open common fields, the soil of which, gradually resembles that of the pastures first described; they contain about four hundred acres, and are rented at ten shillings per acre. There are about fifty acres of enclosed pasture in the hamlet of Thetford, which are of the same quality and value with those first described. The skirty land, common included, amounts to about two hundred acres, and are rented at ten shillings per acre; and there are about six hundred acres of fen land valued at four shillings per acre.

" The fen is of a remarkably good quality, very similar to that of Wilburton, but is reduced to a small value, from the present very defective state of the drainage. The open field land, is kept very well drained, by a wise regulation in this parish, of appointing field-reeves, who have the authority to order any drains to be opened that may require it, at the expence of those to whom such drains properly belong."

SOHAM &c. (a fenside parish, on the border of Suffolk) —P. 135. " On the east of the town is found a black sandy moor, lying upon a gravel; on the west, a deep, rich, black mould, lying upon a blue clay or gault. The greater part of this land lies in pastures of the second quality, and containing two thousand five hundred acres, is rented at twenty-five shillings per acre. South of the village are about five hundred acres of the first-rate pastures,

tures, which are rented at thirty shillings per acre; thence, extending southwardly, are about nine hundred acres of open field arable land, consisting of a rich deep, black mould, lying upon a clunch, proper for the culture of every species of grain, pulse, grasses, and garden stuff, which are rented at twenty-one shillings per acre. North of the village there are about three thousand acres of rich pastures, rented at twenty-five shillings per acre; thence extending northwardly, is an open arable field, of a deep rich and loamy nature, lying upon a tough clay, or gault. This field contains about three hundred acres, and is proper for the culture of wheat, beans, and pease, and is rented at twenty-one shillings per acre. The lands skirting upon the fens, contain about one thousand acres, and are rented at fifteen shillings per acre. The fen amounts to about eight thousand acres, and in its present condition, is not valued at more than four shillings per acre. The bad state of this fen is not attributed to any want of internal works, or powers for lifting the water, but to the constant pressure and soakage of the Highland waters, through the loose and neglected banks of the rivers Cam and Lark. The most inferior fens, and low grounds, in this parish, effectually drained, and properly cultivated, would on a certainty be improved to the annual value of twenty or twenty-one shillings per acre.

" There are here about two hundred acres of rich pasture ground, belonging to the poor, and affording the possessors of a common right, the pasturage of three cows or two horses, no one eligible to hold any of these rights, who possesses or occupies four pounds per ann. There are besides about one hundred and fifty acres of horse common, depastured under a decree from the Court of Exchequer; both these tracts are richly worth, and are valued at twenty-five shillings per acre.

" Soham-mere, which was formerly a lake, is now drained, and brought into a profitable state of cultivation. The soil is a mixture of vegetable matter and brown clay; it contains about fourteen hundred acres, and is rented on an average, at fourteen shillings per acre. No enclosure of the open field has been proposed, nor is wished for, though the laying of the intermixed property together is much desired."—The same remark is made on other parishes.

The largest farm 250*l.*; for 21 years.

ISLEHAM (a commonfield parish on the Suffolk side of the County)—P. 33. " The land skirting upon the fens,

fens, consists of about three hundred acres; is rented at eight shillings and sixpence per acre. The fen, amounting to fifteen hundred acres, has been greatly injured by the practice of cutting turf, and from the deplorable state of its drainage, but a small portion of it is under cultivation: including the draining tax of eighteen-pence per acre, it does not average at this time, more than four shillings and sixpence per acre. There is a small poor's common, of about fifty acres, subject to half a draining tax, or nine-pence per acre."

The largest farm, 250*l*., at will.

P. 35. "The unevenness in the beds of the river Lark and Cam, are much complained of, in resisting the descent of the water. At Prick Willow, six miles below, the water has been found to be no more than eighteen inches deep, when it has been four feet deep, and full between the banks running through this parish. The working of the bear, (?) has been of much service, but the gravels and hards, forming the obstructions in the beds of these rivers, are only to be removed by hand, which done, the drainage of the fen land in this parish, would be greatly improved."

WICKEN—(a fen side parish, in the Suffolk quarter).— P. 134. "A fen common, at present appropriated to the digging of turf, and cutting sedge, rushes, &c. contains about one hundred acres. One hundred and fifty acres of Laas fen land, is annually mown for fodder, and when the fen is not drowned, is rented at five shillings per acre. High fen farm contains about three hundred and fifty acres, which are rented at six shillings per acre; this has long been in a state of uncertain cultivation, from the frequent drownings of the fens. At Spiney Abbey there are forty acres of enclosed pastures, rented at twenty shillings; thirty acres of skirty land, at ten shillings, and one hundred and fifty acres of fen, at six shillings per acre."

The largest farm 440*l*.; for 21 years.

CHIPPENHAM, (an inclosed chalk land parish, bordering on Suffolk).—P. 31. "There are about two hundred acres of fen-land, which ought to be drained through Fordham; but from the obstructions, by mill-dams, &c. in those water-courses, are at present drowned, and in a very deplorable state; they produce little else than sedge, which is cut for thatch, litter, or fuel.

"This parish was enclosed about four years ago."

The largest farm 260*l*.

SNAILSWELL.

SNAILSWELL, (an open upland parish)—P. 25. There are in this parish " about eighty acres of moor or fen common, valued at seven shillings and six-pence per acre. The enclosures in severalty, contain about one hundred and forty acres, and are rented at twenty-one shillings the acre. There are about twelve hundred sheep of the Norfolk breed, which are kept healthy, by preventing them, from feeding upon the wet, moory, fen common; this would be drained, and improved to a very great advantage, were not the water penned back upon it, by a staunch, forming a fish pond, at Fordham Abbey."

The largest farm 340*l.*

BURWELL, (likewise a chalk-land parish, bordering on the fens in the Suffolk quarter).—P. 36. " The fen contains about two thousand acres, a considerable part of which has been greatly injured by the digging of turf; it is constantly inundated, and valued at one shilling per acre. In this most deplorable situation it is considered by the principal farmers, to be far more productive, than if it were better drained, because the water encourages the growth of reed and 'sedge, which is cut by the poor people, and sent by water to the upper country, for the purpose of drying malt. Any attempt in contemplation for the better drainage of this fen, is considered as hostile to the true interests of these deluded people."

WATERBEACH (a fen parish near Cambridge).—P. 128. " On the west of this parish, and extending towards Landbeach, is a well stapled gravelly soil, proper for the culture of rye, barley, turnips, and clover; on the side binding upon the river Cam, a deep, brown loam, without gravel, lying upon a clay, and proper for the culture of wheat, beans, barley, and clover: these contain

acres, and are rented at sixteen shillings per acre. About an equal quantity of enclosures in severalty, are rented at

per acre. One thousand eight hundred and fifty-two and a quarter acres of commons, divided into one hundred and nineteen and a half common rights, at fifteen and a half acres each, or eight cows and four horses, or twelve cows and eight sheep to each common right: about five hundred acres of these commons, are at present out of the reach of the winter floods; the remainder, which are subject to be drowned, can in no way be improved, until that evil be removed, and the commons laid into severalty.

" To assist in some degree the drainage of the adjacent fen common, the chillerin, and the north fen, which

which latter is in severalty, a sluice should be erected at Harrimire head, to issue the waters of the fen into the river Cam, when the level is drowned, or when the water, which is frequently the case, rides higher in the level, than in the river just below. With regard to the scouring out of the bed of the old ouze, or west river, little advantage can be expected to result from that measure, except that, of a better supply of water, during the dry season of summer, to the adjoining country, as the waters descending by the present channel of the Cam, from a higher level, would on a certainty, (were the bed of the west river cleaned out) revert, or flow through it towards Hermitage. Had not the river Cam been diverted from its ancient and original course, from above Clay-hithe, leaving the hurds (?) of Denny-Abbey upon the east, and voluntarily discharging its waters into the ouze, below Cottenham common, the present evils in the navigation below Clayhithe, would not have existed, nor would the country, which is now a melancholy sacrifice to the diversion of that river, have been endangered."

FENNY DITTON (a fen-side parish, a few miles below Cambridge).—P. 45. "There are about two hundred and fifty acres of enclosed arable, and pasture land, in severalty, which are rented at twenty-five shillings the acre, a kindly soil for the cultivation of ash, and elm; a few oaks, scattered about, appear likewise in a thriving state. The remainder of the enclosures, amounting to about one hundred acres, being subject to occasional inundations, from the river Cam, are not valued at more than eighteen shillings per acre. Formerly about two hundred acres of fen common were enclosed, but the very bad state of the general drainage since, has defeated the good effects, expected from this measure; the soil of these enclosed lands, is an absolute *sea-silt*, mixed with small *marine shells*, and vegetable matter, or turf-moor."
The largest farm 380*l*. for 21 years.

WITHOUT the evidence of the interesting circumstance, above mentioned, it might seem to be almost certain, that the tide, heretofore, flowed to the furthermost extreme of the wide spread area which forms the subject under consideration;—and that the whole space, which is now occupied by fens and marshes, was an extension of the bay or estuary which separates the counties of Lincoln and Norfolk.

Judging

Judging from the evidently water-formed lands, in the immediate environs of Cambridge, and the general flatness of the situation, it appears to me probable that the site of the *present* town may owe its existence to alluvion, —to land floods and the tide.—The castle of Chesterton (otherwise Castleton) is seated on a promontory which was once, it seems probable, washed by the tide. The castle may not only have afforded *protection,* but may have given *birth,* to the town of Cambridge.—The bridge may have been originally built for the conveniency of the castle; and the town may have become a consequence, in this, as in numerous other instances that are observable, in various parts of the kingdom.—This, however, by the way.

At the close of his parochial journal, Mr. Vancouver has inserted two Tables. — The first shows,—*so far as his information extended,*—"the contents, in acres, distinguishing each sort of land, the rent or value ;"—"The number of sheep ;"—"The highland produce in bushels per acre ;" —"The population ;" and—"The poor's rate ;"—in the several parishes ;—and, lastly, a column, showing "the produce per acre of wheat, barley; oats, and cole seed,"— in some of the principal "fen parishes :"—a tedious task, which,—incomplete as it is,—and incorrect as it almost necessarily must be, from the short space of time in which the materials were collected, and the several columns framed,—does much credit to Mr. Vancouver, as a Surveyor and Reporter.

The other Table stands thus;—P. 193 :

" A COMPARATIVE

" A COMPARATIVE VIEW of the present Average, and the eventually improved Rental, or Value, of the County of CAMBRIDGE, distinguishing each Description of Land, and the probable Improvement thereon, together with the annual Amount of the Difference in Favor of Improvement.

Description of Land.	Number of Acres.	Present Rental or Value per Acre.			Total Amount of the present Rental, or Value.			Improved Rent or Value per Acre.			Total Amount of Improved Rent, or Value.			Total Amount of difference of Rent in Favor of Improvement.		
		£.	s.	d.	£.	s.	d.	£.	s.	d.	£.	s.	d.	£.	s.	d.
Enclosed Arable	15000	0	18	0	13500	0	0	0	18	0	13500	0	0			
Open Field Arable	132000	0	10	0	66000	0	0	0	18	0	118800	0	0	52800	0	0
Improved Pasture	32000	1	0	4	60666	10	4	1	0	4	60666	10	4			
Inferior Pasture	19800	0	10	9	10642	10	0	1	0	4	20130	0	0	9487	0	0
Wood Land	1000	0	15	0	750	0	0	0	15	0	750	0	0			
Improved Fen	50000	0	15	0	37500	0	0	0	15	0	37500	0	0			
Waste and Unimproved Fen	150000	0	4	0	30000	0	0	0	14	0	105000	0	0	75000	0	0
Half Yearly Meadow Land ...	2000	0	12	6	1250	0	0	1	1	0	2100	0	0	850	0	0
Highland Common	7500	0	10	0	3750	0	0	1	1	0	7875	0	0	4125	0	0
Fen or Moor Common	8000	0	3	0	1200	0	0	0	13	0	5200	0	0	4000	0	0
Heath Sheep Walk	6000	0	2	6	750	0	0	0	2	6	750	0	0			
	443300				226009	0	4				372271	10	4	146262	10	0

The Improved Rent may be multiplied by 3, in order to give the value of the Improved Produce, which consequently cannot be calculated at less than 438,787l. 10s. per annum."

GENERAL INFORMATION.

THIS I collect, *firstly*, from the Reporter's "SECOND
PART,"—consisting of twentyseven pages, placed at the
end of his parochial journal.—*Secondly*, from a very valuable communication, by Mr. STONE of LEVERINGTON (not
the Reporter of Lincolnshire &c.)—"in answer to some
queries sent him." And, *thirdly*, from the PAROCHIAL
JOURNAL, in which are found some miscellaneous articles
of information, other than the main objects attended to, in
making the foregoing extracts.—*These* I shall identify
by the names of the parishes under which they occur.

EXTENT.—In the preceding Table, it may be seen that
Mr. Vancouver estimates (in what manner does not appear) the

	Acres.
" Improved fen of the county	50,000
Waste and unimproved fen	150,000
Together making	200,000"

or more than three hundred square miles of "*fen;*"—distinct from the islets or "*highlands*" (and quere the "skirting lands?") they embrace.—Estimating *these*—the "highlands"—(including the Isle of Ely) as being equal in extent to one-third of the "fens,"—the entire area of the
level lands of Cambridgeshire, with the rising grounds
they contain, would appear to be upward of four hundred
square miles, *in Cambridgeshire alone :* and this agrees
pretty well with an admeasurement of the map of the
county.

CLIMATURE.—We have little information on this subject. I have found incidental mention of it, only, in
speaking of *workpeople;* which see, ensuing.

SOILS.—For much information, on this head, see the
parochial journal, aforegoing.

In Mr. STONE'S communication, are some explicit, and
valuable remarks, on the soils of the three parishes of which
he particularly speaks: namely, LEVERINGTON, NEWTON
and ID ST. GILES'S,—situated at the northern extreme of
the county.

P 165 "The soil is extremely various, each parish
consisting of three districts or divisions of land; *the
marshes, the high lands, and the fens.* The river Nene
runs nearly due north from Wisbeach, on the west side of
which, an embankment was made in these parishes from
the

the sea, about one hundred and eighty, or one hundred and ninety years ago, and lies parallel with it, at the average width of about a mile, bounded on the west by the old Roman bank. This portion of land is called *the marshes*, and consists throughout of a light soil, composed of a mixture of sand, with clay ; the former generally prevailing, and is called by the local term of silt."

P. 167. "The next portion of these parishes to be considered, is the *high lands*, and these lie west of the marshes, between the Roman bank on the east, and the fens on the west. The soil of the high lands, resembles that of the marshes, with a larger proportion of clay, and less sand in them ; so that it may be said, they are, generally speaking, of a heavier soil, increasing in their value as they increase in this particular."

P. 168. "In Tid St. Giles there is some of the best sheep pasture in the kingdom ; the soil is that due mixture, the density and solidity of which, are sufficient to hold the manure arising in vast abundance from the crops of the fen land, whither none ever returns ; capable too of resisting the frost, and yet not so strong a clay as to retain the wet, or to burn in a drought extremely ; that it is on the best of these lands, an unfading verdure is always to be seen. They would be equally good for oxen, could good fresh water be obtained ; of which there is no supply but by rain ; and this in a summer like the last, proves very insufficient."

P. 169. "The *fens* lying on the west side of these three parishes, and remaining nearly parallel with the high lands, as the high lands do with the marshes, and the marshes with the river Nene, form the whole of them. The soil of these (their skirts excepted, which are like the high lands) is a moor, or black soil."

STATE of APPROPRIATION.—See the Reporter's accounts in the parochial journal, aforegoing.

P. 166 (by Mr. Stone). "The marshes are in some places enclosed, in others open, and intermixed in the small lots in which they were originally apportioned, and might receive vast improvements by being laid in severalty."

P. 173 (by the same). "By inclosures I understand the wastes, for which acts of parliament have been obtained for authority to inclose and divide them. These in this country have consisted of interior commons and wastes of the different parishes, whereon right of commoning

ing was vested in the inhabitants of the ancient messuages, &c. also of salt marshes, whereon the like right has been exercised. Three enclosures within ten miles of us, Sutton, Gedney, and Tidd St. Mary's," (in Lincolnshire) "of the former description have taken place, in the course of the last four, or five years ; the first, of about thirty-three hundred acres; the second, about one thousand acres ; and the last, about six hundred acres : and two of the latter description, much nearer us. Walpole and Terrington" (in Norfolk) "salt marshes; the first, consisting of about sixteen hundred acres, and the last, about one thousand acres."

P. 175 (by the same). "Inclosures appear to increase population ; in those made above, cottages are built, which are filled with families: a great proof of their effect in this way is, that the labour in those parishes is double what it was, and it is done with more ease than before. The additional employment seems to attract more than additional assistance, some part of which, becomes stationary, and thus the population is encreased."

STATE of DRAINAGE.—For parochial information, respecting this head, see the foregoing journal.

The subjoined information, by Mr. STONE, is highly important, and creditable to this sensible, experienced, and well intentioned writer.

P. 170. "The larger part of them" (the Fens) "has not been drained more than twelve or fourteen years ; the outfal of this part is through the high lands and marshes into the river, or rather a continuation of the river just mentioned, by means of water mills that go by wind. It was this continuation of the river Nene in a confined, and which when confined, soon became a deep channel, that rendered the drainage of these fens, and indeed a great part of the high lands in these parishes, practicable. For before this a vast expanse of sands or bay, laid in front of the outfal, through which the waters of the Nene used to serpentize in shallow and shifting channels, or rather streamlets, on which it was impossible to navigate but in high tides, or great freshes, and into which it was impossible to drain the adjoining lands. The surface of the bay or sands being so many feet above that of the lands, no interior banks could have been raised sufficiently high, nor no mechanical powers invented to force the waters between them, so as to have rendered the drainage as effectual as it now is, without any increase of banks, or mechanic force, more than is necessary to throw the waters

waters through the high lands and marshes as before mentioned. The leading of the river Nene in a confined channel through part of this bay nearer to a deep water, was part of the great plan known by all who ever attended to the interests of this vast tract of level country, to an immense part of which, besides the parishes under consideration, this partial execution of this plan, has proved a work of salvation: It has served to establish a position before much controverted, 'that a deep and confined channel, ending in an expanse of deep waters, is the only method of uniting the interests of navigation and drainage.'

" These fens were recovered at an immense expence at first; those of Tidd and Newton, having borrowed upon them near ten thousand pounds, contain between three and four thousand acres, and pay an annual tax of four shillings per acre, for the interest of the sum borrowed, and the support of the works of drainage. And here the eye of justice cannot help glancing at a circumstance so very repugnant to her, that as soon as these fens were recovered and rendered productive, they were immediately subject to, and did render a tenth of their produce in corn, or a composition equal to, and often exceeding it, though the rectors deriving this immense advantage, were no contributors to the expence incurred.

" In stating this, I am aware it is only a common evil, but its universality does not lessen it, nor has even one plea from the most ingenious advocate for tythes, ever reached this neighbourhood, in justification, or even palliation, of this suffering. We are told of *communi jure*, but this overturns the cause it is meant to support. It is a fact that the parts of these fens producing corn, have yielded more to the tythes for the first seven years, than to the owners who let their lands to be occupied, and the proportion of such lands for that term was more than two-thirds of the whole. The hazard and disrepute of fens when first drained, that have been long drowned, as these were, even kept the rents low for a time, and before the owner can let his lands for their value, they must be established in good credit, both as to soil and security in drainage."

P. 177 (also by Mr. Stone). " There is no land but what is drained in these three parishes; a field in Leverington, of about two hundred acres, only excepted, called Gorefield; if the owners of this were to solicit the Court of Sewers, to admit them to the common drainage of the
parish,

parish, there is little doubt but they would be admitted on terms proportioned to the relief given ; this I suppose the commoners have power to do. The residue of these parishes are drained by water engines that go by wind, the marshes excepted, which drain naturally. The drains are from twelve to sixteen feet wide at top, cut as deep towards the outfal (through the marshes) as the quickness of the soil (?) will allow, the sides so sloped as to make the bottom about half the width of the top. On the depth of these drains towards the outfal, depends their depth as far inland as the first mill to which a level bottom is necessary, and so from the first to the second mill, &c."

P. 202 (by the Reporter, in his second Part). " Upon this subject, the want of opportunity to revisit the great level of the fens, and the parishes bordering upon them, is a circumstance much to be lamented, as the quantity of fen land that is in an improved and profitable state, and that which is drowned and of little value, would thereby have been more correctly ascertained. Reference, however, may be had to Chatteris, Elm, Leverington Parson-drove, Wisbich St. Mary's, and Thorney, for a comparative view of what the lost country of the fens is capable of, in point of improvement, by recovering the natural outfal of the middle, and south level waters. The fenny land in the above parishes, under improved cultivation, amounts to about fifty thousand acres, and yields a produce far beyond the richest high lands in the county ; averaging a rent of more than fifteen shillings per acre : Whereas the waste, the drowned, and partially improved fens, amounting on a moderate computation, to one hundred and fifty thousand acres, cannot be fairly averaged at more than four shillings per acre. Hence in this County only, an encreased rent of ten shillings per acre, amounting to seventy-five thousand pounds annually, may be reasonably expected from a complete, and effectual drainage of the fens, and restoring to the country, a tract of far more fruitful, and productive land than is to be met with of the like extent, in any part of the island." *

PROVISIONS.

* Mr. VANCOUVER's Paper, on DRAINAGE.—Since this article was ready for the press (see 212, aforegoing) a valuable Paper, on the Drainage of the Cambridgeshire &c. Fens, by Mr. V. has been published.—This Paper was written in *January* 1794 ; being dated, " Hoop Inn, Cambridge, Feb. 1. 1794 ;"—when it would seem to
have

PROVISIONS.—P. 178 (by Mr. Stone). " Beef from one to five shillings per stone, (fourteen pounds to the stone) varying according to the more plentifully or scarce seasons of the year. Mutton from four-pence to five-pence per lb. varying in like manner. Pork generally high, seldom less than four-pence per pound; this owing to the small quantity of grain proper for pig-feed grown hereabouts. None of our soils suit peas, and barley-big is generally used for this purpose, of which but little is grown. Wheat generally below the average of the king-dom. These form the state of Wisbeach market. I see no probability of a fluctuation in these articles of provi-sion. Our population altering but very little, there being no manufactures in this country; the prosperity or de-pression of trade affect us not as to home consumption. Potatoes are grown in great plenty, and contribute greatly to the sustenance of the poor."

MANUFACTURES.—See the close of the last article.

POOR RATE.—By Mr. V's table, the rate of the County at large is 2s. 6½d. But on a par of eighteen fen parishes, noted, it is under 2s. This circumstance, perhaps, may be accounted for, in the superior wages given in the fens; and probably in other advantages of workpeople, there.

TITHE.—For an instance of the flagrant *in-equity* of demanding tithes, on fresh drained lands, see the head *Drainage*, p. 247, aforegoing.

ROADS.—P. 179 (by Mr. Stone). " By public roads, as distinguished from parochial, I suppose are meant turnpikes; these are made of the best silt that can be got, which when pulverized, is nearly all sand. Our parochial roads, where silt can be got, are made in like manner. We carry this some miles for this purpose, but the inner roads of these parishes are and ever must be, bad in winter."

In answer to a query, regarding obstacles to improve-ment, Mr. Stone replies,—P. 184. " The bad roads are certainly

have been sent in, under pressing circumstances, to the Board of Agriculture.

Why it was not printed with his Report,—which did not make its appearance, until *June* 1794,—or why it was,—seventeen years after-ward,—inserted in a Report of *Huntingdonshire*,—rather than in one from *Cambridgeshire* which was published at the same time,—may seem inexplicable to any one who is unacquainted with the Editorship of the Board's works.

This Paper will be further noticed, in the next article.

certainly obstacles; these prevent us from claying our
light silty lands, for in winter, in the part of these
parishes, where clay only can be got, a team cannot be
stirred, and these roads can never be made good.''

Were it not for the circumstance of Mr. Vancouver's
travelling, *on foot*, through the fens, it might well have
been made a matter of some astonishment that he should
not have adverted to the general economy of the roads,
across them.

In a fen country, drains and roads are, in a manner, inseparable; and are equally essential to its habitableness
and culture. In some instances, the same ditch and
bank which form, at once, a *drain*, an *embankment* and a
road, are moreover applied to the purpose of *navigation*.
Thus, by one beautifully simplex operation, an inhospitable
region is rendered not only habitable, and capable of cultivation; but is furnished with the most eligible means
of supplying it with the materials of improvement; as well
as of conveying its surplus produce to market:—an admirable system!—dictated, it is true, by necessity; yet
needing many a fortunate thought, before it reached its
present degree of perfection; much as may be still
wanted to render it perfect*.

Where the top of the Bank is of sufficient width, and
especially when the side next the main drain is guarded
by a rail, a DRAIN-BANK ROAD becomes, in the summer
season, at least, safe and pleasant to the traveller;—who,
being elevated, perhaps, eight, ten, or more feet, above
the general level of the country, gains extensive views;
not only of the water-formed lands, with the villages that
appear to rise out of them; but, frequently, of the distant
uplands which bound them.

But not so where the ridge of the bank is barely wide
enough for one carriage to pass, and without any guard,
on either hand, to prevent its rolling off the roof-like
ridge, into a yawning river bed, or a main drain of equal
depth and dimensions; as is the case, in travelling along
the bank of "Vermuden's drain," between Chatteris and
Whittlesea.

In travelling a road of this description, even in summer
when the carriage path is pretty good, there is some little
cause of alarm to the mere *terra-firma* traveller.—In
                                                    winter

* With long narrow barges, many or most of the larger drains
might, doubtlessly, be navigated.

winter, when the draining wind-mills are at work, close
to the road (their business being to throw the water out
of a minor catch water drain, on one side of the road,
into the main drain, on the other,—through tunnels beneath it) the foaming currents, gushing out in full view
(as I have observed them in Norfolk)—it would seem to
be almost a miracle that a carriage drawn by startling
horses, not used to such a sight, should escape harm.

TENANCY.—P. 188 (Thorney). "The whole parish is
the property of his Grace the Duke of Bedford, and notwithstanding that the farms are all held at will, from
twenty-five to four hundred pound per ann. a spirit of
improvement pervades the minds of every tenant, beyond
what is to be met with in any other part of the County,
and which can only be attributed to the very proper confidence, which the tenants repose in the justice and
generosity of their noble landlord, and to the good sense
and superior abilities, which mark the conduct of the gentleman in every particular, who has directly the management of this valuable property."

For that of several other parishes, see the *parochial
journal.*

COVENANTS.—P. 179 (Mr. Stone). "There are but
few leases; but it has been found, when leases have been
granted, or agreements for farms made, that the covenants
and conditions the best calculated to preserve the fee
simple of the land letten undiminished, are the following:
To restrain the sowing of hemp, flax, woad, madder, and
mustard-seed; and though the police gives rewards for
growing the two first, yet it is the interest of the owner
of the land, to inflict penalties on the sowing them,
as no manure arises from them. The restraining cole
seed from standing for a crop, is founded on the like
objection. Where the first five of these are grown, the
land ought to be expressly let for the purpose, and an
extra rent set upon it; because it must necessarily be the
worse for what it produces, which is never the case with a
farm properly let, and skilfully managed. Every farm
should render the occupier a handsome interest for his
capital employed upon it, in stock, crop, and labour, and
improve in its condition. And here is seen the difference
between a good and bad tenant, which needs no illustration, either to condemn the one, or render the other approved in the eyes of his landlord; the former will always
improve the land he occupies, and his own property together; the latter generally reduces both. The general
covenants

covenants of use for any farm in this neighbourhood, besides the foregoing, are to forbid the ploughing, of the
high lands in general, if water can be got to render them fit
for grazing. Of the portion of fen land belonging to any
farm, not more than one-third of the land permitted
to be ploughed, should be in corn in every year, and the
same as to the marshes, and from neither more than two
successive crops should be taken. To restrain the laying
manure on the ploughed lands is very expedient. I have
seen instances where leases have been silent as to direct-
ing the routine of the crops, and the lands on which the
manure should be laid, of bad tenants manuring the
ploughed lands, and cropping them without intermission
during the terms of their leases. By this abuse the
ploughed land, at the expiration, was extremely foul, and
wanted fallowing and laying down, and the grass land not
improved as it would have been with proper manuring.
Fewer crops of corn and timely fallowing are therefore
insured by forbidding the ploughed lands to be manured.
Moreover the best species of pasture in every grazing
farm, ought to be restrained from being mowed."

RENT.—P. 174 (by the same). "To furnish an idea of
the quality of these lands, (p. 246.) I will state what I
suppose the average rent of them ;

Of Sutton, not less than 30s. per acre⎫ These were the inte-
Of Gedney, about   20s. per acre⎪ rior commons and
Of Tid St. Mary's, not   ⎬ waste lands of these
    less than   30s. per acre⎭ parishes.

Of Walpole and ⎫ 25s. per acre. ⎰The salt marshes of
Terrington, about ⎭   ⎱ these parishes.

" N. B. In these values, the extra rents of lands let for
woad and flax, are not considered, but of the lands only
let for the common purposes of occupation. *

" The hazardous situation of the salt marshes, can alone
account for the rent of them being inferior to that of interior commons and waters, (?) as their quality for growing
corn is much superior : both these salt marshes, produce
the best and biggest crops I ever saw ; no part of the crops
upon them was destroyed by wire worms, or any other
reptile, and their having been so continually and immediately overflowed by salt water, previous to being embanked, may be considered the cause of this. The crops
                                                    on

* This is considerate, valuable Report. Indeed Mr. STONE's
REPORT of THESE PARISHES is full of thought and consideration,

on the interior common and washes, suffered extremely by these at first, and still continue to suffer every year, in a greater or less degree."

The Reporter's estimate (in what manner does not appear) in 1793, of the then "present rents,"—and the "improvable rents"—of the fen lands,—are seen in the foregoing table, p. 243. See also the close of the next article.

FARMS.—On the *sizes* of fen farms *in general*, no Report is given.—For the rental values of the *largest*, see the paroch al journal.

Draining Farm Lands.—An instance is mentioned (in Stow cum Quy) p. 42, of "skirty lands" being raised, by this species of improvement (not very masterly performed) from 8s. to a guinea, an acre.

Homesteads and *Plans* of *Farms.*—P. 179 (by Mr. Stone). " The farm houses in this country are generally esteemed good. The farm yards and offices ill constructed, and from the high price of materials and workmanship, these will probably continue so. Situation for convenience of occupation is little thought of, the property being so dispersed ; there are but few farms that have much land contiguous to the houses."

In the more central parts of the fens, the farm houses are necessarily placed in the villages, situated on the gently swelling grounds, before mentioned ;—and the more marginal, on the uplands which bound them.—Here and there, a few hovels, or a wretched farmstead is seen *in* the fens. But it may, I believe, be said, that the occupiers of the major part of those lands reside one, two, three, or more miles from them. They are of course managed with many disadvantages. This, added to the unwholesomeness of the climature, and the high rate of labor, may serve to account for the lowness of rent, compared with that of lands of equal fertility, cultivated under more favorable circumstances.

OCCUPIERS.—I find no *direct* mention of the occupiers of the fens, in this Report. In the next article, they are incidentally noticed. See also the head, *Tenancy*, p. 251, aforegoing.

PLAN of MANAGEMENT of Farms.—P. 155 (Parish of Elm). " The husbandry of the highland arable is usually, first year, flax, or oats, the flax ground sown with turnips, or cole seed, and fed off with sheep; second year, oats ; third year, wheat ; fourth year, cole seed, beans, hemp, or oats."

P. 166.

P. 166 (by Mr. Stone). " A small part of the parish of West Walton, in Norfolk, extends into these marshes, and is principally intermixed and open. The enclosed parts of them, all consist of both pasture and arable land; the pasture is used for young stock, principally sheep; as the water in general is bad, the   being saline, and there being no possibility of taking in fresh water. The herbage is very healthy, and for young sheep, answers very well; but none of it sufficiently good to fat sheep upon, unless improved by clay or lime; the difficulty and expence of obtaining which, are likely to prevent the experiment from being made. The arable parts of the enclosed marshes have generally two crops of corn taken from off them, are then fallowed for turnips, or cole seed, which when fed off with sheep, the common practice, enable the land to pro-duce two crops of corn more; the first is generally oats, the second wheat, and when the land tires of this round, and becomes foul of weeds, it is seeded down with red clover, and rye grass, (fourteen pound per acre of the first and a peck an acre of the last) is allowed to lie two years and is then taken up again: if clear of twitch, is sown with oats, if not, is fallowed from the swerd for cole seed, or turnips. By this rotine the enclosed part of the marshes is occupied to great advantage; whereas the open and in-termixed parts are in a most wretched state; two crops and a fallow are perpetually taken; the last crop is seldom good for any thing; the land is over run with weeds; i wants resting in pasture, and enriching and compressing by sheep, eating that pasture, which its open state mus forever forbid. If these lands (the open lands) were lai in severalty, and enclosed, they would in general bear double rent, and the occupiers be better off than at pre sent."

P. 168 (by the same). "Of these" (the highlands) " b much the largest quantity is in pasture, and could thes parishes be supplied with fresh water, it is to be presumed but few of the high lands would be ploughed; but th want of this essential in grazing, is an apology for so larg a part, as there is at present, being arable. The manage ment of the high lands that are ploughed, is settled int no system, except that of growing as many crops of cor in succession from them, as they will produce.

"The largest part of these parishes is occupied by th owners, who have become within these few years, the pu chasers of the lands they occupy; and notwithstandir this, there is scarcely an instance of a piece of good hig
                                            pastu

pasture land being ploughed, that is not lowered in the value of its fee simple, five years purchase. A regular and rational system of agriculture may be recommended, and partially adopted in such a country, but cannot be made general or enforced."

P. 171 (by the same). "The culture of these lands, consisting of moor or black soil, is that of paring and burning, sowing with cole seed, feeding off with sheep, taking two crops of corn, the first, oats, the second, wheat, laying down with the last, continuing pasture two years, and then repeating the same course."

P. 181 (by the same). "In grazing considerable emulation exists; in farming very little; the cause of this perhaps is owing to the labour, so scarce and high in this country, necessary to the one more than the other. Labour must be on a better footing before any spirit of excellence in farming can be roused."

P. 185 (Leverington Parson Drove, by the Reporter). "The practice upon the fen of the first quality, is first to pare and burn, sow cole seed, and feed that crop off with sheep, which hitherto has proved the most effectual remedy for the mischievous effects of the wire worm and grub; the second year, oats; third, wheat; fourth, oats; fifth, wheat; the sixth year fallow for cole seed; and it is either then laid down with two bushels of rye grass, and eight pounds of Dutch white clover, or is continued another year with oats, and then laid down, and afterwards the new grass is highly manured. The produce on an average of seven years, is sixty-four bushels of oats, and of wheat twenty-four bushels. The practice upon the fen of the second quality is precisely the same for the two first years; the third crop, oats; fourth, wheat; the fifth year, a fallow for cole seed, which is fed off with sheep, and the sixth year it is laid down with a crop of oats. The produce on an average of six years from this management, is forty-eight bushels of oats, and twenty bushels of wheat."

P. 146 (Sutton). "The fen management is much the same in this parish as at Little-port, the practice being to pare and burn for cole seed, which is fed off by sheep; then oats, or oats and barley, are sown for two years; the latter grain is unfit for malting, and only used for swines food, or change of seed in the highland country. With the last crop of oats, or barley, are sown two bushels of rye grass, with ten pounds of red clover per acre. The red clover is not generally approved of, from the encouragement it is supposed to give to the growth of turn-

hoof,

hoof, or ground ivy, as the roots of this species of ground ivy, are found to be destructive to horses."

P. 188. (Thorney) "The practice here, is first, pare and burn, but with great care, (?) and under proper limitations; sow cole seed, and feed it off with sheep; second year, sow oats; third, oats or wheat, when the land is laid down for not less than six years with proper quantities of rye grass, white clover, and hay seeds. The first year of the new grass it is stocked very hard with sheep, which curbs the partial luxuriancy of the seeds, and makes them unite and mat at the bottom, forming a tender and inviting herbage; for the remainder of the period it is destined to remain at rest."

WORKPEOPLE.—P. 175. (by Mr. Stone) "From Martinmas to Lady-day, fifteen-pence per day—from Lady-day to Midsummer, eighteen-pence per day—from Midsummer to beginning of corn harvest, two shillings and two shillings and six-pence per day—during harvest, from three shillings to five shillings per day, and sometimes six, seven, eight and nine shillings per day—from the end of harvest to Martinmas, eighteen-pence per day. The hours from Martinmas to Lady-day, from seven to five— from Lady-day to Martinmas, from six to six."

"N. B. The want of more hours of work in the summer months, greatly retards the business of the country, and occasions great dissoluteness among the labourers: the day that is not ended in labour, generally is in drunkenness.

" By the piece—mowing of grass, from two shillings to two shillings and six-pence per acre—reaping, from seven to fourteen shillings per acre—threshing, oats from five to six shillings per last, (or twenty-one coom Winchester) wheat one shilling per coom Winchester, and barley eight-pence and nine-pence per coom. The labour in those parishes is very ill done. There are very few resident labourers, that is to say, householders, now in them. These were taken off in the late sickly autumns, and the number of labourers' widows, and families relieved by these parishes, is an incontestible proof of this. Our labourers are generally aukward and unskilled in the processes of agriculture, such as ploughing, sowing, reaping, mowing, stacking, &c. and this happens from having few but the outcasts of other countries among us. That they are immoral and unmanageable in a greater degree than in upland countries, is also certain. The extraordinary number of alehouses conduces to these evils, and since the spirit of revolt from order and duty, so much inculcated

cated by certain publications, has prevailed, the difficulty
of conducting the business of this country, has become
fatiguing and dispiriting in the extreme. The expence
keeps pace with the difficulty, and in proportion as the
wages are high, the conduct of the labourers is insolent
and unfaithful."

P. 169 (by the same).—" An alteration of the ancient
practice of commoning, or depasturing stock, on the wastes
of the parish of Leverington, has been introduced within
these few years, and is continued to the prejudice of the
poor cottagers, who are thereby deprived of keeping cows
for the succour of their families. If the former custom
could be restored, a great benefit to the parish would arise
from it. I believe the labourers families would be much
more comfortable from the article of milk, as well as more
healthy, and our population, which is often greatly reduced
by the unhealthiness of the climate, being good or bad, as
the stagnant waters of our country are made fresh by
rain, or putrid by long draught, would be increased ; the
excessive use of tea among these people would be abated,
and of course themselves and children would be more
vigorous and healthy. This alteration crept in about
eight years ago, on the death of a gentleman, whose pro-
bity and activity, rendered him as much as an individual
could be, the regulator of the parish, and his humanity,
the guardian of the poor's interests in it. It was frequently attempted in his time, but his opposition prevented its taking effect."

These remarks do Mr. Stone's humanity much credit.
In a climate, like this! every reasonable indulgence ought,
in common sense and prudence, to be granted to farm
workpeople ; especially where the water is of a bad quality. And, in a grassland country, milk may be afforded
them, without serious loss to the occupier, the proprietor,
or the community.

WORKING ANIMALS.—I find nothing on this head, relating particularly to the "Fens," in the Report before
me ; excepting the close of the following paragraph (by
the Reporter).—P. 216. "The scarcity of pasture ground,
the want of proper attention in the farmers to the raising
of green food for soiling their horses in summer, and the
great neglect in the culture of artificial grasses, all conduce to an expence in supporting the farm horses in the
upper parts of this country, that is absolutely enormous.
They are kept in the stable throughout the year, each
horse is fed with a peck of corn per day, with as much
                                                    chaff,

chaff, chopped straw, and hay, as they can eat, and work but one journey in the day; which seldom exceeds seven hours, but never eight; except in the neighbourhood of Leverington Parson-drove, and Thorney, where two journies a day are not unusual, ploughing from seven to twelve, and from two in the afte noon until night; or when the day will admit of it, till seven in the evening, doing about an acre each journey." Horses, alone, appear to be in use.

TILLAGE.—*Sodburning.*—P. 177 (by Mr. Stone). "On the fen lands this is general The toughness of the fen swerd is such, that it will not fall to decay, nor be got in pieces unless burnt. Cole seed on fen land will not feed sheep, unless the land producing it is burnt to prepare it for the coleseed. An excess of this practice often consumes a great deal of the soil, and when the land is laid down, a barrenness where this has taken place is very apparent. Goose-grass (or clivers) (?) is the general symptom of this impoverishment. Breast ploughing is certainly the best method, it may be done thinner, and more uniformly than by the plough drawn by horses, though the latter is the practice of this country. And indeed I do not think the damage done by burning, arises from the burning of the swerd, or the quantity pared off, so that it exceeds not one inch and a half or two inches, but from the fire getting hold of the land from allowing the heaps to lie unspread too long, and not watching the fire carefully, and putting it out immediately after spreading, before it gets such hold of the land as to make it difficult to be extinguished; the fire then hits, as it is called, and this is very prejudicial."

P. 201 (by the Reporter). "This practice is admissible to a certain extent upon land, composed entirely of vegetable matter, where the water is at command, and where lowering the surface is not likely to be attended with material inconvenience. Paring and burning is here the only effectual means of quickly bringing land of this description, into a profitable state of cultivation: In such land, wherever there is a considerable depth of vegetable matter, after a few years rest, the surface becomes uneven, resembling a field covered with innumerable ant-hills; and the tops of these inequalities, producing little herbage, and that of an inferior quality, are only to be improved by a judicious application of the plough, and burning about one third part of the thinnest of the *flag*, that can possibly be pared."

MANURE.

MANURE.—P. 172 (by Mr. Stone). "Pigeon dung and soot are sometimes sown upon marsh and high land fallows; whereon turnips or cole seed are sown; and sometimes soot upon wheat at spring, to embitter the surface and upper stratum of the land, to make the wire worms eating the wheat, retreat from it, and where this has been used it has always succeeded; there having been a vast yield after it, when, if it had not been tried, it has been believed the crop would have been entirely destroyed: twenty bushels an acre, is the quantity generally used. Wire worms are the greatest annoyance we experience in our husbandry; they are yellow in their colour, and resemble the centipede, from the number of their feet, but not quite so long in their bodies; the heavy and light soils are equally subject to them."

P. 46 (Fenny Ditton). "Within this enclosure, a considerable improvement has lately been made, by laying on, about fifteen hundred bushels per acre, of the white, chalky, clay, from the highland."

CORN CROPS. - These are fully noticed, in the *parochial journal*, aforegoing.

Enemies of Corn Crops.—See the heads, *Rent, Manure*, and *Plan* of *Management* respecting the WIREWORM.

The *Produce* of Corn Crops, in the fens, appears, on the average of the several instances registered in the Table noticed, aforegoing, p. 242,—to be of wheat 24¼ bushels —of barley 30 bushels— of oats 47½ bushels, and—of rape seed 29 bushels,—an acre.

HEMP.—Mr. Vancouver's observations, on the effect of the hemp crop upon the lands which produce it, is so cheering, at this particular juncture, that it would be unkind to withhold them from the public.—If a crop of hemp be equal to a fallow, not only in destroying weeds (as is generally asserted) but in "fertilizing" the soil, as Mr. V. overtly holds out,—where can be the cause of alarm and dismay, about a supply of that material, for our navy, and other purposes? His strictures are certainly entitled to a place in this Register.

P. 217. "The culture of this important plant, begins deservedly to be regarded in a far more favourable light in the present day than formerly. In those countries where it is generally cultivated, it is considered as an extremely exhausting, and impoverishing crop, but in parts of this county, where the *occasional culture* of hemp, forms a part of a system of perpetual cropping without rest or fallow, it is not only viewed as an ameliorating crop, but experience

rience proves that upon those lands it is the best possible
preparation for a crop of wheat. Flax is cultivated by way
of a change upon the same lands.

"The *fertilizing qualities of hemp* upon the soil, may
possibly be referred to the same cause, which so powerfully operates upon sowing grey peas on land in Ireland,
when it is so far exhausted, as not to yield the quantity of
seed in return of oats, or any other grain. But as the pea
crop seldom fails, the land is thereby brought into so high
a state of preparation, as to insure an abundant crop of
wheat, without manure or fallow. Lands which thus become productive, probably contain a great quantity of
vegetable matter, in an imperfect state of rottenness, and
unfit for the food of plants. The combination of heat and
moisture can only affect its perfect dissolution, and to the
umbrageous influence of hemp and peas, which prevents
exhalation and keeps the surface during the heat of summer, constantly moist, may be ascribed the good effects
arising from these crops."

CULTIVATED HERBAGE.—P. 152 (Chatteris). "From
long experience, it has been found, that the fen land
answers much the best, when it is properly laid down with
the following grass seeds, mixed, (viz.) three pounds of
red clover, three pounds of Dutch white clover, or honey
suckling, three pounds of trefoil, or black nonsuch, three
pounds of narrow leaved plantain, or ribbed grass, and one
bushel of clean rye grass per acre; two bushels of highland hay seeds, are generally preferred to the bushel of
rye grass, when conveniently to be had."

GRASS LANDS.—*Grazing Grounds.*—P. 155 (Elm). "The
general proportion of stock allowed for the highland pastures during six summer months, are twenty-two sheep,
and one steer, or bullock for every five acres; and three
sheep for every two acres, during the winter months; in
which time they will improve in value, but in general not
in grazing or growing fat."

Water for *Grazing Stock.*—P. 168 (by Mr. Stone).
"The want of water in all these parishes is a great hardship. In the parish of Leverington it might be remedied,
as to the highlands; and if the present Honourable Board
attend so minutely to the interests of agriculture as to regard partial and local evils, I pledge myself to shew not
only the possibility, but the facility, of remedying it. I
have frequently suggested it to the principals of the
parish; but the want of unanimity and joint effort among
them, to promote the general good, have left this, as well
as

as many other material matters, disregarded."—It is unfortunate that Mr. Stone has not afforded me an opportunity of conveying to the *public*, the outline of his plan.

See also *Plan* of *Management* aforegoing, on this particular, p. 253.

HORSES.—On the breed, or on the breeding, of this species of livestock, in the fens of Cambridgeshire,—I find nothing, in the Report before me.

In my journey across them, I observed many brood mares and foals, of the black fen breed ; and some young saddle horses of color.

CATTLE.—The following is the only article of information, that I have detected, relative to the cattle of the fens, or waterlands of Cambridgeshire.   P. 208. " In the neighbourhood of Ely, where the herbage is infinitely superior to that in the higher parts of the county, it is a matter of concern to observe that so little attention is paid to the improvement of the common breed of *cow cattle*. (!)   In the neighbourhood of Wisbich, a very sensible alteration in this particular, for the better, is with pleasure observed."

SHEEP (Elm). P. 155. "The sheep are generally of the Lincolnshire breed, though they are occasionally crossed with the Leicestershire ; the three years old wethers of which, when *fattened to the bone*, will weigh upon an average about twenty-six pounds per quarter, and eleven pounds per fleece."

GOOCH's

GOOCH's

CAMBRIDGESHIRE.

THIS REPORT has come out under the same mysterious circumstance, as did Parkinson's Huntingdonshire. See p. 212, aforegoing.

A preface to the Volume before me is dated "*Whatfield Parsonage*, SUFFOLK, 1807 ;" and, in different parts of it, the materials of which it consists would seem to have been collected, in "1806."—Hence, the information it contains, has been "carefully laid up in a napkin,"—has been hidden from the eyes of the public, some four or five years.

I attempt not to speak of the *Reporter's qualifications*, here ; as it is the WATERLANDS, only, of Cambridgeshire, that are required to be attended to, in this place. And it does not appear, in his Report, that Mr. Gooch possessed, in 1806, much knowledge, *of his own*, relating to that particular part of the county.

The NATURAL LANDS of CAMBRIDGESHIRE indispensably form a portion of the MIDLAND DEPARTMENT.

The WATERLANDS of CAMBRIDGESHIRE.

On the HISTORY of those lands we find an undigested mass of matter. By whom it was thrown together does not clearly appear —Many thanks to him who *did* it.

P. 204. " It was the opinion of Mr. Atkins (a commissioner of sewers in the reign of James I. 1604, &c. &c.) that these fens were once ' of the nature of land-meadows, fruitful, healthful, and very gainful to the inhabitants, and yielded much relief to the highland countries in time of great drought.' Sir W. Dugdale (who was born 1605, and died 1686) was of the same opinion, adding as a proof, ' that great numbers of timber trees, (oaks, firs, &c. &c.) formerly grew there, as is plain from many being found in digging canals and drains, some of them severed from their roots, the roots standing as they grew in firm earth below the moor. The firs at the depth of four and
five

five feet. The oaks at three feet; they were lying in a north west direction not cut down, but burnt near the ground, as the ends of them being coaled, manifested. The oaks in multitudes of an extraordinary size, being five yards in compass, and sixteen yards long, and some smaller of a great length, with a quantity of acorns near them.' In marsh-land he says, ' about a mile westward of Magdalen bridge, at setting down a sluice, there were discovered at seventeen feet deep, several furze and nut-trees pressed flat down, with nuts sound and firm lying by them, the bushes and trees standing in the solid earth below the silt.' The Rev. J. Rasbrick, of King's Lynn, (see Philosophical Transactions, No. 279. 1702), and Mr. Elster, (see Historical account of Bedford leve), gives the like testimony respecting the former existence of trees in the fens, the latter remarking that those he saw, appeared to be sawed off. To this day (1806) are found in every part of the fens, many at so short a distance from the surface, that the plough frequently touches them; I witnessed this many times. Mr. A. Young (Annals, v. 37, p. 451), says ' in every part of Europe, where marshy fens and bogs are found, if the soil be peat, trees are commonly discovered at various depths.' It is the same in the lordship of Thorney (in this county); in the upland parts all sorts of trees, and in the lower fen-lands they are all firs; and it is a fact, that Mr. Wing (of Thorney) has often ascertained, that many have been met with sawn off, and lying as they fell by the stump. ' The horns of red deer have been dug up, and are preserved at the abbey.' The commissioners under a law of sewers made 1596, and called ' neat moor law,' speaking of the fens, say, 'which in former times have been dry and profitable, and so they may be hereafter, if due provision be made.'

"Sir H. Hobert, (Attorney-general to James I.) says, ' the grounds now sought to be drained (1604, &c.) are such as naturally and anciently were dry grounds.' Dugdale mentions a gravel causeway three feet deep, (supposed to be made by the Emperor Severus, who was born 146, and died 211), from Denvor in Norfolk, to Peterborough in Northamptonshire, twenty-four miles, and which is now covered with moor five feet in thickness. In deepening the channel of Wisbech river, 1635, the workmen at eight feet below the then bottom, discovered a second bottom which was stony with seven boats lying in it, covered with silt. And at Whittlesea, on digging through the moor at eight feet deep, a perfect soil was found with
swaths

swaths of grass lying on it, as they were at first mown. Henry of Huntingdon, (who lived in the reign of Stephen, 1135) described this fenny country ' as pleasant and agreeable to the eye; watered by many rivers which run through it, diversified by many large and small lakes, and adorned by many woods and islands.' And William of Malmsbury, who lived in the first year of Henry II. (1154) has painted the state of the land round Thorney in the most glowing colours, he says, ' it is a very paradise, in pleasure and delight, it resembles heaven itself, the very marshes abounding in trees whose length without knots do emulate the stars.' ' The plain there is as level as the sea, which with the flourishing of the grass, allureth the eye;' ' in some parts there are apple trees, in others vines.' It appears then on the authority of the authors quoted, that the fens were formerly wood and pasture."

P. 206. " The first attempt at draining any part of the fens (Dugdale) appears to have been made in the time of Edward I. (1272, &c.) many others with various success followed. The famous John of Gaunt (or Ghent who died in 1393), and Margaret, Countess of Richmond, were amongst the draining adventurers; but Mr. Gough in his addition to Camden, says ' the Reign of Elizabeth (1558) may be properly fixed on as the period when the level began to become immediately a public care.' Many plans were proposed and abandoned between that time and 1634, when King Charles I. granted a charter of incorporation to Francis, earl of Bedford, and thirteen gentlemen adventurers with him, who jointly undertook to drain the level on condition that they should have granted to them, as a recompense 95,000 acres (about one-third of the level). In 1649, this charter was confirmed to William, earl of Bedford, and his associates, by the convention parliament, and in 1653 the level being declared completely drained, the 95,000 acres were conveyed to the adventurers, who had expended 400,000*l.* which is about 4*l.* 4*s.* per acre, on the 95,000 acres, and about 1*l.* 8*s.* on the whole breadth, if the whole level contain 285,000 acres; (it is generally supposed to contain 300,000 acres). In 1664, the corporation called ' conservators of the great level of the fens,' was established. This body was empowered to levy taxes on the 95,000 acres, to defray whatever expenses might arise in their preservation, but only 83,000 acres were vested in the corporation in trust for the earl of Bedford and his associates, the remaining 12,000 were allotted, 10,000 to the king, and 2000 to the

earl

earl of Portland. At first the level was an equal acre tax, but upon its being deemed unjust, a gradual one was adopted, which is now acted upon. In the year 1697, the Bedford level was divided into three districts, north, middle, and south; having one surveyor for each of the former, and two for the latter. In 1753, the north level was separated by act of parliament from the rest. In addition to the public acts obtained for draining the fens, several private ones have been granted for draining separate districts with their limits, notwithstanding which and the vast sums expended, much remains to be done; a great part of the fens is now (1806) in danger of inundation, this calamity has visited them many times, producing effects distressing and extensive beyond exception, indeed many hundred acres of valuable land, are now drowned, the misfortune aggravated by the proprietors being obliged to continue to pay a heavy tax, notwithstanding the loss of their land."

P 209. " Much about the same quantity flooded in 1799 and 1800, by downfall and breaches in the interior banks."

DRAINAGE of the Fens.—P. 211. " Many projects for the better drainage of the fens, and the improvement of the navigation, have of late been proposed; the last passed into a law 1795, and is called the Eau Brink cut*, the benefit or evil, however, of which is yet to be known, a difference of opinion after passing the act, having arisen between Sir Thomas Hyde Page, and Mr. Milne, (the engineers named in the act,) for determining the dimensions

" * 1794, Eau Brink cut. It is presumed that the history of tidal rivers does not furnish an instance like that before us, where the upland waters from being confined nearly in a straight line, and to a width of 200 feet (as they are at Germans bridge), are suffered to wander as they approach their outfall into a rambling circuitous course, expanding to a width of nearly a mile, and thence returning to the same line that was before deserted.

" As the case is singular so are the consequent evils. Internal navigation is rendered so defective, that boats cannot pass from Germans to Lynn without pilots, by means whereof great delays and a vast increase in the expence of freight are occasioned; and in blowing weather many lighters have been sunk, and lives have been lost.

" Navigation from the port of Lynn to sea is injured by beds of sand, which are constantly becoming stronger and stronger for want of a proper scower, insomuch that no vessels can navigate, but such as are of a particular form and structure.

" Hence foreign trade is enjoyed by a small number of merchants, who are their own carriers."

sions of the cut, and there being no power in the act to compel these gentlemen to name a third engineer as umpire; nothing has been done but tracing the lines from the dimensions in the act at the lower and upper ends of the cut, and collecting the tax imposed by act; but as this project has long engaged the public attention, and is thought a subject of importance to the county of Cambridge in particular, I have been solicitous to obtain the best information on it. The advocates for the work assert,

" 1st, That upwards of 300,000 acres of land will be better drained.

" 2d, That the harbour of Lynn will be rendered safe and commodious.

" 3d, That the foreign and coasting-trade of the port will be extended.

" 4th, That the danger and uncertainty of the navigation between Lynn and Eau brink, by the present channel will be avoided, and the remainder of the inland navigation improved, &c. &c.

" The opposers of this measure contend that none of these benefits will be the result, but that the reverse of them will ensue.

" Regarding the maxim, ' audi alteram partem;' I will state the opinions I am in possession of, for and against the measure."

For the measure stand the following *Names;* some of which are *known*.

Governor Powell, in 1775.
Mr. John Golburn, 1777.
Mr. James Golbourne, 1791.
Mr. Wattie, in 1791.
" A Member of the Committee" (?) in 1793.
Mr Rennie, in 1793.
The Earl of Hardwick, in 1794.
Mr. Hudson.

Against the measure.

Mr. Humphrey Smith, in 1729.
Mr. Labelye, in 1745.
Mr. Smeaton, in 1767.
Sir Thomas Hyde Page, knight, in 1775.
Mr. Elstebb, in 1778.
Mr. Hodgkinson, in 1792.
" An Inhabitant of Lynn," in 1793.

The

The opinions of Mr. SMITH, Mr. SMEATON and SIR THOMAS PAGE, *against* the measure, are all that I feel myself inclined to notice, here. The *measure, itself,* appears to be, *as far as it goes,* eminently eligible:—provided, I mean, the waters of the Cambridgeshire fens ought to flow through the harbour of Lynn.

It will be right to premise, for the information of my readers, that the "EAUBRINK CUT,"—about which volumes have been written, and year after year has been talked away,—was (and I understand still is), intended to straighten the river Ouse; by cutting off a circuitous bend, near its efflux into the sea.

The length of the proposed channel is some two or three miles; reaching, downward, to within half a mile of the port of Lynn; and, upward, to near the bridge of St. German's.

The present channel is not only circuitous, but wide, and of course shallow;—probably, an estuary, or inlet of the sea, in latter times.—Into this spacious receptacle, the spring tides still force their way; and the waters, there momentarily lodged, tend of course to scour, in their reflux, the haven of Lynn.

The advantages held out to be gained, by a straighter and deeper channel, is not merely that of drawing off the waters of the Ouse more rapidly, and more effectually with regard to the drainage of the lands situated above; but by thus obtaining an increase of current, and a more contracted efflux,—the impetus or force of the stream would thereby be enabled to deepen the harbor of Lynn; and, moreover, to force open the bar which crosses its mouth; so as to permit ships of greater burden to approach that port, than are now able to reach it.

The objections to this plan, by the three engineers last mentioned, were (as stated in the Report under notice) the following:

P. 223. " In 1729, Mr. Humphrey Smith. ' It (the new cut) will (in my opinion) be the utter ruin and total loss of the port of Lynn, for the wide space between German's and Lynn, gives room for the tides, and serves as a large receptacle for a back water to scour out their haven, which if confined by the methods prescribed, the silt and sand of the sea water would raise such a bar, that their shipping could not get over ' "

Same page. " In 1767, Mr. Smeaton. ' I cannot agree in recommending the expedient (the proposed cut) for if the cut be not made equal to the mean capacity of the old

river,

river, it would check the influx of the tides, and *if so made* the event must be uncertain.'"

" In 1775, Sir Thomas Hyde Page, Knt. ' I am of opinion that if (the cut) had not at the first receiving of the water a very considerable breadth and depth, particularly near the outfall, the run of water from the sea into it, being very violent, would carry great quantities of silt, &c. from its sides and bottom, which might be dropped higher up the river, and as the ebb at Lynn is so much slower than the flood, it probably would not have sufficient force to carry it out to sea. This danger might be the greater in a dry season, upon a want of fresh water in the river to counteract the inlet of the tide.'"

Judging from what I have read, as well as from what I have seen, in a cursory view, of the site of this proposed alteration,—those objections, I conceive, might be removed, by the means following.

Form the fresh channel wide enough, deep enough, and with banks sufficiently high, to confine the waters of ordinary floods; and to convey them, *in a body*, to the most eligible POINT and with the best DIRECTION, to clear, from time to time, the haven of Lynn.

On either side of that channel, raise higher banks, at a sufficient distance from each other, to receive the waters of spring tides and extraordinary land floods; also a similar bank across the lower end of such receptacle; to confine them, there, until the tide shall have receded; with floodgates sufficiently numerous and wide, to give vent and the required force, at the proper time of tide, to the waters so pent up; in order to clear, more effectually, the harbor, and to deepen the channel across the bar, at the mouth of it, with more effect, than can possibly be done, I apprehend, by the sluggish reflux of the tide, at present. It would seem to be a great deal owing to the slow return of the tide waters, mentioned by Sir T. Page, that the haven is now silted up; and the bar encreased in height. If the channel of the river, between the harbor and the bar, can be contracted in such a manner, that the collected force of the descending waters could be brought to act immediately on the bar, the effect would of course be rendered the more complete:—and, if the small chart, which is inserted in the Report, be accurate, such a contraction would seem to be practicable.

Regarding the " silt &c." that might be forced up the new channel of the river (as suggested, above, by Sir

T. Page)

T. Page) it may be considered as a circumstance that might be rendered *doubly fortunate* :—first, as it might be made highly beneficial to the lands, above, which are properly situated to receive the suspended matter, as alluvion, or warp ; and, secondly, to the haven of Lynn, as it might thereby, be for ever freed from its encumbrance.—See p. 116, aforegoing *.

On the whole, therefore, it appears to me that, by the means above offered, the port of Lynn might be greatly benefitted ; and, moreover, that a portion of the waterlands of NORFOLK might be effectually drained ; and the lower grounds of that portion be highly enriched.

But how could the Fens of CAMBRIDGESHIRE and HUNTINGDONSHIRE, be much bettered by such proposed alterations,—while the DAM of DENVER remains to obstruct the free and constant influx of the tide ; as well as the uninterrupted descent of land floods, to the point where their action would be the most effective ?

Not only the principal channels, the main drains,— whether in a degree *natural,* or altogether *artificial,*—but the smaller branches, the finest and most distant veins, of the GENERAL SYSTEM, ought to be duly *planned, proportioned,* and *freed from obstructions ;* even as are the arteries and veins of the animal system :—not merely to draw off the superfluous moisture of the lands with due effect ; but in order that the waters laden with alluvion, may flow freely, upward, as far as the tide will carry them : at once to enrich the lands, and to assist in clearing the estuary from mud banks, and the channels of the rivers and drains from obstructions ;—that is to say, from being "silted up."

But while separate and opposing interests are allowed to thwart each other,—to the immense loss of the community!—how can any thing resembling a rational system be carried into execution ?

How discreditable to the administration of public affairs, to suffer so valuable a portion of *our own country* to be kept in a state of unproductiveness, by the jarring interests and cabals of private individuals!—For half a million of money, or perhaps one half, or a smaller part of

that

---

* When I there suggested the *commercial advantage* that might be derived from ALLUVIATION, I was not aware of the particular instance, here in view. There are doubtlessly many instances, in which the principle might be profitably applied.

that sum,—the interest of three millions might, in all probability, be saved *.

The estimated quantity of lands whose surface waters now flow, or are bid to flow, toward the port of Lynn, and which are injured, or rendered in a manner useless to the nation, by an imperfect drainage,—is 300,000 acres.—Admitting that these lands may be improved, by DRAINAGE and ALLUVIATION, only ten shillings an acre, a year, the annual advantage to arise from the improvement would be 150,000 l.; which, at five per cent., would pay the interest of 3,000,000 l.—How many millions—tens of millions—(I cannot refrain from adding) have been expended, during the time the lands under view have been lying in a state of neglect, on the *countries of others,*—without *any* prospect of return!!!

Whether the whole, or the principal part, of the waters of the Fens of Cambridgeshire and Huntingdonshire ought to have their efflux into the sea, through the haven of Lynn, or whether they should meet the tide at Wisbeach, and be discharged into the estuary of the Nene (Cross Key Wash) is an important point that can be satisfactorily cleared up, by no other means than a general plan of the site to be improved; with the comparative elevation of every prominent and depressed part of it, accurately taken, and marked upon the plan.

Until such a GENERAL PLAN of the intire extent of the lands to be drained (no matter as to what Counties they may extend into) with the ELEVATION of every such part, above the sea at low water marked upon it, be produced, let not PARLIAMENT suffer contending *parties* to interrupt their more salutary proceedings. For it is by such a guide, alone, their Committees can form a just judgement of the measure.

If this great national concern—this rich *mine* of CORN and CATTLE—is still to be left in the hands of contending interests, let each *party!* choose an engineer or engineers, to take the levels; and to trace the lines, through every dip and sinking of the surface, that may appear to
them

* The votaries of corruption and speculative commerce may reply with a sneer—"what are three millions!"—Were I to hear them I would say—"A permanent benefit to our own island, of three millions, is of more value to the lasting prosperity of the country, itself, than all the ephemeral schemes of commerce that ever were, or ever will be formed."

them proper to draw off the waters of the entire site, with the most eligible descent;—the engineers, so chosen, naming an umpirage of one or more engineers, before they proceed to business; in order to reconcile, or moderate, any jarrings that may arise;—and by these means produce as perfect a guide, as human endeavors,—under circumstances so irrational and so much to be lamented,—can well furnish *

Should agriculture and commerce clash, as doubtlessly in some cases they might,—for the lasting welfare of the country, and the honor of its government, let agriculture, for once, take the lead †.

On

* It would not be difficult, with such data, to form a MODEL, on an extended scale, to show, in a *summary way*, and with *certainty*, the lines along which the waters ought to flow, and their proper outlet, or outlets, to the sea.

† Since the above Remarks were written, I have perused Mr. VANCOUVER's valuable Paper, mentioned, aforegoing,——Note, page 248.

From that Paper, which has been kept seventeen years! from the public eye, it appears that Mr. V. has (it might be said) made a beginning to take the required elevations, above recommended.—Not, however, the elevations of the interior fens and marshes in detail: but, merely, the descents of the estuaries of the Norfolk or Lynn Ouse, and of the Nene or Wisbeach river,—down to the low water marks, at the terminations of their channels: and, this, principally or solely, with the view of showing the impropriety of *forcing* the fen waters of Huntingdonshire, and the principal part of Cambridgeshire, into the Norfolk river.

Mr. Vancouver's Paper, which extends to forty pages, is divided into

1. " Of the Nature and Origin of the Fens."
2. " Of the general Drainage of the Fens."
3. " Of the internal Works and District Drainage of the Fens."

In the first section, I find nothing that calls, particularly, for insertion, here; the following concise, yet intelligent, account of the nature of fen land excepted.

P. 319. " We find the surface of the fens, which is occasionally exposed to the influence of the summer heats, consists of completely decompounded and putrified vegetables; and regarding the soil only, it is impossible to trace in it any vestige of the original substances that composed it. The sub-stratum, or turf-moor next below the soil, is also a composition of vegetable bodies, but in a less perfect state of rottenness or decomposition; and in this may very plainly be seen the original form and substance of its component parts. Below this again, and lying on the natural and antient surface of the country, is another stratum of vegetable matter, commonly called

bears

On the *business* of embankment and drainage, in the Fens of Cambridgeshire.

Embankment.

bears muck *; this stratum retains every appearance of what it originally was, saving its life and colour, being an assemblage of the roots, leaves and stems of an aquatic vegetation which has undergone but little alteration since the remote period of its first formation; because it has been beyond the reach of the essential principle of heat to combine with moisture and air in effecting its natural and necessary dissolution."

The second section, on GENERAL DRAINAGE, contains much valuable information. The subjoined would seem to be a luminous history of the unpardonable ignorance and folly of those who contravened an unerring law of Nature, and set up their own absurdities in its stead!

P. 321. " As the preceding section contains the amount of my observations and opinion, on the nature and origin of the fens, I shall now direct my attention to the next points which appear to demand our most serious consideration (viz.) the cheapest and most effectual means of forming a good drainage and navigation from the highland country, through the level of the fens to the sea; so as by one and the same means to render commerce more diffusive and beneficial to the country at large, and obtain a more effectual drainage of the fens and low grounds.

" As the drainage of the fens and the navigation of the rivers passing through them to the upper country, are inseparably united, and must ever be regarded in a discussion of this nature as one and the same thing; it is necessary to establish some first principle, which of necessity applies equally to both, and from which, as from a point, we may take our departure, and to which we must return again. The level of the sea I conceive to be this point, since ' all rivers run into the sea, yet the sea is not full; and unto the place from whence the rivers come, thither they return again.'

" The waters of the *middle level*, at this time diverted from their natural course, by the present forced system of drainage in the river Nene at Outwell, arrive within ten miles (reckoned on the general course of the old Ouze river) of Gunthorpe sluice, through which all the waters of the north level are freely uttered. From Outwell church, the waters of the Nene are driven six miles farther, before they can obtain a very slow and languid descent to seaward, through Salterslode sluice. The same enormous system prevails in the whole drainage of the middle, and the greater part of the south level, of the fens; and *is the legitimate offspring of the first diversion of old Ouze from its natural channel, and forcing its waters into the Lynn or lesser Ouze, through the cut which was formerly made from Littleport Chair to Priests Houses.*

" From the highlands in Suffolk (between the Milden-hall and Brandon rivers) to the east of Welney, Outwell, Emneth, and thence to the sea, a positive *dividing ground* exists, formed by the hand
                                                                    of

" * This substance is cut into large sods, about twice the size of a common brick, and forms the red spungy kindling turf, which is sold in large towns for the purpose of lighting fires."

Embankment.—It is a matter of some surprise, seeing the length of time which has elapsed since the genius of
BINGLEY

of Nature, strongly marked and distinctly to be seen between the waters of the Lynn and of the Wisbeach Ouze. The hanging level or natural inclination of the country on the north " (northeast) " side of this *dividing ground*, draws the water off to sea through the lesser Ouze to the outfall of Lynn; and on the south side of it draws them off to the sea through the greater Ouze to the outfall of Wisbeach. *To the cutting through this divided ground in order to force the water of the greater into the lesser Ouze, are all the evils of the south and middle levels of the fens, and of the country below, solely and originally to be ascribed.* At this time the bed of the Ouze, where Denver sluices now stand, was at least *thirteen feet* below the general surface of the surrounding country; and then it was, that by the free action and re-action of the tides, the water flowed five hours in the haven of Lynn, ascended into the Stoke and Brandon rivers, and into other streams which Nature had wisely appropriated to be discharged through that outfall; forming the bed of the Ouze to one gradually inclined plane *from the junction of the principal branches of the river in the low country, to the level of the ocean very near or in the harbour of Lynn.* Then it was, that the province of marshland was recovered from the sea; and all the country which by Nature belonged to the drainage of the Lynn Ouze was effectually drained, and made into good winter grounds.

" The counteracting this disposition of Nature, *by forcing a greater quantity of water into the river than it could discharge into the sea during the time of ebb,* necessarily occasioned the highland and foreign waters to over-ride all those, which during the time of ebb, would naturally have drained into the Lynn river, and gave the waters of Buckingham and Bedford an exit into the sea, in preference to those which lay inundating the country, within a few miles of their natural outfall.—In this condition at present, are all the lower parts of the country bordering upon the Lynn Ouze; and the country above Denver sluices, Downham, Marshland, and Bardolph fens, exhibits the most important of many other melancholy examples and evidences of it. In the higher parts of the country, the consequences of this measure seem to have been severely experienced, on the lands exposed to the unembanked waters of the old Ouze, between Hermitage and Harrimere. The old Bedford river was then cut, from Erith to Salterslode, as a slaker to the Ouze, to relieve the country through which the Ouze flowed, from Erith to Ely. The Ouze waters thus divided, a great part of them descended through the old Bedford river in a straight line of twenty miles into the Lynn Ouze. But as that work was judged insufficient and defective, the new Bedford, or one hundred foot river, was determined upon; and sluices were erected at Hermitage to drive all the waters of old Ouze from Erith, (through the one hundred foot,) into the Lynn Ouze; but that river not having sufficient capacity to utter them to the sea, they reverted up the Ouze, the Stoke, and Brandon rivers, drowning the whole of that country; and finally urging the necessity of erecting Denver sluices as the only apparent cure for the evils with which the County was then oppressed, and seemed farther threatened with. In the execution of this business, with a view of bringing the bottom
of

BINGLEY made the important discovery of " Puddling," and its unlimitted use, in canal making and other water-works,—

of the Ouze on a level with that of the one hundred foot river, (which was cut only five feet deep,) it was judged expedient to raise a dam eight feet high across the bed of the Ouze, upon the top of which the sole or base of the Denver sluices was laid. This measure has not only defeated the purpose it was designed to promote, but has been the unfortunate cause of a body of sand and sea sediment being deposited in the bed of the Lynn Ouze, at least *eight feet deep at Denver* sluices; and only terminating in its injurious consequences at the mouth of the Lynn channel (or low water mark at sea). This shows to every calm and candid mind, the necessity of duly considering the probable effects of counteracting the laws of Nature, in cases where Nature appears experimentally to have had success on her side. By great and continued exertion the strength and ingenuity of man may in some instances delay the evil which otherwise would immediately accrue from a counteraction of those laws; but his energy is not only feeble, but soon expires; whereas that of Nature is potent, and if relieved only from the operation of incidental obstacles, as it is unalterable in its essence, so it must be uniform in its effects, from the beginning of time till time shall be no more.

" From a due consideration of the obstacles which will appear at this time to exist in what has long been considered the principal outfalling drain to the middle and south levels of the fens, it is surely reasonable to direct our attention to the general inclination of the country with respect to the sea, and to what has all along been pointed out by Nature as the main outlet thither, for the waters of the middle and south levels, and see if some means cannot yet be devised for recovering the general course of the ancient and voluntary passage of the waters through their natural channel of Wisbeach to the sea."

How far this evidently considerate and well written account is founded in fact, would be *proved* by the measure, suggested aforegoing.

The following minutes and remarks will convey to my readers, Mr. Vancouver's laudable, ingenious, and well concerted attempt, to ascertain *the action of the tide*, at the mouths of the two discharging rivers, and the *elevation* of the *lands on the coast*, above the sea at low water.

P. 325. " To begin this inquiry we must take our departure from the low water mark from sea; and trace the effect of the tidal waters as they regard the discharge of the land waters, through the channels of Lynn and Wisbeach. On this occasion, I have been as accurate as the time and means in my power would enable me to be, but still I must lament the necessity I have been under of resorting to the materials of art rather than adhering closely to those of nature to establish my facts upon.

" The flowing of the tide above the haven of Lynn, at stated distances to Denver sluice at the times I was moored at the entrance of the Lynn and Wisbeach channels, would be more satisfactory and conclusive to my mind, than any scientific authority, however high, and deservedly to be depended upon. Such data however as I have been able to collect from the flowing of the tides, will be found in the following tide tables. TABLE

works,—that it should not, long ago, have found its way into the Waterlands of Cambridgeshire and its environs; especially

"TABLE of the flowing of the tide on the 19th day of November 1793, in the harbour of Lynn, and at the mouth of the Lynn channel, two miles below the Terror Sands, at the White or Flag Buoy, distant about fourteen miles on a straight line below the harbour of Lynn.

In the Harbour of Lynn.

Time Hours.	Time Min.	Rise Feet.	Rise Inches.	
At 5				dead low water, or the first flow of the tide.
5	30	6	6	
6		6	5	
6	30	3	3	
7	32	2	5	
7	40	1	11	Ebb began.
				flow.
In 2	32	14	6	

At the Mouth of the Lynn Channel.

Time Hours.	Time Min.	Depth of water in which we anchored Feet.	Depth Inches.	Rise Feet.	Rise Inches.	
At 2		19				in which we anchored at dead low water.
3	30	21	6	1	10	
3		25	4	5	8	
4	30	28	2	8	6	
4		31		11	6	
5	30	33	8	13	2	Young flood at Lynn.
5		36	3	16	9	
6	30	38		18	6	
6		39	6	20		
7	23	40	6	20	6	
7	40	41		21		Ebb began.
In 5	40	a flow of		21	6	

" N. B.

especially when we perceive the immense advantage it is
capable of affording to the fen banks, and their inade-
quateness without it, or a substitute. See p. 213, aforegoing.

Mr. SMITH of Chatteris has struck out a method of improving the fen banks, which, tho not equally accurate as
that of " Puddling," must be of great use to them.—The
following is the substance of Mr. Smith's " Communication
to the Board."

P. 246. " Previously to my describing a valuable and
improved mode of banking, I will concisely observe that
the great level of the fens is divided into three large
levels, and that each of these levels is subdivided into numerous districts by banks; but as these banks are made
of fen-moor, and other light materials, whenever the rivers
are swelled with water, or any one district is deluged
either by rain, a breach of banks, or any other cause, the
waters speedily pass through these bright, moory, porous
banks, and drown all the circumjacent districts. The fens
have sometimes sustained 20,000*l.* or 30,000*l.* damage by
a breach of banks; but these accidents seldom happen in
the same district twice in twenty years; the water, however, soaks through all fen banks every year in every district;

" N. B. The above observations at the Flag Buoy in the Chops of
the Lynn Channel, were made by Mr. Lionel Self, Mr. Middleton (master pilot), and the Author; and those in the Harbour of
Lynn, by Mr. Thomas Breame, and Mr William Durham; a gentle breeze blowing from the south-east the whole time.

" ☞ To explain in some measure the phenomenon that appears
from the within tide tables, of the ebb in the harbour of Lynn, being
noticed at the same point of time, it was felt in the mouth of the
Lynn channel, fourteen miles on a straight line nearer to the sea, we
must recur to the set of the tides in the bay, which is formed by the
coasts of Lincolnshire and Norfolk. The flood tide makes in Brancaster Bay on the coast of Norfolk about two hours sooner, and off
Hunston one hour sooner than at the Flag or White Buoy, which is
placed in the entrance of the Lynn channel, and of course returns in
the same proportion of time before it is high water in the mouth of
the channel. During the last hour's flood at the Flag Buoy, the tide
off Hunston sets eastwardly, and towards the sea between the sunk
sand and shore; in consequence of which, the water along shore in
the old eastern channel, between Hunston and Nottingham point,
is affected; and ebb in the harbour of Lynn, is felt sooner, than
would be expected, from the harbour of Lynn being fourteen miles
farther from the ocean than the mouth of the channel. At the time
these observations were made, the Terror Sands, which are about two
miles above the Flag Buoy, had not at low water more than four feet
depth upon them.

" TABLE

trict; and when the water-mills have lifted the waters up out of the fens into the rivers in a windy day, a great part of the

sluice, about six miles below the town; also on the north side of the Bar Buoy, about eighteen miles below the town, being in the entrance of Wisbeach channel; and also, in the harbour of Lynn.

On the North Side of the Bar Buoy.

Time.		Depth of water.	Rise.		
Hours.	Min.	Inches.	Feet.	Inches.	
At1	20	12		9.6	in which we anchored at dead low water.
2	0	13	1	6	
2	30	16	4	4	
3	0	19	7	3	
3	30	22	10	6	
4	0	24	12	6	flood at
4	30	27	15	6	
5	0	31	19	6	
5	25	32	20	6	high water.
5	30	32	20	6	
6	0	33	21	3	
6	20	33	21	3	
6	30	33	21	3	sensible ebb.
6	40	32	21	6	
In 5			21	3	rise or flow of the water.

N.B. The above observations were made by the Author, assisted by Sam. Gardiner, Tho. Gardiner, and Sam. Bouch. A gentle breeze at south by west the whole time.

At Gunthorpe sluice.

Time.		Rise.		
Hours.	Min.	Feet.	Inches.	
5	25			the first flow of the tide.
5	55			
6	25	4	2	
6	55	6		high water.
In 1	35	7		rise or flow of water.

N.B. The above observations were made by T. Pears, who lives at and has the care of the sluice. There were 2 feet 7 inches of water, at the time of young flood, over the threshold of the sluice.

In the town of Wisbeach.

Time.		Rise.			
Hours.	Min.	Feet.	Inches.	10ths.	
At6	20				the first flow of the tide.
6	50	1	0	3	
7	20	2	6	3	
7	50	3	5	3	
8	0	3	6	3	high water.
In 1	40	5	6	3	rise or flow of the water.

N.B. The above observations were made by Mr. John Turpin, of Wisbeach.

In the harbour of Lynn.

Time.		Rise.		
Hours.	Min.	Feet.	Inches.	
At4	12			dead low water, or the first flow of the tide.
4	42	5	8	
5	12	3	10	
5	42	2	6	
6	12	1	3	
6	30		9	high water.
In 2	38	14		rise or flow of the water.

N.B. The above observations were made by Mr. Thos. Breame of Lynn.

" From

the water soaks back through the porous banks in the night upon the same land again. This land" (water) "that soaks through the bank, drowns the wheat in the winter, washes the

"From the preceding tables the following summary may be drawn.

"When the tide at the mouth of the Lynn channel has flowed three hours, and has there risen thirteen feet two inches, it is young flood in the harbour of Lynn. But as it flows in the mouth of the Lynn channel, two hours and twenty minutes longer, the whole flow or rise of the water there is twenty-one feet six inches, in five hours and twenty minutes of time ; while the whole flow of the water in the harbour of Lynn in two hours and thirty-two minutes, is fourteen feet six inches ; and (adjusting the difference between the watches) at forty minutes past seven, ebb has made, and is first noticed, as well in the harbour of Lynn, as in the mouth of the channel. The inference is plain, allowing a small effect for the operation of the tide in the eastern channel (as before explained), there is an absolute acclivity of seven feet perpendicular height, between the low water mark in the entrance of Lynn channel, and the low water mark in the harbour of Lynn ; to overcome which acclivity and the obstructions upon it, in three hours of time, a force of moving water from the ocean of thirteen feet two inches perpendicular pressure is required.

"Secondly—When the flood tide has been made four hours and five minutes at the mouth of the *Wisbeach channel*, it has there risen twenty feet, and at this time it is young flood at Gunthorpe sluice. It flows in the mouth of the Wisbeach channel fifty-five minutes longer, making in the whole time five hours, and the whole flow or rise of the water is twenty-one feet three inches The time from first flood at Gunthorpe sluice, to high water there, is one hour and thirty-five minutes ; in which time the tide flows or rises seven feet in perpendilar height ; from whence it is plain that there is an acclivity of fourteen feet three inches, from the level of the sea at low water, to the low water at Gunthorpe sluice. Again, when the water has flowed five hours in the mouth of the Wisbeach channel, and has there risen twenty-one feet three inches, the first flood is perceived in the town of Wisbeach. At this time it is high water at sea ; though from the momentum of the tide, the water is continued flowing in the town for one hour and forty minutes longer, and there rises three feet six inches three tenths. From hence it is also plain that there is an acclivity of seventeen feet eight inches seven tenths between the low water at sea, and the low water mark in the port of Wisbeach ; to overcome which acclivity, and the obstructions upon it in five hours of time, a pressure of water from the ocean of twenty-one feet three inches perpendicular height is required. It is also to be remarked, that when the water has flowed in the entrance of the Wisbeach channel two hours and fifty-two minutes, and risen thirteen feet nine inches, it is young flood in the harbour of Lynn ; it continues to flow two hours and eight minutes longer in the mouth of the Wisbeach channel, where the whole flow or rise of the water is twenty-one feet three inches. In the harbour of Lynn the same tide flows two hours and thirty-eight minutes, and there rises fourteen feet. From hence it follows that there is a declivity of three inches more between the harbour

the manure into the dykes, destroys the best natural and artificial grasses, and prevents the fens from being sown till too late in the season. This stagnant water lying on the

bour of Lynn, and the mouth of the Wisbeach channel, than between the same harbour and the mouth of the Lynn channel; or in other words, that the low water in the mouth of the Wisbeach channel is three inches lower than that in the mouth of the channel of Lynn, or so much nearer to the low water mark at sea. From this view of the Lynn and Wisbeach rivers, the following opinions are fairly to be drawn : First, that the low water in the harbour of Lynn, is ten feet nearer to the low water mark at sea, than the low water in the port of Wisbeach. And secondly, allowing a fall of six feet four inches in the distance of near sixteen miles from Denver sluice to the harbour of Lynn, that there exists at the former place the same obstruction to the descent of all the middle and the south level waters as the waters of the north level uttered through Gunthorpe sluice have to encounter and completely overcome, (víz.) about fourteen feet perpendicular height above the level of low water at sea. This difference however must be observed, that whereas Gunthorpe sluice is situated within twelve miles of the absolute and lowest level of the sea (and within a much shorter distance of where there is a constant and eternal depth of from seven to ten fathom at low water), Denver sluice is not within thirty miles of this lowest level, and to which point the land waters must descend, before it can with reason be said that we have got compltely rid of them."

P. 331. "This being the present state of the Lynn and Wisbeach rivers, as they relate to navigation and the discharge of the land waters to the sea ; the next objects which command our attention are the cheapest, the quickest, and most effectual means of removing the obstructions at present existing in their respective channels; and bringing deep water, or the level of the sea, as near as the laws of Nature will admit of, to the seats of the present marine navigations; to the end, that by their improvement the drainage of the country may be rendered more immediate and compleat, and a more permanently valuable property be restored to individuals and secured to the nation."

This brings Mr. Vancouver to the consideration of the Eau brink scheme :—and this to Section the third, of which it is in reality a part ;—namely—"the internal works and DISTRICT DRAINAGE of the fens :"—joint subjects that have employed the pens of various writers. But they having had no firm ground on which to tread, their strictures must necessarily be, in a degree vague, and contradictory, and, of course, not entitled to a place, here.

Until a general plan of the country to be drained, and the elevation of every particular point of it's area, be accurately made out, no complete arrangement regarding its drainage and alluviation, can be drawn, with any degree of certainty. Every attempt will be, as it has hitherto been, little better than groping in the dark. On the contrary, with such a ground work to act upon, added to deliberate study of the site itself,—a high degree of perfection may be reached; without hazarding a miscarriage, or unnecessary expence; most especially, if a MODEL, *on a large scale*, were accurately formed, from such materials.

the surface, causes also fen agues, &c. thus the waters that have soaked through the porous fen banks have done the fertile fens more real injury than all the other floods that have ever come upon them. I have been much concerned in fen banking from my youth, and though I now farm upon a large scale, yet I am still much employed in superintending fen banking, and draining low lands; not only in the fens, but also in some highland counties, at a considerable distance. I had some time back devised the plan which I now find to answer so well, but found it extremely difficult to prevail with any gentleman, who possessed a proper district, to give it a fair trial; however, this last autumn, I prevailed with a gentleman in the parish where I reside to try the following plan, which proves equal to my most sanguine expectations.

"Plan of improved banking.

"I first cut a gutter eighteen inches wide, through the old bank down to the clay, (the fen substratum being generally clay,) the gutter is made near the centre, but a little on the land side of the centre of the old bank. The gutter is afterwards filled up in a very solid manner with tempered clay, and to make the clay resist the water, a man in boots always treads the clay as the gutter is filled up. As the fen moor lies on a clay, the whole expense of this cheap, improved, and durable mode of water-proof banking, costs in the fens only sixpence per yard. This plan was tried last summer on a convenient farm, and a hundred acres of wheat were sown on the land. The wheat and grass lands on this farm are now all dry, whilst the fens around are covered with water. This practice answers so well on this farm, that all the farmers in this parish are improving their banks in the same manner, and some have begun in adjacent parishes."

Draining Fen Lands.—In the subjoined extract, we find another instance, and a more striking one than that noticed, aforegoing (p. 167.) on morasses being liable to be drained too dry.

P. 242. "Necessary as drainage is to fen-lands, there are instances of its having been absolutely ruined by it: a remarkable one is at Chippenham, at Mr. Tharp's mill. where a very deep cut was made to carry off the tail water; the effect on the land on each side (a fen moor) is, it cracks in summer to that degree that it produces nothing, and no cattle can go upon it in safety; when, therefore, fen

is

is drained, it is necessary to have a command of water to be kept within a foot (?) of the surface.   Mr. Tharpe has done this with great judgment by sluices."

The GENERAL MANAGEMENT of Fen Lands, in Cambridgeshire.—P. 104. " The perfection of fen husbandry is to be seen at Thorney, under the direction of Mr. WING, whose management is so superior, that it is to be lamented his jurisdiction as superintendant of draining and embanking, does not extend over the whole level of the fens.   His cropping process is: ' pare and burn, and spread the ashes immediately ; 1st crop, cole fed by sheep; 2d, oats; 3d, oats or wheat; with either, layer for as long time as it remains good.   The layer ray grass two bushels, white clover eight or ten lbs., and on lands not liable to be flooded in winter, one sack of hay-seeds, six or seven lbs. of rib-grass, seven to ten lbs. of white clover, a small quantity of ray-grass; on the latter lands, the seeds are sown on the wheat.' "

THE

THE WATERLANDS

OF

NORFOLK and SUFFOLK.

THESE being a natural part,—forming the southeastern margin,—of what may be emphatically termed the WATER-LANDS of ENGLAND,—I think it best to assimilate the partial accounts of them, which have been collected by the Board, with those of Lincolnshire, Northamptonshire, Huntingdonshire, and Cambridgeshire; and thus to consolidate the whole of the information gained, by the Board of Agriculture in their County Reports, relating to this extraordinary passage of country.

The REPORTS, in which the information concerning this passage is contained, are

Kent's Norfolk,

The Secretary's Norfolk,

The Secretary's Suffolk.

KENT's NORFOLK.

SOIL.—P. 14. "Marshland may be considered as a hundred by itself. The soil is a rich ooze, evidently a deposit from the sea: the north part is highly productive; but the south part very much injured for want of better drainage, which, it is presumed, will now be effected, as there was a bill passed in the last session of parliament for that purpose."—The "Eau-brink Cut" has been spoken of, aforegoing.

P. 52. "The Marsh-land comes next under consideration. The greatest part of the hundred of Freebridge marsh-land may be considered of this kind.—The chiefest part of this soil is a rich ooze, evidently a deposit from the sea. The north part of this hundred is highly productive; but the south part very much injured, for want of a better drainage, which it is now likely to have, as a recent act of parliament for this, and other purposes, has been lately obtained.

"A second

" A second division of Marsh-land, lies upon the north coast, between Brancaster and Cley. These are of a very good quality; but they are kept embanked at a very considerable expence, for if the sea were to overflow them, they would be ruined for a very considerable time."

ARABLE CROPS.—P. 56. "In some parts of Marshland, there is a considerable deal of rape seed grown : in the parishes of Outwell, Upwell, Emneth, and some others in the neighbourhood of Wisbeach, there is likewise a considerable deal of hemp and flax sown."

THE SECRETARY's NORFOLK.

A MINUTE, made in 1784, on "COUNT BENTINCK's EMBANKMENT," in the MARSHLANDS of NORFOLK, will be the best introduction to the other notices of the Secretary, relating to that valuable tract of country.

P. 435. "The tract of land in Norfolk, between the rivers Wyne and Ouze, called Marshland, is one of the richest districts in the kingdom. It spreads also into Lincolnshire, and forms altogether by far the largest salt-marsh we have. As the sea still retires from this coast, it is easy to perceive in what manner all this country has been the gift of that overwhelming element, which in other places encroaches so severely, and is, at high tides, restrained even here with so much difficulty.

" The soil of the whole is the subsidence of a muddy water, with a considerable portion of what the waves, powerful in their agitation, wash from the bottom of the adjoining gulph, which forms the embouchure of two considerable rivers. It is a mixture of sea-sand and mud, which is of so argillaceous a quality, that the surface of it which covers the sand, gives it the common acceptation of a strong clay country. Is its extraordinary fertility at all owing to the marine acid, with which every particle is impregnated? That cause has every where on the coasts of every part of these islands, as well as other countries, some effect. If the sea leaves only a running sand, the saline particles are soon washed away or exhaled; the land may be barren, though never in the degree of vulgar conception. But when the sand is mixed with, or covered by a more retentive substance, such as an argillaceous or calcareous earth, then the particles, whether saline or mucilaginous, are retained, and the surface classes amongst, or rather is at the head of all, fertile soils.

" I observed that the whole country has been a present from the ocean : this is obvious from numerous appearances ; but those who wish to know its history particularly, should consult DUGDALE. I may remark, that there are ranges of banks at a distance from each other, which shew the progressive advances which industry has effected, eager to seize the tracts which so dreaded an enemy relinquishes. One of these banks is called the Roman, which naturally brings to our mind the vast exertions which that people made in agriculture, wherever their victorious eagles flew. The distance of this bank from the shore, if it really is Roman, and not a misnomer, is not so great as it would have. been, had the sea in all ages been as liberal as it is in this. It probably varies considerably in this respect in different periods : at present it retires very rapidly, so that though Count BENTINCK's embankment has been finished but a few years, there will be, in twenty years, a thousand acres more ready to be taken in, belonging to Mr. BENTINCK, the present possessor.

" The mud deposited by the sea, is at first, and for some years, bare of all vegetation : the first plant that appears is the marsh samphire ; by degrees grasses rise, which, from their appearance at the time I viewed them (October), and eaten close down by cattle, seemed to be the common ones of the improved salt-marsh, but not the *diadelphia* family, which come afterwards.

" Long before it is raised enough by successive deposits of mud from high tides, it lets to the farmers of the contiguous improvement for 5s. per acre ; some years since at 2s. 6d. Broken as it is by holes and little creeks of water, it lets, immediately after embanking, at from 20s. per acre ; a few years ago to 40s. ; and 42s. at present. I observed one or two pieces within Count BENTINCK's new bank, that were left in that rate for cattle, but in general they were under the plough, and the grass-fields laid down after a course of tillage.

" The business of embanking to take in a new piece of marsh, is done sometimes at the expense of the farmers, who make the bank, to have the land rent-free for 21 years. Adjoining to the Bentinck improvement, is a piece of 80 acres thus taken, but the bank very ill made, at no greater expense than 40s. a rod. Those constructed by landlords, were deficient in not having slope enough given towards the water. Count BENTINCK laid out his upon a scale never practised here before ; and his son, the present possessor,

sessor, has far exceeded it. The former extends about four miles, and added to his old estate, 1000 acres. The base of the bank is about 50 feet. The slope to the sea, 36 feet, forming an angle, as I guess from my eye, of 25 or 30 degrees. The crown is four feet wide, and the slope to the fields, 17 feet, in an angle, I guess, of 50 degrees; the slope to the sea, very nicely turfed. The first expense of this bank was 4 l. per rod, but a very high tide coming before it was finished, not only made several breaches, but occasioned an additional height and slope to be given to several parts, to bring it to the above dimensions, all which made the gross expense about 5 l. a rod. The whole cost something above 5000 l. The expense of the buildings, and other things, amounted to as much more, for five new farms, with houses, barns, and all necessary offices, were immediately raised; this was, however, going to a greater expense than necessary, for the land would have let as well in two or three farms, as it did in five. Calculating the expense at 10,000 l. and the new rental at 1000 l. a year, it is just ten per cent. for the capital. The expenses certainly ran too high; for the value of the marsh, at 2s. 6d. an acre before embanking, reduces it to less than nine per cent.; after which, there is still to be deducted, the almost periodical repairs, which remarkably high tides still occasion, and which may be averaged at once in ten years. So that when we consider it not as a purchaser of a new estate, but an agricultural improvement of a waste, the profit is not equal to what might be made on other species of waste lands.

"This is probably owing to the husbandry of these stiff wet soils being very ill understood, and managed in a manner that is reprehensible in almost every particular.

"Instead of a system of miserable tillage, with weeds the chief signs of fertility, the plough ought to be introduced only as a preparation for the most perfect grass system that can be devised. These lands, when well laid down, will fatten the largest bullocks and sheep in England, which is the right employment of them; and in which application they would be better worth 30s. than in their present state 20s. Hence it should be an improving landlord's business to farm the marsh till he got it to a very fine grass, laid down himself, for I scarcely ever saw a tenant that would do that well. Ray-grass, and the weedy rubbish of a loft, which he calls hay-seeds, with, perhaps, some common clover, are what he has recourse to; and, under such management, the wonder is, that he
ever

ever gets a pasture worth even 20s.   In all improvements,
where the previous steps are very expensive, like embanking a marsh, draining a bog, &c. it is essential to profit, that the land be advanced to the highest perfection
possible, as those preparations to culture cost no more for
a great than a small rental.

" Count BENTINCK had one idea in the execution of his
work, which had considerable merit; he planned a navigation from a quay to each of his farms, over the whole
estate, by a large ditch capable of admitting long-boats,
some of which he actually built ready for the business : by
this means the farmers would be able to carry their corn,
or bring manure from Lynn, if they chose to do it, without the least land-carriage; but his death, which was occasioned by too assiduous an attention to building the
bank, living in a tent, in a bad season, and aguish situation, without the precautions of adapting his diet to those
circumstances—prevented the execution.

" One circumstance of folly in his neighbours, prevented
the improvement from being so considerable as the Count
had planned.   At the further extremity, towards the Wisbeach river, there is a common belonging to the parish of
Terrington, to which the sea, by retiring, makes additions similar to those by which individuals have profited.

" A continuation of his bank, in nearly a right line to
the Wisbeach river, would have taken in about 500 acres
of that common.   Mr. BENTINCK applied to the parish for
their consent to do it. which would have been the means
of shortening his bank.   Though several individuals would
have been glad of making use of so favourable an opportunity, the body refused their consent.   They were even
so preposterous in their opposition, that when he afterwards offered to be at the sole expense, provided they
would give him a lease of 21 years of the land recovered,
they still refused it.   Upon which he was obliged to follow the irregular outline of his own property.   The motive of the parish, for refusing their consent to a proposa
so advantageous to themselves, arose from this circumstance.   It is of great extent; the proprietors adjoining
the common, make, at present, nearly the whole advantage of it; but when embanked and let, those at a dis
tance would come in for their share, a jealousy of which
occasioned the failure of the scheme *   " Th

" * This tract has been since embanked, and allotted by act of par
liament, passed in 1790."

"The spirited and unlimited attention, even to the loss of his life, with which Count BENTINCK planned and executed this great work, ought to render his memory dear to every lover of agriculture. His active mind had taken a strong and most useful turn towards that art; apparent, not only in this great and successful project, but in the original invention of an admirable machine for drawing up trees by the root, which executed that difficult work with expedition and cheapness.—*Minute, in* 1784."

This minute, I have pleasure in saying, shows that the Secretary of the Board, when he will allow himself time, to think and write, is capable of conveying useful information, in appropriate language.

SOIL.—P. 14. "The whole district of marshland is probably a relict or deposition of the sea; it is a silt, or warp clay of great fertility, upon a sandy silt at various depths, but usually eighteen inches or two feet. The stiffer clays are the worst arable: the more mild and temperate ones, the best and easiest worked of course; but the strongest clay is the best for grass."

APPROPRIATION.—P. 138. "The Smeeth (?) would, under the hammer, let at 3 l. an acre; and the Fen, at 25s.

"This great tract of land was, in its former state, worth little: the Fen not above 1 s. an acre in reed, being two or three feet deep under water: the Smeeth (?) was often under water, in parts to the amount of half; and then at the Midsummer after rotted the sheep that fed it."—

"Above 30,000 l. a year is added to the produce of the kingdom, by this most beneficial undertaking.

"The poor people who turned cows, geese, and ducks upon the common, without possessing *rights*, have suffered, as in so many other cases; and it is to be regretted, that some compensation is not in all such cases provided by the act. There cannot be a doubt, that the immense system of labour created, is worth far more than such practices; still many individuals are injured, and without any absolute necessity for being so."

RENT.—P. 40. "The Marshland clay, 28s."

STUBBLES.—P. 433 (section, "Manuring"). "I found many oat-stubbles in the new enclosure of Marshland Smeeth burning, ready to put in wheat or cole for seed: the crops had been immense in straw, and reaped, and the land quite black with the ashes; but many partially and badly done, not half burnt. Mr. JOHN THISTLETON, of Walpole, had burnt his completely: I saw the fire spread over several in an unbroken moving wall of flame, and must

must be to the utter destruction of many insects, and all grubs and slugs not buried in the earth."

This, in a dry autumn, may, in many cases, be eligible. But, before fire be put to a tall rank stubble, the situation of the field, in regard to buildings and rickyards, and the nature of its fences,—should be looked to;—lest the flames should not be confineable to the stubble field; but be led away from it, to distant buildings;—as has been the case, in burning "feg"—dead grass—in the spring of the year, in the Midland Counties;—where the greater part of a village was consumed, through the want of this precaution. See my MIDLAND COUNTIES, vol. II. p. 77.

MUSTARD SEED.—P. 325. " Much cultivated from March to Wisbeach, and about the latter place. A good crop will yield five or six coombs per acre, and it sells at from 8s. to 21s. a bushel. It is, after being in full blossom, subject to a fly, which damages it greatly.

" In the newly-inclosed lands of Marshland Smeeth, mustard is the chief crop. They ploughed the old grass of that rich common once, and after one or two harrowings, sowed a quarter of a peck of seed per acre, from Candlemas to the end of March; hand-hoed the plants once or twice, as wanted, thinning and setting them out at nearly equal distances. The crop is reaped the beginning of September, and tied in sheaves, leaving it three or four days on the stubble: it is stacked in the field, and these stacks are called *pies*. If it gets rain in the field, it turns grey, and loses half its value. The Smeeth is now full of these stacks, and the season has proved highly favourable. It is threshed in the autumn, being left for a sweat, which improves the colour. A good crop, such as they have got this year, amounts to six or seven coombs an acre, and the present price at Lynn is 20s. a bushel. From this account it is not surprising that the Smeeth of 1500 acres, letts at 3l. The price, however, is sometimes so low as 7s. 6d. to 10s. a bushel. They intend, according to the common practice near Wisbeach, &c. to sow four crops in succession; the second is usually as good as the first: and after four years mustard, a crop of wheat, then fallow.

" In old cultivated lands, four or five coombs a good crop."

Considerable quantities of mustard seeds are still (1810) grown on those lands.

THE

THE SECRETARY's SUFFOLK.

Soil.—P. 6. "Of the fen district it is only necessary to observe, that the surface, from one foot to six, is the common peat of bogs, some of it black and solid enough to yield a considerable quantity of ashes in burning; but in other places more loose, puffy, and reddish, and consequently of an inferior quality; the under stratum generally a white clay, or marl."

Draining.—P. 6. "Part of these fens is under water, though subject to a tax for the drainage, which has failed; but in Burnt Fen, by a late act of parliament for improving the banks, 14,000 acres are completely drained, and under cultivation."

Plan of Management.—P. 42. "The course of crops generally pursued in this district, is to sow cole-seed on one ploughing, after paring and burning; which is for sheep-feed or seed, according to circumstances; then oats twice in succession; with the last of which crops they lay down with ray grass and clover, for six or seven years, and then pare and burn, and repeat the same husbandry."

Sodburning.—P. 161. "This husbandry, which, properly managed, is the most admirable of all improvements, and improperly, the most mischievous, is known only in the small angle of fen. In that district they could not cultivate without this capital assistant. It is scarcely possible, profitably, to bring boggy, moory, peat soils, from a state of nature into cultivation, without the assistance of fire, which is the most effective destruction of the spontaneous growth, and never fails, but because the men employed do not pare deep enough. In these fens, the original surface is rough and unequal, from great tufts of rushes, &c. called there *hassocks*. Some persons cut them with spades, at the expence of five to ten shillings an acre; others with the plough. Paths for the horses were, in that case, to be cut by hand, and the plough made on purpose, and called a hassock plough, cut laterally much beyond the line of its draught. But opinions are, in general, that hand work is the cheaper: in either case the hassocks are dried, heaped, burnt, and the ashes spread. After this they go over it again with a very complete and effective tool, called a fen-paring plough, the furrow of which is burnt."

Rape.—Same page, in continuation.—"Cole-seed is then sown on one shallow ploughing; never harrowed, in order
not

not to disturb the whole furrow, but rolled, or lightly bush-harrowed."

P. 74. "There is a considerable quantity of cole-seed sown in all parts of this county; but in the fen district, it is one of the principal crops.

"*Preparation.*—The preparation is the same as for turnips, but manure not commonly bestowed for it; in the fens it is generally sown on one thin ploughing, on pared and burnt land.

"*Seed.*—A quarter of a peck is the common quantity of seed; but I have known half a peck sown by many.

"*Time of Sowing.*—If for sheep feed only, it is sown in the turnip season; but if for seed, in the beginning of August.

"*Harvest.*—It is reaped, and left on the *gavel* till fit to thresh.

"*Threshing.*—Threshed in the field on cloths, and the straw burned, which is wasteful management, for there is no vegetable substance, however apparently dry, that will not rot, and make manure, when bedded in a farm-yard for the urine and dung of cattle to mix with it *.

"*Produce.*—Various; from four to ten sacks an acre; five coombs, or two quarters and a half an acre, probably the medium; and as it sells from thirty shillings even to forty shillings a sack sometimes, it is a very profitable crop to the farmer.

"*For Sheep.*—The application most important, and most beneficial *to a farm*, is this; it is excellent for sheep, and exceeds turnips both in fattening and giving milk.

"*Succeeding Crop.*—When seeded, it is commonly succeeded by wheat, which farmers are fond of representing as excellent, in order to convince their landlords that the crop is innocent, in not exhausting: I have seen very good wheat after it; but it is certainly an exhausting crop. When fed, it is followed by barley or oats."

GEOLOGICAL REMARKS, on the FORMATION of the WATER-LANDS of CAMBRIDGESHIRE and its ENVIRONS.

IN ABSTRACTING the Reports from Lincolnshire, I incidentally touched on this subject (pp. 40 and 94); and in going through those from Cambridgeshire, and the neighbouring Counties,

---

* Cattle will eat the upper parts of the stems, freely. See my YORKSHIRE, Art. *Rape.*

Counties, my attention has been repeatedly led to the same topic.—It is far from my intention to attempt a general theory, concerning this, at least, interesting subject. Nevertheless I think it right to register, here, what may serve to furnish materials for such a theory.

The different descriptions of *lands*, spoken of by the several Reporters, are—" Highlands"—" Road Hams"— " Marshes"—" Skirty Lands"—" Fens."

And the different sorts of *soils* and *substrata*, mentioned, —are Clay—Loam—" Silt"—Sand—" Fen Moor"— " Bear's Muck"—" Gault"—Gravel.

" HIGHLANDS."—This is merely a provincial term, that is used in speaking of lands which rise a few feet, or a few inches, above the general level of the adjacent fens or marshes.

It is on lands of this description that the interior villages are situated.—The sites of Chatteris and Thorney are, to the eye, evidently raised a few feet above the surrounding levels.—The rise of that of Whittlesea, on the contrary, in approaching it from the south, is barely perceptible. And the site of Crowland is imperceptibly raised above the wide-spreading circumjacent fens.—The minor villages, seen in crossing the "great Bedford Level," between Ely and Chatteris, appear to stand very little above it.

I was, at first, struck with the idea that those gentle risings might be *natural islets*.—But further observation and reflection induced me to consider them, rather, as the productions of floods and tides, in far distant times, when the surface of the ocean, it is possible, rose higher than it does at the present day *.

Are

---

* What is the fact?—Does the sea *decrease* in depth? Do earthquakes, or other agitations, by causing internal fractures, make room for surface waters? Or may they not, in some cases, force up interior waters to the surface, and thus *raise* that of the ocean? In other words, is not its depth liable to be encreased or diminished, from time to time, by such internal ruptures? And may not these intimations, duly considered, tend to reconcile the disputes, respecting this dark, yet most interesting, branch of Geology? It is a subject, indeed, about which the minds of the inhabitants of this globe can scarcely be more interestingly employed ;—the general fracture of its surface, (such as evidently appears to have heretofore taken place) or its total dissolution, excepted.

When we reflect on the extremely small portion of the earth which is liable to our examination,—the highest mountains being as grains
of

Are those insular swells and the "SKIRTY LANDS" of a kindred nature?—I was led to the idea that such may be the fact, by my observing *gravel pits* characterising, equally, the insular and the marginal lands,—from my leaving the neighbourhood of Cambridge, until I reached *land*, again, in Northamptonshire.—And see Mr. Vancouver's parochial journals, aforegoing.

The surface soils of these lands are, of course, various; from their having been formed with such heterogenous materials, as shifting currents and other fortuitous circumstances, during a succession of centuries, might furnish. —They may be seen in Mr. V's journals.—See also the remarks of Mr. Stone (of Leverington) on the soils of his neighbourhood, p. 244, aforegoing.

"ROAD HAMS."—See Mr. Vancouver's description of them, p. 229.

"MARSHES."—This term is chiefly applied to "Salt Marshes," or alluvious lands in the neighbourhood of the sea, or toward the mouths of rivers.—See Mr. Stone's account of them, p. 244; and the Secretary's, p. 283.

"FENS."—This is provincially applied, in Cambridgeshire, &c. more uniformly than in Lincolnshire, to low, black-soiled, moory lands.

The distinct SPECIES of SOILS are only two; namely, alluvion and vegetable mold.

ALLUVION.—From this, many *varieties* of fossil soils are formed; according to the circumstances of situation, currents, and obstructions of the channels of soil-bearing waters.—Thus, sand, silt, loam, and clay, in endless variety, may be formed.—See p. 113, aforegoing.

The origin of the vegetable mold is to be looked for in the nature of aquatic plants growing on beds of mud covered with water; thus producing, in the process of time, a morass; and thus filling with decayed vegetables, the hollows which the waters previously occupied.

The prevailing substratum of the "fens' cannot, I conceive, be other than alluvion of former times:—chiefly, it is probable, the finer particles, or mud, which would have the best opportunity, and the most time, to subside, in the wide-

of sand on the surface of an egg, and the deepest oceans as dimplets in its shell,—it appears to be consonant with human reason that the aggregate ocean might be suddenly absorbed, or twice the quantity of the water which it now contains, be discharged, by internal agitations.—Earthquakes and volcanos *prove* the existence of those agitations and irruptions.

wide-spreading and stagnant or slowly moving waters, in which the vegetable mold of the fens have evidently been produced *.

The manner in which those receptacles were filled with water is a subject which probably will remain in a degree conjectural.—In Gooch's Cambridgeshire are found the following intimations :—

P. 206. "The engineers were of opinion that the country in question formerly meadow and wood, now fen, became so from partial embankment, preventing the waters from the uplands going to the sea, by their natural outfall; want of proper and sufficient drains to convey those waters into the Ouse; neglect of such drains as were made for that purpose ; and that these evils increased from the not embanking the river Ouse, and the erection of sluices across it, preventing the flux and reflux of the sea; and the not widening and deepening where wanted the river Ouse, and from not removing the gravels, weeds, &c. &c. which from time to time accumulated in it."

These circumstances may have rendered the mischief permanent, but could not have been the original cause of it. The overflowing, the "drowning,"—as I have before observed,—must, necessarily, have been done instantaneously, or at once;—else, how came it that not only fallen timber and faggot wood, but hay in swath, were left to perish, in the woods and fields?

The "Roman Bank" is an immense mound of earth, even at this day, where it remains unbroken.—With such a mound, reaching from the rising grounds of Norfolk, to those of Lincolnshire, the entire level of the waterlands, now under notice, would be secure from the overflowings of the tide ; saving such part of it as might flow up the channels of the rivers; and if these were embanked, in like manner, the waters of the tide might be said to be brought, in that instance, under man's control.

This extraordinary mound, it is highly probable, was really raised while this island was a Roman province. The *Romans* knew the value of *territory* to a populous country. *They* let not immense improvements lie neglected; nor did things by halves. And we may safely conclude, I think, that they would not merely raise *embankments,* but would make *drains,* in unison with them ;—in order to lay
the

* For descriptions of " Gault," and " Bear's Muck," see pp. 229 and 272.

the entire site under consideration sufficiently dry for the purposes of cultivation, or other economical uses ; and, in all human probability, kept them in that valuable state,— as one well organized whole;—even as Holland is now kept.

How the banks were broken,—whether by tempest,— or by an enemy, to inundate the country,—or by way of precaution, to prevent its being taken possession of,— those who have more leisure than I have, to examine the earlier stages of our history, may possibly be able to ascertain.—That an immense work did heretofore exist, and that it was suddenly thrown down, and the country laid waste, may, I think, be deemed selfevident.

Were the proposed plan and elevation executed in their full extent, such traces of the ancient system would probably appear, as might assist in forming a modern work of similar intentions.

NORFOLK.

NORFOLK.

THIS COUNTY, tho not so strongly featured as Lincoln-shire, readily admits of being divided into NATURAL DISTRICTS.

In proceeding, geographically, the first and most striking feature, in the face of Norfolk, is formed by the CHALK HILLS, which stretch along its northern coast.

The WATERLANDS,—the marshes and fens that unite with those of Lincolnshire and Cambridgeshire,—next present themselves.

To those succeed the HEATHLANDS of West Norfolk.

Eastward of these,—even to the eastern coast,—occupying the central and eastern parts of the County,—lies, the wide and spreading tract of SANDY LOAMS, which give character to Norfolk, and its husbandry.

In the southeast corner of the County,—in what may be termed the YARMOUTH QUARTER,—is found a plot of stronger, more fertile loams;—Lands of a superior quality. It is provincially known by the appellation of " Fleg," or the " Fleg Hundreds."

Lastly, on the SOUTHERN BORDER of the County, adjacent to Suffolk, is situated an extent of COOL LANDS, widely differing, in natural character, from the other lands of the county;—whose prevailing characteristic is absorbency:—whereas those which occupy its southern margin, rest on a repellant base;—requiring the soil to be raised into beds, to free it from superfluous moisture. But little if any of it, I believe, is so retentive as to be thought entirely unfit for the turnep husbandry;—tho some of it would seem, from a cursory view of it, to be so.

MY OWN KNOWLEDGE of Norfolk has chiefly arisen, during a constant residence of two years, in the county (as appears in my Register of its Rural Economy). Its Wolds, or chalky Downs;—its water-formed lands; and the cool-land passage last mentioned;—were the only parts of it that I had not formerly examined.—I therefore made them the more particular objects of my attention, in my recent Journey of Observation, through the County. See p. 11, aforegoing.

FROM NORFOLK, as from Lincolnshire, we have two distinct REPORTS. One of them by Mr. KENT;—the other by the SECRETARY of the BOARD.

" GENERAL

"GENERAL VIEW

OF THE

AGRICULTURE

OF THE

COUNTY OF NORFOLK:

WITH

OBSERVATIONS FOR THE MEANS OF ITS IMPROVEMENT.

DRAWN UP FOR THE CONSIDERATION OF THE

BOARD OF AGRICULTURE AND INTERNAL IMPROVEMENT.

BY

NATHANIEL KENT,

OF FULHAM, MIDDLESEX.

WITH ADDITIONAL REMARKS FROM SEVERAL RESPECTABLE GENTLEMEN

AND FARMERS,

1796."

THE QUALIFICATIONS of this REPORTER, to write on rural subjects, are known to many;—by his long and extensive practice, in different parts of the kingdom, as an estate agent of the highest class;—and by his " Hints to Gentlemen of Landed Property;"—a literary work of considerable merit;—so far as it treats of the subjects more immediately pertaining to the author's own profession.

But neither in that work, nor in the Report now under consideration, do we recognize, in Mr. Kent, a *practical agriculturist* of minute attention, or mature experience. On *English* husbandry, Mr. K. writes more like an *observer*, than a *practitioner.*—On this branch of rural affairs—PRACTICAL AGRICULTURE—I have therefore been
less

less solicitous, either to *extract*, or to *correct*, than otherwise I should have been.

There are, however, a few passages, very unfortunately inserted in the volume before me, that are so radically wrong,—so subversive of good husbandry,—and are
brought forward in so obtrusive a manner,—that it would
be an unpardonable offence in a Reviewer who professes
to censure (where censure is due) as well as to praise,—
to suffer them to pass, without confering on them the
attention they require.

Regarding Mr. Kent's *Report* of the *established practices*
of agriculture, in Norfolk, it may be remarked that Mr. K.
was employed in the character of a *gleaner*, only.—The
harvest had been previously reaped, and a principal part
of what he collected, might well have been left in the
field.—I am happy in being able to say, however, that
(unless in one instance, and there through mistake) Mr.
Kent has not found occasion—or has not done me the
justice—to correct, or to controvert, in any sort, my RE-
GISTER of the RURAL ECONOMY of NORFOLK.

But let not the above intimations respecting this Reporter, as a writer on *English agriculture*, lower, in the
minds of my readers, his abilities, and the value of his
observations, on ESTATE AGENCY,—on the EXECUTIVE
MANAGEMENT of LANDED PROPERTY. On this important
branch of rural concerns, I have to regret that Mr. KENT
has not afforded me opportunities of encreasing the number and length of my extracts. His mind must be amply
stored with matured knowledge, concerning this ill understood, and, in the prevailing practice of the present day,
ill conducted, department of the rural science.

Regarding the SURVEY, from which the volume under
consideration was written, it had doubtlessly been going
on, during a length of years, previously to the composition
of the Report;—which bears no marks of an *actual Survey*
of the County, at large, having been taken for the especial purpose of making it.

Mr. Kent's Report of Norfolk is not a mushroom production,—hastily formed of hearsay information.—So far
as *established practices* are reported, it appears to be, in
most cases, the result of long observation, in the County
of which it treats.—The *speculative* matter, it contains, is
the most objectionable.

Respecting the AUTHORSHIP of this volume, I have to
say, that it is written in a clear intelligent manner, and,
mostly, in the plain, simplex, style of Report.—The *arrangement*

rangement is, in a great part, the Reporter's own. It is far from judicious.—But this, with me, is a venial fault. All I ask for is valuable matter, conveyed in intelligible language. Let me be favored with this, and I will, with pleasure, bring it under an arrangement that is, at once, natural and practical.—In the present instance, we find a copious index, which renders the deficiency of system the less inconvenient.

I can truly say,—and it would be a crime in me not to say it,—that I have not analyzed and re-arranged any work, since I sat down to my present undertaking. with so much facility and satisfaction (in some *extraordinary* instances excepted) as I have KENT'S NORFOLK.

This being a " reprinted Report," the author has properly inserted the more valuable of the NOTES made on the broad margin of the " original Report;" tho not in the most convenient way, to the reader. The notes are separated from the text;—not appendent to the passages to which they belong. The sections, in this case, however, being mostly short, the inconveniency is less, than on a former one   See NORTH. DEPART. p. 335.

The ANNOTATORS are Sir Thomas Beever, Mr. Wagstaff, Mr. James, Mr. Howlet, Mr. Strachy, and others whose names will appear, in the course of the Review.— Their remarks, however, tho frequent, and of some length, are rarely such as to demand particular notice, in this concentration of what is really valuable in the Board's Reports.

The number of pages, in the body of the Work, 194;— in the Appendix, 34.

A sketch of the rivers, market towns, and outlines of hundreds;—also two plates of implements, and one of livestock; are attached to the volume.

SUBJECT THE FIRST.

NATURAL ECONOMY.

EXTENT.—Norfolk, Mr. Kent says, p. 6. may be considered—" as containing, as nearly as can be ascertained from the maps hitherto published, about 1,710 square miles, and 1,094,400 statute acres."

The

The following is Mr. K.'s analysis of the above gross amount of acres.—P. 7.

"The space on which the towns stand . .	1500
Public and private roads	16416
Lakes and rivers	2000
Sedgy and swampy ground	1500
Unimproved commons	80000
Woods and plantations	10000
Arable land, computed at two-thirds of } the whole county . . . . }	729600
Meadows, parks, and upland pasture . .	126692
Marsh lands	63346
Warrens and sheep-walks	63346
Total of acres	1094400"

SURFACE.—P. 12. " The surface, except in some few parts, near Norwich, and upon the coast near Sherringham and Cromer, is mostly a dead flat."

CLIMATURE.—P. 10. " Being open to the German Ocean, north and east, and lying on the marshy parts of Cambridgeshire and Lincolnshire on the west—the air is on that account extremely cold in winter, and during the early parts of the spring, vegetation is generally kept back by sharp easterly winds, and a vast quantity of sleet— cattle on this account, often suffer severely as well from this inclemency of weather, as from want of a proper supply of nourishment in the spring; for when the turnips happen to perish early, from the frequent change of frost and thaw, the farmer finds himself obliged to dispose of his stock to a very great disadvantage."—P. 11. " In summer, the showers are rather more frequent than in the midland counties—storms and tempests, such as thunder and lightning, are frequent, and as violent as in other parts of the kingdom, but seldom last so long as in hilly districts, but in general pass in a quick direction from the south and west, towards the sea, which strongly attracts them; and I have remarked that it is but seldom that these storms come from the sea."

WATERS.—For the *Rivers* of Norfolk, see *Inland Navigation*, ensuing.

SOILS.—P. 12. " The greatest part of the arable land is sandy. The prime parts of the county lie north and north-east of Norwich; comprising the hundreds of East and West Flegg, South Walsham, Blofield, Happing, Tunstead, and the greatest part of North and South Erpingham;

pingham; all which may be denominated a true sandy loam, equal in value to the best parts of the Austrian Netherlands, to which it is similar. It is highly fruitful, and so temperate and pleasant to work, that it is rarely injured by wet or drought, so that the occupier is seldom put out of his rotation of cropping."

P. 13. "The district south and south-east of Norwich, consisting of the hundreds of Lodden, Clavering, Henstead, Earsham, Diss, Depwade, and Humilyard, as well as some parts of Fourhoe and Mitford, though chiefly sand, have an occasional mixture of clay, and are in many parts wet and full of springs; but yet these parts are fruitful, though to a less degree than the former; they are likewise less pleasant and more expensive to work.

"The largest portion of the County lies west and northwest of Norwich; comprising the hundreds of Taverham, Eynsford, Holt, North Greenhoe, Gallow, Launditch, Brothercross, Smithdon, Freebridge, and Clackclose. There is some very good land in different parts of this district; but, upon the whole, it is a very inferior country to the two preceding districts. It runs, in general, light, and its best dependence is upon the fold."

It is rather remarkable that Mr. K. did not particularize, in this quarter of the County, the *chalk* lands, similar to the Wolds of Yorkshire and Lincolnshire, and the Downs of the Southern Counties,—which are there found.

P. 14. "The hundreds of Shropham, Guiltcross, Weyland, South Greenhoe, and Grimshot, lying south-west of Norwich, run upon a still lighter sand; so light, that in the last mentioned hundred, the sand very often, in a high wind, drifts from one parish to another."

The soil of "Marshland" appears, aforegoing, p. 232.

I have transcribed, with greater readiness and pleasure, Mr. Kent's Report of the Soils of the County at large; as my own account related most particularly, to the more eastern parts of it.

SUBJECT

SUBJECT THE SECOND.

POLITICAL ECONOMY.

APPROPRIATION.—P. 6. 'It is extremely difficult to state, with any degree of accuracy, what are the different proportions of cultivated and uncultivated land, as this could only be done by a general survey, but from the best enquiry and observation that I have been able to make, I will hazard the following calculation:" see p. 299, aforegoing.

In that statement 80,000 acres are set down as the estimated quantity of "unimproved Common."—The quantity of *common field lands*, at the time Mr. K. *originally* wrote, in 1793, does not appear. But, in the volume before me, are the subjoined conjectures concerning them.

P. 32. " In my general estimation of the quantity of arable land, I have supposed the whole to be about two-thirds of the County, or 729,600 acres, of which, perhaps, about three parts out of the four may be inclosed; the other fourth part in common fields."

P. 72 (Section " Common Fields and Inclosures ").— " There is still a considerable deal of common-field land in Norfolk, though a much less proportion than in many other Counties ; for, notwithstanding common rights, for great cattle, exist in all of them, and even sheep-walk privileges in many, yet the natural industry of the people is such, that wherever a person can get four or five acres together, he plants a white-thorn hedge round it, and sets an oak at every rod distance, which is consented to by a kind of general courtesy from one neighbour to another." —In this way, many or most of the common fields of East Norfolk appear, pretty evidently, to have been inclosed.

Mr. K's remarks on the *disadvantages* of *Common Fields,* —tho not new or very striking,—are entitled to a place, here ;—as corroborative and *authentic* evidence, tending to show the unfitness and folly of suffering to exist any impediment to the removal of those disadvantages ; few men having had more opportunities of observing the mischiefs arising from those fragments of feudality.

P. 73. " Land, when very much divided, occasions considerable

siderable loss of time to the occupier, in going over a
great deal of useless space, in keeping a communication
with the different pieces. As it lies generally in long
narrow slips, it is but seldom it can receive any benefit
from cross ploughing and harrowing, therefore it cannot
be kept so clean ; but what is still worse, there can be
but little variety observed in the system of cropping ;
because the right which every parishioner has of commonage over the field, a great part of the year, prevents
the sowing of turnips, clover, or other grass seeds, and
consequently cramps a farmer in the stock which he
would otherwise keep. On the contrary, when land is
inclosed, so as to admit of sowing turnips and seeds, which
have an improving and meliorating tendency, the same
soil will, in the course of a few years, make nearly double
the return it did before, to say nothing of the wonderful
improvements which sometimes result from a loam or
clay ; which will, when well laid down, often become of
twice the permanent value in pasture, that ever it would
as ploughed ground. Most striking effects of this sort
are to be seen in Leicestershire, Northamptonshire, and
other Midland Counties. This, indeed, has been urged
by some as an argument against inclosing, as they would
infer that it lessens the quantity of arable land too much,
and tends to make corn dear ; but the excess of grazing
and ploughing will correct itself. If arable land be laid
down, there is a great deal of coarse old pasture land
which may be broken up, the turf of which wants renew-
ing ; and this old grass land, which could not so well have
been spared before, is, of all land, that which is most
adapted to the growth of potatoes, hops, hemp, and flax
The markets will ever regulate the proportion of arable
and grass land, better than any fixed plan that can be
suggested."

The Reporter next adverts to the *effects* of inclosing, or
the *population* of a country ; and produces evidence of its
having promoted it, in Norfolk ;—of which there can be
little doubt. In every *arable* country, that, I conceive
must necessarily be the case.

In a section entitled " Commons considered," the sub
jects of *population* and *public benefits* are renewed, and
placed in a more striking light.

P. 81. " These lie in all parts of the County, and are
very different in their quality. Those in the neighbour
hood of Wymondham and Attleborough, are equal to the
finest land in the County, worth, at least, twenty shilling

a

an acre; being capable of making either good pasture, or producing corn, hemp or flax. There are other parts which partake of a wet nature, and some of a furze and heathy quality; but they are most of them worth improving, and all of them capable of producing something: and it is a lamentable thing, that those large tracts of land should be suffered to remain in their present unprofitable state."

P. 82. " From observation and enquiry, I find, that in the most fertile parts of England the people employed in agriculture, and the rural trades connected with it, are in about the proportion of one to six acres; and if a proportionate number be added for the towns, and people employed in other trades, not connected with husbandry, the number will be, perhaps, as one to four acres of land. But as the more ordinary parts will not carry so high a population, the safer average may be set to the scale generally, as one to five acres; and as these lands do not support a third of the number of people which they would do, if they were cultivated; however, supposing they do, at this time, support a third of what they would do if improved, still there is an apparent loss of 10,666 persons, in this County only, which being highly agricultural, with a large proportion of manufactories and trade, I shall leave the benefits which would result from the inclosure of this great tract of land, to the estimation of the financier."

Under the head " Poor Rates," we find the subjoined notice, respecting another great evil of Commons.

P. 158. " There is another observation which I have made, which is, that the larger the common, the greater number, and the more miserable are the poor.

" In the parishes of Horsford, Hevingham, and Marsham, which link into each other, from four to nine miles from Norwich, there are not less than 3000 acres of waste land, and yet the average of the rates are, at least, ten shillings in the pound.—This shews the absolute necessity of doing something with these lands, or these, uncultivated, will utterly ruin the cultivated parts; for these mistaken people place a fallacious dependence upon these precarious commons, and do not trust to the returns of regular labour, which would be, by far, a better support to them."

Convinced, as this writer must be, of the numerous disadvantages to the country, in its present state,—in regard to unappropriated lands,—it was no more than might have been expected, that he should turn his mind toward

facilitating

facilitating the amelioration of their condition. Accordingly, we find Mr. Kent an advocate for "one general Act of Parliament," suitable to the furtherance of so great a public good.

His remarks, however, are too cursory to merit a place here, after what has been published on this topic; excepting so far as they point out, in a forcible manner, the almost incredible grievances which are permitted to strow the way, so as to prevent, or retard, the obtaining of private bills.

P. 76. "The great expence, when a bill is solicited, which always operates as a powerful discouragement to undertakings of this kind, and sometimes sets them wholly aside; especially, as the fees are double, if another parish has the smallest share in the emoluments, though the trouble to those who pass the act is not doubled by it. But this is not all the discouragement, for in the course of obtaining the bill, the evidence must go up to town, and attend a committee of the Commons, afterwards be sworn at the bar of the Lords, and attend their committee also: and as these attendances are often at intervals considerably distant from each other, the evidence must all this time either be supported in town, at a great expence, or make three or four journies; and as this sort of evidence is generally given by professional men whose time is valuable, these delays are very inconvenient, and frequently operate so powerfully upon the minds of the people, that many an inclosure is passed over which would otherwise be effected. This in a great measure will account for so many of our commons and common fields having remained so long in their present state."

PROVISIONS.—See the head, *Markets*, ensuing.

POOR RATES.—On this topic, Mr. Kent has furnished some valuable information.—P. 156. "Poor-rates, which no longer back than twenty years, were so light, that a farmer, when he went to take a farm, hardly thought it worth while to enquire the amount of it; but now it is become the first question he must ask.

"The causes of the astonishing increase of these rates, it is presumed, will chiefly be found in the rise of provisions, beyond the proportional rise in the price of labour. There may be some other causes, but this is the chief.

"When this great alteration first began to be felt, the Houses of Industry, of which there are several in this County, took their rise, and, for a time, there was great expectation

expectation of advantage from them, but I am informed, that some of them, at least, have been for some time upon the decline, and this last year of scarcity, they are *minus* in their accounts, so that, it is to be feared, they will not answer the end that was expected from them. The griev-ance, therefore, in and out of the houses, is become of a most serious nature ; there are few parishes now, that pay less than five or six shillings in the pound, upon the rack-rents. In the parish of Hevingham, where I reside, they are nine shillings in the pound; in the parish of Buxton, on one side of me, they are ten; and in the parish of Marsham, on the other side, they are sixteen ; so that, in the latter place, more is paid to support the poor, than the landlords put in their pockets : for, after they have paid land-tax, and kept their buildings in repair, they do not get above fifteen shillings. The obvious consequence of this is, that where an acre of land would be worth twenty shillings, if there were no poor rates, it can only be worth ten shillings subject to them.

" There is one material reason, however, to be assigned why the poor-rates are so very high in the parish of Marsham, and many other parishes, not far distant from Norwich. In the year 1712, an act of parliament passed, for regulating the workhouses in that city, in which act, there is a clause which prevents any apprentice, taken from any country village, from gaining any settlement in Norwich *.—This was evidently done to encourage the manufactory, when it was upon a prosperous and flourish-ing footing—but it has had a cruel effect upon the parishes, which, originally, furnished the city with these apprentices ; many of them married in Norwich and else-where, and, upon the decline of the trade, the city pre-ferring its own poor, these strangers, for want of work, were obliged to return to their original place of residence, and many of them brought with them large families. This seems to prove the necessity and propriety of taxing trade, when it is flourishing, to provide a fund for its poor, when it declines."

And, in another section, entitled " the State of the Poor," we find the following sensible, humane, and liberal sentiments,

---

* What an *inconsiderate* act!—Or what an abandoned, and bare-faced sacrifice of the *landed* to the *commercial interest*.—The blighted harvest raised by *such management !* is now (1811), wellnigh literally, ——rotting on the ground.

sentiments, which reflect equal credit on the head and the heart of the writer.—P. 170   " The poor-rates have increased in this County in a full proportion to others, and with a view of stopping this increase, several houses of industry have been established; but they are grievous things in the eyes of the poor, and I am afraid, are not found to answer the end that was expected from them.   I know of no law that can enforce industry; it may be encouraged, and great good will result from it ; but it never can be effected by compulsion.

".There are two principles which should be kept alive, as much as possible, in the minds of the poor—pride and shame : the former will lead them to the attainment of comfort by honest means ; and the latter will keep them from becoming burthensome to their neighbours.   But many of the modern plans, for making provisions for them, have tended to destroy these principles.

" A man born to no inheritance, who assiduously devotes his whole life to labour, when nature declines, has as great a claim upon the neighbourhood, where the labour of his youth has been devoted, as the worn out soldier or sailor has to Chelsea or Greenwich ; and this reward ought to be as honourable, as it is comfortable, and not to be administered in a way that is repugnant to that natural love of rational freedom which every human mind sympathizes in the enjoyment of.—Such a man, as I have here characterized, ought to be distinguished from the lazy and profligate wretch, who has seldom worked but by force.   The one ought not to be crowded into the same habitation with the other; but in houses of industry there can be no distinction."

TITHES.—In Mr. Kent's general remarks on tithes, there is little to interest.   No reasonable man can doubt the *right* of the clergy and lay rectors to tithes, *as the law now stands*.   Nor does any one, conversant with rural affairs, doubt that tithes, collected agreeably to such law, are an *obstacle* to *agricultural improvements*.   Nor can any man, who has bestowed much attention on the subject, doubt that there might be *some* " difficulty," in fixing a suitable equivalent for them.   But what great good was ever obtained without some difficulty ?

Having already spoken, repeatedly, and at length, on these topics, I will, here, merely insert Mr. K's account of the present state of tithes, in Norfolk.—P. 154.   " As to the general scale upon which tythes are let in this country, I do not think it can be said, that they are exorbitantly

tantly high; I believe the highest price, for all tythes, is
five shillings an acre, upon the very best arable land, and
two shilling upon the best meadows and pasture, at least it
is so, with very few exceptions. The more general composition is three shillings and sixpence an acre, for the
arable, and one shilling and sixpence for the grass.—In
the very light parts of the County, it is two shillings an
acre, for the former, and ninepence for the latter; and
there is hardly an instance, in fifty parishes, of tythes being set out, or taken up in kind."

INLAND NAVIGATION.—P. 17. " The principal rivers
are the Ouze, the Waveney, the Yare, the Wensum, and
the Bure. The great Ouze is navigable from Lynn,
twenty-four miles through the County, and then com-
municates with seven of the Midland counties; the Little
Ouze branches out of the Great Ouze, and is navigable
by Brandon to Thetford; the Waveney from Yarmouth
by Beccles to Bungay; the Yare and Wensum from
Yarmouth to the populous city of Norwich; and the Bure
from Yarmouth to Aylsham: besides which, there are
several small cuts to private estates.

" These inland navigations are of great use to individuals, and to society at large—they give aid to agriculture, and spirit to trade; and tend to lessen the number
of horses, which are the greatest devourers of the produce
of the earth : I could therefore wish to see them improved
upon, and extended as far as possible, and it is a consideration worth the attention of the gentlemen of the
County.

" The most obvious improvement of this sort, which
presents itself, is that of extending the navigation of the
Wensum from Norwich to Fakenham, which I believe is
not only practicable, but would be found to answer the
expence extremely well, as it would pass through a corn
country the whole way, from which the corn is now conveyed a vast way by land carriage : I am told there were
formerly some steps taken towards effecting this desirable
object. I am at a loss to know why it failed of success,
but should be glad to see it revived without loss of
time."

Mr. Fox, an annotator, suggests the plan of uniting the
Thetford and Bungay, that is to say, the Ouse and the
Waveney navigations: and, thus, not only obtain an
inland communication, between the ports of Lynn and
Yarmouth, but encircle the entire County with the means
of WATER CARRIAGE.—And Mr. COLHOUN, in a letter to
the

the President of the Board, mentions (p. 19.) a plan which
—"was offered to parliament about five years since,
(but was rejected) by which it was proposed to make a
canal from the Brandon river, by Newmarket and Saffron
Walden, to London;"—whereby, not only would an inland navigation be opened, between the metropolis and
the two ports above mentioned;—but the entire surplus
produce (of grain, flour, and other articles) of the western
and southern parts of the County,—would find a ready
and safe conveyance, to the London markets.

ROADS.—P. 16. "The roads in this County, afford
the farmer a very great advantage over many other parts
of England, being free from sloughs, in all parts (except
the marshes), and though the soil is sandy, it resists the
pressure of the wheels at a small distance from the surface,
and the ruts are kept shallow at a very little expence;
and after the longest and hardest rain, become dry and
pleasant in a few days, which is not only an agreeable circumstance to a traveller, but a great comfort to cattle in
their drift; so that I may venture to say, that the roads
are better, in their natural state, than in almost any other
County; so good, that no turnpike was thought of in
Norfolk, till they became common in most other parts."

In a note, p. 79, Mr. STRACHY wishes to see "an act
for making turnpike roads, where a majority of persons,
possessing a certain property, agree amongst themselves.
An act of a moderate length now costs 200 l. which is a
great discouragement. The fees to the clerks of the
House of Commons and House of Lords, are considerable;
but upon the passing such an act, for the public convenience and honour of the country, either House might
contrive a compensation to those, who would be deprived
of the emoluments which now arise to them, from the
turnpike bills annually brought in."—Mr. S. might well
have noticed, in addition to the unnecessary expences,
within the Houses of Parliament, the inconveniences, not
to mention the great expences incurred, *out of doors*, by
the present *unreasonable* practice.—See the head, *Appropriation*, p. 304, aforegoing.

MARKETS.—What we find, on this head, in the Report
under consideration, is no otherwise noticeable, than as a
subject of censure.—Take the following extract:

P. 167. "The markets, as far as relates to the pitching of corn, are every where dropt, and the whole trade is
carried on by sample, which is greatly against the labourer,
artificer, and little tradesman, as it has a tendency to throw

the

the corn into the channels of monopoly, and I do not
think a better thing could be done for the community,
than that of giving all possible encouragement to public
fairs and markets; for, among other good effects that
might result from them, I am of opinion, it would tend
more than any thing, to check the increase of large farms,
as I have before ventured to observe."

I know no County in which fairs and markets are so
well attended, as in Norfolk*. As to "the pitching of
corn," in markets;—dragging the immense produce of
Norfolk to, perhaps, a distant market town, and, thence,
back again, probably, to a distant granary or mill, situated on the opposite side of the place of its growth,—let
the impropriety speak for itself.

The following particulars, relating to the rise of provisions, during the twenty years preceding 1793, are not
applicable to Norfolk, alone. Similar alterations of
prices have taken place, in other Counties :—more owing
to the depreciation of the value of money, than to markets
not being well attended (Norwich, Lynn, and Yarmouth
markets, for instance!) or to the entire produce of grain
(in Norfolk!) not being "pitched" therein!—There is
not another County, in the kingdom, to which such
groundless argument, could have been so unfortunately
applied†.

P. 168. "Butter was then 7d. a pint, of 20oz.—last
year it was 1s.—cheese is increased from 3d. per lb. to 6d.
—poultry and eggs in the same proportion—pork and
butcher's meat from 3d. per lb. to 5d.—meal from 1s. to
1s. 6d. per stone, of 14lb.—malt from 1l. 12s. to 2l. 8s.
per quarter."

Surplus

---

* This, indeed, appears in the writer's own account of them.—
P. 168. "As to the markets for other provisions, such as poultry,
butcher's meat, and vegetables, I do not think any part of England
can exceed that of Norwich, nor are those of Lynn and Yarmouth inferior, except as to size."

† The Reporter must surely have been in the habit of holding col-
loquial *arguments* on these controversial, and (a few years back)
party-forming topics ; and thus, have riveted the errors on his mind.
Seeing the good sense and sound judgement manifested, in many
parts of his performance, there seems to be no other way of account-
ing for these and a few other prejudices and partialities, that are
zealously propagated in different parts of his work. And nothing but
language, powerful as his own, can mitigate their mischievous
tendency.

Surplus Produce.—On this topic, too, we see the Reporter in the character of a *prejudiced* man; desireous to aggrandize his favorite County (great in agriculture as it truly is) beyond its deserts.—Norfolk—the nature of its soil being duly considered—has, for more than a century past, stood proudly pre-eminent, as an arable County. But, in my opinion, this writer gives too much of its merit to "art and industry," and too little to *marl* and *turneps;*—both of which, if they have not already *had their day,* have certainly been *living very fast.*—Thirty years ago, marl, in many instances, had nearly lost its efficacy; and turneps, it will be seen, under that head (ensuing) are not everlasting. The immense quantity of grain sent out of the County (whether providently or not, is not material to determine, here) has necessarily caused a reciprocal exhaustion of its lands. And had it not been for the fossil manure which those lands happened to cover, they doubtlessly would, even under the present admirable system of management, have long ago been exhausted; if not reduced to the lowest stage of poverty; or, without it, many of them would never have been brought into a state of cultivation;—would, to this day, have remained in that of sheep walk and rabbit warren.

That the occupiers of Norfolk have extraordinary merit in their profession,—are great in art and industry above most other Counties, and were, some years back, above all others,—I am willing and happy to allow. My chief intention, in making these remarks, is to *moderate* what I conceive to be extravagant praise; which ever will, sooner or later, injure the object on which it has been bestowed.

Mr. Kent, however, has not only an extensive knowledge of the County, but appears to have paid considerable attention to the subject here under discussion. He is, therefore, entitled to an attentive hearing.

P. 144. " In a good corn year, when there is a free exportation, *it has been said,* that the four Norfolk ports export as much corn as all the rest of England ; which I believe to be true, for it is seldom less than a million sterling in value, and often more; and though some of the corn comes down the Waveney out of Suffolk, and some down the Ouze from two or three of the midland counties, this addition seldom bears the proportion of more than an eighth part of the Yarmouth export, and a third of the Lynn, which is not more than a tenth upon the whole.

" The following is the nearest calculation I can make of

of the usual excess of corn, and other articles of provision, sent yearly out of the county, after reserving not only a sufficiency for its people employed in agriculture, but for fifty thousand home manufacturers, and six thousand seamen.

" The *corn* I am able to state with accuracy, as I have obtained it from the Custom-house books, where the quantity exported is registered *.

" The *cattle* I cannot be so confident of; but I have taken all the pains in my power to glean up the best information that could be obtained; and where I have deduced any thing from comparison, I have taken care to be within the limits of justification. The bridges of St. Germain and Magdalen, ascertain, in some degree, the number of Scotch and Irish cattle brought into the county; and the turn-pikes leading out of the county, together with the assist-ance which I have had from Mr. Archer, and other intelli-gent salesmen at Smithfield and St. Ives, enable me to come pretty near to what I conceive to be the truth.

" Last year there were actually 20,594 fat bullocks, brought from Norfolk to Smithfield and Islington, and about 3000 to St. Ives and other places; but, either from the war or some other cause, this is considered rather as a larger supply than usual; but they may be safely taken at 20,000 as a yearly average, about *one-quarter* of which are *home-bred* beasts, and the remainder Scotch and Irish The sheep are supposed to be upwards of 30,000; at least they may be safely taken at that number. Objects, such as swine, butter, rabbits, poultry, &c. are not of so much consequence, but suffice it, that they shall all be mode-rately estimated."

After

" * Lord Roseberry has the following remark:—'Where duties are not to be paid, the Custom-house books are not a rule to judge by, as every exporter enters, at random, any quantity he pleases, and always more than he is likely to export, to prevent the trouble and expence of a second entry, there being no necessity or obligation for entering the exact quantity they are to export. The debentures being given on corn afterwards, on the real quantity shipped; and it is from the register of the entries only, however, that this calculation is made, or even the reports to parliament, which make them very fallacious, and this members of parliament should advert to.' How far this may effect my calculation, I cannot presume to say: I have given my statement, on the best information I could obtain, and *flatter myself*, at least, that it is not far from the truth."

Thus, may we here say, the foregoing statements, so far as they relate to the export of *corn*, are not to be implicitly relied on.

After making some observations on the manufactures of Norwich (not of moment) Mr. K. proceeds—P. 146. " I shall begin my recapitulation with the corn, which is to be considered as *the yearly average* which has been exported to foreign parts and coastways, for the last three years, which were far from being prime one

Particularized statements are, accordingly, formed of the numbers of quarters of *wheat,—wheatflour,—barley,— malt,—rye,—peas,—beans,*—with their several prices,— shipped from the ports of YARMOUTH, LYNN, WELLS, and BLAKENEY with CLAY,—respectively. But,—for the substantial reason, contained in the foregoing note,— I will, here, omit the particulars of those statements, as not being sufficiently accurate, for the use of the Political Economist; to whom, alone, even if well ascertained, they could have been valuable.

P. 149. " The total amount" (in *money,*—the numbers of quarters of each species of grain are not given, in the aggregate) " of the whole County,—after deducting for the Suffolk and Midland proportions, 901,521*l.* 9*s.* 0*d.*"

The estimate of the value of " cattle,"—or rather the *animal produce,* stands thus:

	£.	s.	d.	£.	s.	d.
" 5,000 home-bred bullocks, at 10*l.*	50,000	0	0			
15,000 Scotch and Irish, the fatting profit which may be set at 5*l.* each	75,000	0	0			
30,000 sheep, at 1*l.* 10*s.*	45,000	0	0			
Swine, not less than	10,000	0	0			
Rabbits, at least	10,000	0	0			
Dairy articles, about	80,000	0	0			
Poultry and game	3,000	0	0			
Wool, conjectured to be about	20,000	0	0			
The herrings exported	50,000	0	0			
50,000 lambs, at 12*s.*	30,000	0	0			
				373,000	0	0"
which added to the surplus of the *vegetable productions*				901,521	9	0
The total value of surplus produce, annually sent out of the County, is, according to these statements				1,274,521	9	0

Mr. Kent thus concludes his strictures.—P. 150. " I have purposely brought the whole into money, with a view of shewing

shewing with the greater ease, what number of persons this extra, or superabundant produce is equal to the support of. And if we apportion ten pounds for the sustenance of a human being, one with another, which must be acknowledged to be a liberal allowance, where luxuries are excluded, it will appear, that this county sends out a foreign supply for upwards of 127,000 persons*. And if we take the 56,000 employed in the home manufactures and navigation, from the whole population of the county, it will shew, that the county furnishes more than a sufficiency for double the number of persons employed in agriculture and its appendant trades.

" Every impartial man, who considers this vast produce, must be struck with astonishment; and as Norfolk is far from being naturally a good county, it must, undoubtedly, be to *art* and *industry*" (assisted by *marl* and *turneps*), " that this great source of treasure is to be ascribed. It is evidently so great, that no part of England, not even the famous vales of Taunton, White Horse, or Evesham, are supposed to exceed it in proportion of corn.

" Government must certainly draw from this county a much greater portion of revenue, than from any other; for as nearly one-third part of all the arable land is sown with barley every year, and as the barley crop is generally very good, (half of it being sown upon clean land after turnips)" (and the other half generally the most productive crop) " the return which it must make, when traced through the malt-house, brew-house, and distillery, will be found to amount to a sum almost incredible†.

" I do not exhibit this statement as a panegyric on the county; but to point out to the Board of Agriculture, how beneficial this kind of husbandry is above all others; not only to the individual, but to the public revenue: a most powerful argument this, for Government to give all possible encouragement to inclosures in general; and a grand inducement *for other countries to follow the like course of husbandry*, wherever the soil will admit of it:"—that is to say, a system of MIXED CULTIVATION;—an ALTERNACY of

ARABLE

---

* Under the head, *Workpeople*, ensuing, it will seem to appear, that, in a " Hundred House," with " every species of economy," human beings cost 18*d.* a day, in " mere eating and drinking." Eighteen pence, a day, is 27*l.* 7*s.* 6*d.* a year.

† NORFOLK HUSBANDRY.—Be it remembered that, in the above paragraph, we clearly see the *six-crop system* considered, by Mr. KENT, as the ESTABLISHED, and " nearly" the UNIVERSAL COURSE of the COUNTY.

ARABLE CROPS and HERBAGE;—of products for *sale*, and of
products for *consumption*;—of crops that tend to *foul* the
ground;—and of such crops, half crops, or no crops, as
will admit of a due quantity of tillage, in due season,
whether with the plow or hoe,—to *cleanse* it,—and fit it
for future crops of saleable produce:—a plan of management, this, which has long been practised, in different
parts of the kingdom; and, in the southwestern peninsula
of it, probably, long before it was known, or adopted, in
Norfolk:—in other words, while Norfolk was, principally,
a County of heathlands—of sheep walks and rabbit warrens.

Norfolk, it is probable (speaking generally of the
County) has not borne grain, in abundance, much above
a century.—During the passed century, a principal part
of it was *fresh land*,—a newly discovered country, in
regard to grain crops.—The productiveness of it, therefore, is the less astonishing and wonderful. There can,
indeed, be no *mystery* in the matter. Its actual produce
must be owing to natural causes,—assisted by industry,
and a judicious plan of management.

But how are " other countries to follow the like course
of husbandry"?—The Norfolk system is not, *in itself*, a
whole. How could it be carried on, without foreign assistance? Only " one quarter" of the cattle fatted in the
County (the main support of the Norfolk husbandry) are
" bred" in it. It requires another County of land, nearly
as large and good as itself, to breed and rear cattle for it.
How, then, are " other Countries (that is to say the United
Kingdom at large) to follow the like course of husbandry?"

Were it not that it might be deemed officious, if not
invidious, I would not hesitate to say—now is the time,—
high time, or more than time, I conceive,—for the occupiers, or rather the proprietors, of Norfolk, to turn their
attention toward breeding the whole of their fatting stock;
and no longer continue to exhaust the country of its naturally scanty means, by sending out of it the immense
quantities of grain which are *really* exported, annually.
It is no longer a fresh-land country (the northwestern
parts excepted) and let it not,—by continuing to force
and exhaust it, and transporting from it an inordinate
and *unnatural* abundance of grain crops, be reduced to a
state of profitableness (to the proprietor and the community) beneath that in which it lay, a century and a half
ago.

SUBJECT

SUBJECT THE THIRD.

RURAL ECONOMY.

DIVISION THE FIRST.

TENANTED ESTATES.

ESTATES.—*Proprietors.*—Mr. Kent is (perhaps decorously) entirely silent, as to the present state of landed proprietorship, in Norfolk. We are not informed whether its lands are in few, or in many hands;—whether large or small owners are the most prevalent;—of course, we do not, in this, as in others of the Board's Reports, find a list of large proprietors, with the rentals of their several estates.

Tenures.—On this topic, Mr. Kent is quite *at home.* His professional experience, in different parts of the County, had given him peculiar advantages, and entitles him to every attention.

P. 28. " It is almost impossible to give the different proportions of each tenure, in so extensive a county as Norfolk; I must therefore be allowed to take it partly upon conjecture, and partly upon a comparative examination of the particular districts with which I am most acquainted; from which, I shall make the following deductions:—

" The copyhold is of two sorts, the one subject to, what is called here, an arbitrary fine, that is, a fine at the will of the lord, who, upon such estates, generally takes near two years value on descent, and a year and a half on alienation :—this copyhold is considered in value, about five years short of freehold. The other copyhold, is only subject to a fine certain, so that a lord of a manor can seldom take more than four shillings an acre, and sometimes only sixpence :—this is nearly of equal value to freehold.

" The money rents are, in most instances, easy and light, but a corn rent is sometimes reserved, which comes heavy.

" Heriots, generally speaking, are not known in this county,

County, which is a happy circumstance, as they are, un-questionably, the most cruel badges that remain of the ancient feudal system.

"There is some leasehold, for terms of years, under the bishop and dean and chapter of Norwich, and corporate bodies; some little under other ecclesiastical and colle-giate bodies, not resident in the County; but very little on lives, and that little only under the church or colleges.

"The practice which lay-lords have of leasing their estates upon lives, in the Western Counties, is in no in-stance, that I know of, followed in this County; though it is to be much wished, that it was the custom with respect to cottages, as it would be the best means of making them more comfortable than they are.

"Considering the whole of the County, perhaps I shall not be much wide of truth, if I state the freehold lands to be three-fifths; the church, collegiate, and corporate estates, at one other fifth; and the remaining fifth copy-hold, under lay-lords."

Mr. K. is friendly to "subordinate Tenures," which he thinks (p. 30) "have their advantage in society; by keep-ing up a sort of barrier against the monopoly of land, they tend to keep estates distinct, and preserve some lots of land, to which small capitals and industry are most ap-plicable."—But, in my mind, his best "argument in favor of copyhold is, the greater certainty of its title, and the cheapness of its conveyance compared to that of freehold." p. 31.

Why, then, not institute NATIONAL COURT ROLLS,—or TRANSFER OFFICES of *landed*, as well as of *monied*, pro-perty?—See my TREATISE on LANDED PROPERTY;—Divi-sion, *Purchase* of *Landed Estates*.

IMPROVEMENT of ESTATES.—*Sodburning.*—To this oper-ation Mr. Kent is a decided enemy. He would seem to prefer even *fallowing* to "burn-baking." But he rests his antipathies, on the opinions of others (the Board's Re-porters) rather than on his own experience.—Norfolk, in which sodburning is not in use, cannot be a proper place in which to discuss this subject.

Irrigation.—Respecting this valuable improvement of landed Estates, the writer of the Report under notice, might be said to be less than unacquainted;—having had, it would seem, a smattering of unsuccessful practice; and having caught a few *fashionable* ideas that were afloat, at the time he wrote. I should, of course, have passed over his remarks upon it, in silence,—had he not mis-stated what

what I had said upon the subject, in my register of the
Norfolk practice, Vol. I. p, 317 ;—wherein, speaking of
the improvement of the Norfolk meadows,—and, among
other means, by watering,—I have said—" *without* this
advantage, great as it would be, in *addition*, I will venture
to assert, from an extraordinary attention to this subject,
that the present rental value of the meadows of East Norfolk might be doubled."—Whereas, the Reporter says
(p. 51) " Mr. Marshall recommends watering, and says it
would double their value."

Many of the meadows of Norfolk are very similar, in
soil and surface, to those of Salisbury and Amesbury; and,
with a similar water, and with their surfaces formed in the
same manner, their improvement would, doubtlessly, be
of a similar nature.— In the valleys, and at the feet, of the
calcareous hills, in the northern quarter of ·Norfolk, Irrigation might, more than probably, be practised with great
advantage.

For a systematized detail of the theory and practice of
Irrigation, in its different branches, and as it is applicable
to grass lands of varying surfaces, as well as to arable
lands,—See TREATISE on LANDED PROPERTY.—Article,
Watering Lands.

EXECUTIVE MANAGEMENT of Estates.

TENANCY.—Here, again, we have the pleasure of seeing
Mr. Kent in his own element.—The following remarks are
so luminous, and so replete with good sense, and liberal
sentiments, it were a crime not to express the satisfaction
I experience in transcribing them; though of considerable
length.

P. 122. "The ancient feudal tenures had undoubtedly
a strong tendency to enslave mankind, by subjecting
tenants to the controul and power of an arbitrary lord;
but, like all other things, there were some advantages to
be found in the system. Every man, who held land, had
a certainty in it, as the tenant generally held his possession
for life. When these tenures were discountenanced, by
the liberal spirit of modern law, some new compact became necessary, and terms of years were substituted in
lieu of the former; for as land, properly managed, requires great expence, and seldom answers that expence in
one year, it was but reasonable that the man, who applied
his judgment, devoted his labour, and ventured his capital,
should have some reasonable time allowed him to reim-
burse himself, and derive some proportionate reward for
what he had done.

" In

"In the course of time, this term began to be reduced into a regular number of years. As most of the land was formerly under the regulation of two crops and a fallow, the time allowed was from three to twenty-one years, and the latter, in the end, became the most general limitation, and is the most prevalent term for leases at this time.

"That leases are the first, the greatest, and most rational encouragement that can be given to agriculture, admits not of a doubt, in my opinion; but, of late years, there are very strong prejudices entertained against them. In this county, it is rather the fashion to grant leases, which, in a great measure, accounts for the improvements that have taken place in it; most of the great estates have been made from it: for, without leases, no marling, to any extent, would have been undertaken, nor so much ground brought into cultivation, by one-third, as there now is. The Holkham estate, alone, strongly proves this assertion, as it has been increased, in the memory of man, from five to upwards of twenty thousand pounds a year, in this county only, and is still increasing like a snow ball. Mr. Coke, the present owner of it, is a real friend to agriculture, and justly considered as one of the best landlords in the county. From my particular knowledge of him, I can say, that at least two years before his leases expire, he puts the tenant upon a footing of certainty, by stating to him, the terms he expects for a renewal of his lease, that he may have time to look out for another farm, in case he does not like the conditions that are offered to him; but, though the advance of rent is often very great, I have never seen an instance of any tenant leaving him, unless grown too far in years to be able to continue. The stipulations and reservations in his leases are founded, too, upon principles of equity, and consist in no unnecessary repetition, or unreasonable exactions, being couched in plain terms, such as ought to compose a liberal contract between a gentleman and an industrious tenant; which may be worth imitation, in those who are fond of crowding their leases with overbearing compulsatory clauses, tending more to create obedience and servility in their tenants, than to promote good husbandry. There are some few estates, in this county, of a very considerable size, where leases are entirely withheld; but it is evident, that these estates are obliged to be let for, at least, 20 per cent. less than what they would be, if leases were granted. In many other counties the prejudice is so strong, that an owner would almost as soon alienate the fee simple of his

estate,

estate, as demise it for a term of years. I will not be so
harsh as to say, that this dislike to leases arises from ob-
stinacy or want of sense, but it is certainly an unfortunate
prejudice, which the proprietor takes up, and tends greatly
to injure the public. One of the arguments made use of
is, that it makes the tenant insolent and independent.
There may be some few instances of this sort, but they
ought not to be allowed to operate to the general injury of
a country, however indifferent a gentleman may be to the
advantage of his own purse. A man of large landed property owes, in my opinion, something to society, and
ought to get rid of his prejudices, where they affect the
community. Providence, who put him in possession of
his property, undoubtedly meant that he should in some
sort act as a public steward, and it cannot be right that he
should wrap up the talent entrusted to his care in a napkin. It grieves me to go into a country, which I often do,
and find it almost in a state of nature, because, the soil
being wet and expensive to cultivate, the tenant cannot
afford to do it without encouragement, and the owner's
insurmountable objection to leases, keeps him from granting the sort of encouragement which is essentially necessary. The yeomanry," (tenants) "in such parts, are
upon a wretched miserable footing; the public sustains a
vast loss; and the owner has, in lieu of the comfort he
might bestow, and the good he might do, no other conso-
lation than that he has the county more at command. But
even this is a mistake; for I have, except in few instances,
always found a tenant as obliging and well behaved to his
landlord, when he had a lease as when he had not. (?)

"The arguments in favour of leases seem to me so powerful, that I could not, on this occasion, suppress giving my
full sentiments relating to them ; and it seems unreasonable, to the greatest degree, to expect a tenant to hazard
all he is worth, and devote the best part of his life, upon
an estate, which, upon the death, or perhaps the mere ca-
price, of his landlord, he is liable to be turned out of at
six months notice. I will not, however, deny, that there
may be some reasonable exceptions against the practice I
wish to recommend, where lands lie near a gentleman's
house, part of which it may be an object to take into hand;
or, if a minor be very near of age, or if there be any immediate design of selling an estate, it is not prudent to grant
leases, because, in the latter case, a purchaser may wish
to enter into immediate possession, and may have particular objects in view, which will induce him to give a higher
price

price than he would, under the idea of purchasing merely to pay him a reasonable interest. But, except in these instances, leases, in my opinion, cannot be too strongly recommended; for I am certain, that where estates are under an entail, or in a family that has no idea of parting with them, leasing is, unquestionably, the most effectual means of raising their value, as the owner, by this means, has it in his power to stipulate for improvements, in what manner and proportion he pleases, which he cannot do by any other means so well."

Here, I think it right to remark, that,—rational, and highly beneficial, to the landlord the tenant and the community, as *long leases* undoubtedly are,—*abstractedly considered*,—and would be, *positively*, provided the value of money were as permanent, as the nature of lands;—and superlatively advantageous as they are to tenants, while the value of money is in a state of rapid depreciation,—as it has been of late years;—it appears to be, in the latter case, not only *irrational* on the part of landlords, in general, but *unfair*, in those of a certain time of life, to grant them.—The nominal value of land,—the rental of the kingdom,—has been almost doubled, during the last twenty-one years. And many proprietors, no doubt, are now receiving only half the present value of such of their lands, as have formerly been let on twenty-one years' leases.

In the present unsettled state of the value of money, leases for SIX YEARS CERTAIN, and THREE YEARS NOTICE, are, under those circumstances, all that a proprietor can prudently grant, and all that a tenant can reasonably expect.—If marling, draining, or other expensive improvements, are required,—let the landlord effect them, or agree to remunerate the tenant, for the remainder of such improvements.—It is not vainly to recommend a species of tenancy of my own invention, that I have said this; but from a clear and firm conviction of its rectitude.

Covenants. —(respecting Crops)—P. 60. " Though it is highly proper to confine tenants to a regular system of cropping, yet there are some little variations, that under certain circumstances, they ought occasionally to be indulged in.

" When, for instance, a piece of land is well cleaned, mucked, and sown with turnips, and the crop, notwithstanding all possible care, does not succeed; in such case, if the tenant be allowed to sow wheat, and, in the ensuing spring, clover among it, no harm can result from it, as it would

would have been seeded with barley if they had succeeded.

" No landlord ought to object to this, as the land is neither injured, or ultimately put out of course by it ; at the same time that the difference in value, between a wheat and a barley crop, will be a full compensation for the inconvenience the tenant sustains, by the loss of his crop of turnips.

" Sometimes it will happen, that grass seeds will not take root. In such case, it would be a hardship to confine a tenant to keep that piece of land in an unproductive state for two years : he should, when this happens, be allowed to take a cross crop, being confined to turnip or vetch it, after such extra crops."

P. 115.—(respecting Repairs)—" When farms are leased, the landlord generally engages to put them in repair, and the tenant to keep and leave them so. But estates, under this regulation, are very often neglected, for when the landlord is not called upon, it is very natural for him to be careless, and, at the expiration of the demise, there is often a heavy unexpected charge brought on, for want of a little timely attention ; and it seldom happens that a landlord can prevail on the departing tenant, to be at much expence in making good defects, and it is very unpleasing to be obliged to compel him to do a thing by force. Constant attention not only reduces the expence of repairs, but brings them to a more regular and even charge. But, as no exertion or assiduity, whatever, in an owner or steward, can be sufficient to attend to every accident that happens, upon a large estate, it seems essentially necessary, that the tenant ought, some how, to be interested in the preservation of the buildings, as well as the landlord, because, as he is always on the spot, he can remedy a breach at the expence of a shilling, by taking it in time, which will cost the landlord a guinea, by being neglected. He too, by being on the spot, can better attend to the workmen, to see that they do not idle away their time, when they work by the day.

" This obvious inconvenience I have, in a great measure, remedied upon the estates under my care, in this county, by obliging the tenants to be at one-half of all the expences of workmen's wages, not exceeding three per cent. however, to their share upon the rents ; this, with three per cent. more from the landlord, and the allowance of the materials, besides, after buildings are once put into good repair, will, in general, be sufficient to keep them so.

" The

"The advantage resulting from this, does not merely consist in the saving of the three per cent. but the tenant, by this means, becomes interested in the preservation of the buildings; and by that means the adage is verified, of A STITCH IN TIME, &c."

P. 223.—(in the Leases of T. W. Coke, Esq.) "Tenant will not assign, transfer, set over, or part his interest in the estate, to any person, except to his wife, child or children, without the licence of his landlord, first obtained in writing, under penalty of forfeiting his remaining term. —He will not lop, top, or prune any maiden tree, or cut down any young sapling, like to become timber, under penalty of paying three times the value of such timber-tree or sapling so lopped, topped, pruned, or cut down.— That he will not break up or convert into arable, any old meadow or pasture land, without licence so to do, under penalty of five pounds an acre additional yearly rent, to be paid from the time of such breaking up to the end of the term; and double that penalty for the last year.—That he will, during the whole of the term, endeavour as much as possible to adhere and conform to the course of cropping all his arable land, under six shifts, or equal portions, of which one shift shall be in turnips, or vetches fed off with sheep; two other shifts in grass seeds (which shall not be broken up till the same have lain two years); one other shift in wheat, and the remaining two shifts with lent grain.—But in case it shall so happen that the grass seeds shall at any time fail, so as to render it reasonable to break up any particular piece of land, after it has been in grass only one year, then he shall be permitted to break up such piece of land after one year's lay, taking only one crop of corn or grain after such one year's lay, and then summer-tilling the same for turnips, and so bringing it round again as soon as possible under the regular course of six shifts before stipulated —That he will in the last year of the term leave one full sixth part of all the arable land hereby demised in grass seeds of one year's lay; one other sixth part in two years' lay; one other sixth part in turnips, sown upon a fourth earth, well mucked and twice hoed.— That he will expend and consume all his hay, straw, and stover, upon some part of the premises during the whole of the term, and lay and spread all the muck, dung, and compost arising therefrom upon such parts of the land as is most proper to bestow the same upon.—And that he will imbarn and stack all his last year's crop of corn or hay upon the premises in the last year of the term, and leave

the dung arising from the last crop but one properly
turned up in heaps, in the yards or some other suitable
part of the premises, on or before Midsummer day in the
last year of the term.—That he will keep all his hedges,
ditches, mounds, and fences in good order and condition
during the whole of the term; and new make or repair
one-twelfth part of the whole every year; and at the time
of such making or repairing the same, will lop such pol-
lards as have been usually lopped close to their heads, and
cut down all the bushes, thorns, and stemwood, close to
the stools on which they grow, and effectually scour and
cleanse the ditches belonging to the same, and also permit
and suffer any trees to be planted in or near the same
which the said Thomas William Coke may think proper
to plant, and do all in his power to protect the same.—
That he will carry all materials for repairs, pay all carpenters', bricklayers', and other artificers' wages, find
allowance beer, nails and gate-irons, straw for thatching
and clay for daubing, and likewise keep gates, stiles, rails,
locks, bars, and bolts in good repair, being allowed timber
in the rough, bricks, tiles, lime, and hair, for doing the
same.—That he will at any time during the term hereby
demised agree and submit to any exchange of land that
may be proposed, having other land of equal quantity or
value laid to him in lieu of what he may be required to
give up.—That he will permit and suffer the succeeding
tenant to sow any grass seeds he may choose upon such
part of his land as he may sow with lent grain in the last
year of the term, and that he will sufficiently harrow in
the same gratis.

"LASTLY it is agreed, for the mutual convenience of
both parties, that the hay and turnips which shall be left
upon the premises at the expiration of the term, shall then
be valued by two impartial persons competent to value the
same; and if they cannot agree in such valuation, they
shall have power to call in and appoint any third person
they may choose as an umpire, to settle the difference between them; and the value so settled shall be paid by the
in-coming to the out-going tenant.—That the out-going
tenant shall be suffered to retain the use of the barns and
stack yard till the first of May next after the expiration of
the term, for the purpose of superintending the threshing
out and dressing his last year's crop of corn.—That the
in-coming tenant shall have liberty to enter upon the
yards, part of the stables, and upon the sixth part of arable land, being the second year's lay, at Midsummer previous

vious to the expiration of the term, for the purpose of
carrying out the muck and *making the summer fallows for
an ensuing wheat crop.*—That the in-coming tenant shall
be entitled to the straw, chaff, and colder, arising from the
last year's crop of corn ; but shall be at the expence of
threshing out the said corn, and carrying it to the usual
markets, for and in lieu of the said straw, chaff, and
colder."

. RENT.—Still we follow Mr. Kent with pleasure and instruction.—P. 57. " Respecting the scale of rent, it is the
most difficult question to answer, with precision, of any
the Board requires ; for there is nothing so unequal in the
kingdom, as the rent of land. Corn, and all articles of
merchandize, preserve some degree of proportion ; but
the price of land, is so much affected by local circumstances, that it has no regular standard, though it would
be a great advantage to agriculture if it had. Persons
of small fortune, and tradesmen, when possessed of a little
land, are naturally induced to get as much as possible for
it ; and farmers, above all others, when they become
owners, make the worst landlords in the kingdom. It is
therefore to large estates, that we are to look for moderation in rents, as they are generally let upon a fair and
consistent scale. From this consideration, more than any
other, great estates are of advantage to the public, as they
have a tendency to keep the price of land down to a proper level, which otherwise would, in many places, become
so excessive, as to give no encouragement to an industrious occupier.

"As to the general standard however, of rents in this
county, subject to poor rates and tythes, I believe it varies
from 20s. to 16s. an acre, in the first division of the county,
which I have described ; from 18s. to 14s. in the second ;
and 14s. to 8s. in the third ; from 12s. to 4s. in the fourth ;
and, in the Marshland hundred, from 30s. to 20s. The
average of the whole county is about 15s. * ; and though
this would be a dear rent, for the same soil, in most other
counties, the nature of the husbandry, and the industry of
the inhabitants, render it easy, and rents are better paid
in this county, than in almost any other, as there is hardly
any such thing as an arrear known ; at the same time, the
farmers live, as they are entitled to do, with comfort."

DIVISION

* In 1782, I estimated the general average, at 12s.

DIVISION THE SECOND.

WOODLANDS.

NATURAL WOODS.—P. 86. "In my first Report, I stated, that the woodland, of an old standing, was not considerable; that a single wood, or coppice, was found here and there, but no great tract together; and that the county was not remarkable, for any particular application of the underwood, further than the mere purpose of sheep hurdles and materials for thatching.   At that time, I considered Foxley Wood, which is three hundred and nine acres, belonging to Sir John Lombe, Bart. as the largest in the county, which I still believe to be the case; but I have since learnt from Sir Thomas Beevor, that there are several other considerable woods in Ashwell Thorpe, Hetherset, Ketteringham, Hethel, Bunwell, Hempnall, and Shottisham, of eight hundred or a thousand acres, in the aggregate, besides several other smaller woods in other parts, and that the underwood is used for hoops, as well as thatching, and other purposes of repairs."

PLANTING.—This is a subject to which Mr. Kent would seem to have paid considerable attention;—both as an observer and a practitioner.   His remarks,—however, are mostly of a desultory nature :—and, seeing the systematized details, concerning the theory and practice of this valuable art, that are already before the public, there is little in his Report of Norfolk that is entitled to preservation, in this Register.

Among the planters of Norfolk are mentioned Mr. MARSHAM of Stratton (who might be styled the first of English planters), Mr. BERNEY of Bracon, Mr. COKE of Holkam, and Mr. WINDHAM of Felbrig.

The few extracts which I shall make, on this occasion, relate, principally, to the natures of individual timber trees; namely, the larch, the chestnut, and the pinaster.— Not that there is much that is new, in Mr. K's remarks (unless in regard to the last species); but they will serve as respectable corroborations of what the public have already in possession.

The *Larch.*—P. 89.   Mr. Berney has put the timber of this tree "to almost all the purposes of buildings, such as
principals,

principals, spars, lath, and boards; likewise to many cabinet uses, such as doors, tables, window-frames, book-cases, chimney-pieces, and many beautiful specimens in carving. In short, he entertains the highest opinion of it; and, having made observations upon the proper season for felling it, as well as all other firs, he recommends it to be done in the months of July or August, as he has found, by experience, that the liquid which oozes out at that time of the year, almost immediately turns to a sort of rosin, which operates as a stiptic, so that the wood is not so much drained as at other seasons, but hardens and comes into use sooner, which is a hint worth notice."

The *Chestnut.*—P. 220. " In 1676, an ancestor of the present Mr. Windham, of Felbrigg, in Norfolk, had the merit of being a considerable planter of chesnut. In the space of fifty years, it is presumed these plantations required thinning, as his successor, about that time, began to apply this timber to useful purposes upon his estate.

" The first account is of the branch or limb of a chesnut, about thirteen inches square, which, in the year 1726, was put down as a hanging post for a gate, and carried the gate, without alteration, fifty-two years, when, upon altering the inclosures of the farm where it stood, it was taken up, under my direction, and appearing to be perfectly sound, was put down for a clapping-post in another place.

" In 1743, a large barn was built with some of this timber, and is now as sound in every part, beams, principals, and spars, as when first the barn was built: about the same time, several chesnut posts and rails were put down, which I have since seen removed, and after standing thirty or forty years, generally appeared so sound, as to admit of being set up in some other place.

" The last instance I shall mention, though not of long date, will shew the great superiority of this timber over oak in fences. In the year 1772, the present Mr. Windham made a large plantation in his park, which was fenced with posts and rails, converted from young oaks and chesnuts of the same age and scantling, such as were picked out of a place where they stood too thick. Last year, upon Mr. Windham's enlarging his plantation, it was necessary to remove this fence—when the chesnut posts were found as sound as when they were first put down, but the oak were so much wasted, just below the surface of the ground, that they could not be used for the same

same purposes again, without the assistance of a spur to support them."

The *Pinaster.*—(a variety of the Scotch Fir) P. 95. " As a decided proof of its advantage over the Scotch·fir in growth, and consequently in value, I need only state, that about forty years since, his late Royal Highness William Duke of Cumberland made a plantation of nearly a hundred acres on a remarkably poor sandy land, adjoining to Bagshot Heath, in Surry, chiefly with Scotch firs, but with a smaller proportion of pinasters intermixed with them. The plantation is reckoned to have succeeded extremely well, and has been a great ornament to the country; but the Scotch firs do not average more than five cubical feet, whilst the pinasters are full forty; some of them I have measured, and found to be upwards of seventy feet."

These, if accurately ascertained, are extraordinary facts. I have frequently observed its rapid growth; and, some years ago, had an opportunity of examining its timber; which, tho of a standard, or single tree, in a bleak situation, but tolerably good soil, and of mature age, and large size, was, as might well be expected from its quick growth, remarkably coarse-grained, and open in its texture; but particularly tough, in the splinter.

I am happy to find Mr. Kent an advocate for propagating woods, from *seeds*, rather than from *plants.*—P. 96. " When new plantations are made, it is always best to make them in as large a body as the ground will admit of, and if there is a time to clean the land well, I recommend such plantations to be made from seed in drills, rather than with seedlings, keeping the ground clean till the plants get high enough to protect themselves."

DIVISION THE THIRD.

AGRICULTURE.

FARMS.—On the *sizes* of farms, this writer sets out by saying—P. 129. " It is a subject on which no person can stand neutral, but must take a decided part one way or another"! and he goes on, for several pages, as an advocate for *small* farms;—but by no means a powerful one.

His

His positions are frequently untenable, and his argument inconclusive; as those of *party* writers often are.—At length, however, the good sense of this writer prevails; and he closes his strictures with the following concessions.—P. 135. " I will, however, admit, though I am an advocate for small farms, that, as the country is now situated, no farm should be under 30*l.* or 40*l.* a year, and even these should be dairy farms, nor would I have any arable farm under 50*l.* I will still go farther, and say, that the greatest number should be from 80*l.* a year to 150*l.* none ought to exceed 200*l.* where the land is of a good quality; or 500*l.* even upon the poorest land, where great farms, on account of a large flock of sheep, are most admissible. The greater the difference in their size, between the preceding extremes, perhaps, the better, as they will better play into each other's profits; some will raise cattle to more advantage than they can fat them, and others will fat them to more advantage than they can raise them."

This passage does not appear, in the *original* Report. And it cannot, I trust, be deemed improper to be noticed, here, that, previously to the publication of the *reprinted* edition, now before me, I had disseminated (in the most public manner) sentiments of a similar nature:—in consequence of which, it is possible, not only the sticklers for *small farms,* but the more powerful argumentalists for *large farms,* were convinced of their errors, and the folly of their violent disputes;—which subsided about that time.

For a full investigation of this very important subject (more recently written) see my TREATISE on LANDED PROPERTY.

On the prevailing sizes of farms, in the several Districts of Norfolk, or in the County at large, not a scrap appears, in this Report!

HOMESTEADS.——On this prominent part of estate agency, Mr. Kent's practice, and opinions, are entitled to full attention.

New Erections.—P. 110. " That a farmer should have reasonable accommodation, cannot admit of a doubt; but it is highly improper that he should be indulged in unreasonable or unsuitable buildings.

" Farm-buildings in this county are upon a very respectable footing, but, in my opinion, they are upon too large a scale."

P. 111. " Farmers are very averse to stacking, though wheat

wheat is preserved sweeter and better on staddles than in barns; they are always crying out for barn room; and they certainly are indulged in a greater proportion of it, than farmers in any other ·county. It is not uncommon to have barns, upon 100*l.* a year, which cost 300*l.* there are many single barns that have been lately erected, which have cost considerably more than that sum; and some few farm-houses, upon farms of about 300*l.* a year, have cost 1000*l.* This is certainly wrong, for such buildings make a great waste of timber, and are unnecessary and, moreover, very bad examples, as one farmer will always covet a similar thing to what he sees his equal in possession of. I should much rather see a disposition in the country, to build a sufficient number of comfortable cottages, for the industrious labourers, than to run into an excess of indulgence, where no good purpose can be answered by it."

The following hints, in *rural architecture,*—tho not new,—are entitled to the greater attention, as coming from a man of Mr. K.'s extensive experience.—P. 113. " Not to build any thing but what will be really useful. To build upon a small compact scale, and, as much as possible, upon squares or parallelograms; not in angles, or notches. * To build, at all times, substantially, and with good materials. Not to lay any timber into fresh mortar, because the lime eats up and wastes the ends of it, long before the other parts decay; but to lay the ends into loam or clay. Not to put any window-frames or door-cases into new brick-work, at the time the walls are carried up; but to introduce a discharging-piece, or lintel, over such door and window spaces. The reason of the last caution is obvious; for as brick-work settles, soon after it is up, the window-frames and door-cases, on account of their strength, will not yield to it, but occasion cracks and flaws; but, when a lintel is made use of, the whole work settles regularly together, and door-cases and window-frames may be then introduced, with more propriety than before."

On *Repairs,*—I find little, in Mr. K.'s remarks that is either new, or excellent.—At whose *expence* repairs are done, or ought, according to Mr. K.'s opinion to be done,

in

* This good *general* rule is liable to an *exception.* An *octagonal* FARM YARD is preferable to a *square* one; in as much as it prevents " angles and notches."

in Norfolk, appears, aforegoing, under the head, *Cove-nants*, p. 321.

The annual *percentage* of repairs Mr. Kent says (p. 111.) he has found, by experience, to be not less than " 10 per per cent, including materials."

On the *materials* of building and repairs, in Norfolk, I find nothing, in the Report before me, to be added to my own account of them;—which is much fuller than that of Mr. K.

Cottage Grounds.—I will quote what Mr. Kent offers on this subject.—There is meaning and moderation in his remarks. Not only may it be allowable for men of fortune to indulge their philanthropy, and grant cow grounds to their laborers; but it may, in some cases (as where grass grounds are abundant) be *convenient*, for " great farmers," to do the same,—*to a certain extent.*

P. 172. " There is one thing which is incumbent on all great farmers to do, and that is, to provide comfortable cottages for two or three of their most industrious labourers, and to lay two or three acres of grass land to each, to enable such labourer to keep a cow and a pig*—such a man is always a faithful servant to the farmer who employs him: he has a stake in the common interest of the country, and is never prompt to riot, in times of sedition, like the man who has nothing to lose; on the contrary, he is a strong link in the chain of national security.

" There are but few great farmers, however, inclined to accommodate cottagers with these little portions of land, and when they do let them any, it is generally at double the rent they give for it. But I am persuaded, that if there were a certain number of cottages, of this description, in proportion to the size of the estates, and they were accommodated in this manner, and those places were bestowed as a reward to labourers of particular good conduct, it would do wonders towards the reduction of the rates, and the preservation of order; for I have been witness to several striking proofs of this, in two or three labourers, who have been thus favoured, whose attachment to their masters was exemplary, as they were not only steady in themselves, but by their example kept others from running into excess. There cannot well be too many of these places attached to large farms; they would

---

* It would require four or five acres of Norfolk land to keep a full sized cow and pig.

would be the most prolific cradles of the best sort of population."

But still the scheme, even in this view of it, remains theoretical and impracticable, *to any considerable extent.*—Where grass lands are scarce, it can seldom be convenient, to a " large farmer," to part with it to his laborers!—or to be encumbered with their stock!—Beside if " there are but few great farmers inclined to accommodate cottagers with these little portions of land," how is even Mr. Kent's diminutive part of the grand scheme to be carried into effect?—And, again, if only " the most industrious"—that is to say those who are able and willing to support themselves and their families,—are to be selected,—how can the partial regulation, above proposed, " do wonders towards the reduction of the rates?"—As to the " stake" and the " link," above hinted at, it cannot be reasonably expected that " farmers"—of any class—will prefer political regulations, to their own interest.—In fine, the more this sentimental scheme is investigated, the narrower its foundation appears.

OCCUPIERS.—Neither of the sizes of estates, of the sizes of farms, nor of their occupiers, in the County under Report, do we find any mention made, in the work of a writer who had a more general knowledge of each, than almost any other man.

PLAN of MANAGEMENT of Farms.—P. 32. "The landlord generally wishes to fix the management and course of cropping under a six-course shift, viz. wheat the first year—barley or oats the second, without clover—turnips the third—barley or oats, with clover, the fourth—the clover mowed for hay the fifth—and the sixth grazed till Midsummer, and then broken up for wheat in succession.

" But the occupier will often *endeavour* to contract it to a five-course shift, by sowing his wheat upon clover of one year's lay, and in *some* of the best parts, as in the Flegg, Tunstead, and Blofield hundreds, *some* tenants carry on only a four-course shift: thus, wheat, turnips, barley, and clover."

Mr. K. then proceeds to remark on those three different rotations. His observations, however, only tend to show (and perhaps were only made with that intent) that he had formerly seen something of *Flemish* husbandry;—but without attempting to prove, or even to intimate, that it is superiorly calculated to obtain the objects aimed at, in the prevailing system of *Norfolk*:—that system, by which
the

the extraordinary products of corn and cattle, stated aforegoing, are brought to market. He is not, indeed, decided upon any point whatever; except that (p. 33) "in the great western parts of the County, the course of six shifts ought to be strictly adhered to; and there is" (the Reporter truly says) "something very rational in this six-course husbandry upon a light soil, for though the exhausting and fertilizing crops, do not follow alternately, as in the four-course shift, yet there is an equal number of each observed in the rotation."

The same remarks equally apply to every part of the County, where the practice of fatting bullocks on turneps, and finishing them on raygrass, in early spring, prevails; in order to obtain the advantageous prices, in the London market, which ever takes place, between the supply of stall-fatted beace of winter, and the grazed stock of summer.

This is the TRUE NORFOLK HUSBANDRY; by which Smithfield market, from the middle of May, to the middle of June, is supplied with the best meat it receives in the course of the year; and without which an ill-supplied chasm would, necessarily take place:—a supply which neither the Flemish, nor the five-shift, husbandry could afford.

In the neighbourhoods of Yarmouth and Norwich, where large supplies of manure may be purchased, the four-crop course may be followed. But there will be little risk in saying that, in four-fifths, perhaps nine-tenths, of the County, (at the time this Report was made,) the legitimate Norfolk husbandry prevailed *.

WORKPEOPLE.—P. 159. "Some little difference is found in different parts of the County, but the following is the nearest general average that can be offered :

Yearly Wages.

A head carter—nine to ten guineas.
An under carter, or lad—five to seven guineas.
A shepherd—about ten pounds.
A yard man—about eight pounds.
A dairy or house maid—four guineas.

Daily Wages

Of a labourer, till within a few years, was 14d. in summer, and 1s. in winter, but they are now increased, in most parts of

* For evidence, bordering on proof, that Mr. KENT really considered this to be the case, see note p. 313, aforegoing.

of the County, to 18d. in summer, and 14d. in winter.—
Carpenters, thatchers, and bricklayers—20d. a day."

The Reporter continues his list to sundry articles of
task work. But, as I had previously published a fuller
list, I forbear to copy it. The two lists, in most cases,
agree; allowing for a rise, during ten or twelve years, of
fifteen to twenty, per cent., on yearly and day wages.

The subjoined remarks, from the foot of Mr. K's list,
are more than interesting ;—they must excite the stronger
feelings of every man who is not callous to the sufferings
of a numerous class of his own species.

P. 163. "This scale of wages, and price of labour,
may do for a man with only one or two children, but if
he has more, it is evidently not sufficient, according to the
present rate of provisions ; for in the houses of industry,
where every species of economy is observed, and where
they have the advantage of boarding a great number together, and buying in their provisions at best hand, the
mere eating and drinking, alone, costs 18d. per head,
which I have authority to state from Sir Edmund Bacon,
who shewed me the account of their expenditure, and
whose attention to these institutions, is distinguished by
every species of humanity and benevolence that is in his
power to bestow. Therefore, as a cottager must purchase
his comforts at a great discount, it is clear, that when his
family exceeds what I state, he must have considerable
help, let him be ever so industrious."

If it "cost 18d. per head," a day, to support even an
infirm or aged individual, in "mere eating and drinking
alone," how wretched must be the lot of a hungry labor-
ing man, with a wife and even one or two children (and
still more with half a dozen !) without any other means of
support for meat, drink, washing, rent, fuel and cloaths,
than fourteen to eighteen pence, a day !!

How reasonable, then, it would be, for every man who
has no other dependence, for the subsistence of himself
and his family, than his own hand labor, and who has
more than two children,—to have the *right* of claiming,
—as a contributor to the well being of the state, (by adding to the number of the working class, and thereby,
strengthening the sinews of society) a PENSION from the
PUBLIC.—See the WESTERN DEPART. p. 326.

Equally humane and liberal, as the foregoing, are the
subsequent sentiments, which evidently flow from a kind
heart, and amiable disposition.

P. 192. "In the prosperity of agriculture, there are
three

three persons who have a natural tye upon each other : the gentlemen of landed interest—the farmer—and the labourer. Their degrees of interest are different, but their connection must be permanent, as they cannot subsist without the aid of each other. Protection is due from the first—humanity from the second—and obedience from the third. Sound policy dictates a due observance of this mutual obligation, and the preservation of a proportionate and just scale in respect to every thing which mutually affects the parties : a departure from this, will, in the first instance, prove very detrimental to one of them, and cannot ultimately be of any advantage to the others.

" Admitting this, as every impartial man must, and comparing the advanced price of provisions, with the present rate of wages, and the price of labour, the cause of the increase upon the poor-rates must be obvious. I would, therefore, advise every gentleman in the commission of the peace, carefully to peruse a book I have before recommended in this work, namely, Fleetwood's *Chronicon Preciosum*, which will show him the proportions which were observed at that time, and likewise to advert to two particular acts of parliament, framed by the wisdom of our ancestors, viz. the 5th of Elizabeth, chapter iv. and the 1st of James, chapter vi.; where sufficient power is given to regulate this important business.

" Every farmer I would advise, to consider the labourer not as an incumbrance upon him, but as essentially necessary to carry on his business, without whom he could not live or support his own family ; but the present weak policy has arisen from a misconception of the utility and real importance of the labourer to society. No farmer will slight his horse, or give him the less hay or corn for its being dear, if he did, he would expect the animal to decline in condition.—Why then should the human servant be less attended to ?* He is, undoubtedly, the first sinew that puts the labour of the farm in motion, and without which it cannot be carried on : if, therefore, his full earnings will not keep him, it is a duty incumbent on his master, to let him have a sufficiency of corn, for his own

* In countries where human servants are *slaves,* the principle of conduct here indirectly recommended, is observable. But, in England, laborers change their employers when they list : and are not always grateful for indulgencies received.

own family, at the same rate or price by which he is paid
for his labour, and not to suffer the spirit of a poor man,
of this description, to be broken. *

" The force of this argument is grounded in my heart,
and I hope it will strike those with conviction, who have
power, in their different stations to administer the comfort I recommend—and that no dispassionate person
will blame me, for thus standing forth—the steady friend
of the helpless."

WORKING ANIMALS.—Mr. Kent is an advocate for *oxen.*
But, on their comparative merit with *horses*, we find nothing (after what has been written on the subject) either
new or excellent.—His strictures, however, on the pernicious effects of horses, abstractedly considered, are well
entitled to public attention. I, therefore, insert them ;
tho they do not, in detail, altogether accord with my own
opinion.—Nevertheless, in as much as they convey, in
an impressive manner, a general idea of the destructive
tendency of horses, I cordially agree to them ; and the
more readily, as they regard the horse tax (in part at
least) as a "real advantage to the community."

P. 141. " The more the number of horses can be
lessened, the better for all ranks of people. The consumption by horses, especially horses of pleasure, and
luxury, is astonishing ; for though a horse in agriculture,
does not consume above three acres (?) of the fruits of the
earth in a year, a horse kept upon the road, eats yearly,
in hay and oats, the full produce of five acres of land. A
man, allowing him a pound of bread, and a pound of
meat a day, or in that proportion, not quite an acre and
a quarter ; and as the poor eat but very little meat, it
cannot be put at more than an acre to them : so that one
of those horses eats nearly as much as five men. The
more, therefore, we reduce our number of horses, the more
plentiful will be the fruits of the earth for man. Under
this idea, perhaps, the tax upon horses of pleasure and
luxury may be a real advantage to the community. Let
any person but consider how these horses sweep off the
produce

* An evil tendency of this method of relieving laborers, in times
of scarcity, has, I trust, been fully shown. See NORTH. DEPART.
p. 377.

But let not that be a hinderance to the due relief of workpeople in
such distressful times. It makes no difference to their employers
whether they give them money, or "money's worth." But to the
community, the difference is material.

produce of the earth : I am told, and I believe, from good
authority, that in the city of Norwich, not quite fifty years
since, there were only twelve carriages of pleasure and
luxury, and there are now seventy-two, including post-
chaises, and thirteen hackney coaches besides ; and if we
allow three horses to each carriage, upon an average, allowing for change, this will make a difference of 219 horses in
the city of Norwich only.   At that time, there was only
one coach to London ; now there are two mail coaches,
and two heavy coaches , and, as there cannot be allowed
less than sixty horses to each mail coach, and fifty to each
of the others, this makes an increase of 170 horses
more.—There is also a coach to Lynn, and another to
Yarmouth, which cannot take less than twenty horses
more—here then is a difference, upon a round calculation,
of 409 additional horses, in what affects Norwich only;
which, at five acres to a horse, consume the additional
produce of 2045 acres.   If this mode of calculation be extended to other towns in the County, it will amount to a
very great number of acres, in the aggregate, and multiplied by a similar increase in all other parts of England,
will shew, that one great cause of the dearness of provisions, is owing to the number of horses which are kept
more than formerly."

Truth, however, requires that some deduction should
here be made for the decrease of saddle horses, used in
travelling, which has taken place, during the period
spoken of.

IMPLEMENTS.—Inserted, in this Report, are two plates
of implements.   One of them showing a Norfolk plow,
and the other a Norfolk harvest carriage (" maphrodite ")
and a Berkshire waggon.

I find nothing noticeable, in the Reporter's section,
" Implements," which is very short; except the admirable thought conveyed (not very intelligibly) in the subjoined extract; and which, if duly carried into effect, and
followed up, bids fair to be productive of a valuable acquisition to tillage.

P. 120.   " There is also another instrument, just introduced into the Flegg hundred, which is an iron bar
fastened upon the plough beam, and projecting out so as
to be dragged by the plough along the middle of the last
furrow, to that which is turning over ; the end of the bar
being cut into a sort of an edge, is loaded with weights to
keep it down, and, by this means, makes a little dent (?)
which catches a great deal of corn, and what it does
                                                          catch

catch, is deposited (where land is only once ploughed) in the middle of the furrow, so that the seed, when it strikes root, has the benefit of the best part of the flag or inverted turf. This has not been much proved, but it promises to be of some benefit, and, I am inclined to think, it will be of most use in barley sowing."

MANURES.—On the amelioration of the soils of this pre-eminently arable County, the Report under consideration is in a manner silent!—I perceive not, in the Section "Manures, &c." a passage, in *husbandry,* that is entitled to extraction.

The theory and practice of *marling,* in Norfolk, the Reporter has politely conceded to his predecessor.

Sea Sand ("the small sand from the beach"—quere *Shell Sand?*) has lately been used for bottoming farm yards. And

River Weeds have been found to be an excellent manure for turnips.

To *men* of *fortune,* the following hint may have its use. —P. 25. "There is another source, which I here offer more particularly to gentlemen who are in possession of parks, plantations, and lands in hand, and that is, to cause a permanent fold, during the winter months, to be pitched, in some sheltered spot, near their woods, and to pen their store flock in it, giving the sheep the quantity of hay they are accustomed to have, in racks, in the fold, and littering it every night with fresh leaves of trees, with rushes, moss, or any other similar rubbish that can be collected ; this turned up together, in the month of April, and mixed with about one-sixth part of lime, rubble from old walls, or any sort of ashes, will make as good a sort of manure as can be laid on turnips—and the quantity will be very consi-derable : suffice it, that on one of His Majesty's farms at Windsor, I made, in one winter, six hundred cart loads from six hundred sheep."

In the Appendix is a paper of some length, by Doctor Hinton, on the advantages of peat and lime, for manure. But I perceive nothing in its desultory contents that would add to the value of this Register.

TILLAGE.—Here, I am completely " at check," for the first time, in pursuing the devious track of the work now before me ;—in which, beside a brief account of the prac-tice of "*ploughing*" in Norfolk, we find, in different parts of it, the author sporting among the wildest speculations; —uttering the very crudities, or first thoughts, of a tyro, or town farmer :—the whole forming a tissue of error and truth,

truth, or the semblance of truth, which, I fear, will cost me more time and thought (and certainly more irksomeness) to unravel, than I have bestowed on the rest of the volume. But the erroneous principles propagated by a man of Mr. Kent's fair fame (in his own profession) must not be passed over, without due examination and notice.

P. 37.—(Section, " Modes of Culture.") " As ploughing is done here with so much ease, it is an encouragment to the farmer to give it the more tilths, which, in some measure, accounts for the land being so clean ; but I apprehend there is another reason, which is, the shallow ploughing observed in this county, compared with many other parts of England. * Land is undoubtedly kept cleaner by shallow than deep ploughing, and, in light land, the moisture is more preserved by having a pan at the bottom ; and there is likewise a much less body of earth to manure and keep in heart. The great secret with ploughed land seems to be in keeping it so clean that nothing shall grow but what is sown upon it ; and to keep the surface in a pulverized state, so as to be open and mellow to receive benefit from the influence of the atmosphere."

From the tenor, and mode of expression, observable in this passage, (which closes what is said in that part of the work, on tillage, and which is, in fact, insulated, and itself a whole,) it is evident, that the writer meant it, not as being applicable, merely, to the practice of *Norfolk ;* but as containing a GENERAL PRINCIPLE of TILLAGE, which ought to be pursued, in " many other parts of England"—or may we not fairly add in England at large ; and, of course, on all soils, and in every situation? It could not have been written with any other intention, than that of impressing the reader with such an idea. And it must, necessarily, by it's general bent, and complexion, have the pernicious tendency of inducing many inexperienced practitioners, to adopt *shallow plowing,* in all cases,—*on Mr. Kent's principle.*

With what contempt must every experienced strongland farmer hear such doctrine.—In cases where the base of the land is repellant of superfluous moisture, after the pores of the cultivated mold are supplied, and where of course a certain quantity, only, can be lodged in it, the rest

* The shallow plowing of Norfolk is evidently owing to the natures of the soil and the subsoil (or " pan") of that county.

rest of the rain water, that falls upon it, is shot off the surface, and lost to the purposes of vegetation, during a succeeding drought. It follows, of course, that if the cultivated soil is not deeper than the immediate region of the main roots, of corn, or other arable crops, they are drowned with every shower, or moderate fall of rain, and parched for want of moisture, by the shortest drought:—thus becoming the sport and victims of the weather.

On the contrary, if a proper depth of porous, absorbent soil be prepared, by what is called "deep ploughing,"—(as eight, ten, or more inches)—a receptacle is formed beneath the crowns of the roots;—which, unless in long continued rainy seasons, are free from the annoyance of water, or fluent-mud;—while the moisture, lodged beneath them, invites the feeding fibres, downward, and, at the same time gradually sends up to the surface,—like water lodged beneath a garden pot,—the required coolness and moisture: thus tending, in a twofold manner, to frustrate the evil effects of a droughty season.

Hence, in stiff-land districts, it is common to see deep-plowing farmers growing rich; while their neighbours, —poor in knowledge, or spirit, or weak in teams,—are pining in penury. I have known a succession of shallow-plowing tenants beggared on a stiff-land farm; and their successor, by deeper tillage, make a farmer's fortune upon it.

Why, let me ask this writer, is land "kept cleaner by shallow than deep ploughing?"

It is certainly true, that, "in light land the moisture is more preserved by having a *pan* at the bottom."—But a *pan* may be at any *depth*.—In Norfolk, it is mostly found at three to six inches deep.—The remark, above quoted, therefore, is without meaning or import*.

The position, that, "there is likewise a much less body of earth to manure and keep in heart,"—is almost equally vague and unmeaning. When applied to soils and arable crops, in general, it is wholly so.

The final period of the above extract is fraught, not only with meaning, but with good sense; and shows, in a happy manner, the valuable effects of *fallowing foul lands*. For nothing can bring foul lands into the state there described,

* The nature and use of a "PAN;" and a circumstantial account of the TILLAGE of NORFOLK, may be seen in my Register of its Rural Economy.

scribed, but a COURSE OF TILLAGE;—for which the term
" fallowing" has been immemorially established, throughout the kingdom.

Nevertheless, the writer of that period has set apart an
entire section,—for the purpose of decrying that very process,—under the appropriate quack title of " FALLOW-
ING EXPLODED!!!"   That is to say, for ever doomed
to disuse,—if not to contempt and ridicule,—on all soils,
and on every occasion.

P. 66. " It is a question with some persons, whether
summer fallowing be necessary or not? I am one of those
who do not think it is.   Nature does not seem to require
any *pause* or *rest* (!) of this kind; all plants make their
annual shoots, as regularly as the day succeeds the night.
The earth was evidently designed to yield a regular uninterrupted produce; and it does so, *where we leave it to
itself*. If you do not sow corn it will produce weeds: its
productive quality never ceases. * It is therefore our
business, by good culture, to *expel the unprofitable plant*,"
(by a course of tillage; otherwise " fallowing") " and introduce another, from which we may derive benefit.   The
idea of leaving land to rest is ridiculous; keep it clean,
and intermix the crops sown upon it judiciously, so that
one may *fertilize* (!) as much as another exhausts;" (ha!
ha!) " and it may be sown as a garden is planted, from
one generation to another."

Yes, if the same labor and attention could be paid to
field, as to *garden* culture.   In a garden of an acre or two,
we see three or four men, constantly employed.   A hundred acres, cultivated in the same way, would require the
laborers of two or three parishes to cultivate them.   Were
the population of England proportionate to that of China,
a sort of garden culture might be transferred to the field.
But writers on *English* agriculture, at this day, should now
and then advert to the existing circumstances of their own
country; and not draw their conclusions from China,
Flanders, or any other country, that is differently circumstanced.

Again, in continuation,—" Look at half the common
fields in England, where the system established by the old
school is called two crops and a fallow.   What does this
exhibit, but a conflict between the farmer and his weeds,
                                                         in

* How does this apply to the artificial culture of arable crops? It
is merely *fine* writing.

in which the latter generally get the better; for they are only half stifled, and never effectually killed?"*

So, because it is wrong, in the present state of this country, longer to pursue the feudal system (founded as it was, in wisdom, at the time it was instituted)—because it is inexpedient to leave, uncropped, lands of all descriptions, every third year, the process of " fallowing" is to be " exploded"—as the pellet from a pop-gun.

This is, in truth, flying from pillar to post—from light to darkness—from one extreme to another; as men who write or talk on subjects they have not duly studied, in all their parts and bearing, have ever been wont.

All the " works of men's hands"—all human institutions, —tho the plans may be well laid and the executions well performed,—are liable to be *out of order*. Is not a clock, a watch, and every other machine of man's making, wont *to go wrong;* and, sooner or later, to require a *thorough repair,*—a *complete fallowing?*—A garden may be said to be, perpetually in a state of fallow, or fallow crop; and, with the care and labor, above mentioned, to be *daily under repair.* But the same plan of management, it has been shown, cannot, in the present state of society, in this country, be extended to the field.

P. 67. " On the other hand, view this county, which yields a crop every year, without being exhausted; and though the soil in many parts is light and ordinary, *by being kept clean,"* (by fallowing) " seldom fails of a fair return, which enables the farmer to employ more hands, and give a better rent; which are two important considerations, the one being beneficial to the country at large, the other to the land-owner.

" This subject seems to have excited some doubt and objection, as will be seen by some of the comments annexed. I do not, however, see any reasonable ground for the support of fallowing. The Austrian Netherlands, one of the most productive districts in Europe, allows of no such useless interruption in the rotation of its annual crops, nor does this county, which is the nearest copy to it of any part of England. The turnip crop, in fact, is here the fallow

---

* How silly to put the above paragraph in the place it occupies! It is a finely picturesque description of SLOVENLINESS. But not of any particular " system."—Such slovenly management is seen under every system of management in the kingdom.

fallow, and certainly brings land into a cleaner state (?) than any other mode of cultivation."

With how little attention must this writer have even *observed* the Norfolk husbandry, or how unfairly has he *described* it.—Those who have no other knowledge of it, than what appears in this writer's description, cannot fail to be astonished when they are told,—and with strict truth, —that, under the *legitimate practice* of the *County*, namely, the six-crop rotation, the lands of Norfolk are regularly *fallowed*—are positively *summer fallowed*, every sixth year *;—and very much after the manner in which feudal farmers, formerly fallowed, and some farmers still fallow, their common fields; namely, by breaking them up, after spring seed time (in Norfolk, about the middle of June) and continuing to "fallow" them, in other words, to plow and harrow them, *throughout the summer*, for wheat:—and this, in addition to the tillage given for the turnip crop,—which we are told, by this Reporter of the Norfolk practice, "is here the fallow:"—so that the lands of Norfolk, are in effect, and absolutely, fallowed twice, every six years,—as were the feudal fields of old! And, of course, nothing but unpardonable slovenliness (such as that mentioned above) can prevent their continuing, perpetually, in a state of cleanness and good tilth.

In the same way, any *absorbent* lands,—'lands that may be plowed any day in the year' may be kept in *constant repair*, with a degree of moral certainty.

But not so *retentive* lands,—lands that can rarely be worked, with profit, either *late in autumn*, or *early in spring;* and that are, in their nature, unsuitable, either for the turnip or the barley crop.—These would seem to be a description of lands, which our Reporter,—judging from the internal evidence of his work, had never even heard of, —much less observed,—certainly never cultivated,—or it were impossible, for a man of his discernment, to have written the section now more particularly under consideration.

This, however, would be the most improper place, in which to discuss the general management of lands of *that* description. Nevertheless, it may be proper to notice, here, the USES of FALLOWING. For I cannot expect to meet, in going through the Board's Reports, with another

text,

---

* See the head, Covenants, p. 324, aforegoing.

text, so apt and suitable to the purpose, as that which presents itself, in the section now open to my view.

P. 67. " Those who talk of resting land, seem to consider it in the nature of an animal, which undoubtedly must have rest as well as food, to go through labour; but surely this does not hold good when applied to the nature of land, which, by proper attention, will be found grateful and productive without ceasing."

This, in the mouth of an orthodox, commonfield farmer, might excite a smile: or, if sarcastically vociferated by a *knowing* drill maker, might induce one to exclaim, with a laugh, ' what a keen clever fellow.' But, coming from a sage author, while writing on one of the most serious subjects that can occupy the mind of man (that of providing sustenance for a populous nation) less grateful sensations are excited.

Two distinct advantages, both of them highly valuable, are produced by fallowing, or a continued course of tillage, while the ground is uncropped;—no matter as to the season of the year, or the length of time that may be occupied by the process.

The first is to free the soil from weeds:—from root-weeds, by destroying them; from the seeds of weeds, by exposing them to the influence of the atmosphere, and inducing them to vegetate; and, then, to destroy the seedling plants, by repeating the different operations of tillage.

The other is to meliorate the soil, by exposing it to the action of the atmosphere.

A piece of productive ground whose soil and subsoil, or immediate under stratum, are of the same original or specific nature (not difficult to be found) would be a proper site of experiment.—Remove the cultivated soil. Immediately plow and sow part of the substratum, and observe the produce (if any). Fallow another part; that is, throughout the four seasons, continue, to expose every part of it to the atmosphere, by repeated plowings; sow it, and compare its produce, with that of the other part.

Or, what is more easily done, and which *is* done, every year, or ought to be done, occasionally, by every stiff-land occupier,—select a piece of ground of a meager sickly complexion; owing to a diseased habit, brought on through a want of tillage, and wearing much of the appearance of a meager, sickly, hidebound animal.—But let not this figurative animal, " lie to rest!"—Rouse it into action. Tear it up, in autumn; as soon as the half starved crop

is off;—by a rice-balk, or half plowing; that the frosts of
winter may duly operate upon it.—In the spring, cross-
plow the ribs, so raised (if opportunity permit) and let
the winds of March search into it.—In later spring, move
the rough clods; and thus enable the summer suns to
penetrate every side and part of them.—This being effected, reduce them; and mold the surface, again, into
ribs; thereby enlarging it, and giving the sun and the
air the greater power over it; as well as to give the weed
seeds, the soil may contain, more room to vegetate.—
And continue the operations of tillage, with the plow, the
harrow, and the roller, as the state of the soil, the season,
and the intended crop, may dictate.—And, by those plain,
obvious, and certain means, bring it to that clean, healthy
state, and prosperous appearance, so well described,
above, by this writer.

By an EIGHTEEN-MONTHS FALLOW (by which
only one year's rent and taxes are sunk, and one crop
nominally lost) assiduously conducted, through tolerable
seasons, and followed by a spring crop (or no grain crop)
and cultivated herbage,—the most foul, degenerate, churlish, *sluggish*, soil may be cleansed, pulverized, ventilated,
rarefied, and *roused into profitable action*, for some length
of time.

By the help of beans and cabbages, in rows, with wide
intervals, duly cultivated, strong lands, that are suitable
for those crops, may, *afterward*, be kept sufficiently clean,
and in sufficient tillage, for many years; as ten, fifteen,
or twenty, according to seasons, and the attention of the
cultivator.

But, whenever a state of foulness, or a want of tillage,
returns, he must be an ignorant, or an improvident, husbandman, and unfit to partake in the cultivation of a circumscribed territory, who neglects to *repeat* the operation
of FALLOWING :—not by merely " summer fallowing;" but
by continuing a COURSE of TILLAGE, through every season
of the year*:—a REGENERATING PROCESS, this,
which,

---

* The great and prevalent ERROR, in FALLOWING, is that of
closing the operation when it is barely *beginning* to produce the required effect.—The root weeds having been broken into sets, and the
seeds of weeds released from their confinement, they are left, alive,
in the soil, to propagate their respective species, and contend with
the crop to be placed in conflict with them.—One plowing, toward
the finishing of a fallow, may be more radically efficacious,—in regard to the complete extirpation of weeds,—than three or four, at
its commencement.

which, in a course of years, will do more for the occupier, the proprietor and the community, than all the plausible schemes of amateurs, listeners, and superficial observers,—added to all the quackery of interested individuals, that has so long been poisoning the minds, and debasing the practice, of inexperienced occupiers.

It now only remains to notice the concluding paragraph of the section—" Fallowing exploded ;"—in which paragraph this " ANTIFALLOWIST,"—after all we have heard, allows " Fallowing" to be, in some cases, " absolutely necessary !"

How inconsiderate, or how ill judged, to hold out, in a " catching light,"—that the most valuable operation in English agriculture, at this day,—when judiciously applied, and properly executed,—is a fit object to be held up to public ridicule and contempt.—It is to be feared that three readers, of four, whom the volume under review is calculated to direct, will be led by the *title!* and *general drift*, or body of the section under censure,—than by the three last lines of it,—which few readers of experience will have the patience to reach.

I will insert the final paragraph, entire, and thus let my readers see the *whole* of this *section extraordinary!* Not that I think it, in itself, at all entitled to the distinction ; but lest any one should accuse me of having unfairly garbled its precious contents.—P. 68. " I apprehend, the custom of fallowing, originated from the ancient state of the common fields, before the introduction of turnips and artificial grasses; in this early period of our husbandry, fallowing was absolutely necessary, as there was but little stock then kept in proportion to what there now is, therefore land could not be so often or so well manured as now; with the inclosure, therefore, of common fields, fallowing ought to have ceased, in other parts as well as here; but where farmers still continue the reprehensible practice of taking three crops in succession, which is still the case in many parts of England, there fallowing is absolutely necessary; but it is by no means a necessary part of Norfolk husbandry."

I leave the reader to say, here, " this I deny."—For, in the Norfolk husbandry,—emphatically or strictly speaking,—fallowing,—summer fallowing,—has ever been an essential link in the chain of management.

SEMINATION.—On *dibbling*, we have the following notice of the Reporter.

P. 38. " In treating of the process in seeding, I shall begin

begin with wheat. This is partly dibbled and partly sown broad-cast: the former is not in so high estimation as it was some years since; but I am of opinion, that when wheat is planted upon clover of only one year's lay, it is the best practice, especially if the dibblers are well looked after, for in this case it will admit of a saving of a bushel of corn to an acre."

I perfectly agree with Mr. Kent, in that dibbling is best adapted to a clover ley of the first year;—and, it may be added, on moderately deep soils; on which the practice was, probably first adopted,—on the southern border of the County.

I am not surprized to hear that the practice (highly valuable as it doubtlessly is, on a suitable soil, and under a proper course of management) is declining, in the thinner-soiled parts, of the County; especially where the six-crop course is practised.—This decline, it is probable, is not more owing to the shallowness of the soil, than to the practice, *as it is now performed*, interfering with the established course of the country; by depriving it of the SUMMER FALLOW, that raised it to the enviable height, at which it has long been stationed. Even the modern innovation, mentioned by the Reporter, in the same page with the last extract;—namely that of the second year's ley being, at the time he wrote, " seldom touched till after Lammas,"—is calculated to damp its fair and well earned fame.

But let not the above remark, on the probable effects of dibbling on the thinner soils, and in the established routine of practice, in Norfolk, be any disparagement to the practice in general. It has ever struck me as being highly valuable;—an impression which induced me to examine into it, while on the spot, by every mean I had in my power; and to analyze and digest the minutiæ of its operations, in such a way, as to enable those who have not had an opportunity of observing it, to enter on its prosecution.

Mr. Kent does not attempt to describe it. But, in the Appendix to his Report, are inserted several papers, relative to it: jointly, however, they contain nothing resembling a whole;—even were the several items of information systematized. All I have to remark, concerning them, is, that I find nothing in them to add to my own account; nor any thing that contradicts it, or in any way renders doubtful its accuracy.

Viewing the threefold advantage of dibbling in the

seeds

seeds of grain crops; namely,—the even distribution of the seed in the *heart* of the soil,—the saving of human food arising from it,—and the employment of young laborers, thereby enuring them to industry;—and seeing, at the same time, the many advantages of the legitimate husbandry of Norfolk, one is naturally led to a desire of incorporating them;—and the practicability of it is evident.

Break up the raygrass leys as soon as the finished bullocks are sent off to market; fallow, through the summer;—harrow down the last, or seed plowing; and run over it a MARKING ROLLER;—namely a wooden roller, with rings or hoops of iron round it, at every eight, nine, or ten inches, rising above the wood, so as to make lineal impressions, on the surface; to guide the dibbler, in the same manner as he is directed by the "flags," or whole furrows, of one plowing.

The rolling and treading of the fallow, by this method of putting in the seed, could not fail of being advantageous to the light dry lands of Norfolk.

HARVESTING.—The harvest of Norfolk is certainly reaped in what a Kentish man would call a slovenly manner. But this Reporter, I think, is too severe in his censure of it.—When we see, in the writer's own statement, the immense quantity of corn grown in the County; and the comparatively few laborers that the Norfolk farmer can collect, to gather it in (there being no mountainous, or extensive manufacturing district within reach, from whence to draw them); we can only wonder how its crops are gathered together.—The dispatch made by the laborers of the County is most extraordinary; and altho some waste may occur, in the nature of this dispatch, the saving of wages, to the *grower*, is probably much greater. Were it not for the internal manufacture of the County, it would be difficult to conceive how the crops grown within it, could be harvested.

WHEAT.—On the culture of the different arable crops of this superiorly arable County, or on the after-management of its abundant produce, we look, in vain, for any thing resembling *an account*, by this Reporter of its practice.

Under the foregoing head, Semination, something of the *seed process* of wheat is seen; so far as relates to the method of depositing the seed.

On the *time* of *sowing*, we find the subjoined observations; which I insert, here, as a further specimen of this
Reporter's

manner of thinking and writing, on *agricultural* subjects.—
P. 39. " It has been remarked, that, as near the time as
possible that nature sheds any particular seed, it always
grows with more certainty, and therefore less seed is required, when sown early, than when sown late: about
Michaelmas is the height of the season here; it never
should be delayed above a fortnight after."

This reasoning applied to native plants, growing in the
state of nature, may, or may not, be just. But applied to
exotics, under the controul of *art*, we may safely affirm,
from the unerring evidence of experience, that it has no
better foundation, than a wild untutored idea.—All *cultivated plants*—all arable crops—if suffered to stand, in this
climate, would shed their seeds, in summer or autumn.
But confining ourselves to wheat (without mentioning
" spring crops"!)—which, if suffered to stand, would, in
the greater part of this kingdom, shed its seed, in August.
Why, let it be asked, defer the time of sowing, until
Michaelmas?—Why not pursue the practice of the Cotswold, and Wiltshire Down, cultivators, and sow in harvest?—They sow not, however, the seed which has just
dropped from the ear; but that of the year preceding:—
while, in the vale of Glocester, closely bordering on the
Cotswold hills, the most profitable time of sowing has
been found, by long experience (under the established
management of the County), to be November and December*. And, in the district in which I am now writing,
the north of Yorkshire,—it has recently become a practice, founded on experience, to sow wheat (winter wheat)
in February or the beginning of March. Even grass lands
of several years laying, I have seen sown in early spring
with good success.

On a majority of the lands of England, I am of opinion,
October is not only the most convenient, but on a par of
years and seasons, is the most profitable, time of sowing
wheat,—on fallowed, or on ley ground.

It is not the practice, recommended, in this case, that
I mean to condemn; but the unfledged principle, laid
down; which is capable of misleading the student, and,
thereby, of doing mischief, without a probability of producing any good.

　　　　　　　　　　　　　　　　　　　　　　　The

* Even in Norfolk (notwithstanding what we read in the last extract) wheat is (or was in 1732) principally sown between the middle
of October and the middle of November. See my Register of the
Norfolk Practice, Vol. I. p. 216.

The *produce* of wheat, in Norfolk, is stated, by Mr. Kent, to be as follows.—P. 56. " There are some parts of Marshland and the Flegg hundreds, which will produce six quarters of wheat, and ten of oats, upon an acre; but, in very light parts of the county, the farmer is glad to get two quarters of wheat, and three of barley. However, I believe the general average crops of the whole county, one year with another, may be estimated as high as three quarters of wheat and four of barley, and other articles in proportion."

This estimate, I conceive, is too high. Norfolk is not, generally and emphatically speaking, a wheat country. The " Marshland" and " Fleg" Districts bear but a small proportion to the County at large. Twenty bushels, an acre, on a par of years, would be found, on a minute enquiry, I believe, much nearer the general average of the whole County."

BARLEY.—In the following short paragraph, we see the whole of the ostensible article, concerning barley,—the most prevalent and productive crop of Norfolk,—in this Report of the highly extolled practice of the County.

P. 39. " The barley is, at all times, put in the ground in excellent condition. When it follows wheat, the stubble generally has turnips thrown upon it till Christmas, when it is scale ploughed in two furrow ridges; and afterwards has four earths."

TURNEPS.—On this prevailing crop, by which Norfolk has deservedly gained so much praise, and truly well earned honor, we find, in Mr. Kent's Report, some interesting particulars of information.—They principally relate, however, to

The *history* of the turnep crop, in Norfolk.—P. 40. " Not only this county, but many other parts of England, are indebted to the Townshend family, for the original introduction of this root into this country. Before that time, turnips were only cultivated in gardens and small spots, and hoed by gardeners; but in the reign of George I. the then Lord Viscount Townshend, grandfather of the present noble Marquis, attended the King to Hanover, in the quality of Secretary of State, and observing the advantage of this valuable root, as there cultivated at that time, and the fertility it produced, brought the seed and practice into England, and recommended it strongly to his own tenants, who occupied a similar soil to that of Hanover. The experiment succeeded, and by degrees, it gradually spread over this county."

P. 43.

P. 43. " Having stated, that turnips came into this country from Hanover, one would naturally expect, that they were managed to great perfection there, at this time; but I doubt this is not the case, for I had this summer the honour to be introduced to a very intelligent Hanoverian nobleman, at Windsor, Count Hardenberg, who was very inquisitive into the state of Agriculture in England, and upon my conversing with him about turnips, I found that they did not know the use of them there, at this time, so well as we do, which is a matter of surprise, that an article of such great benefit should ever decline in repute; I doubt it must have arisen from the ground growing tired of them."

How thoughtless, or ill judged, then, to talk about the *Flemish* husbandry of four crops, and one of these turneps; and thus indirectly recommend it to the notice, if not to the imitation, of the Norfolk husbandman,—in preference to his long established and profitable practice.

The proposed substitution of vetches*, lucern, and potatoes!—for clover and turneps occasionally,—is barely entitled to notice. It is a mere reverie of a closet farmer. It is not the clover, but the raygrass which follows it, that gives character and excellence to the established practice of Norfolk.

Again,—P. 41. " I wish I could close this short history of turnips, without lamenting, that the ground does not relish them so well as formerly, so that great care is necessary in raising them, and more seed is required; and after all, it is a teasing and precarious crop, and admits of no certain rules to ensure absolute success; though some cautions may be worth stating in this place."

The Reporter accordingly proceeds to dictate;—and, in a few lines tells us (in the cookery book manner) how to get a crop of turneps. But, neither on the *culture*, nor the *consumption* of this crop, do I find a line that is entitled to insertion, here:—excepting an ingenious method of *manuring* with *rape-cake*, which has been discovered, and in a degree established, since I published my detail of the culture and consumption of the turnep crop, in that County.

P. 41. " Some persons use rape-cake for turnip manure;

---

* In the northwest part of the County, where *sheep* are the principal fatting stock, vetches may be eligible. But not so, in the County at large, under its present system of management.

nure; and Mr. Styleman of Snettisham, a gentleman of considerable fortune, who farms part of his estate upon a large scale, and is trying many ingenious experiments, uses it in a pulverized state, to which he reduces it by means of two mills, worked by two women, each mill being formed of two cylinders, revolving towards each other. The first breaks the cake into pieces of the size of a walnut, by the operation of cogged cylinders; the second is constructed of plain cast-iron cylinders, similar to those used for grinding clay to make bricks. Thus reduced to powder, he puts it into the very drills, where he had just before deposited the turnip seed, by means of Cook's machine, which requires no other contrivance or alteration, than substituting different cups and funnels. The quantity of cake used is a quarter of a ton per acre, which has never exceeded 1 *l*. 5*s*. in its price. He assured me, that this method had never failed to insure him a good crop."

Other forcing manures might probably be used, in a similar way, to enable seedling turnips to push up, and escape the depredations of their enemies.

SAINFOIN.—P. 63. "Where land has a chalk or marl at the bottom, let not saint-foin be forgotten upon such a soil as this; or even where there is gravel under a good surface," (yes, if the gravel is of a *calcareous* quality,) "it is impossible to say too much in its favour. In this country it is but little known; I believe the first person who brought it into Norfolk, was the late Sir Henry L'Estrange; next to him it was countenanced by Mr. Rolfe and the Rev. Armine Styleman; but the greatest planter of it is Mr. Coke, who has, this dry summer, cut two hundred and sixty-five loads of excellent hay, rather exceeding a ton to a load, from one hundred and four acres. This was from a plant of four years old, upon land not worth more, for any other purpose, than twelve shillings an acre."

GRASS LANDS.—The perennial herbage of Norfolk is chiefly found in the marshes and fens, on the Lincolnshire and Cambridgeshire side of the County (already noticed p. 282.);—or in those on the southeast or Yarmouth quarter;—or in the narrow boggy bottoms that are scattered over the face of the County. The whole of these are *waterformed lands;*—the effects of alluvion and aquatic plants.

There are very few *natural lands,* in Norfolk, that are well adapted to this species of produce; unless on its southern border.—Nevertheless, in parks, and other demesne grounds, of men of fortune, old grass lands are observable, in different parts of the County.

Mr. Kent, it is true, has not appropriated any considerable portion of his volume to the subject under view. It is, however, a matter of concern to find a man of Mr. K's ability and use in society (when rightly directed) spending his time and talent, so unprofitably, as in filling, even a few pages, with cursory remarks, on a subject,—the bog meadows of Norfolk,—which had, previously been fully discussed *.

HORSES.—On this subject of Report, Mr. Kent has, properly enough, bestowed no other attention, than what relates to horses, as working animals, in husbandry. Norfolk is not, emphatically speaking, a breeding County, for horses of any other description.—In this chapter " Livestock," however, he has inserted the subjoined remarks, which I have, of course, some satisfaction in transcribing.—P. 100., "The horses, as I have before observed, are short, compact, active, and hardy; those of the original standing, and those of the Suffolk cross, in my opinion, may be considered equally good; those which have the Lincolnshire cross, as Mr. Marshall very properly intimates, are not so well adapted to the country."

CATTLE.—Neither on the *breed;*—the *breeding* and *rearing;*—the *dairy;*—nor on the *procuring* or *fatting*— of this first and most prominent object of the Norfolk husbandry,—do we find a syllable,—after the ample details of which the public are in possession,—that is entitled to public attention. Indeed, this Reporter has not, himself †, furnished quite two pages of matter (of any sort) relating to an article of market produce, which brings into the County, annually, the extraordinary sums, that are stated aforegoing.

I, therefore, willingly conclude (though nothing of the kind is expressed, or even intimated) that the Reporter politely intended to concede, to me, the entire merit of bringing

---

* For minutes, and general remarks on the MEADOWS of NOR FOLK: see my Register of its RURAL ECONOMY; Vol. I. p. 312 and the *minutes* thence referred to.

And for systematized details of the nature and improvement o Marshes and Moory Grounds, in general ;—see the TREATISE O LANDED PROPERTY—Articles *Draining* and *Reclaiming.*

† In the "Appendix," are inserted three notices, concerning thi subject. But none of them is sufficiently estimable to be entitled to place, here.

bringing this distinguished branch of English husbandry,
before the public.

SHEEP.—Again, I am gratified, in coinciding, in opinion, with Mr. Kent;—who strenuously advocates the *native* breed of Norfolk;—and he is pleased to appeal to my remarks, on the same topic, in corroboration of his own.

When I wrote on the subject, the breed of Leicestershire, alone, had invaded their long possessed territory. The Southdown breed were, then, confined to their own native hills; and had not, yet, become *fashionable*, in Norfolk;—where the "Leicestershires" were, at that time, *all the rage*;—ill adapted, as they are, to the arable lands of that County.

There can be little doubt, I conceive, of the Southdown breed *doing*, on the Wolds or *calcareous Downs* of Norfolk; as these have a close affinity to their native soil; to which their habits have been molding, during a succession of ages*. But whether they are equally well suited to the far more widely spreading *sandy loams* of Norfolk, experience, alone, can determine†. That they are not so well adapted, as the native breed, to the *heathlands*, on the west side of the County, wants not, I think, the gift of prophecy to foretell.

The *history* of the native breed of Norfolk is well given by

* Yet, in travelling over those calcareous grounds, in the midst of summer (1810) I witnessed a striking instance of the *climature* of North Norfolk being too severe for them. The day, it is true, was rainy and rather cool for the season, and the few flocks that fell in my way had been recently shorn. But such tender-looking creatures, in the shape of sheep, I never before beheld, under any circumstances: —turning their tails to the wind (not strong) and sticking up their backs, like some caterpillars, in the act of crawling, they exhibited themselves in attitudes the most *picturesk!*
Those flocks, however, might not, could not, be of the genuine breed of the Southdowns of Sussex,—a robust, hardy race of animals; —but, more probably, were a delicate, *improved* variety,—molded to the taste and fashion of the day.

† On the *slatey loams* of Devonshire (in one instance, at least, that I have ample knowledge of) they have *not* done well; though many of the original flock were real "old Southdowns."—Notwithstanding they have now been several years on the ground, the deaths continue to be numerous.
These truths are not told to *deter* sheep farmers, in any part of the island, from *trying* the Southdown breed, which, on the chalk hills of the southern Counties, are a most valuable variety of sheep;—but to *caution* those, who may wish to make the trial, not to *run* at the breed, too rapidly, in any other situation.

by Mr. Kent.—P. 102. "The sheep come next under consideration; and here it is necessary to premise, that great part of this county is known to have been, within the space of a century, a wild, bleak, unproductive country, comparatively with what it now is ; full half of it was rabbit-warrens and sheep-walks; the sheep were as natural to the soil as the rabbits, being hardy in their nature, and of an agile construction, so as to move over a great deal of space with little labour. When great tracts of this land were brought into a better state of cultivation, the Norfolk sheep gave great aid to the new improvement, as they fetched their sustenance from a considerable distance, and answered penning as well as any sheep whatever. Folding became in high estimation, and, aided by marling, brought the improvement of the country rapidly forward. Soon after, the turnip system followed, which enabled the farmer to improve his stock considerably by better keeping; so that, at this time, they are become respectable and profitable in their return, and in as high estimation, at Smithfield, as any sheep whatever, for no better mutton can be put upon a table ; and though they produce but little wool, it is of good quality."

On the *management* of sheep, whether in *breeding* or *fatting*, Mr. K. is silent; excepting (in the section " irregular crops"), while speaking of a waste of fodder, we have the subjoined intimation.—P. 64. " Sheep are still more apt to create waste ; therefore the cutting of hay, in like manner as straw is cut, into chaff, is a frugal and excellent practice; for by this means, there is no waste at all: and it is certain, that hay given in this way, will go considerably farther, than if given in the old way."

SWINE.—The following lines are all we find, in the Report under view, concerning this species of livestock.— P. 106. " The pigs are remarkably thin-haired and small, compared to the Hampshire breed, but very prolific, and the pork excellent ; but the inhabitants have no idea of making bacon, farther than as to hams and cheeks, which, however, they prepare extremely well. The number of swine used to be very great, but is now somewhat less, on account of the decline of the dairies."

POULTRY.—P. 106. " The poultry is superlatively good, especially the turkey, which has no equal, at least in flavour, which I attribute to the dryness of the soil, and to the greater range which they have more than in other counties."

On PIGEONS, DECOYS, RABBITS and GAME, are the subjoined short notices.—P. 107. "The pigeons are much fewer than formerly, as many of the pigeon-houses have been dropt, on account of the injury which the pigeons do to thatched buildings.

"The decoys are but few to what they were formerly; but, as there are so many marshes, and several pieces of water called broads, it is presumed, that many of them might be revived to advantage, as wild-fowl is become more valuable since the communication to London is made easier and quicker, by means of the turnpike roads.

"Rabbits are very numerous, as the warrens are not only very considerable, but many other parts are full of them, particularly near plantations, where they do great injury, and are very difficult to keep down.

"The game is still in great plenty, though not equal to what it was formerly. Many of the gentlemen are too tenacious of it, which makes the farmer, its natural guardian, less careful to preserve it; and it is too often a source of discord in the county."

In the final section of this Report, named "General Observations,"—are contained the following well conceived admonitions;—with which I will close my extracts from this valuable work:—and I beg the author of it will accept a thousand thanks, for the pleasure and information it has afforded me;—hoping that he will not think unkindly of me for the free animadversion, which I have deemed it my duty to the public, to apply to some particular parts of it. He may be assured that nothing but a solicitous regard, for the same love of truth, and the same ardent desire to serve our country, as is manifested in various parts of his own performance, could have urged me to so unpleasant a task. *

P. 191. "In this Report, it has been my aim to give a faithful account of the Norfolk husbandry, and such other customs as are necessarily connected with it, without extenuation or exaggeration; and the intelligent farmer, in other parts, will be under no difficulty in determining which parts to adopt, and which to reject.

"In the perusal of a treatise of this kind, it is incumbent on the reader to lay aside all prejudice, and suffer his mind

* Many months after this article was written, and had been revised for the press, I observed with concern, in the public prints, an account of the DEATH of Mr. KENT; whose character, as an ESTATE AGENT, I have long admired. May he have left many PUPILS who will follow his example.

mind to be open to conviction—otherwise, I shall have written, and he will read, in vain. I should not have thought it necessary to introduce this caution, if it were not almost generally allowed, that husbandmen are more obstinately attached to old practices, let them be ever so bad, than any other description of men, and are consequently averse to the introduction of any thing new, let it come ever so well recommended ; at the same time, it is highly proper to be careful against adopting the visionary recommendations of modern theorists, who, upon hypotheses of their own, hold up wild systems of delusion, which are apt to mislead the credulous and do great injury.

"True judgment seems to lie in selecting such objects for imitation, as are either the result of well attested experiments, or that come from such respectable authority as cannot be doubted."

"GENERAL

"GENERAL VIEW

OF THE

AGRICULTURE

OF THE

COUNTY OF NORFOLK;

DRAWN UP FOR THE CONSIDERATION OF THE

BOARD OF AGRICULTURE AND INTERNAL IMPROVEMENT.

BY

THE SECRETARY TO THE BOARD.

1804."

THE QUALIFICATIONS of this writer are noticed, afore-going, p. 65. How far they have been well applied, in compiling the Volume, now under Review, may be enti-tled to a few moments consideration.

Why the County of *Norfolk*, which had been reported, *two deep*, should have been selected by the Board, as a fit subject on which to employ the time and talents of their principal Secretary, does not fully appear. The Secre-tary's own *apology* for it is as follows.—" Introduction.—A second Report for the County of Norfolk, by a different writer from the gentleman who executed the first, demands a short explanation, to obviate any idea tending to lower the estimation in which the original Report is justly held. There have been various instances of second, and even third Reports of the same County, all by different hands;" (a precident!) "but in the case of Norfolk a new Report was demanded, for a local reason. The introduction of a new breed of sheep, and the rapidity with which the prac-tice of drilling spread in the County, had effected so great a change in the state of Norfolk husbandry, that all former works on the Agriculture of that celebrated County must necessarily be deficient, however excellent in other respects.

The

The present Report does not appear to the exclusion of the former, but merely in assistance of it; that such objects as were unnoticed, or but little attended to, from their being at that moment in their infancy, should now be registered, for the use of such other Counties as may not yet have made similar exertions."—" July 14, 1804."

These, surely, might well be deemed "lame excuses."— Why follow the " Southdown"—a *Sussex* breed of sheep, into *Norfolk*?—Why not rather study the breed and its improvement, on its native soil; where it had reached its highest degree of excellency; and where it had been *long established*; rather than in Norfolk, where it was but under *experiment*; and where (even from what appears in the Report itself) it was chiefly or wholely confined, to a particular, and narrowly circumscribed quarter of the County;—being, in the County at large, a very stranger?

Again.—Why make the tour of Norfolk to see something of *drilling*; which had been practised, more or less, in almost every County of the kingdom, for more than twenty years; and which, in Norfolk, might then have been deemed a comparatively new thing?

Had the Reporter's excuse been, that he made the tour of Norfolk, to study the art of *dibbling*; which, there, received its birth; and where, only, it was an *established practice*;—it would have been,—as far as this circumstance would have warranted it,—admissible:—Provided, I mean, its rise, progress, and establishment had not been previously possessed, in detail, by the public.

How inexplicable, then, it is, that the precious time of the principal Secretary of the Board should have been so unprofitably employed; as in filling a full bodied octavo volume, principally, with unimportant opinions, and vague assertions, picked up, in conversation, or casual enquiry; concerning practices with which the public were previously acquainted!—The most apt motto to have been placed, in the title page of his volume, would surely have been—

" Vanity of vanities, altogether vanity."

However, as the volume is now before me, I will go carefully through it, and mark what may appear to be useful to the public,—and is not included, in my own Register; or in the foregoing Review of Mr. Kent's Report.

The MODE of SURVEY, in this instance, or rather the manner in which the materials of this volume were obtained,—

tained,—would seem to have been (for nothing is *explicitly* stated concerning it) by occasional *visits*, from time to time, to men of fortune, in the northern part of the County; and, by a *tour* through the County at large, previously to the compilation of the Report,— as in Lincolnshire.

In point of AUTHORSHIP, no comparison will bear, between the Report of Norfolk, and that of Lincolnshire. Were it not for the title page, no one would, from the manner observable in the two Works, suspect them to be from the same pen. The volume, now under consideration, is mostly written in readable, intelligible language; and, to the arrangement of its materials commendable attention has been paid. Not only are the several topics, or heads, pretty generally kept distinct; but the more complex subjects are analytically systematized:—much in the way, in which I have usually treated of them.— Further observations, on the EXECUTION of this Work, will be made in passing through it.

The number of pages 532.

No Index.

A Map of the Soils of Norfolk; and seven small Plates of Implements &c.

SUBJECT THE FIRST.

NATURAL ECONOMY.

EXTENT.—See Mr. KENT's statement, p. 298, aforegoing.

CLIMATURE —On this topic, too, the Secretary follows Mr. K. who agrees with me, in regard to the backwardness of the seasons, in Norfolk.

SOILS.—The Secretary has appropriated twelve pages, to this subject; over and above the " Map of the Soil," afore noticed; on which some considerable share of thought appears to have been bestowed. But, after Mr. KENT's valuable detail, we find very little, in the Secretary's account, that demands public attention.—The following estimate of the extent of each species of soil, set down in his account, may, if sufficiently accurate, have its use. No authority is given.

P. 4. " The relative contents of these districts are found by measurement" (by whom?) " to be:

	Square Miles.
Light sand,	220
Good sand,	420
Marshland clay,	60
Various loams,	900
Rich loam,	148
Peat,	82

1830"

It may be remarked, of this statement, that, in the district of " *Good Sand*," is included the *chalk hills* of Norfolk; and the rich silty lands—*the marshes*—of the north coast. And that the sweeping designation "*various loams*" (which emblues half the map) is altogether indeterminate;—as equally covering, and of course confounding, the *cool strong lands* of the southern border of the County, with the *light sandy loams* of the central and eastern parts of it:—or, to use the Reporter's own words (see *farms* ensuing)—" the *dry* soils and the *wet* ones:"—consequently, *levelling* the almost only, and certainly the most radical, *agricultural distinctions* of lands, in Norfolk!

SUBJECT THE SECOND.

POLITICAL ECONOMY.

APPROPRIATION.—The chapter, " Enclosing" occupies seven *sheets!* of letter press:—Itself a small volume.—The subjoined is the Reporter's prefatory account of it.—P. 75. " The number of parliamentary enclosures that have taken place of late years in Norfolk, and the remarkable improvements which were known to have flowed from them, made it an object of considerable importance to ascertain the result, as far as it could be procured by visiting the respective places, or obtaining information from the Commissioners, or other persons interested in the work thus effected. With this view I visited many of them, and gained the best intelligence to be procured concerning the rest. The following alphabetical table contains

contains the result of these inquiries, with such additions, not immediately relative to enclosing, as circumstances induced my attending to."

Six of those seven sheets would seem (in *turning them over*, for who could endure to *read* them?) to be filled with " baptisms and burials"!

On the PRINCIPLES of APPROPRIATION; or on the BUSINESS of " ENCLOSING," not a page, out of the one hundred and twelve, could be well formed. And on the EFFECTS of APPROPRIATION, we find no GENERAL STATEMENT, nor any CONCLUSION drawn:—not even regarding *population* (which occupies so large a portion of the chapter)—as to whether, on the whole of the information adduced, it has encreased, or lessened, in consequence of Appropriation and Inclosure!

Under the head, " General Observations," at the close of the chapter, are a few pages of particulars,—chiefly communicated by, or *extracted* out of, Commissioners of Inclosures.—But how astonishingly strange, that, even from men of this description, scarsely any thing of *practical* information, relating to the immediate subject of Appropriation, or " Enclosing," has been collected.—The few following lines are all that appear to me worthy of extraction.—P. 184. " In all the enclosures in which Mr. Algur has been concerned as a Commissioner, it has not been the practice to put poor men to the proof of the *legality* of their claims, but the mere practice, and if they have proved the practice even of cutting turf, it has been considered as a right of common, and allotted for accordingly."

Regarding the scattered crumbs, observable in the main body of the chapter, it is not likely that any man,—seeing the writer himself has not thought them worth concentrating,—will ever take the pains and labor of picking them up, and applying them to any useful purpose;— even were they capable of such an application.

In the chapter, " Wastes," we are told,—P. 385. " Nothing can cause more surprize in the minds of many strangers on their first visiting Norfolk, than to find, on entering the county by Brandon or Thetford, a long stage of 18 miles to Swafham, through a tract which deserves to be called a desert: a region of warren or sheepwalk, scattered with a scanty cultivation, yet highly improveable."

POOR RATES.—The average of forty minutes, made by the Reporter, in different parts of the County, is set down

at

at 5s. 6d. in the pound;" (p. 47):—But whether on *nominal* rents, or on *real* rents paid, or on *rack* rents estimated, is not (except in a few instances) mentioned!

In a section entitled, " Comparison of Times" (which will be further noticed) the *rise* in " parish rates," between 1790 and 1803, is made out to be thirty per cent. p 510.

TITHES.—The " general average of 37 minutes," comes out at " 4s. 9d. per acre" (p. 41) and the rise per acre, between 1790 and 1803, fifty eight per cent. p. 510.

MARKETS —P. 490. " Mr. OVERMAN, of Burnham, has a small ship, which he keeps constantly employed in carrying his-corn to London, in bringing rape-cake for manure from Holland, London, Hull, or wherever it is to be procured best, and at the cheapest rate. When his farm does not in this manner produce employment, he sends her for coals, or deals, or on any service which times and markets render eligible."——" Mr. MONEY HILL, of Waterden, has also a sloop of 50 tons, which goes to sea, with two men and two boys: he built her, and the employment is the same as Mr. OVERMAN'S. Mr. DAVY has likewise one."

SUBJECT THE THIRD.

RURAL ECONOMY.

DIVISION THE FIRST.

TENANTED ESTATES.

ESTATES.—P. 17 " Estates are of all sizes in Norfolk, from nearly the largest scale to the little freehold: one of 25,000l. a year; one of 14,000l.; one of 13,000l.; two of 10,000l.; many of about 5000l.; and an increasing number of all smaller proportions. When the larger properties are deducted, the remainder of the county will be found divided into moderate estates, and in the hands of gentlemen who pay a considerable attention to the practice of agriculture."

RECLAIMING HEATHLANDS.—P. 385. " Mr. Bevan, after trying

trying several methods of bringing old heath lands into cultivation, gave the preference to the following : sow oats and seeds on one earth after the drill roller ; after harvest feed hard with sheep for two years, in order to rot the old turf."

DRAINING ESTATES.—P. 389. " Mr. Freeman, of Swanton Morley, possessing a tract of meadows on the river, at Billingfold, poisoned by the water being pent up by the mill at Elsing, and no fall to be gained on his side for draining it, laid a truck under the river, and by permission, cutting a drain on the other side, gained a fall, and by it drained 120 acres, to his great profit, and also to lowering the soakage of his neighbours' meadows. The improvement doubled at least the value of the land."

MILLS.—*Steam.* P. 73. " Mr. Gooch of Quiddenham, in Norfolk, having a water-mill which was sometimes unemployed for want of water, erected a steam engine contiguous, at the expense of about 500l. The stove which heats the boiler, is so contrived as to burn coal to coke for his malt-house. One man attends both the engine and the cinder oven. It was, in the drought of 1800, of singular use to the whole country, for wind and water having both failed in a great measure, corn was brought from ten miles distance, to be ground by this engine : he has two pair of stones to the water-wheel, and two pair to the engine. The power, that of twelve horses."

Water Mill.—P. 391. "In going from Waterden to Rainham, passed by Sculthorpe Mill, and there enter a region that must make a farmer's heart ache. Of the nuisances that a country can be plagued with, certainly water-mills class very high in the black catalogue : for the sake of this beggarly mill, which apparently cannot be worth more than from 20l. to 30l. a year, here is a noble tract, from a furlong to a mile wide, of what, ought to be rich meadow, poisoned with water, and producing rushes, flags, sedge, and all sorts of aquatic rubbish. Who would not suppose the two sides of the river belonging to little proprietors, as beggarly as the mill, who could meet over their tankard to wrangle, but never agree? No such matter. Marquis Townshend on one side, and Mr. Coke on the other. It would not be amiss to couple the two stewards of the estates up to the chin in one of these overflowing dykes, till they settled the matter, *for the benefit of the public.*"—Bravo! Bravo!

TENANCY.—P. 47. " The great improvements which for 70 years past have rendered Norfolk famous for its
husbandry

husbandry, were effected by means of 21 years leases; a circumstance which very fortunately took place on the first attempt to break up the heaths and warrens in the north-west part of the County. These leases established themselves generally; and were, more than any other cause, powerfully operative in working those great ameliorations of wastes which converted that part of the County into a garden."

The Reporter proceeds to *dissertate*, on this subject. But the following information, respecting the prevailing practice, at the time he wrote, is worth a " power" of argument.—P. 48. " Sorry I am to perceive, that contrary ideas seem to be gaining ground in this County; that some landlords will give no leases, and others only for 7 or 9 years. That the agriculture of the Country will suffer in proportion as these ideas prevail, I have not a doubt; and it is a very fortunate circumstance, that Mr. Coke, the possessor of the largest estate in it, adheres steadily to those principles which improved his noble property, never giving a shorter term than 21 years."

My sentiments on granting twenty-one years leases, under existing circumstances, appear p. 320, aforegoing.

Covenants.—P. 50. " *The New Covenants* * in *Letting the Farms of* T. W. COKE, *Esq. M. P.*—

" Supposing a farm to contain 540 acres arable land:

" Shall and will at all times, keep and leave ninety acres, part of the arable land, laid to grass of one or more years laying. Also ninety acres grass of two or more years laying—each to be laid down with a crop of corn, after turnips, and to continue laid two years at least; the time of laying to be computed from the harvest next after sowing the said seeds; and upon breaking up the same †, after January 1st, 1804, may be permitted to sow forty-five acres (part thereof annually) with pease, or tares, for seed, to be twice well hoed: other part thereof with tares, for green food, buck-wheat, or any leguminous or other vegetable plant, for ploughing in as manure, or summer-tilling any portion of the remainder.

" Shall not sow any of the lands with two successive crops of corn, grain, pulse, rape, or turnips, for seed, (except

* For the former covenants of that estate, see p. 322.

" † The land intended to be sown with pease should not be till 4¼ years after the commencement of lease, upon supposition that *new tenant* may not be so situated as to have the turnips (covenanted to be left by old lease) completely clean."

(except the above-mentioned pea and tare stubble), without the leave or consent of the said ——, his heirs, or assigns, being first had and obtained in writing.

" Lands for turnips, four clean earths at least.

" The turnips covenanted to be left in the last year, ninety acres to be mucked, so far as the same will extend, and to be paid for by valuation ; at the same time a due regard to be had to the cleanness of the land upon which they grow.

" Sheep, cattle, and all other live stock, to be lodged upon some part of the premises, when consuming the produce of the farm.

" Straw, chaff, and colder, to be left without allowance.

" Incoming tenant to carry out the crop of corn, not exceeding the distance of ten miles, gratis.

" Rent payable forty days before St. Michaelmas (whereever a thrashing machine is, or shall be erected), if demanded, by notice in writing being left at the farm-house to that purpose."

RENT.—The " Recapitulation " of a few pages of memoranda made in going through the country, stands thus :
P. 40. " The light sand district, as marked on the Map, I conceive, lets, on an average, at 6s. an acre.

" The various loams at 16s.

" The better sand 12s.

" The rich loam 26s."

In the section, " Comparison of Times," it appears that the rise of rent from 1790 to 1804, was " 35 per cent." p. 510.

DIVISION THE SECOND.

WOODLANDS.

On this branch of Rural Economy, little information is adduced.—Mr. COKE of Holkham, and Mr. BEVAN of Riddlesworth, are mentioned as principal PLANTERS. The first, we are told, has planted more than two millions,— and the latter nearly one million,—of " trees and shrubs."

The following anecdote, relating to the LARCH, is well worth preserving, here.—P. 384. " Colonel BULLER shewed me a circumstance relative to this tree, which
merits

merits noting : old sows, if allowed to get at them, will
bark them for the sake of rubbing themselves in the tur-
pentine : he had some killed, in this manner, before he
knew by what cause ; when informed, he ordered the sows
to be watched, and had it confirmed by his own view."

DIVISION THE THIRD.

AGRICULTURE.

F ARMS.—*Sizes.*—P. 26. " Upon this subject we must
divide the County generally into two parts—the dry soils
and the wet ones. Upon the former the farms are large,
and upon the latter much smaller.

" The rich districts which, though dry enough for turnips, are strong enough for yielding great crops of wheat,
possess some moderately-sized farms, such as from 400 to
600 acres; but many smaller. The wet land is more
commonly held in small occupations. The poorer sands
are usually in very extensive farms." See *Soils*, p. 360.

Homesteads.—P. 19. " In the species of building properly appropriated to an Agricultural Report, greater exertions have, I believe, been made in Norfolk than in any
other County of the kingdom. One landed proprietor,
Mr. Coke, has expended above ONE HUNDRED THOUSAND
POUNDS in farm-houses and offices; very many of them
erected in a style much superior to the houses usually
assigned for the residence of tenants; and it gave me
pleasure to find all that I viewed, furnished by his farmers
in a manner somewhat proportioned to the costliness of
the edifices. When men can well afford such exertions,
they are certainly commendable.

" One of Mr. Coke's barns at Holkham is built in a
superior style ; 120 feet long, 30 broad, and 30 high, and
surrounded with sheds for 60 head of cattle : it is capitally
executed in white brick, and covered with fine blue slate.

" At Syderstone, he has built another enormous barn,
with stables, cattle-sheds, hog-sties, shepherd's and bailiff's
houses, surounding a large quadrangular yard, likewise
in a style of expense rarely met with. In discourse with
the

men at work in this barn, they informed us, that to one
man who *unpitched* the waggon at harvest, seven others
were necessary on the *goff* to receive and dispose of the
corn (!) after it was raised to some height; at a great expense at a time of the year when labour is the most valuable."—The Reporter adds—and his observation I believe might be applied to the whole County—" the farmers
are, however, very generally advocates not only for barns,
but for great barns."—And it may be further added—The
proprietor of the Holkham estate is not the only one
who has indulged a passion for gorgeous farm buildings;
and thereby entailed lasting incumbrances on estates. A
convenient homestead is much more profitable to a tenant,
than a *great* one. Yet judging from the close of the
chapter, " Buildings,"—*that* valuable quality has not,
hitherto, been sufficiently attended to, in the County of
Norfolk.—P. 25. " I wish I had it in my power to add,
that I saw a good farm-yard in the county, manifesting
contrivance, and in which no building could be moved to
any other scite without doing mischief. Where is such an
one to be seen?"

The following hint, in *rural architecture*, is not new,
but eligible.—P. 20. " In building the walls around a new
farm-yard for Mr. Coke, Mr. Overman, after a certain
height, draws them in to a brick's length at the top, a
saving in these erections which merits notice."

Building Materials.—P. 21. " Mr. Coke has, at Holkham, a brick manufactory, which ranks very high among
the first in the kingdom; bricks in all sorts of forms are
made, so that in raising an edifice, there is never a necessity for breaking a whole brick to have a smaller of a very
imperfect shape, which takes time, and creates waste;
cornice, round column, corner, arch bricks, &c. are made
in great perfection."

OCCUPIERS.—Within the section, " Farms," the Secretary brings together the *names* of more than fifty occupiers (names that are constantly recurring, thro the volume):—but without noticing either the quality or the
natural situation of their several holdings;—as to whether
they lie on the *chalk hills*, in the *fens* or *marshes*, or
among the *heathlands*, the *sandy loams*, or the *cool strong
lands* of Norfolk! The *names* even of the farms, or the
parishes they lie in,—were they always to be found in the
Reporter's map,—would avail but little; as the labor of
searching for them, *in the map at large*, would deter
readers

readers in general from the pursuit *.—The list is introduced, with the subjoined *neat* eulogy.—P. 32. " Those who have visited Holkham as farmers, will not accuse me of flattery, if I assert of Mr. Coke, that he is *fairest where many are fair*."

PLAN of MANAGEMENT.—Under the head, " Farms,"— " Course of Crops,"—and " Arable System," are found ample and extraordinary remarks, relating to "the Norfolk husbandry !"—In these remarks we perceive *one* of the Reporter's *real* motives for loading the agricultural book market with an unnecessary volume.

In *my Report*, I spoke of the PRACTICE of EAST NORFOLK, as the long established system of NORFOLK HUSBANDRY ; by which the immense, almost incredible, surplus produce, mentioned aforegoing, was principally obtained.—This would seem to have given umbrage to the splendid meteors which then blazed, or were beginning to blaze, amid the dark region of rabbit warrens and wild sheepwalks, in the more *northern* parts of the County ;—in which last-enlightened part of it, the writer of the Report, now under consideration, appears to have received his first impression of " Norfolk husbandry."

Delighted, no doubt, with the hospitality, and that still more delightful repast, the fierce argument, which seldom fails to arise, during a state of *revolution*, whether in politics, or in agriculture,—he has gratefully stepped forward to blazen forth the practices which *there* prevailed, in 1804.—Even in his map, we see the words " NORFOLK HUSBANDRY," displayed in capitals, over NORTHERN NORFOLK † : and this, notwithstanding, if we were implicitly to

* For further remarks, on this topic, see the head, *Turneps*, ensuing.

† The Reporter not unfrequently designates the scroll of the County, here spoken of, by the term, " WEST NORFOLK ;"—a name which, naturally and indispensibly belongs to the *marshlands, fens,* and *heathlands* of Norfolk :—certainly not to the *chalk hills* and their environs.—" Northwest Norfolk," which this writer sometimes uses, is more allowable. But, seeing, not only in Nature, but in the Reporter's map, that the narrow range of country, about whose revolutionary proceedings this Reporter has more particularly written, stretches away along the north coast, (from the inlet of the sea, which divides Norfolk from Lincolnshire on the west, toward the eastern coast of the County),—NORTH NORFOLK is the appropriate term which, indisputably, belongs to it ; and by which I shall distinguish it.

to rely on his own details, scarsely any two principal occupiers in it, thought and acted alike ; even in 1804.

In what state, then, must this corner of the County have
been, in 1782 ?—I would have as readily registered Abbe
Seiyes's pigeon-hole constitutions, while revolution raged
in France, as the unestablished practices, which,—even at
the time this Report was written,—were fluttering to get
on the wing, in North Norfolk.

A quarter of a century, hence, men's minds may become assimilated, and a regular system of management be,
there, established :—similar, in much probability (unless
on the chalk-down lands) to that which has prevailed, in
the eastern and central parts of the County, for a century
and a quarter past,—with a success unequalled.—Yet this
writer prides himself on having been instrumental in attempting to pull it down ! !

P. 362.   " For the last four or five and thirty years that
I have examined West Norfolk with the eye of a farmer,
the change in the tillage system has not been great.   At
that period the course was, 1. Turnips; 2. Barley; 3.
Grasses for two, or, in a few cases, three years; 4. White-
corn ; on the better soils wheat; on others, rye, &c.   The
only change that has occurred has been in the grasses : the
variation, which I believe first took place from forty to
fifty years ago, was shortening the duration, from three
years to two : in both cases giving what may be called a
bastard fallow the last year, by a half-ploughing, soon
after Midsummer.   Above thirty years ago, *I contended*,
both in print and in conversation, *against it*, but was held
cheap for entertaining any doubts of the propriety of the
practice.   I have lived, however, to see this change also
in a great measure take place amongst the best farmers,
who now give only one ploughing for the winter corn."

Will it, can it, be generally credited, that the Secretary
of the Board, the strenuous advocate for " old establishments," should ever have been a stickler in a REVOLUTION !
—had ever been detected in attempting to break up a
" regular order of things," that had stood the test of ages ;
and had raised the County of Norfolk, to a height of
improvement, profit, and fame, which rendered her the admiration, and envy, of every other County of this proudly
agricultural kingdom ?

It is with some reluctance, that I insert the following
licentious, demi-jacobinical remarks, in addition to the
preceding ;—lest they should be caught at by revolu-
tionists in politics.—P. 31.   " In respect to their husbandry,
the

the farming mind in this County has undergone TWO
pretty considerable REVOLUTIONS. For 30 years, from
1730 to 1760,* the great improvements in the *north
western* part of the County took place, and which rendered the *county in general* (!!) famous. For the next 30
years, to about 1790, I think they nearly stood still ; they
reposed upon their laurels. About that period a *second revolution was working :* they seemed then to *awaken to new
ideas :* an experimental spirit began to spread, much owing,
it is said, to the introduction of drilling ; and as so new a
practice *set men to thinking,* it is not unlikely : *nothing
can be done till men think,* and they certainly had not
thought for 30 years preceding."—Why, this is in the very
marrow of " Jacobinism"! †

Hence, according to this account, the husbandry of
northwestern Norfolk was in a state of disgraceful turpi-
dity, in 1780, 81, and 82; and no wonder it did not particularly engage my attention, at that period.—It so happened, however, that *the* DURSGATE and *the* MALLET were
then in full blaze,—the Etna and Vesuvius that astonished
" the natives " of that day. A fact this, which militates
against the above general position.

Having already represented the Secretary's endless details of " course of crops" (in the present case filling a
sheet and half of letter press) in what appears to me to be
the true light,—in reviewing his Lincolnshire Report (see
p. 136, aforegoing) ;—and having spoken my sentiments
on the Norfolk system of management, in reviewing Mr.
Kent's Report, *(before I had read a line of the Secretary's) ;*
—it would be a waste of time and paper, to extend the
present article ‡.

WORKPEOPLE.

* Then it was that northwestern Norfolk emerged from the *pastoral*
and entered the *agricultural* state.

† May it, or may it not be, that this " tractable man" (to borrow a
phrase from the impressive dialect of Downing-street) is here writing
the genuine dictates of his own mind?

‡ The most reasonable objection that could be raised against the
six-year rotation of Norfolk, is the taking of two crops of corn, in
succession.—But, so long as the barley crop, after wheat, continues
to be equally, or more, valuable, on a par of years, than that after
turneps, there can be no doubt of the superiority of the system, in
point of *present profit,* whether to the *occupier,* or the *existing* community.

The exhaustion of the land is, in my opinion, the only radical objection to it. See p. 314, aforegoing :—also a note on the article,
Tares, ensuing.

WORKPEOPLE.—It appears, aforegoing p. 333,—that between the years 1782 and 1796, a rise of 15 to 20 percent., on yearly and day wages took place; and, in the section " Comparison of times," in the Report now before me, a rise of about forty percent. was incurred, on day labor, between the years 1790 and 1804; and that the rise, during that time, for " husbandry labor in general," —including day labor, yearly wages, and task work,—was nearly fifty percent.

P. 484. " A custom is coming in around Waterden, &c. of allowing board-wages to farm servants, instead of the old way of feeding in the house ; 8s. a week are given."

WORKING ANIMALS.—By several memoranda (pp. 479, and 480) it appears that, in Norfolk, the proportion of horses to the number of acres occupied, is from three to four percent. ;—the Reporter noting,—and I apprehend with much truth,—"the larger the farm, generally the smaller the proportion."

P. 480. " Mr. Burton, of Langley, (?) never lets his horses remain in the stable at night, always turning them into a well-littered warm yard, contiguous to the stable. This is the practice of the farmers in the angle of country formed by Woodbridge, Saxmundham, and the sea."— In Suffolk.

P. 481. " Mr. Purdis, of Eggmore, works 32 Devonshire oxen in yokes and bows, four to a plough. I saw them at work, and was much pleased to see them step out so nimbly, as to be fully equal to the horses ploughing in the same field, in point of movement : they plough an acre and an half in one journey."

IMPLEMENTS.—The only thing that arrested my attention, in going over the chapter, " Implements " (of considerable length) was—that the Reporter is not a *plowman.*

MANURES.—The Secretary's section, " Manuring," fills two sheets.

On *marl,* we find a long line of " facts," strung together. But, after the ample details I have given of marl, and of marling, in Norfolk, they can be of little consideration with the public.—The Reporter's recommendation of one-horse cars, instead of three-horse carts, is highly *entertaining;* and Mr. Colhoun's " contrivance to draw the carts of any size, out of the pits, by the mean of a capstan," may, in many instances, be truly valuable.

P. 405. " He uses large three-wheeled tumbrels, and to save the extra number of horses, which are used in common to get the load out of the pit, he applies a boy and

and a horse to the lever of a capstan, and draws up the load with so little loss of time, that the whole operation takes but three minutes and a half."

For an instance of bringing sunken marl to the surface, see the head, *Tillage,* ensuing.

" *Sea Weed,*"—a strange misnomer of " the ruins of a forest of large trees." But no matter. The idea it represents belongs to the most striking facts—the most *interesting* information—which is comprized in the volume now under review.—Altho this extraordinary phenominon belongs to the science of GEOLOGY, rather than to that of AGRICULTURE, (being, as a sourse of manure, merely local) I allow it to occupy the situation which the Reporter has assigned it.

P. 414. " Sea Weed. What other name to assign to a very singular manure on the coast at Thornham, I know not. In the great and accurate map of the County, published by Mr. Faden, there is a mark on the shore for what is called *crabs, scalps, and oak-roots.* Mr. Rishton had the goodness to take me to view this spectacle, which is an extraordinary one: it is evidently the ruins of a forest of large trees, the stubs and roots remaining, but so rotten, that with a spade I dug into the centre of many, and might have done of all, with as much ease as into a mass of butter. Where the stumps are not found, on digging I turned up a black mass of vegetable fibres, apparently consisting of decayed branches, leaves, rushes, flags, &c.; to what depth this vegetable stratum extends is not known, but at some creeks on the very edge of the sea, at low water, there is a very fine soapy sea ouze, at two or three feet depth. The extent of this once sylvan region, which every common tide now covers, can scarcely be less, in one place only, than from 5 to 600 acres. There is not an appearance of any tree lying at present from the stump, as if blown down or left after falling, but rather that of a forest cut down in haste, the stems cleared and hurried away, leaving the branches to rot: but this is mere conjecture. It is remarkable that there is not, as I am informed, any mention of this ruined forest in the old historians of the County; nor does tradition offer the least conjecture or report on the subject. Trees, roots, and stumps, are very common in bogs, wherever found; but here is not the trace of any thing like a bog, the earth is solid, and all a fine ouze or sea-clay.

" Mr. Rishton viewed these relicks with the eye of a farmer; for experiment, he sent his carts down for some, and

and spread 10 loads per acre of it, for turnips : it answered
perfectly, and on comparison, equalled his yard-dung:
and also rape-cake."

Aquatic Plants.—Mr. Kent mentions " river weeds," as
an excellent manure, for turneps. And the Secretary has
the following notices, respecting " pond weeds."

P. 416. " Several persons in Norfolk are in the regular
habit of clearing their rivers and ponds just before turnip-
sowing : they cart them immediately on to the land, and
plough in as muck, and load for load they are equal to
farm-yard dung. Mr. Coke thus manures from 20 to 30
acres annually from the lake at Holkham.

" Mr. Crowe, of Lakenham, manures four acres annually
for turnips with the weeds of a river that runs by his farm;
the plants are chiefly the *Phelandrium aquaticum & Sium
nodiflorum* (water-hemlock and water-parsnip). He lays
20 loads of 30 bushels per acre, and ploughs in directly:
are as good on sand and mixed loam as the best dung,
but not equal on stiff soils.

" Mr. Bloomfield, of Billingfold, has been in the habit
of manuring his turnip-land with weeds fresh from the
river, and ploughed in quickly; they have answered as
well as yard-muck."

Sticklebacks,—are used as a powerful manure, on the
coast of North Norfolk; as on that of South Lincolnshire.
—See p. 143, aforegoing. They "are caught in immense
quantities, in the Lynn rivers, about once in seven years."
p. 417.

Rape Cake,—is still, it seems, a prevailing manure, on
the north coast of Norfolk. See p. 350, aforegoing.

Buckweet.—See that head, ensuing.

Yard Dung,—would seem to have been in a state of high
fermentation, in Norfolk, at the time of this Reporter's tour.

Endless opinions and assertions are crouded together,
on the controversial point respecting *long dung* and *short
dung ;*—(and whether straw should be *eaten,* or *trodden*
into *dung)*—a dispute much resembling, in difference of
opinion, and contrariety of argument, that about *long
horns* and *short horns, long wools* and *short wools* (see Lincolnshire). No two men appear to have possessed the
same ideas on the subject. The pros and cons, if duly
weighed, would probably poize, each other.—Nothing
comes fairly out, that is worth a moment's thought.

I have repeatedly said—" the more we know, the less we
seem to know." And this Reporter appears to have
reached the acme of rural knowledge; namely, the point
of

of diffidence where men may seem to know nothing. He, therefore, (let us conceive) industriously notes down all he hears, without due discrimination. But, surely, a profici- ent in short hand, tho he might not possess an idea, in agriculture, would make a more eligible Reporter; for as much as his notes, in the excellence of his art, might be more uniformly correct.

When speaking of farm yard manure,—its specific qua- lity,—the nature and state of the soil,—and the crop for which it is intended,—require to be accurately defined :— otherwise, all that is said about it, is vague;—and is more liable to be injurious, than profitable, to students, and in- experienced practitioners.

On FOLDING SHEEP, for MANURE.—In p. 475, the Re- porter mentions an "accidental experiment"—that is to say an INCIDENT—in which there appeared a great differ- ence, in the verdure of a ley, or young-grass field; one part of which had been eaten off with sheep, in the ordi- nary way, but from the other part the sheep had been folded on a fallow ground.

The truth of this no one, who has had experience in sheep-folding, will doubt.—What, therefore, is the use of noticing it, without at the same time declaring the benefit which the fallow field received by the process? If the fal- low did not receive more advantage, than the ley ground and the flock received injury, the management was bad. But, the reverse, the reverse.

It can seldom, I apprehend, be right to fold from a TEMPORARY LEY ;—unless to improve particular parts of its own area, in order to equalize its productiveness.

But this is no good reason why sheep may not be folded, with profit, from OLD GRASS LANDS, whether upland *sheep walks,* or lowland *grazing grounds,* that have, for ages, been depastured with that species of stock, and where their dung, it is more than probable, has lost much of its efficacy, as manure:—or from rich *watered meadows,* that do not require manuring.

TILLAGE.—*Fallowing.*—P. 192. "The grand fallow of Norfolk is the preparation for turnips, which will be men- tioned under that article. The common summer-fallow takes place on strong, wet, and clayey soils ; upon which, however, turnips are too generally ventured. One fault in the husbandry of the county, and of Norfolk farmers when they move into very different districts, is that of being wedded too closely to practices which derive their chief merit from a right application to very dry or sandy soils.

" Mr. Overman, whose husbandry merits every attention, having taken a farm of Mr. Coke, at Michaelmas 1800, and the outgoing tenant possessing a right to sow some layers which were very full of spear-grass, &c. Mr. Overman gave him, to the surprize of his neighbours, 5l. 10s. per acre to desist; not that he might himself sow those fields, but for the sake of *completely fallowing them.* Some I found had undergone the operation, and were clean; others were in it, and almost green with couch. *He destroys it by mere ploughing and harrowing, without any raking or burning;* conceiving that by well-timed tillage, any land may be made clean ;* and that on these sandy soils, a July earth in a hot sun will effect it : but whenever or however done, his object, whether with much or little tillage, is sure to be answered; and as the successive cleanness of the land depends on its being once got perfectly free from weeds, his great expenses, he expects, will in the end prove the cheapest way of going to work. He gives four earths in all ; the first before winter, only two inches deep; another in the spring; the third two, or two inches and a half deep, in July, in a hot time; the fourth after harvest."

P. 29. " Mr. Johnson, of Thurning, entering 500 acres in sad order, he ploughed up and *fallowed* the seeds, for which he had given 30s. an acre."

P. 238. " Mr. Haver's bailiff assured me, that he gets as good barley on a fallow without muck, as he does after turnips on the same strong land that was well dunged : a good crop ten coombs; rarely less than eight in any management. The husbandry is well conducted, After harvest the fallow is laid on to ten-furrow ridges, so that in spring they have only to plough and sow."—The Reporter adds—"to scarify and sow would be better, the horses going only in the furrows." (!)—" Mr. Pitts," (same page) "of Thorpe Abbots, also gets much better barley on a fallow without manure, than after turnips well manured for, if the land be heavy."

Yet, in the very same Volume which contains the above instances of the good effects of fallowing, is the subjoined remark. The Reporter has wantonly mentioned the man's name who made it. I will not, however, be guilty of the same cruelty.

P. 214.

---

* I am happy to find a man of Mr. Overman's good sense perfectly coinciding with me, in this particular of management.

P. 214. "Mr. ———, at ———, applied summer-fallowing, the first year of his taking his farm, much of which consists of various loams and sands, on a strong marley and clayey bottom, and abounding with springs; but after that, he has never fallowed, and never will.—His expression was, "*a man is a madman that summer fallows.*"—Would it not be allowable retort to say—that a man must be an ideot (in aration) who could make use of such an expression?—and simple must he be who sent it to press!

There would seem to be only one excuse for the remarker. He appears to be a *young* farmer. For we are told—"he is very regular in the four-shift course."—And if he found his farm, on entering it, *quite clean,* or rendered it so, "the first year," by *summer fallowing;* and moreover enjoys a situation in which he can command *extraneous manures;*—he may be right. See p. 332, aforegoing.

In this section, "Tillage," we perceive many pro-and-con opinions about *deep* and *shallow* plowing. But not a syllable is entitled to a place, here.—Neither the nature of the subsoil, the depth of the natural soil, nor whether a "pan" intervenes between them, is not, except in a very few instances, accurately, or at all, stated!

The subjoined passage, relating to marl, but found in the section "Tillage," is worthy of notice.—P. 189. "Mr. Willis observing the marle on his land was sunk below the common path of the plough, turned it up again by going a deeper pitch, and found it to answer nearly as well as a new marling."—Where the subsoil, or immediate basis of the cultivated mold, is not of an ungenial quality, this expedient might, doubtlessly, in many cases, be eligible.

Price of *Plowing.*—P. 191. "Thirty years ago" (says the Reporter) "the common price of ploughing was 2s. 6d. an acre in every part of Norfolk, except Marshland: it is now 4s.; in some places 3s. 6d."

Semination.—Dibbling.—On this *native practice* of Norfolk, we find only a few notes, in the Report under view. The reason of this is clear. It was not in *vogue,* in *North* Norfolk, at the time of reporting.—Indeed, we are informed, not in the Section Dibbling, but in that of Wheat, —P. 293,—that the enquiry "is not of consequence in North-west Norfolk, for they have no population equal to dibbling becoming general: and a circumstance which tends much to impede this husbandry, is the imperfect manner in which it is performed, for the sake of making great earnings; this has, in many instances, given a preference to drilling."

In

In the County at large, dibbling appears, in travelling through it, to be still the favorite, and still in full practice.

Drilling.—This Reporter is a travelled man; and has doubtlessly experienced the comforts which flow from an observance of the sage maxim—" When you are at Rome, &c."—Hence, in Lincolnshire, we find him an anti-drillist, in the first and boldest rank. In Norfolk, on the contrary, during the Revolution in the northern part of that County, when the delightful rage for drilling was at its height, and, of course, a constant topic of table-talk, and hard-fought argument,—we see him a willing convert to the practice;—and filling pages after pages with its praises;—closing his notes (p. 360) with this observation. —" From these notes it appears, that, notwithstanding some failures, and probably many prejudices, the drill culture has very completely established itself in West Norfolk, and is spreading into the other districts of that extensive county. The success appears, on the whole, to be very flattering:"—the author adds—" but there is one singular circumstance which should, so far as Norfolk only is concerned, check the unlimited panegyrics sometimes too generally heard *in conversation*, and that is, there being, at least to my knowledge, but one farm (Mr. Hoste's) on strong or clay land, where this practice is thoroughly introduced. Suffolk affords multitudes; but Norfolk is at present our business; and here the farmers on strong land, have hitherto rejected it. This is remarkable, as I have heard some very able drillers give it as their *opinion*, that this husbandry has greater merit on strong than on light land." (!)

Having thus given the Reporter's *own observations*, at large,—it will be proper to notice two passages in his book (not inserted under the ostensible head "Drilling!")—which militate forcibly against the position, that " the drill culture has very completely established itself in West Norfolk."—They are these :

P. 250. "Mr. Rogerson, of Narborough," (between Swafham and Lynn) " was amongst the earliest drillers in Norfolk, and on a very large scale, especially for barley; but this year (1802) I found he had put in all his crop with one-horse ploughs, preferring this method, after long experience: he never had a better crop."

P. 288. "Mr. Dalton, of Swafham, has drilled largely at Bilney;" (still farther *northwestward)* " but his success for the two last years has been so bad that he leaves it off, convinced that the broad-cast answers better. If he drills early,

early, the poppy gets greatly a-head; if late, the frosts turn the drilled wheat out of the ground; by ploughing the seed in he avoids the latter evil."

Might it not, here, be aptly suggested, without giving great offence to the Reporter or his friends, that, had he deferred his tour a few years longer, he might have found many a Norfolk drillist following those gentlemen's examples;—dropping off, like withered fruit, one after another, according to the dates of their respective commencements?

The Norfolk practice of " *two-furrowing*,"—of sowing the seed between two thin furrow slices,—is not mentioned, by this Reporter. It was deemed, perhaps, to be of too plodding, and *immechanical* a cast, to assimilate well with "modern husbandry!"—This being as it may, it is, in my mind, the most *rational* method of depositing the seed of *corn* crops, in *broken ground*,—that husbandry, ancient or modern, has yet brought into practice.—It is, in effect, the gardener's and nurseryman's practice of sowing seeds of a similar size.

In Norfolk, it is true, the seed, in this operation, is sown, *by hand;* but how readily might a *machine*—a two-furrow plow—be contrived, to spread it, more evenly, and of course with better effect.

For a description of this mode of Semination, see my NORFOLK, *Minute*, 43. And for general remarks on the DRILL HUSBANDRY see my SOUTHERN COUNTIES,—District *Isle* of *Thanet :*—the cradle of the practice, in England.

ARABLE CROPS.—For the first time, I here behold the Secretary of the Board, in the character of a *systematist.* In the Volume before me, the more important of the arable crops are treated of, *analytically*, nearly (as I have said before) in the manner in which I have usually registered the materials of my own surveys.

To discuss the doubtful points, and combat what appears to be erroneous, in the eight sheets of letter-press to which this subject, is extended,—would be an irksome, and might prove an ungrateful, task. I will, therefore, merely select such passages as will, I conceive, throw additional light on the Norfolk practice.

Prefatory to this selection, it may be proper to inform my readers, that the materials, collected by this Reporter, on the arable crops of Norfolk, principally consist of conversational notes—of insulated, unsupported assertions and opinions, thrown together, under each head, or sub-head, in the shape of unconnected cementless memoranda;
—with

—with, here and there, a remark of the compiler;—perhaps on some particular crop which happened to succeed a favorite process or operation; but, generally, without detailing the CIRCUMSTANCES, of *succession, soil, tillage, manure,* &c. &c. which *preceded, accompanied,* or were intended to *follow* that particular crop!!

IT IS NOT ONE CROP IN A COURSE, (nor even one course of a series) THAT CAN DETERMINE the PROPRIETY of a PRACTICE.

What must more particularly surprise, if not disgust, the experienced arable farmer, on going through the sections now under notice, is the extraordinary circumstance of this veteran writer, on agriculture, being an enemy of the *plow!*—a friend to the " scuffler,"—" riffler,"—" scarifier,"—" whiffler," (no glossary);—still a very TYRO, in the PRACTICE of ARATION.

WHEAT.— *Tillage.*—P. 272. "One of the most remarkable circumstances of the Norfolk husbandry, and the most difficult to account for, is the system, very common, of ploughing a lay intended for wheat, three or four times, beginning in June or July."

Why, this is the very corner stone, the firm foundation, of the NORFOLK HUSBANDRY! which has *covered the County with glory,*—filled its farmers' pockets with money,—and the markets of the metropolis with corn and cattle,—for more than a century past!!—Yet this Reporter of its practices—this occasional visitor of revolutionary North Norfolk—wonders how the Norfolk farmers can follow it! and has bestowed upon it much reflection:—such as any other stranger to the uses of tillage, and the practice of the County at large, might have done.

Smut, in Wheat.—P. 299. " Many farmers about Houghton are troubled with the smut, but Mr. Stanton, of Darsingham, sows only old wheat, and never having been known to have any smut from such seeding, others are getting into the same practice.

" Captain Beacher, of Hillingdon, always sows old wheat, and never has any smut: no brining or liming, as that injures old seed. He has sown old and new seed in the same field, and had the smut in the latter, but not an ear in the former."

Dibbling Wheat.—P. 284. "Mr. Salter, of Winborough, dibbles all his wheat on layers, or on whatever land is proper for the practice, and what deserves particular attention, all is done by women, with only one confidential man for superintending them: he gives 10s. 6d. an acre for two
rows

rows on a flag. He thinks that women dibble better than
men, from being more obedient and manageable. This
practice deserves universal imitation: his women also reap
wheat."

As a proof of this valuable process having greatly encreased in practice, since I wrote upon it, the subjoined
notices, among some pages of others, may suffice.—P. 285.
" Mr. Brown, of Thrigby, thinks that there are five times
as many acres of wheat and pease dibbled in Fleg as are
sown broad-cast."—P. 286. " Mr. Syble, of South Walsham, this year (1802) dibbled 60 acres; Mr. Heath, of
Hemlington, the whole of his crop on a farm of 500 acres.
Mr. Francis, at Martham, all for some years past." *

Wheat and *Turneps.*—I insert the following extraordinary instance of practice (for such, it would seem, to have
been, considered)—as something new, rather than as an
example to be incautiously followed.—Yet, on light absorbent lands, and with a favorable season, for eating off
the turneps, I do not see why it might not be followed with
success.—If such a season should not occur, mow off the
tops and *necks* of the turneps, let the roots rot, and roll
them down, for manure, for the wheat.—This by the way.

P. 294. " Mr. Walker, of Harpley, some years ago,
introduced and practised a husbandry in which he was entirely original. I viewed his farm, while these experiments were going on, for two years. In order to give a
greater degree of stiffness to his sandy soil, he thought of
putting in wheat without any ploughing at all, immediately before sowing. He began with six acres of turnips,
hoeing in the wheat seed at the second hoeing of the turnips: these were eaten on the land by bullocks and sheep.
The wheat proved good, and answered expectation. The
next year he did the same on 35 acres: this also succeeded; but the best wheat was where the turnips were
eaten in the driest weather. The following year he extended the culture to 70 acres, which also succeeded to his
satisfaction. The year following, he had 100 acres. Upon
the whole, the culture produced not better than the common crops, but equal. The most adverse circumstance is
a wet season for eating the turnips, but at the worst, it can
amount to no more than the loss of the seed."

Teathing

* In travelling thro the center of the County, from the Burnhams
to Scole Inn, in July 1810, luxuriant, yet tall, straight-standing crops
of DIBBLED WHEAT. were most abundant.

Teathing wheat.—This is another novel practice; and of a tendency somewhat similar to the last. On very *loosely textured, absorbent lands,* and in a *favorable season,* for the operation, it can scarsely fail of being eligible.

P. 296. " *Tathing.*—This is a singular husbandry, which I did not meet with till I entered Fleg, from Yarmouth. It consists in carting turnips on to wheat in February and March; they call it to *pull and throw* on wheat, eating them on that crop by sheep and bullocks, if sheep are kept; but if not, by bullocks alone."

A string of pro-and-con opinions succeed. But the specific qualities of the lands, on which it had been unsuccessfully applied, not being given, the information, on the whole, is unsatisfactory.

Roots of wheat.—P. 299. " Mr. Thurtell has traced the fibres of the roots of wheat, five feet deep, on the side of a marle pit."

Harvesting wheat.—Early cutting.—P. 300. " Mr. Parmenter, miller, at Aylesham, a considerable farmer also, and a very intelligent sensible man, remarked to me, that the farmers let their wheat stand too long before cutting. They were apt to have a notion, that when millers gave this opinion, it was speaking for their own interest: but he cuts his own wheat before it is ripe, and would do so on the largest scale, if he was not a miller: the quality is far superior, and the crop just as good."

Produce of wheat.—The subjoined statement is worth preserving.—P. 301. " Mr. Repton, at Oxnead, favoured me with an accurate account of all his crops for some years back.

		Acres.		Coombs.	Bushels.
1773	-	77	-	3	3
1774	-	50	-	5	2
1775	-	46	-	6	2
1776	-	56	-	5	2
1777	-	30	-	6	3
1778	-	71	-	5	1
1779	-	50	-	6	0
1780	-	61	-	5	0
1781	-	53	-	9	0
1782	-	46	-	7	2
1783	-	47	-	6	3
1784	-	50	-	5	3
1785	-	58	-	7	0
1786	-	59	-	8	2

1787

		Acres.		Produce per acre.	
				Coombs.	Bushels.
1787	-	42	-	8	0
1788	-	56	-	7	1
1789	-	47	-	7	0
1790	-	58	-	7	2
1791	-	58	-	8	2
1792	-	57	-	7	0
1793	-	54	-	9	1
1794	-	48	-	5	$1\frac{1}{2}$
1795	-	59	-	5	$1\frac{1}{2}$
1796	-	52	-	8	0
1797	-	53	-	7	1
1798	-	53	-	9	2
1799	-	57	-	5	0
1800	-	55	-	7	3
1801	Books not made up.			—	—
	Average	-	-	6	$3\frac{1}{2}$"

That is to say—twenty seven bushels and a half, on the average of nearly thirty years.

There are few farms, in this kingdom, tho of much higher rental value than the farm of Oxnead, can equal such a produce.—Yet this farm has long been conducted on the *true*, the *legitimate*, the CONSTITUTIONAL HUSBANDRY of NORFOLK;—as may be seen in the Reporter's own account of it.—P. 200. " Mr. Repton, at Oxnead, has been, from the year 1773,* regularly in the six-shift husbandry, of

1. Turnips,	4. Seeds—ollond,
2. Barley,	5. Wheat,
3. Seeds—hay,	6. Barley;

which is common throughout the country."

RYE.—P. 304. " There is a practice in the South-west district, which has merit—that of ploughing up the rye stubbles in harvest, and sowing one or two pecks of seed additional per acre, with intention of burying the scattered grains, and thus having a crop of spring food for sheep. The tillage has its use for the following turnips. consequently the expence merely consists in the small portion of seed added."

BARLEY.—*Succession.*—For barley, after fallow, see the head, *Tillage*, aforegoing.—The following are the remainder of the Reporter's notices, on this topic.

P. 238.

---

* And his predecessors, perhaps, for near a century preceding that time; Oxnead being situated toward the center of the long established practice of the County.

P. 238. " Mr. Cubit, at Catfield, and his neighbours, get more barley after wheat than they do after turnips drawn ; but the cleanest and the best coloured is after turnips; and they find that the barley after wheat, in a six-year's shift (the seeds lying two years), is much better than in the five shift, in which the seeds remain but one year.

" Mr. Cubit, of Honing, also gets the best crops of barley after wheat, but attributes it to the pulling and throwing turnips on the wheat stubbles; but he remarks, that the throwing business seldom answers, except in very dry weather.

" Mr. Repton, at Oxnead, generally gets better barley after wheat than after turnips, but the latter all drawn.

" Mr. Johnson, at Thurning, gets as good barley after wheat on four earths, as after turnips.

" Mr. Everit, of Caistor, in Fleg, observes, that if turnips are fed off by sheep early, that is, by December, then the barley is much better than what is gained after wheat; but if the turnips are fed in the spring, in March for instance, the barley after wheat beats it.

" Mr. Francis, of Martham, upon the whole, has rather better barley after turnips than after wheat, but the latter the greatest bulk: the turnips carted away."

Barn management of barley.—P. 256. " To free barley from the awn, in years or crops when it is very tough and adhesive, Mr. Bevan has a horse rode by a boy repeatedly over the floor when six to eight or nine inches deep in barley, and it is found effectually and cheaply to free it.

Malting barley.—P. 256. " In 1800, Mr. Gilpin, of Heacham, a considerable maltster, bought some beautiful barley that had not received a drop of rain, and trying a small parcel of it, found it malted badly : he tried a most uncommon experiment, and founded upon an idea very contrary to all common ones on the subject : he kiln-dried it by a gentle heat, watering it lightly with a watering-pot twice or thrice, six hours intervening; dried it: after which operation it malted well, every grain sprouting, and no malt could be finer. Hence observes the very intelligent gentleman* from whom I had this account, it is evident that a good shower of rain in harvest, or a sweat in the stack, is beneficial to the maltster.

" By

" * Maxey Allen, Esq. of Lynn."

" By the same gentleman it was remarked to me, that malt keeps better with the *comb* in it, screening when wanted.

" The best trial is to swim it in water; all that swims is good malt; what sinks, is barley rather than malt."

PEASE.—P. 308. " Mr. Overman, from various observations, is of opinion, that if pease are repeated oftener than once in eleven or twelve years, they are very apt to fail.

" Mr. Syble, of South Walsham, has found that pease are a very uncertain crop: this is known to all farmers; but he has remarked further, that they will not bear repeating. If sown often on the same land, they are almost sure to fail."

BEANS.—This Reporter informs us that he had " been calling out for beans;" but scarsely any one would vouchsafe to answer him.—There are, no doubt, a few lands, on the southern border of the County, on which beans would *grow.* But there is scarsely any other County (aggregately considered) in the kingdom, which is less adapted to their *culture.*

TARES.—P. 319. " The culture of this plant has increased very considerably in Norfolk of late years. Within my memory they are multiplied at least tenfold."

On a *sheep* farm, they might be well introduced in the following rotation.—P. 197. " Mr. Purdis, of Eggmore, a very uncommon variation from the general husbandry:

1. Turnips,		4. Seeds,
2. Barley,		5. Tares,
3. Seeds,		6. Wheat."*

BUCKWEET. P. 317. " Mr. Francis, of Martham, has sown buck-wheat after turnips, and got eight or nine coombs an acre, and wheat after the buck: the reason of this uncommon course was, because part of the field was coleseed, and it brought the whole into wheat; the crop nine or ten coombs an acre.

" Mr. Cubit,

---

* Should the proprietors of Norfolk determine to rear their own *livestock* (see p. 314, aforegoing) and thereby prevent the too great exhaustion of their estates, by raising an inordinate produce of *corn,* the above rotation of crops, I conceive, will be well entitled to their consideration.—Its peculiar merit consists in continuing the Norfolk lands *three years in herbage;* which, on the suggested plan of rendering them *permanently productive,* is, I conceive, a principal point to be aimed at, in their culture.—With a view to *present profit,* no plan is, nor perhaps ever will be, found equal to the long established practice of the County.

"Mr. Cubit, of Honing, finds that nothing cleans land so well for wheat as sowing buck; he gets seven or eight coombs an acre; but oftener ploughs it under, putting a bush under the beam to sweep it down for the plough—a poor succedaneum for the skim coulter. He finds it as good as a mucking; but this only on strong land. He sows it on a second year's layer, as soon as barley sowing is over, from the 15th to the 20th of May; about the 1st of August ploughs it under, harrows well in September, then throws on the seed, and ridges for wheat: always good crops."—Other instances are mentioned of similar success.

HEMP.—The hemp culture of Suffolk extends into Norfolk.—We find the following notices respecting its *decline*, in the latter County.—P. 326. "This culture, in the vicinity of Diss, has greatly declined; there is scarcely one-tenth grown of what there was some years past: this is chiefly attributed to the high price of wheat."—P. 330. "Mr. George Eaton, linen-weaver, informed me, that about Diss there is not so much hemp grown as before the price of wheat was so high, by a third or fourth. It is affected also by the high price of turnip seed; for the cottagers, &c. sow turnips on their hemp grounds, and if seed be high, they let them stand for a crop, instead of sowing hemp every year in the common manner. I he necessity of manuring for every crop of hemp, impedes much the increase of it under any circumstances."—P. 333. Mr. Richardson.—"Not half the hemp raised now, that he remembers, though the price is doubled. Where they used to have hemp, they now have wheat. And little farmers had more than large ones at present."

P. 329. "*Estimation* of the *quantity* of hemp *raised* in the hemp district of Norfolk.

	Acres.		Acres.
Old Buckenham	20	Shelfhanger	5
Carleton	8	Burston	5
Banham	20	Gissing	5
Winfarthing	12	Aslacton	5
Kenninghall	6	Forncet	3
The Lophams	30	Waketon	2
Garboldsham	8	Tibenham	2
Roydon	5	Titshall	1
Bressingham	10	Shimpling	1
Fersfield	10	Drickleborough	3
Diss	10	Harleston	5
			Starston

	Acres.			Acres:
Starston	1	Fretton		7
Schole	3			
Brockdish	7			202
Needham	8			

It may amount to about 200 acres."

The Secretary closes his section with "an answer he sent to some queries transmitted him" (by whom does not appear) "on the subject of *the* encreasing the growth of hemp." The following is his proposal.

P. 335. " The land which will produce profitable crops of hemp, is applicable to various other beneficial purposes; and to induce men who possess such land to vary from their common objects, would demand a very powerful impulse.

" There seem to be but two ways to give this impulse; one by a general bounty per acre (per stone would be more liable to fraud) on all hemp that produced 35 stones and upwards per acre: the other, to dispatch intelligent persons through all the hemp districts, and others where the soil is rich enough, to form contracts with all persons willing and able to raise the commodity largely; engaging to take all they produced, not less than   tons, at a given price, for five years."

I am unfortunate in differing, entirely, in sentiment, from the Secretary of the Board, on this, at present, important subject.

At a time, when it would seem to be generally understood, that corruption is suffered to stalk abroad, barefaced, in open day,—" bounties" and "contracts" are equally inadviseable ; and ought not to be *unnecessarily* resorted to :—and certainly should not, in the case under consideration ; while a more simplex, and, to my mind, a more practical, and more probably productive, expedient presents itself.

ESTABLISH READY-MONEY MARKETS for HEMP ;—fix the price to be given for it, at such a height as will pay the cultivator better—somewhat considerably better—than the ordinary crops in cultivation ; and a supply will naturally, follow.

The price, required, is such as will not merely remunerate the tenants handsomely, for labor, seed, and *ordinary rent ;* but such as will enable him to offer an *extra rent,* for permission to cultivate it, on *restricted* lands.

The hemp lands of this island lie mostly toward the coast,—are principally situated within twenty miles (a
day's

day's journey *out)* of a SEA PORT and CUSTOM HOUSE:—
There, let samples and prices be exhibited; and there, at
the proper season, let a *man* of *business,* an *acting agent*
(with a sufficient, but moderate salary) be placed; to receive the hemp; deposit it in warehouses (in charge of
the officers of the customs); *and pay down the money for
it, on delivery.*

Thus will the produce of the island be immediately
placed in the hands of Government,—in detached quantities (and of course the least liable to accidents)—ready to
be shipped, and conveyed to wherever it may be wanted.

The prices may be settled, annually, or occasionally,
according to the estimated demand, required:—due notice
being given of the prices for the succeeding season.

The great, and indeed serious, objection to growing
hemp in this island, for the uses of its navy, might be the
breaking up of perennial grass lands, for that purpose.—
If, however, it cannot be imported,—nor be raised without
that sacrifice,—necessity might warrant the expedient.—
But see p. 259, aforegoing.

TURNEPS.—With prompt memoranda, respecting this
important article of produce, in the Norfolk husbandry,
this Reporter has furnished twenty pages.—They are, it is
true, arranged, analytically, according to the points of
practice into which the turnep culture is resolvable. But,
in regard to the natural districts in which the several instances of culture took place, the nature of the lands to
which they severally relate,—readers in general are left
wholly in the dark. To a man who knows the situation
and soil of every village, every principal farm, and every
capital farmer, in the County, these memoranda may be
intelligible:—But not so, to ordinary readers.

This defect is not peculiar to the article, now immediately under notice; nor is it confined to arable crops, in
general; but may be said to pervade the entire volume.
(See occupiers p. 367, aforegoing.) Had the author of it
prefixed an alphabetical LIST of the CULTIVATORS whom he
quotes, with sketches of their several situations,—the soils
they occupied,—their agricultural *educations,*—and the
degree of *maturity* of their respective practices,—practical readers would have been able to appreciate their assertions and opinions, with sufficient accuracy, to improve
their own.—The unaccountable contradictions which now
appear, among men who stand high in their profession,
might, perhaps, by the help of such an interpreter, have
been satisfactorily reconciled. Men, whom we see con-
tradicting

tradicting each other, may, each of them, be perfectly right; their opinions and assertions having been drawn from the peculiar circumstances of their own experience; —having grown out of different situations and soils.

Hence, the inexplicit method of this writer, not only renders his book barren of useful information; but must place his informants in unpleasant, if not aukward, predicaments, with respect to each other.

I now proceed to extract the few short passages, that I have marked, in this Reporter's Section, "Turnips."

Preparing the *Seed.*—P. 224. "Mr. Shepherd dresses all his turnip seed with train oil and sulphur; three pints of the oil and one pound and a half of sulphur to a bushel of seed: dresses the seed with the oil by thorough mixing in a tub, and dries it with the sulphur, keeping it 12 hours before sowing: he has tried it repeatedly, and in comparisons, and is firmly persuaded of the benefit, from the superiority of the dressed seed in crops attacked by the fly, not only in experiments side by side, but also in saving crops when turnips have in general been destroyed."

Drilling Turneps.—P. 225. "The application of this mode of culture to the turnip crop has not yet made any considerable progress in the country; nor are the opinions of the farmers settled upon the question of its propriety."

Thus we find, in *modern* Norfolk, the fashion of drilling extended (we may say with little latitude) to every thing but turneps!—Several instances, it is true, are noticed of drilling them, as wheat or barley, *on the flat;* and mostly with *narrow intervals.* But none, in the TWEEDSIDE MANNER;* (see NORTHERN DEPARTMENT) not even to be carried off.

Raising the Turnep Crop.—P. 225. "Mr. Coke having heard that ducks had been used to clear turnips of the black canker, tried them on a field of 33 acres; he bought 400 ducks; on the 16th of July they were turned in, having water

---

* There is one instance noted, however, which *resembles* that practice.—P. 226. "Mr. Bloomfield, of Harpley, finding that his turnips were very apt to fail, like those of his neighbours, on a chalk soil, varied his husbandry; he spread the muck, and then sowed the turnip seed, and ploughed them in together, by two furrows meeting, but not lapping the one on the other, and the seed coming up along the centre of the flat ridge thus formed, before winter he ploughs between, to earth them up powerfully, for preservation against the frost. The success has been great, and much exceeding the common practice on that soil."

water at one corner of the field, and in five days they
cleared the whole completely, marching at last through
the field on the hunt, eyeing the leaves on both sides with
great care, to devour every one they could see."

Carting off Turneps.—P. 227. "Mr. Drake, of Billing-
ford, carts off his turnips with quarter-carts, the horse and
one wheel going in the furrow, and only one wheel on the
land, and that on the crown of the ridge. The mischief
thus done, he says, is less than in any other method he has
seen. The soil strong and wet.

"Upon good land Mr. Coke draws half and feeds half;
but on the weaker soils feeds all.

"It is common with many farmers in West Norfolk to
draw out the largest roots for carting home to bullocks,
and for feeding the smaller ones in the field by sheep.
Carting damages many ; but there is a great advantage in
leaving the small ones, which resist the frost the best."

Eating off Turneps.—This would seem to have been a
favorite practice, in 1804, with some of the large occupiers
of *North* Norfolk. But not with those of the *eastern* parts
of the County ; who then proceeded as in days of yore ;—
whose practice, in point of stability, might be likened unto
the laws of the Medes and Persians.

A hint to the sheep farmer.—P. 230. "In *feeding
turnips* (!) by sheep, Mr. Johnson remarks, that it is right
to begin at the poorest end of a field, or where the worst
crop is, as the flock, by falling back, will double dress it :"
—more especially, let it be added, if the lower end of the
field happen to be the poorest.

Preserving Turneps.—I copy the following enteries,
tho the former of them is scarsely intelligible.—P. 231.
"The Rev. Dixon Hoste practised a method, with this intention, that answered well ; he took the coulters out of
his ploughs, and then ploughed in the turnips ; and they
held good through a very bad March.

"The Rev. Mr. Munning has published his method : it
is drilling at eighteen inches, and two feet, and ploughing
furrows between, to bury them as well as may be effected.
This method has been practised with great success, by Mr.
Repton, at Oxnead, and other farmers."

Produce of Turneps.—P. 229. "Mr. Ferrier, at Hemsby, carts his whole crop to the *par* yard, the roots being
first tailed in the field. At Hemsby, &c. in Fleg, 30 great
cart-loads an acre (!) ; and single roots as much round as
a middle sized man's body.

"They have been sold at Ormsby, to the Yarmouth
cow•

cow-keepers, at 7*l*. 7*s*. an acre. A price fixed by appraisement, at Michaelmas, to incoming tenants, often 4*l*. 15*s*. He has known 36 large loads an acre; and 24*lb*. a turnip, and quite brittle, no flockyness."

The *stability*, or *duration* of turneps, as a crop in husbandry.—The information gathered, on this head, is most contradictory. Yet had the nature of the land, its degree of freshness to the crop, and the rotation in which it had been cultivated, been stated, with sufficient accuracy, in each instance,—something valuable, it is possible, might have been made out.

The only *probable fact* which rises from among the croud of opinions adduced, is, that, formerly, turneps could be grown *without manure;* but that, now, manure is essential to a crop; unless on *fresh land.*—This, if substantial, is admissible, evidence, tho no proof, that land may be " tired of turneps." See p. 350, aforegoing.

P. 222. " The practice of manuring for the turnip crop is universal in Norfolk. Before the culture had been for a long period general, good crops were sometimes gained without, but for many years past none are to be procured except on *new land,* without much attention to this necessary branch of the management."

This, by the way, is the Reporter's own assertion; and, this, notwithstanding the following passage; which occurs in the same section.—P. 234. " From these notes it appears, that opinions vary, and I wish the reader to have the ideas of the farmers, rather than any general notion of my own, formed from those opinions—such might be erroneously given. I make it a rule to let the county speak for itself on every point."

The subjoined notice may serve to corroborate the foregoing extract.—P. 233. " Mr. England, of Binham, has no other idea of land being sick of turnips, than what results from the fact, that this crop was to be gained twenty years ago without dung, but not so at present."

For instances of growing turneps, with wheat, see p. 380, aforegoing.

CABBAGES.—P. 322. " Mr. Reeve, of Wighton, has every year a few acres, to use in frosty weather."

CULTIVATED HERBAGE.—This Reporter's section, " Clover," extends over ten or twelve pages; which are principally filled with opinions, assertions, and uncircumstantially reported practices, respecting that crop.—From the whole, and almost every part of the information, there drawn

drawn together, it is evident, that the lands of Norfolk (the *fresh* lands of course excepted, tho not a word on this circumstance appears) are " sick of clover:"—a fact, this, which the Reporter himself, toward the close of his section, proclaims in these words.—P. 266. " From the preceding notes it appears, that one of the greatest diffi-culties which have for some years been found in the Nor-folk husbandry, has been the failure of clover. I have often heard this, as a general fact, denied by men whose practice ought to have taught them better: in the com-mon management there can be no doubt of the fact."

Yet, incredible, as it may seem, the writer is still harp-ing, on his favourite string—" the four-shift husbandry;" and has actually formed his arrangement of the arable crops of the County, on that basis; treating of them in the succession of *turneps—barley—clover—wheat!*—and this notwithstanding he is conscious of its impracticability. —P. 265. " At Grimstone it is no wonder the land is sick of clover, for they are in the four-shift husbandry."!!!

It is painful to see a man persevering in conscious error:—For, in the section, " Clover," there is good evi-dence that, in the six-year husbandry, the clover crop, in 1804, still remained tolerably permanent:—much in the same state in which it was, in 1782:—a strong evi-dence of the superior excellence of that husbandry.—The two following extracts (the first being the Reporter's own) will warrant these remarks.

P. 259. " In Happing hundred I find the approach of a change in practice: they admit at Catfield, that if clover recurs too often the land will not yield it, but their method is not an alternate substitution of other seeds, or baulking the land for a round, but to take a six-course shift instead of a five, and mixing white clover and trefoil and ray, by which two precautions they suc-ceed well."

P. 260. " Mr. Margateson, of North Walsham, very rarely misses of clover in the six-shift husbandry; if it does fail the loss is great, for he thinks trefoil very un-certain for hay; when it does happen, the clover of the next course is sure to be good."

For my account of the six-year rotation of Norfolk, as it more particularly relates to the subject now under no-tice, see the RURAL ECONOMY of that County, under the heads *Succession* and *Cultivated Herbage.*

RAYGRASS.—Still we find the Secretary caviling at this most

most valuable of grasses*;—and, in revolutionary North Norfolk, we are given to understand, that it is condemned as an *exhauster!*—Is not wheat an exhauster? Are not potatoes exhausters? Is not every superiorly nutritious plant, that is cultivated and carried off the land, an exhauster?—The herbage of raygrass, while young, and its hay when cut at the proper age, are, beyond all *dispute*, singularly nutritious.

If a full crop of raygrass be suffered to stand for "hay," until it become *straw*, and shed its seeds in making—or to run up, in the spring, until it be unpalatable to pasturing stock,—it will exhaust, without an adequate return; as would wheat, or other grain crop, under similar mismanagement.—But, in the long established husbandry of Norfolk, the quantity of seed sown is so small, that the crop is scarsely seen, the first year;—being barely enough to assist the clover hay in drying; and, the second year, is never suffered to run up, and acquire a "benty" state.—Having, in early spring, while the blades, or root leaves, remain of a tender, sacharine quality,—forced the stock forward to a profitable market, the turf is plowed under; and the roots, while full of sap, together with the manure afforded by the spring feedage, are assimilated with the soil; as a matrix for wheat;—and the land, by a course of tillage, put into a profitable state, for succeeding crops.——Under this demonstratively wise plan of management, not a particle of soil can be *unprofitably exhausted.*

The subjoined extract may serve to corroborate the ideas that I have long been propagating.—P. 267. " Mr. M. Hill thinks that the common prejudice against raygrass arises from a mistaken practice; approves the use, but not the abuse of it. Whenever it is sown for feeding, he particularly recommends the bare feeding in the spring; if suffered to grow more than two inches long, it will imperceptibly rise and run to bent, and then only it is injurious."

ORCHARD GRASS—" Cocksfoot"—DACTYLIS *glomerata.* —P. 269. " Sir Mordaunt Martin, in 1788, observing, by an experiment, that this grass grew four inches in less than three days, determined to attend more particularly to it: he remarked, that when sheep were let out of a fold, they ran over every thing, to get at a baulk that was full

* See his *Lincolnshire*, p. 162, aforegoing.

full of it, and there ate it in preference to other grasses.
In some parts of Norfolk it is called cow's grass, from
their being very fond of it. He began to cultivate it in
1794. It grows at Midsummer, in a drought, when every
thing else is burnt up. He sows it with nonsuch, instead
of ray-grass, and finds it much more profitable.

" Mr. Overman, observing the eagerness with which
sheep, when let into a field at Burnham-market that had
some cocksfoot grass in it, ran over ray-grass, and every
thing else, to get a bite of this plant, thought it worth
cultivating, and sowed about an acre, on the dry gravelly
part of his farm, just above the marsh. This-spot was
the only one, in a large field, that did not burn in the severe drought of 1800, and convinced him of the excellence of the grass."

I have grown this valuable species of cultivated herbage, in rows, as lucerne; and have cut it three or four
times, in the course of the summer.

SAINFOIN.—An instance of *sowing it without corn* is
mentioned in this Report.—P. 340. " The Earl of Albe-
marle made an experiment which, though not in the
bounds of Norfolk, is in sight of it, and therefore I shall
mention it here: taking into his own hands an immense
farm of 4000 acres, with 3000 sheep, and wishing to provide all sorts of food as early as possible, he ventured to
sow a field, in extremely bad order, with sainfoin alone in
June: the foulness of the land such, that his Lordship's
hope was not sanguine. This was in 1801, and the crop
this year, 1802, was among the very finest he had ever
seen, at least two tons and a half per acre."

On *breaking up* sainfoin ley.—P. 340. " Mr. Overman,
of Burnham, has broken up sainfoin layers, and suffered
such losses by the red-worm, that he was fearful of sowing
corn upon the last field he ploughed. He therefore
ploughed it before winter, and summer-fallowed it for
turnips without manure. After these he sowed barley,
which crop I viewed, and found very fine; not having suffered the least attack. He remarked, that the ploughing
before winter probably contributed to the destruction of
the worm, as well as the summer tillage."

LUCERN.—Different instances are noticed, in this Report, of lucern being cultivated, with success, in the
broadcast, or random manner; and one of *raising it with
clover*, in that way.—P. 345. " Mr. Bevan sowed at Riddlesworth, in 1793, thirteen acres broad-cast, with barley;
seed ten pounds an acre, and also six pounds an acre of
red

red clover, on good sand, worth 12s. an acre. In 1794 he mowed half for soiling and half for hay; the latter two tons per acre; the lucerne was predominant, rising four or five inches above the clover.

" Mr. Bevan's is now nine years old, and is still very profitable, and had it not been attacked by the parasitical plant (?) which infests it, would have been now in full perfection. He has sown twelve acres more, which is now in the second year, and promises to be very productive."

Laying down arable lands, for perennial herbage.— P. 377. " Mr. Coke, at Holkham, has laid down various pieces with good success, and he is decidedly of opinion, that the best method is that of a fallow, till about the middle of August, and then sowing the seeds alone; keeping off all stock in the autumn, and sheep feeding for two or three years."

GRASS LANDS;—or established perennial Herbage.— I am concerned to find that many of the meadow lands of Norfolk, still remain in a neglected state; tho the work of improvement would seem to have been going on, of late years.—I perceive nothing new, however, or differing much from the plan I formerly recommended;—excepting the wonderful discovery of *sowing tares* on grass land —" wherever any earth was spread, or any other operation had laid bare the surface, harrowing in those seeds:" —" to draw up as well as protect the old plants"—p. 371: —Instead of sowing the seeds of grasses and other perennial herbage;—as is usually done, in such cases.

After expatiating with rapture, on this astonishing improvement, the Reporter adds, p. 372,—" if making known this single discovery had been the whole result of examining the county, the Board would not have failed in the object of ordering the district to be reported."

Some years ago, when farmers were so ignorant, as to believe that the grasses and other cultivated herbs could not be raised without a crop of grain,—" to draw them up and protect them,"—the expedient under notice might have been gravely spoken of, as a good thought. But, now,—since it has been discovered that the best method of *making* a meadow (and why not in *mending* one) is to sow the seeds, alone, in the manner described in the final extract of the last head (above)—would it be too severe to say, that such raptures border on the ridiculous?

CATTLE.—On the *breed* of cattle, in Norfolk, little information

formation is found, in this Report. The *native* breed of the country has been too long *established*, to merit especial notice, by a *fashionable* Reporter.—After speaking of the cattle of Scotland, that are annually purchased, he says, p. 445,—" Cattle in Norfolk of other sorts, do not offer much that is interesting : they have a breed of their own which possesses no qualities sufficient to make it an object of particular attention."

Nevertheless, in the *eastern* and *central* parts of the County, let us hope a remnant of them is saved,—by the " old-fashioned farmers " of those districts *.

In

* On the IMPROVEMENT of LIVESTOCK.—In travelling through Norfolk, in 1810, the SUFFOLK BREED (a hornless variety)—or a mongrel cross with that breed—appeared to be fast overrunning the County.—This change has doubtlessly been effected by the fashion and folly, which has of late years been prevalent of *crossing* and *changing* instead of *improving*, the ESTABLISHED BREEDS which centuries of experience have adapted to the soils and climatures of the DIFFERENT DISTRICTS of the KINGDOM.—In the Lynn quarter, the native breed of Norfolk, unpolluted by fashion, were the most observable.

For a description of that valuable breed, for the lands and climature of Norfolk, see my register of its Rural Economy.

I MUST, here, be permitted to remark, that, had the intimation there offered (p. 328) been adopted, by a man, or by men, of skill and capital,—namely, that of SELECTING INDIVIDUALS, from the best of the pure Norfolk breed, and IMPROVING the SELECTION, so as to adapt it, by enlarging the frame, to the improved state of the Norfolk husbandry,—a variety of cattle, might long ago have been produced, much resembling, in general appearance, the best of the North Devonshire breed, but somewhat smaller, and, of course, better adapted to the thin weak soils, and comparatively severe climature of Norfolk, than the *foreign* breeds that have been fetched into it, at great cost.

One great man had the good sense, ingenuity and perseverance, to improve the different breeds of livestock, which he found in his own district, from a low state of degeneracy, to the highest state of perfection, perhaps, their natures would allow.

But instead of this EXTRAORDINARY DISCOVERY being embraced as a fit example to be followed, by other men, in other districts, occupiers from every quarter of the kingdom—from every soil and climature—flew to Leicestershire for stock ! without considering that their own long established breeds were not only enured to their own situation, but were, perhaps, in most cases, superior, in natural or acquired properties, to the unprofitable sorts from which Mr. BAKEWELL raised his valuable breeds of stock.

In regard to CATTLE, however, the breeders on the banks of the Tees (between Durham and Yorkshire) having seen the advantages of Mr. Bakewell's plan of improvement in raising the " long-horned " breed

In *the north*, all appears to be still in a state of anarchy, —with respect to this species of livestock :—"longhorns" in disgrace ;—"Devons" the reigning favorites.—Therefore pass we on to the subject of

Fatting Cattle.—P. 365. "Mr. Marshall, who considers the practice of East Norfolk as alone deserving the title of *Norfolk* husbandry, mentions 40 or 50 bullocks, on turnips, as a matter of exultation. In 1768, I registered the fact, that Mr. Mallet, of Dunton, had 280 bullocks fatting on turnips, on a farm almost wholly arable."

How wonderful!—and, yet, the wonder would have ceased, if the reader had been told that Mr. Mallet's farm, in North Norfolk, was seven times the size of farms in East Norfolk ;—and that Mr. Mallet was merely pursuing the East Norfolk practice; by which he acquired an ample fortune.

The number of bullocks *now* to be seen (or were in 1804) on that magnificent farm, the Reporter does not mention. But the subjoined extracts will enable us to form some judgement of it.—Men who have not adopted any fixed plan to go by—no settled point to rally at—are very liable to swerve, and, perhaps, to wander from one side of the line of truth to the other.

P. 231

breed to a high state of excellence, set about the improvement of their own established breed—the "short-horned" variety. And, of later years, the breeders of Herefordshire, Sussex, and Devonshire have been making fainter efforts towards improving their established breeds—the "middlehorned" variety ; which, in a general view of the uses of cattle in this country, is far preferable to either of the former breeds.

But, most unfortunately, the cattle of Norfolk,—evidently a variety of the middlehorned breed, reduced in size, by soil, climature, and management, during the earlier stages of the Norfolk husbandry, and now only require to be raised to the standard of its present improvement,—are still suffered to remain in their deteriorated state:—the breeders of Norfolk, during the last thirty years, may be said to have been aiming at any sort but their own!

The Suffolk breed are doubtlessly better adapted to the present practice of Norfolk than any of the breeds above spoken of. But the degenerate sort now observable in the County is much inferior to what the native breeds might have been raised to, by twenty-four years of attention (without much expence) bestowed on their improvement. Still, no doubt, the breed may be saved from annihilation ; but the improvement, cannot, now, be made to spread so rapidly, as it might a quarter of a century ago, when the native breed was in possession of the country.

WHAT MISCHIEFS TO A COUNTRY MAY NOT BE EFFECTED, BY ILL FOUNDED FASHIONS, INCONSIDERATELY FOLLOWED.

P. 231 (section "Turneps"). "Mr. Dursgate is such a steady friend to feeding turnips on the land by sheep, that he would not have a bullock on his farm, except for the purpose of treading his straw into muck."

P. 364 ("Arable System"). "A great and a very important change has, however, taken place in the application of crops to sheep instead of bullocks and cows. Formerly the farmers *consumed* much of their straw by cattle: now the best *tread* it all into *dung*. (!)

"Sheep are the main grazing stock, and no more cattle kept than for *treading*, not eating straw, while feeding on oil-cake, &c."

Nevertheless, and notwithstanding what is here said, we are subsequently told, in general, and apparently considerate, terms, (p. 444, section "Cattle")—"The cattle predominant in Norfolk are Scotch, bought in every year from the drovers of North Britain. The quantity of these is very considerable indeed ; as there is scarcely a farmer of any consideration in the County, that does not turnip-feed a lot proportioned to the size of his farm."

Which of these "facts" is the reader to believe? Both of them are the Reporter's *own*.

The following curious and well reported fact (for such we *must* allow it to be) is too extraordinary to be passed, unnoticed.—P. 445. "I saw upon Mr. Money's farm at Rainsham, a Norfolk horned cow, which is *undoubtedly* 35 years old ; she has not had a calf for about ten years; she is old to the eye, but in good condition, and no marks of extreme age, except a stiffness in her motion, and a halting gait, as if her feet were sore."

SHEEP.—*Breed.*—The Secretary prefaces his section "Sheep," with a *caricature* of the NATIVE BREED of Norfolk.—He next copies Mr. Kent's account of them; and then mine. This done, he proceeds to string his collection of memoranda, heterogeniously, as they rose to hand ;—concerning the "breeds, crosses, and various circumstances "—relating to the different sorts that happened to be propagated in the County, at the times of making them :—introducing his list by the following remark.— P. 449. "I proceed to the minutes I have taken in the County at different periods; in all such cases (!) the opinion of strangers must fall before the *experiments* (?) of the natives : (!) *their* practice," (yes) " *their* opinion, are what County Reports should contain."

May it not here, be warrantably suggested, that a man, who had spent a length of years in practical pursuits, in different

different parts of the County, and had been in the habit, not only of *calling upon*, and *conversing* with professional men of the highest classes, but of *viewing*, and frequently no doubt *examining* their *farms*, at different seasons ;—or one, who had *constantly resided* some years, in the best cultivated part of the County; and had, during that time, not only *viewed* and *examined, through every season*, the practice of others, and constantly *registered* their several practices; but had, *himself, practised*, on an extended scale, every branch of the Rural Art, in that situation ;—was much more likely to understand the agriculture, and rural concerns of the County ;—than an occasional *visitor*, in one particular quarter of it,—" to *talk* about *farming ;*" or, at most, a *transient tourist*, calling upon professional practitioners, and *hastily putting down whatever might casually arise in conversation?*

Having already explained myself fully, concerning this mode of book-compiling, and having, also, given my sentiments relating to the sheep of Norfolk, in reviewing Mr. Kent's Report (before I opened the Secretary's) I have the less to perform, here.

The Southdown breed of sheep, however, being held out as one of the leading motives toward compiling the volume under review, and the author of it claiming the high consideration of having first introduced that breed into the EASTERN DEPARTMENT, it would be a want of common civility to pass over the two sheets of letterpress, of which his section, " Sheep," consists, without further notice.

The Secretary, it appears, first introduced this breed into Suffolk, in 1784, and, not long afterwards, was instrumental in gaining them a footing, in Norfolk.—But, here, the history of the " Southdowns "—otherwise "Downs"—in Norfolk, ends. For we have nothing resembling a regular, or comprehendible history of them, afterward. Whether, the present stock, in Norfolk, which, perhaps, principally assisted in giving birth to the volume, under review, sprang from the race of Houghton, or from that of Holkham, does, by no means, clearly appear.— Even the progress they have made (no matter from what point or points) toward the conquest of Norfolk, in 1804, is not explicitly declared.—From the chaotic, and frequently (for want of requisite *localities)* unintelligible, mass of matter before me,—they would seem to be confined, principally, or wholely, to North Norfolk ; which is certainly their most *natural* country.

The

The following is the only direct information, that I can find, respecting this particular.—P. 449. " The South Down breed is getting rapidly in possession of all the country from Swafham to Holkham; but from Brandon to Swafham many Norfolks remained : I observed, however, some mixture even in that district."

By this sketch, one is led to conceive, that, in 1804, they were in possession of only one line of country, even in North Norfolk*.—While, on the calcareous hills of Wiltshire and its environs (as I some time ago predicted) they may be said to have gained entire possession.—One may now travel fifty or a hundred miles across them, without seeing any other breed of sheep.—Yet the Secretary of the Board has led us down into Norfolk, to hear men talk about Southdown sheep, to which they may be deemed, or might have been, in 1804, little better than strangers ;—as pretty evidently appears, from the different and contradictory opinions that were then maintained, concerning them. They were then, it is plain, highly *fashionable*, but in nowise *established*, even in North Norfolk.—What a hoax !

Before I close this article, it will be proper to speak my own sentiments—make my own *assertions* and give my *opinion*,—respecting these mystic matters.

When I left Norfolk, in 1782, the *Norfolk* breed were in full and quiet possession of the country;—excepting a few inroads that had recently been made, by the *Leicestershire* breed.—As to the " *Southdowns !*"—they were, then, grazing, peaceably, on their native hills ; having never so much as dreamed of conquest!---I was not then aware of the existence of such a breed.---They might be said to have been, at that time, *unknown ;*---unless in the neighbourhood of their own recluse, and narrowly circumscribed hills.---The hills of Hampshire, Wiltshire, and Dorsetshire, were, then, inhabited by tall, whitefaced, horned sheep.

The first knowledge I gained of the Southdown breed was in 1791 ;---when I examined them on their own little territory ;---appreciated their merit,---as *arable upland folding*

---

* And in travelling, even the more northern part of this line,—namely between Houghton and Burnham (see note p. 353, aforegoing) I observed only two or three flocks (only two of size) and these were near its northernmost extremity.—On the demesne of Houghton a fine flock of *natives* were seen!

*folding sheep ;---*and have, ever since, been speaking highly of them, as such. But let me add, I never considered them as any thing *more than sheep!*

When I had finished my examinations and practice, in Norfolk, I was convinced, from the rigid attention I had paid to the subject, that no other breed of sheep, *then publicly known to exist*, were better suited to its lands, than its own long established breed.---And I have, now, full conviction on my mind, that, had the same exertions,---the same talking, the same bragging, the same puffing, the same showing, and one half, or a much smaller proportion, of the expence which has been bestowed, on " Southdowns" and " Leicesters,"---had been judiciously laid out, in IMPROVING the NATIVE BREED---the established flocks whose ancestry had long been naturalized to the soil and climature of the country,---each district adapting them to its own soil and situation,---the County at large would have been infinitely more benefitted, than it has hitherto been, by the devious line of conduct that has been pursued; and which has, of course,---by throwing the native breed into the background, and slandering them while there,---tended to prevent the improvement, which, otherwise, almost necessarily would, in these improving times, in regard to the different breeds of livestock, have taken place.

It would be laughable, were it a laughing matter, to hear *comparisons* gravely commented upon, and inferences exultingly drawn, from comparisons made, between the individuals of a breed, on whose improvement thousands ---tens of thousands probably---have been expended (not in Norfolk altogether) and those of another---perhaps the very worst of another---which has long lain in a state of neglect!

I leave it to the good sense of the professional occupiers of Norfolk, to make their election; and, I doubt not, they will, when the present ferment shall subside, choose the breed that will be most profitable to themselves and the community.—What has principally induced me to say thus much, on the subject, has been a desire to relieve the native breed from the false impression which the public may have received, from the *unfairplay* they appear, to me, to have had, in the volume under review.

SWINE.—On the *rearing* of pigs, the following incident may have its use.—P. 479. " Mr. Wiseman, at Happsborough,

borough, having occasion to wean some pigs much too young, from the death of a sow, or some other cause, tried boiled pease for them "—with success.

On *fatting* Hogs.—The two subjoined *opposite* methods, are worth preserving.—P. 478. " I found Mr. Salter, of Winborough, fatting 180 pigs in August, by throwing down pease in a well littered yard, and says the pigs lose none at all : they have the run of a meadow, and he is clear, from long observation, that they fatten much better and quicker than if confined."

P. 479. "I found a new piggery building by Mr. Havers, at Thelton, in which the most singular circumstance is the sties for fatting, being single, for one hog, and so narrow that he cannot turn himself."

For an instance of sows peeling off the bark of growing larches, to anoint themselves with their sap,—see p. 365, aforegoing.---Quere, can that incident afford any useful information, or hint, to the hog doctor?

EXPENCE of FARMING.—In a section, entitled "Comparison of Times," is the following notice.—P. 504. "The Board of Agriculture having, in consequence of a requisition from the Corn Committee of the House of Commons (1804), procured returns from the several counties, of the expenses on arable land in 1790 and 1803, I am permitted to insert here the result of their inquiries for the county of Norfolk, which will be found in the following tables."

A few extracts have been made, aforegoing, from those tables. In p. 520, we find the subjoined explanation of them.—"The reader will perceive, on consulting the preceding table of the expense of cultivation, that the object is incompletely ascertained. Some correspondents returned only the amount of labour; others excluded rent and rates; others omitted seed, &c. The returns from some other Counties were still more deficient. To remedy the omissions, the Board ordered a second letter to be written, requesting an answer to the following question : *What are the charges upon* 100 *acres of arable land, under the following distinct heads."*

In p. 526, this business is further explained.---" In remarking on the preceding particulars, I am, in the first place, to note, that the Board is not in the least committed in drawing any of these averages. That Body simply ordered circular letters to be written; and every reply stands distinctly on the personal authority of the writer.

There

There ends the authority of the papers as I received
them. The calculations, to draw them into one view,
I have made, for the satisfaction of such readers as
might wish to know what such a general result would
be."
The Paper thus concludes.---P. 527. "Now, if the
rise upon these be estimated from the first series of letters,
viz. Rent 35, Tithe 58, Rents 30, Wear and Tear 42,
Labour 47, Manure 76, and taking the advance in the
articles, Seed, Team, and Interest, from the answers to
the second letter (not having place in the first), the result
would stand thus :

	1790.			Rise per cent.	1803.		
	£.	s.	d.		£.	s.	d.
Rent - -	80	0	0	35	108	0	0
Tithe - -	15	19	6	58	25	0	0
Rates -	17	13	5¼	30	22	10	0
Wear and tear -	18	0	0	42	25	0	0
Labour - -	94	18	10	47	138	0	0
Seed - -	30	6	0	11	33	13	0
Manure -	10	16	0	76	19	0	0
Team -	46	10	0	18	54	16	8
Interest of capital	34	0	0	16	39	13	4
Total	341	11	3¼		465	13	0

Which is a rise of $36\frac{12}{34}$ per cent.
"And this I take to be as near the truth as these data
will permit an estimate to arrive."
I have the more readily noticed those statements, tho
inconclusive (and not quite correct), as they form the first
specimen I have had a favorable opportunity of laying before my readers, concerning the labors of the Board.

RETROSPECTIVE OBSERVATIONS.

ON a careful and even *critical* examination, of the
foregoing decisions, on the Work still before me, I have
not been able to detect a single passage, which,—with
strict justice to the principles invariably adhered to, in
the prosecution of my present undertaking,---namely,
those of drawing forth useful truths, and exposing dangerous errors, wheresoever they are found,—I can subject
to

to further alteration ; desirous as I am *(for various reasons)* of giving as little offence to its author, as the extraordinary circumstances of the case will permit.—To allow what appears to me enormous improprieties, in any of the Board's Reporters, would, in my own mind, be highly criminal ; and doubly so, when they are found in the Reports of the Board's principal Secretary ;—whose situation, as such, must naturally impress many readers with an idea of superior acquirements, and a maturity of knowledge and judgement of every subject he may bring forward, concerning "Agricultural and internal Improvement."

SUFFOLK

SUFFOLK.

MY personal knowledge of this County is not sufficient to entitle me to undertake the arduous task of analyzing its component parts, and separating them with the required accuracy, into NATURAL DISTRICTS.

This, however, I regret the less, as its REPORTER has long been a *resident* owner and occupier within it; and can scarsely fail of being well acquainted with its *natural*, as well as with its *rural*, ECONOMY.

While I was resident, in Norfolk, I passed repeatedly through Suffolk, in my way to and from the metropolis ;— crossing it by three different lines :—namely, by Newmarket,—by Bury St. Edmunds,—and by Ipswich. The eastern side of the County may therefore be said to be the only part I had not *seen*.

In my late journey, through this Department, the more particular objects of my attention, in SUFFOLK were—the *hemp*, the *dairy*, and the *carrot* districts. I therefore shaped my route, from the southern border of Norfolk, by Eye and Debenham, to Woodbridge; and, there, crossed the estuary of the Devon, into the carrot quarter;— pursuing my route from Woodbridge, by Ipswich and Stratford, toward Colchester.

The Board, I believe, has received only one Report from Suffolk.

" GENERAL

GENERAL VIEW

OF THE

AGRICULTURE

OF THE

COUNTY OF SUFFOLK;

DRAWN UP FOR THE CONSIDERATION OF THE

BOARD OF AGRICULTURE AND INTERNAL IMPROVEMENT.

BY

THE SECRETARY TO THE BOARD.

1797."

IN this Report, we find the SECRETARY of the BOARD writing, in a character widely differing from that under which he
appears, in his Reports of Lincolnshire and Norfolk. He is,
in the present instance, writing, principally, from his own
knowledge of the Country whose rural concerns he is reporting;—and is rarely employed in piling up the unsupported assertions of those with whom he happened to
converse.

The Secretary being, in this case, the "original Reporter,' and also the Editor (I take for granted) of the
"reprinted Report," we find several ANNOTATIONS appending, at the feet of pages, to the passages on which they were
made (it would seem) by different hands, on the margins
of the primary Report.—A few of those notes are apt cor-
rections of the text. But, viewed collectively, they are
not of great consideration.

In arrangement and manner, this resembles the Norfolk
Report; but, in propriety of matter, far exceeds it.—We
meet with *few* stumbling blocks, and *fewer* dangerous
errors that require to be exposed and corrected.—The
work of criticism will therefore be rendered easy, and that
of abstraction, pleasurable.—There are, I find, some sentiments,

timents, that do not coincide with my own; but they are *seldome* (I regret that I cannot say *never)* of such a nature as can give rise to unpleasant sensations in the mind, either of the Reviewer, or the Reviewed.

The quantity of matter, in this instance, is comparatively small.

The number of pages 314.

A map of soil, and two other engravings.

SUBJECT THE FIRST.

NATURAL ECONOMY.

EXTENT.—After mentioning Hodskinson's Map and Templeman's Survey, the Reporter says (p. 1.) Suffolk "may be computed at about 800,000 acres:"—Or 1250 square miles.

CLIMATURE.—P. 2. "It is unquestionably one of the dryest climates in the kingdom: with which circumstance two others unite: the frosts are severe, and the N. E. winds, in the spring, sharp and prevalent. In these northern latitudes, and insular situations, the most humid countries are the most free from frost and snow, till you arrive on the western coasts of Ireland, where the rains are incessant, and frost unknown. Severe winters and dry springs have a strong influence on agriculture: the former render turnips a precarious dependence, and the latter lengthen the winter, to the great expence of the keepers of live-stock. On the whole, however, the climate of this county must be reckoned favourable."

WATERS.—P. 6. "Suffolk may be esteemed a well watered country: its boundaries to north and south are rivers partly navigable; and it is every where intersected by streams."

SOILS and SUBSOILS.—A " Map of the Soil of Suffolk" is prefixed to this Report.—It appears to have been sketched with a degree of consideration.

At the northwestern extremity of the County, a plot of *fen land* appears; being a portion of the Cambridgeshire fens; and has been already noticed.

Adjoining to this is a tract of *light sandy heathlands ;*— similar, it would seem, to those of West Norfolk.

Along

Along the seacoast lies a border of *sandy loam* of a better quality than the foregoing :—the southern end of it comprising the celebrated *carrot lands* of Suffolk. And,

On the southern verge of the map, bordering on Essex, appears a plot of "*rich loam.*"

The remainder of the County,—the more central, and by far the largest part of it,—is denominated "*strong loam.*"

Something of the *specific qualities* of those soils may be caught in the subjoined extracts.

P. 2. "There is not, perhaps, a county in the kingdom which contains a greater diversity of soil, or more clearly discriminated.

"A *strong loam*, on a clay-marl bottom, predominates through the greatest part of the county, as may be seen by the map annexed; extending from the south-western extremity of Wratting Park, to North Cove, near Beccles. Its northern boundary stretches from Dalham, by Barrow, Little Saxham, near Bury, Rougham, Pakenham, Ixworth, Honington, Knattishal, and then in a line, near the river which parts Norfolk and Suffolk, to Beccles and North Cove; but every where leaving a slope and vale of rich friable loam adjoining the river, of various breadths. It then turns southward by Wrentham, Wangford, Blithford, Holton, Bramfield, Yoxford, Saxmundham, Campsey Ash, Woodbridge, Culpho, Bramford, Hadleigh; and following the highlands on the west side of the Bret, to the Stour, is bounded by the latter river, with every where a very rich tract of slope and vale from thence to its source. Such is the strong land district of Suffolk taken in the mass; but it is not to be supposed that it takes in so large an extent without any variation : a rule, to which I know few exceptions, is, that wherever there are rivers in it, the slopes hanging to the vales through which they run, and the bottoms themselves, are of a superior quality, in general composed of rich friable loams: and this holds even with many very inconsiderable streams which fall into the larger rivers. The chief part of this district would in common conversation be called clay, but improperly. I have analyzed many of these strong loams, and found them abounding with more sand than their texture would seem to imply ; so that were they situated upon a gravel, sand, or chalk, they would be called *sandy loams ;* but being on a retentive clay-marl bottom, are properly, from their wetness, to be termed *strong*, or *clayey loam.*"

This cannot be accurate. "Wetness" may be the cause

cause of *cold,* but surely not of *strong* or *clayey* land.— Wetness does not alter the specific quality, the component parts, or materials, of a soil.

Concerning " the district of *rich loams,*" nothing satisfactory is said.

Of "the *sandy maratime district,*" we have the following remarks.—P. 4. "Of that district I must observe, that my arrangement will startle many persons, who speak of *clay* in a loose and indefinite manner. I was told of large tracts of clay near Pakefield and Dunwich*, and particularly on the farm of Westwood Lodge; but when I examined them I could not find a single acre: I found rich loamy firm sand worth 20s. an acre, but nothing that deserved even the epithet *strong.* I was assured that there was little or no sand in Colness hundred, where I saw hundreds of acres of buck-wheat stubbles. All these expressions result from the common ideas of soils being not sufficiently discriminated. Land of 15s. or 20s. an acre, in the eastern parts of the county, is never called sand, though deserving the epithet as much as inferior ones. The error has partly arisen from the title of *sandling* being given peculiarly to the country south of the line of Woodbridge and Orford, where a large extent of poor, and even blowing sands is found; but speaking with an attention to the real quality of the soil, and not at all regarding the rent, the whole of the maritime district may be termed sandy; towards the north, much inclining, in various parts, to loamy sands, and in others to sandy loams; but so broken, divided, and mixed with undoubted sands, that one term must be applied in a general view to the whole."— P. 5. "The under stratum of this district varies considerably, but in general it may be considered as sand, chalk, or *crag;* in some parts marl and loam."

P. 5. "*The western district of sand* is a much poorer country, containing few spots of such rich sands as are found on the coast, but abounding largely with warrens and poor sheep walks: a great deal under the plough *blows,* and consequently ranks among the worst of all soils, black sand on a yellow bottom perhaps excepted. Parts of the district take, however, the character of loamy sand; the

---

" * There is not an entire acre of clay near Pakefield or Dunwich; but almost all the corn lands thereabouts have been made by opening pits, and laying from 60 to 120 loads of clay per acre. That is what in Suffolk is called *clay,* though more properly marl."

the whole angle, for instance, to the right of the line from Barrow to Honington, in which no blowing, or even very light sand is found. A more striking exception, though of small extent, is found at Mildenhall, where there is an open field of arable land of capital value, dry yet highly fertile, and friable without being loose; its products almost perpetual, and its fruitfulness almost un-varied. The under stratum, through almost all the dis-trict, is a more or less perfect chalk, at various depths, but I believe uninterrupted; and it may be received as a rule, that the whole of it, low vales on rivers only excepted, is proper for sain-foin."—How comparatively profitable, then, must be its culture on such superficially infertile lands.

For further remarks on the specific qualities of the soils of Suffolk, see the head, *Rent*, ensuing.

MINERALS.—P. 6. "There are no mines in the county; nor other fossils connected with agriculture, except such as are necessarily mentioned under the titles of *soil* and manure."

SUBJECT THE SECOND.

POLITICAL ECONOMY.

APPROPRIATION.—P. 30. " Suffolk must be reckoned amongst the earliest inclosed of the English counties, but there are very large tracts yet open, that want the benefit of this first and greatest of all improvements. Some modern inclosures have been made by act of parliament, but the spirit is not active; the examples have not been well followed, though the success has been as great."

P. 147. " I have calculated from much information, of different kinds; and from comparing and combining vari-ous data, conclude that there are in Suffolk *wastes* to the amount of nearly, perhaps quite 100,000 acres, or $\frac{1}{8}$th part of the whole; comprehended under the terms *sheep-walk*, common, *warren*, &c."

POPULATION.—On this subject, the Secretary has be-stowed particular attention. He wrote to "all the rectors and vicars of the County, requesting the *births* and *burials*, from their registers, for the last twenty years;" and there-from formed a table; which must necessarily have given him much trouble.—But, since the late census was taken,

of

of the population of the kingdom, in general, local registers have become of less value.

In the "Appendix," p. 297, we find the following particulars;—which I insert, here, as a caution to political
arithmeticians; and as a specimen of the *negligent* manner in which the *home* department of government has long
been administered.—" The parish of Barnham, near Euston, contains 5302 acres, viz.

In 1764. Infield arable, inclosed,   -   -   381
          Outfield arable,   -   -   -   -   2626
          Meadow and pasture,   -   -   -   559
          Heath, or sheep-walk,   -   -   1735
                                          _____

                Total,   -   -   -   -   5302

And consists of four farms. The whole belongs to his
Grace the Duke of Grafton, to whom I am obliged for
these particulars. There are 3300 sheep in it, 60 cows,
and 43 horses.

Land-tax,   -   -   -   -   -   -   101 *l*. 2*s*.
Poor-rates in 1764,   -   -   -   -   -   -   £. 53
            1765,   -   -   -   -   -   -   41
            1767,   -   -   -   -   -   -   45
            1787,   -   -   -   -   -   -   131

Windows in the assessment,   -   -   -   -   94
Houses appearing on the duplicates,   -   -   9

But this number being very small, for a village which I
recollected had quite another appearance, I counted, and
found them to be forty-six.

" Hence, whatever examination a political arithmetician
could make at the Tax-office, to discover the population
of this parish, would give him not more than the number
of forty-five souls, at five to a house; but the fact is, there
are at that ratio 230, or nine" (five) " times as many."

PROVISIONS.—P. 203. "Throughout the county, the
average of mutton, beef, and veal, to take no *weighing*
meat, (?) on contract for the whole year, may be stated at
5d. per pound. But mutton usually a halfpenny per
pound dearer than beef; and the coarse joints of the
latter, bought *in the afternoon*, may be had in general by
poor housekeepers, at 2d. or 2½d. the pound. Pork 5½d.
Butter, salt 8¼d. 9d. and 9¼d.; fresh 10d.* and to 1s. at
                                                      scarce

" * At Hoxne, fresh butter is always sold by the pint (a pound and
a quarter), and during many weeks of this winter, it hath been sold at
one shilling per pint: a very rare circumstance indeed.—*Note by a
Correspondent of the Board.*"

scarce seasons, Cheese 5d., but Suffolk 3½d. and 4d. The price of all these is risen considerably in twenty years. Bread 1¼d. and not risen."

FUEL.—P. 204. "The fuel of the poor, is in general wood ; but for the last twenty years, coals have been gradually introducing in some cottages ; and in parts of the county joining to heaths, fens and commons, they burn, as in other countries, heath and peat."

MANUFACTURES.—P. 209. "The principal fabric of the county, is the spinning and combing of wool, which is spread throughout the greatest part of it ; except in the hemp district, where hemp is spun and wrought into linen.

"At Sudbury, they have a manufacture of *says.*" (?)

HERRING FISHERY.—P. 208. "At Lowestoff, the principal support of the place is the herring-fishery, in which they have 40 boats, each of 40 ton, which they build themselves, at the expence of about 6 *l.* to 7 *l.* a ton : to each boat there are two fleets of nets, the price of which are 300 *l.* Each boat requires eleven men. They catch from 10 to 40 last of herrings per boat ; average 20 ; and the mean price 12 *l.* a last, rising from 6 *l.* to 20 *l.* A last requires 5 cwt. of salt. The men are paid wages, except the master, mate, and one other ; these by the last. To four herring-smacks, there are two boats employed in landing the herrings ; they are carried immediately to the salting-house, washed in fresh water, spitted. and hung up in drying lofts ; fires are made under them ; the fuel, oak, elm, or ash-billet, cut out of the arms of timber-trees ; other wood not so good ; when dried, they are packed up in barrels and shipped for the Mediterranean. The nets and casks are all made in town.—The boats are laid up all the year, except from September 22 to November 22, which is the season. If built larger than 40 ton, they are not so well for the fishery."

POOR.—On the recent *rise* of the poor rates are inserted, in this Report, lengthened remarks, by "the Rev. Mr. BUTTS"

After showing the valuable influence of an attentive magistrate, residing in or near a parish ; and after strongly recommending "the incorporation of hundreds," or subdivisions of counties ;—Mr. Butts thus concludes his remarks.—P. 22. "It may be said, that if magistrates attended properly to their duty, such incorporations would be needless, as every abuse of the poor laws might be immediately remedied on an application to them. No doubt.

doubt, were a sufficient number of active and intelligent
men appointed by the Lord Lieutenants in every county,
to fill the most important and useful office in which it is
possible that any member of the community can be employed, much might be done towards correcting the growing abuses; but where the residence of a justice is at the
distance of six or seven miles from the existing grievance,
there is but little chance of its being removed : ignorance,
and want of leisure, in the small occupier and pauper,
secure the overseer from any interruption in his inattention
to those laws which were enacted for the benefit of society;
but which, I am confident, without the intervention of the
magistrate, become, in many instances, oppressive.

" The following extract from the rate-book of an adjacent parish, will render every thing that can be further
said on the subject, to prove that the evils complained of
arise from the causes I have mentioned, entirely needless.

						£.	s.	d.
Easter	1770	to	Easter	1771	- -	1091	17	5
Ditto	1771	dittc	1772		- -	1320	5	7
Ditto	1772	ditto	1773		- -	1886	1	3
Ditto	1773	ditto	1774		- -	1276	1	8
Ditto	1774	ditto	1775*		- -	848	2	3
Ditto	1775	ditto	1776*		- -	817	9	10
Ditto	1776	ditto	1777*		- -	966	7	9
Ditto	1777	ditto	1778		- -	1113	6	11
Ditto	1778	ditto	1779		- -	1151	17	3
Ditto	1779	ditto	1780		- -	1202	19	5
Ditto	1780	ditto	1781		- -	1146	10	11."

And, in the section, " Poor," the Reporter says, p. 212,
" the most singular circumstance relating to this subject,
in the County of Suffolk, is the incorporation of various
hundreds, for erecting and supporting *houses of industry*."
—He continues,—" Thomas Ruggles, Esq. a friend of
mine, having examined these, with great attention, is so
kind as to communicate the result of his inquiries in the
following memoir, which I insert, as the most satisfactory
mode of introducing them in this Report."

This memoir occupies fifty pages (no inconsiderable
part of the volume!) many of which are filled with unimportant details (but not all of them equally uninteresting);
without any recapitulation, or general statement, of the
scattered

" * During these three years, a committee of gentlemen attended
to the parish business."

scattered items; or any conclusions drawn, that can
serve as guides to other establishments of a similar nature,
—saving what may be caught in the extract, below ;—
which I insert in this Register; altho,—from the observations that I have incidentally made, in different parts of
the kingdom,—1 am by no means convinced of the fitness,
either in a moral, or a political light, of such establishments. Mr. Ruggles' flattering description of the " hundred houses of Suffolk" is too exquisitely drawn to be
wholely overlooked.

P. 228. " In the incorporated hundreds, the houses of
industry strike one in a different light from the cottages of
the poor; they are all of them built in as dry, healthy, and
pleasant situations, as the vicinity affords ; the offices,
such as the kitchen, brewhouse, bakehouse, buttery, laun-
dry, larder, cellars, are all large, convenient, and kept
exceeding neat; the work rooms are large, well aired ;
and the sexes are kept apart, both in hours of work and
recreation.

" The dormitories are also large, airy, and conveniently
disposed; separate rooms for children of each sex, adults
and aged: the married have each a separate apartment to
themselves; mothers with nurse children are also by
themselves.

" The infirmaries are large, convenient, airy, and comfortable ; none without fire places.

" All the houses have a proper room for the necessary
dispensary, and most of them a surgeon's room besides.

" The halls, in all, are large, convenient, well ventilated, with two, or more fire places in them, and calculated,
with respect to room, for the reception of full as many as
the other conveniences of the house can contain.

" The chapels are all sufficiently large, neat and plain.
Several of them rather tending to grandeur and elegance;
there were two houses which had no chapel ; one of them
made use of a room ample enough for the congregation,
properly fitted up, and kept very neat; the other house
attended the parish church.

" The apartments for the governor were in all the houses
large, and conveniently disposed ; in one or two of the
houses of industry, these apartments were rather more
spacious and elegant than necessary ; there are also convenient storehouses and warehouses, for keeping the manufacture of the house; the raw materials and the clo-
thing, &c. for the use of the inhabitants.

" The land about the houses belonging to them, particularly

larly the gardens, are all calculated for producing a sufficient quantity of vegetable diet; so necessary to the health, as well as agreeable to the palate of the inhabitants.

" In general, the appearance of all the houses of industry, in the approach to them, somewhat resembles what we may suppose of the hospitable large mansions, of our ancestors, in those times when the gentry of the country spent their rents among their neighbours.

" The interior of these houses must occasion a most agreeable surprise to all those who have not before seen poverty, but in its miserable cottage, or more miserable workhouse.

" In looking over my notes, I find that the affirmative neatness which prevailed from the cellar to the garret, in all the houses, with very few exceptions in particular departments, occasioned not only a memorandum of the fact, but gave rise to a conception, which possibly lies more in imagination than reality; that where a deficiency in this respect is observable in any domicile, a concomitant deficiency is also observable in the healthy looks of the inhabitants.

" This neatness, which had so pleasing an effect on the eye, was the cause also, that the other senses were not disgusted by that constant attendant on collected filth and foul air, a noisome stench; as deleterious to human life, as it is in general nauseating to those who accidentally breathe such an atmosphere.

" The practice of frequently white-washing, does much in preserving the air of these houses wholesome and sweet; but the constant attention of those who perform the offices of the house, is absolutely necessary; and even that is insufficient, unless the halls, working rooms and dormitories, have the external air admitted through the windows, whenever it can be done with safety to the inhabitants, with respect to catching cold. This practice of keeping the windows open cannot be trusted to the paupers themselves; for, strange to tell! the general complaint against them was, that they would, not only, not attend to keeping them open, but if the adults and aged had their choice, such depravity arises from habit, that they would live in that atmosphere of putrid air, which would undoubtedly produce contagion.

" The neatness and *proprieté* which prevailed in their halls at the hour of refection, were also laudably observable; most of these houses of industry being visited at the hours of breakfast, dinner, or supper. At times I have felt disgust,

disgust, when requested to take some refreshment which has been offered to me in a cottage; a disgust arising from the absence of that neatness which attends the tables of those among whom it has been my lot to live; but no want of neatness in those houses created disgust: a breakfast, dinner, or supper, might have been ate at their tables with a keen appetite.

" Their bread was, in all the houses, particularly pleasant; it was good brown bread, made from the flour deprived of the coarsest of its bran : white bread was also baked, for the infirm, the convalescent, and young children.

" Their cheese was in general good, although frequently the cheese of the country. In one house they bought Dutch cheese, which was stronger in its taste, and consequently to some palates not so pleasant. The small beer was also pleasant; no wonder, they bought the best malt and hops, brewed a large quantity at a time, and kept it in excellent cellars. Ale was also brewed in inferior quantities, and given to the convalescent, and to those whom the governor thought proper, either as a necessary refreshment, or as a reward ; and it was also distributed at stated times to the whole house.

" It did not occur to me to take minutes of the bill of diet in any of the houses, because no doubt has been suggested that it is not wholesome and sufficient. That, in some instances, it has been too abundant, may be suspected, as well from the relicts which were seen after their meals, as from the idea thrown out by one of the directors."

Mr. R. then proceeds to answer the following questions.

" 1. Have these institutions amended the morals of the poor ?

" 2. Have they tended to diminish the burthen of expence to society attending their relief and maintenance.

" 3. Have they increased, or do they tend to decrease, the chance of human life ?"

But, in twenty or thirty pages of discussion, I perceive nothing to induce me to alter my opinion, respecting those establishments.

Such aggregations of the most ignorant, and, of course, the most dissolute, part of society, bear, in my idea of them, too near a resemblance to *other* houses of manufacture, to be radically serviceable, either to the morals, or the health, of their inmates,—even under the wisest regulations,

regulations, and the strictest attention.—And, without these, an establishment of that sort, might, without great impropriety, be classed with the *cotton mill ;*—that sink of health and morality, which none, but a nation, maddened with inordinate commerce, could have suffered to exist.

PROVIDENT SOCIETIES.—P. 262. " Box Clubs. This admirable institution," says the Reporter, " has flourished considerably in Suffolk, as may be seen by the following list of them in the office of the clerk of the peace for the County."—P. 265. " Number of clubs 219—7709 members ; average of members, 35 in each club."

In each of those societies, the number of members, admissible, is fixed.—The highest number is sixty-one ;—the lowest thirty-one.

TITHES.—P. 17. " There is as great a variety in the circumstances attending the receipt of tythes in Suffolk, as in most other districts of the kingdom. They are gathered in kind by some ; and the compositions admitted by others vary in proportion to the liberality, and situation in life, of the possessors. In the mass they must certainly be considered as favourable to the occupier, and to do credit to the moderation and feelings of the gentlemen, who, having the power to require what would be a very heavy payment from the farmer, content themselves with compositions under the real value.

" These are, in some parishes by the acre, and in others by the pound of rent. They vary too much to allow of general description, consistent with accuracy.

" Mr. Nesfield, of Wickhambrook, informs me, that for 75 years they have been there invariably 3s. an acre for corn, when a fore crop ; 2s. the after crops ; and 11d. an acre for hay."

INLAND NAVIGATION.—P. 205. " For the following account of the new navigation from Stowmarket to Ipswich, I am indebted to the Rev. Henry Hill, of Buxhall."

The account is not sufficiently satisfactory, to be inserted, here, at length.—The subjoined extract (from the same page) may serve as a caution to trustees, in undertakings of a similar nature.—" The expence of making was greatly enhanced by the trustees being forced into a law-suit with the first contractors who had began the work, sometime before they were dismissed ; and as their work was began at the lower end, at different places, and could not be settled for till after the law-suit was concluded, the trustees were obliged to begin their works at the upper end, consequently the carriage of many of the heaviest
materials,

materials, which would have been brought by water-carriage (had the works been finished below first), were brought by land." !

P. 207. " *Effect.*—Reducing the price of land-carriage more than one half, and a reduction (of *carriage only*) of four shillings per chaldron on coals, and consequently raising the rent of land considerably.

" *Tonnage.*—The charge, one penny per ton per mile, from Stow to Ipswich; and from Ipswich to Stowmarket, one halfpenny per ton per mile."

ROADS.—P. 205. " These are uncommonly good in every part of the County; so that a traveller is nearly able to move in a post-chaise by a map, almost sure of finding excellent gravel roads; many cross ones in most directions equal to turnpikes. The improvements in this respect, in the last twenty years, are almost inconceivable."

MARKETS.—*Weights* and *Measures.*—P. 293. "Under this head, there is nothing peculiar in the County. The Winchester bushel is universally used."

Surplus Produce.—N. P. 184. " The quantity of butter supposed to be sent from Suffolk to London, annually, is about 40,000 firkins."

Toward the close of the volume, under consideration, appears a section, entitled " Statistical Division of the Produce of Land in Suffolk."—It is thus prefaced.

P. 266. " I have often reflected on the most simple method of bringing into the shortest compass possible, a view of the gross produce of the soil, diffusing itself through the variety of classes most nearly concerned in the culture, receipt, and consumption, of the earth's products. What may be called, without impropriety, political agriculture, depends altogether on this division being clearly understood. Volumes have been written diffusely upon the subject, and have perhaps failed in utility in proportion to their bulk; but if tables, on a plain and simple plan, could be constructed, which would present the leading facts in a clear view, the road to this branch of knowledge, so unquestionably important, would be greatly shortened. Inquiries, however, of this nature, must be long pursued, and by many persons, before any thing near perfection is to be attained. I present the following sketch to the Board, as an attempt which may in time be ameliorated, in more able hands, into a general view of the kingdom, which shall contain, in a very small space, abundance of useful information."

Altho

Altho I perceive not,—either in the *plan* or the *execution* of the six statements displayed in that sketch, any thing which, in itself, merits transcription,—I will here insert one of them (the first); with the intent to induce some one of sufficient leisure, compass of mind, depth of penetration, and soundness of judgement,—to form a more judicious plan, and to execute it more scrupulously, than that which is now before me appears to have been. For, without scrupulous accuracy, every statement on the subject must necessarily prove injurious, not useful, to the public.

Nothing, it might be said, can be more selfevident than —*that* plan of management which furnishes the community with the largest *permanent* supply of human necessaries, from a given portion of territory, is the most profitable to a nation.—But how are we to draw any thing bordering on accurate knowledge, relating to this subject, from the arrangement of figures exhibited in the subjoined extract?

P. 267.—" SUFFOLK RICH LOAM.

STATISTICAL DIVISION OF THE PRODUCE OF AN ACRE OF WELL-MANAGED ARABLE LAND.

Rent, 15s.
Farmer's capital, 5*l.* per acre.
Course of crops :

    1. Turnips,
    2. Barley,
    3. Clover,
    4. Wheat.

GROSS PRODUCE.

	£.	s.	d.
1. Turnips, keeping 6¼ sheep 26 weeks, at 3d.	2	0	0
2. Barley, 4 qrs. at 21s.*	4	4	0
3. Clover, 7 sheep 26 weeks, at 3d.	2	5	6
4. Wheat, 3 qrs. 42s.	6	6	0
Divide by 4 years,	14	15	6
Per annum,	3	13	10

THE

" * For the price of wheat and barley in Suffolk, see Annals of Agriculture, vol. xv. p. 33."

The landlord	-	-	£0 12 0	net rent,
The state,	-	-	0 2 6	land-tax,
Artizans,	-	-	0 0 6	repairs,

		0 15 0	gross rent,
Industrious poor,	-	1 1 0	labour,
Indigent poor,	-	0 3 6	poor-rates,
Artizans, and sundries,	-	0 0 6	other rates,
Artizans,	-	0 2 0	wear and tear,
The church,	-	0 4 0	tythe,
The farm,	-	0 7 0	seed,
Ditto,	-	0 10 0	$\left\{\begin{array}{l}\text{team of 4 horses,}\\ \text{at 12 l. 10s.}\\ \text{per 100 acres.}\end{array}\right.$
The farmer,	-	0 10 10	

£3 13 10

Produce,	-	-	-	-	£ 3 13 10

Seed,	-	-	-	£0 7 0
Team,	-	-	-	0 10 0
Half wear and tear,	-	-	0 1 0
Five-sixths of labour,	-	-	0 17 6
Three-fourths of poor-rates,	-	0 2 6

1 18 0

For market,	-	-	-	-	£ 1 15 10

" In order to form such a table as this, it is necessary to simplify the business, more than it admits in every case, in fact. The clover is supposed to be the food of sheep alone; but in common practice, the horses, hogs, cows, and, in general, all the stock of a farm consume it; but for the great objects of such an inquiry, to substitute sheep does not affect the principles of the calculation.

" To discover what portion of the produce comes free to market, is always an inquiry of considerable importance; for if the subject was thoroughly analyzed, it would probably be found, that that system of rural economy, whether respecting the size of farms or the conduct of the soil, would be found politically best, which sent the largest *surplus* to market. In order to discover what this is, deductions should be made of that portion of the produce
consumed

consumed by the necessary neighbours of the farmer in the village, including a very large portion of the labour, a smaller proportion of poor-rates, and a still smaller one of the wear and tear; all the seed, and (but not with positive accuracy) the team. The farmer's personal consumption should also be deducted; but this is more difficult to estimate. When the consumption of these several classes is deducted, the remainder forms that portion of the produce which may be said to go *free* to market, and forms the great basis which supports towns and manufactures."

Were this a proper place (in which to discuss points of political arithmetic) I should not have leisure, even if I could collect resolution, to combat every error and impropriety which those statements appear to me to contain *.

One prominent error, however, I must not refrain from noticing, here.—It relates to the FARMER's DIVIDEND; and, in effect, to the PROFITS of FARMING.

His capital is put down at 5*l.* an acre; and his share of the produce is made out to be 10*s.* 10*d.*, an acre; from which deduct 5*s.* for the interest on the capital, the remainder is 5*s.* 10*d.*;—the only requital left him, for his skill, industry, hard labor, disappointments, and vexations, incident to the raising of that produce. For the whole of those considerations, a farmer of 100 acres would not, on the statement which appears above, receive more than 29*l.* 3*s.* 4*d.* a year.—And, in the next statement his dividend is set down at 7*s.* 7*d.*, or 12*l.* 8*s.* 4d., a year!

If such is not the real intention and meaning of the item—" the farmer 10*s.* 10*d.*."—what does it mean?—Yet this is all the occupier is *made to get*, in following the Reporter's favorite course!

In pursuing other arable courses, the occupiers are not permitted to pocket *quite so much;*—possibly to show the superiority of "four shifts"!—While, by a slight alteration—the mere dash of a pen—in *making up* either of the statements,—that is to say, by slightly altering any of the items, whether of gross produce, or of deductions, especially the former,—a farmer might be made to get half as much more, or half as much less (say 15*s.* 10*d.* or 5*s.* 10*d.*) as might best suit the *fancy*, or the *view*, of a calculator:—an alteration, which, seeing the diversity of opinions respecting

* Had I casually picked them up, without a celebrated name to them, I should not have hesitated to have considered them as the reverie, or day dream, of a visionary mind.

specting rents, and the wide extent, in quantity and value, of arable crops,—no man on earth could successfully controvert, much less *prove* to be *wrong*.

How perfectly vague and useless are such calculations. —Calculations, I mean, in which a number of particulars are brought together; some of them for, others against (let it here be put for the sake of argument) a preconceived result; many or most of them, perhaps, being in a considerable degree *arbitrary* or *unfixed;* and without any settled PRINCIPLES of CALCULATION having been *previously laid down.*—With such pliable materials, and loose rules for employing them,—how easy it must be to stretch and twist them, this way or that, as may best suit the intended purpose of *any* calculator.

In the instance before us, the farmer's dividends being *nearly* the same, in the several statements, and agreeing with the calculator's general idea of a farmer's profit,—as will presently be seen,—it seems evident that he intended them as proper rewards, or as nearly bordering on proper rewards, for the farmer's toils:—notwithstanding what he says, in p. 273.—" It is proper to explain here, and the observation is applicable to all these estimates, that the proportion assigned to the farmer concerns no farm in general, but merely land precisely thus managed. If any of the expences run higher, or the products lower, that proportion is of course affected. The general profit of his business has no place in this inquiry, which is confined merely to such fields as are cultivated in the course assigned, and under the circumstances minuted."

What else, let it be asked, has a *farmer* to make profit of, but his lands—his " fields " in the aggregate—his *farm?* —" The general profit of his business," according to the above-transcribed statement (which includes both live and dead stock) supposing him to occupy 100 acres, and to keep the whole under the course on which that statement is made, can be no other (beside the pittance of *profit* which his wife may make by her poultry) than one hundred times 5s. 10d., or 29l. 3s. 4d., a year?

Again, in the statement relating to " grass land applied to cows,"—the farmer is allowed (in print) a somewhat better dividend; namely 12s. 8d.; or 39l. 3s. 4d., a year. But this, it would seem, was done with the view of stating the superior profitableness of grass lands:—not only to the farmer, but to the state:—or, to let the calculator set forth his own motive (p. 278)—to show that " grass land being, on comparison with arable, injurious to the public interests,

terests, is extremely ill-founded, and that, on the contrary, the support of great cities and flourishing manufactures very intimately depends on a large proportion of
the soil being thus employed."

Nevertheless, we have found this writer (after the above
was written and printed, in 1794) aiding and abetting the
plan of breaking up such profitable lands.—See p. 138,
aforegoing.

The contents of another section of the volume under
consideration, entitled " Expense and Profit," will best
assimilate with that just noticed ;—as they equally tend to
propagate a FALSE PRINCIPLE of CALCULATION :—a principle, which, it is to be feared, has been unfortunately
adopted, by one of the ablest writers on rural subjects, of
the present time *.—How necessary, then it is, to scruti-
nize, with rigid attention, the works of this *ostensible* Reporter; and to hold up his errors, in the most overt manner, to public view.—I here insert the section, entire.

P. 25. " Inquiries into these circumstances of the
national husbandry, can only be suggested by the Board
of Agriculture with a view to excite a spirit of industry, and
to shew the importance of investing in agricultural pursuits,
a sufficient capital to insure to the cultivator of the soil a
fair return for his exertions and skill. There may be nothing improper in stating, that it is conceived that the usual
farming capital is estimated to amount from 3*l.* to 6*l.* per
acre, according to soil, and other circumstances ; and certainly, the farmer who has skill and experience, ought to
make at least *ten percent.* on his capital. He must in
many cases make much more. The old estimate, here as
elsewhere, was, that the produce amounted to three rents ;
but for many years past, that idea has been utterly erroneous—was he now to make no more, he would soon be in
gaol. He ought to make five, and in some cases more."

Concerning what portion those five rents the occupier
is entitled to, in the opinion of this calculator, we are not
informed. Let us suppose *one* of them the number of
acres 100 ; the rent 75*l.* and the capital 500*l.* ; as before.
—A dividend of 75*l.* on 500*l.* principal is *fifteen percent.*

Supposing him to be entitled to *one third* of the *whole*,
— as has long been the popular idea,—his dividend would
be *twenty-five percent.* upon his capital employed; or
125*l.*

* See NORTHERN DEPARTMENT—*Northumberland*, p. 106.

125 *l.* a year;—from which deduct five percent, for legal interest, the remainder is 100 *l.* for skill, industry, hazard, &c. &c.:—instead of 29 *l.* 3*s.* 4*d.* (or 12 *l.* 8*s.* 4*d.*!) the pittance assigned him, in the Reporter's statement, aforegoing.

From this view of the subject, I think, we may fairly conclude that " *ten percent,*" on the capital employed is, in all cases, far beneath the true percentage by which to calculate a farmer's profit; and that it is in nowise admissible in calculations on the subject.

For, calculating on a farm of 100 acres, at 20*s.* an acre, and the capital employed 500 *l.*, agreeably to this writer's ideas *,—the farmer who should receive only ten percent on his capital, including the legal interest, would not get the common day wages of one of his laborers. The legal interest of his money is foreign to the calculation;—he can get this and sit still:—so that he has only five per cent, for his skill, industry and attention; which, on 500*l.* principal, is only 25 *l.*; while in many parts of the kingdom, he is, now, (1810) paying his servant or laborer 35 or 40 *l.*

If we admit that a farmer who is capable of stocking and managing a farm of 100 *l.* a year, ought to have double the earnings of a common day laborer,—the calculation is required to be on *twenty percent,* (in the proportion of 5 *l.* capital to 1 *l.* rent) including legal interest, or *fifteen percent,* without it : that is to say *three times as much,* as ten percent with it!—And even, before this be taken into the account,—insurance, risk and hazard of every kind (not seen in the foregoing statement!) ought to be deducted from the gross produce,—with equal propriety, and as necessarily, as rent, repairs of every denomination †, government taxes, parish rates, tithe, labor, extraneous manure, and seed.

SUBJECT

* For general remarks on the due proportion between rent and capital,—see my TREATISE on LANDED PROPERTY, p. 391 ; or the ABSTRACT of it, p. 407.

† REPAIRS incident to HUSBANDRY.—

Roads,	Water Courses (for the watering of
Buildings,	Livestock and Lands),
Gates,	Wear and Tear of Working Animals,
Fences,	Implements, Furniture,
Drains,	&c. &c. &c. &c.

SUBJECT THE THIRD.

RURAL ECONOMY.

DIVISION THE FIRST.

TENANTED ESTATES.

Estates.—P. 8. " The state of property in Suffolk may
be considered as beneficial in its division. The largest
estate in the county is supposed not to exceed 8000 or
8500*l.* a year,* and it is a singular instance of the rise in
the value of land within the period of forty or fifty years.
There are three or four other estates which rise above
5000*l.* a year; and I have a list of about thirty others
which are about 3000*l.* a year and upwards. Under this
there are numbers of all sizes; but the most interesting
circumstance is of a different complexion—I mean the
rich yeomanry, as they were once called, being very numerous, farmers occupying their own lands, of a value
rising from 100*l.* to 400*l.* a year."

Tenures.—P. 8. " The great mass of the county is
freehold property, but copyholds are numerous, and some
of them large. Of college leases, scattered in various
parts, nothing particular is to be noted.

"Under this head, however, may not be improperly arranged some customs which are very 'great impediments
to the due cultivation of the soil ; these are the rights of
commonage and pasture, which exceed the ordinary cases.
At Troston, on the borders of the western sand district, I
found open field lands in which the course is one crop to
two fallows ; and these consist in leaving the land to weeds
for the flock of one farmer, who, by prescription, is the
only person that can keep sheep in the parish ! Nothing
can be imagined more beggarly than the husbandry and
crops on these lands; the same farmer has even the right
of sheep-feeding many of the inclosed pastures and meadows

* This, however, will be found to be materially contradicted,
under the head *Homesteads,* ensuing.

dows after the hay is removed. In return for such privileges, he is bound to fold a certain number of acres for the other farmers."

And was such an absurdity really suffered to exist, in this enlightened nation, at the close of the eighteenth century!—Had it been discovered in the East or West Indies, it would probably have been done away.—It is not, however, the only one of equal irrationality, to be found in the land we live in. See my GLOUCESTERSHIRE V. I. p. 198.

IMPROVEMENT of Estates.—*Draining.*—P. 151. "This most excellent practice is general on all the wet lands of the county."

P. 152. "The materials used for filling, bushes covered with straw, sometimes straw or stubble only; and the expence, if with bushes, amounts, on an average, every thing included, to two guineas, or forty-five shillings an acre, the men being paid three shillings a score rods for the work. The duration varies, according to the goodness of the work and materials, from 12 to 25 years; and some filled with straw only, have been known to last much longer."

Irrigation.—P. 7. (Section "Waters") Suffolk we are told (p. 406, aforegoing) is every where intersected by streams—"which" says the Reporter, "would be invaluable, was that most beneficial of all practices, irrigation, understood : but unfortunately, these waters have from the creation ran in waste, to an incalculable loss. There are, however, some thousands of acres which might easily, by this improvement, be advanced to a state infinitely more productive."

Before this unqualified assertion was made, the specific qualities of those waters should have been given. For, on the nature of a given water its fertilizing quality principally depends. If the substrata of the two sandy districts of Suffolk are, as set forth aforegoing, chalk, marl, or other calcareous substances, the waters which issue from them can scarsely fail of proving highly beneficial to the soils they may be spread over. Again,

P. 176. (Section "Irrigation"). "Of all the improvements wanting in this county, there is none so obvious, and of such importance, as watering meadows. The rivers, streams, and brooks, in every part, are numerous; few countries are better watered with small streams; yet is there not a well-watered meadow in the county; at least, not one to my knowledge."

EXECUTIVE MANAGEMENT of Estates.—*Tenancy.*—P. 24.
" In Suffolk, the more common terms for leases are seven,
fourteen, and twenty-one years ; much land is occupied
by men who are tenants at will. There are few counties
that have been more improved by leases of twenty-one
years than this has been. The tracts in the sandy districts,
which have been converted from warren and sheep-walk
into cultivated inclosures, by means of clay, marl and
crag, have seen these improvements effected by means of
such leases giving the tenant that security in the invest-
ment of his money, which induced him to lay it out : nor
have they operated only in such capital undertakings ;
they have caused large tracts to be hollow drained, and
have occasioned an improved cultivation in almost every
respect where it depended on larger sums being expended
than common to farmers who are not able or willing to
make such exertions."—See p. 320, aforegoing.

Rent.—The following observations are highly creditable
to the industry of this Reporter.—P. 16. " To ascertain
the rent of the several districts is impossible ; nothing
more is to be expected than to guess, with some degree of
approximation to the truth. On the foundation of as correct information as I could, from residence and examination, procure, I am inclined to believe, that the several
soils are at present rented as under, the whole country included, sheep-walk, waste, commons, &c. which are very
large deductions from the rate of the cultivated land.

	£.	s.	d.
The strong or wet loam, at per acre,	0	13	0
The rich loam, - - - - - - -	0	14	0
The maritime district of sand, - -	0	10	0
The western ditto of ditto, - - -	0	5	0
The fens, - - - - - - - - -	0	2	6

" It should be noted, that there are in all these districts,
except the fen, tracts that let at 20s. and 25s. and even
higher rents, and meadows higher still : but the rents here
minuted are those of the whole county, as viewed in the
map.

" GENERAL VIEW OF THE RENTAL OF THE COUNTY.

" Dividing the county according to the soil in the annexed map, and weighing each division accurately, I find
the proportions are, to the total of 800,000 acres, as under ;
to which I have added the rent and totals.

30,000

ACRES.		£.	s.	d.
30,000 fen, at 2s. 6d. - - - - -		3,750	0	0
46,666⅔ rich loam, at 14s. - - -		32,666	13	4
156,666⅔ sand, at 10s. - - - - -		78,333	3	4
113,333⅓ do. at 5s. - - - - - -		28,333	6	8
453,333⅓ strong loam, at 13s. - -		294,666	13	4
800,000, average rent, 10s. 6d.		£.437,749	16	8"

DIVISION THE SECOND.

WOODLANDS.

T IMBER.—P. 144. "The strong loams of Suffolk formerly contained considerable quantities of large oak; these, as in every other part of the kingdom, have been much lessened, and the succession that is coming on, bears no proportion to the growth that preceded it."

DIVISION THE THIRD.

AGRICULTURE.

F ARMS —*Sizes.*—P. 13. "These, in Suffolk, must, in a general light, be reckoned large; and to that circumstance, more perhaps than to any other, is to be attributed the good husbandry so commonly found in the county. In the district of strong wet loam, there are many small ones from 20 *l.* to 100 *l.* a year; but these are intermixed with others that rise from 150 *l.* to 300 *l.* and some even more. In the sand districts they are much larger, many from 300 *l.* to one of 850 *l.* or 900 *l.*; that of West Wood Lodge, near Dunwich, in the occupation of Mr. Howlett, and belonging to Sir John Blois, Bart. consisting of above 3000 acres, is without exception the finest farm in the county." The Reporter, notwithstanding the principle laid down,

in

in the Introduction*, is led to a general "observation relative to the profit of cultivating different soils;"—in
which he says (p. 13) "there is no comparison between
the wealth of our farmers on dry and on wet land. On the
former, the occupation of a farm of 200*l.* or 300 *l.* a year,
has been throughout the county, generally found attended
with a very handsome profit, visible in various circumstances, and ascertained on the death of the farmers. But
on the wet land, though numbers are very much at their
ease, yet the advantages, and fortunes made, have been
exceedingly inferior, and mixed with many instances that
will not allow the idea of considerable profits."—He attempts to account for this; but neither in the text, nor
in the notes upon it, do I find any thing sufficiently satisfactory for insertion, here.

Homesteads.—P. 10. "The farm-houses are much improved within the last twenty years; but they are still
very inferior to what, it is to be hoped, they may become
in some future period. They are too often built, even at
present, of lath and plaster, which decaying in a few years,
occasions repairs being so heavy an article of deduction
from the annual receipt of an estate, as to lessen considerably the net profit resulting from landed property.
The extent to which this evil operates in the eastern part
of the kingdom in general, may be conceived from a curious fact; that the repairs on one estate of about 15,000 *l.*
a year, came in eleven years to above 40,000 *l.*"

If the estate alluded to is situated in Suffolk, the remark
is contradictory of a former assertion (p. 424). If not, it
ought not to have appeared in *this* place, without explanation.

Cottages.—P. 11. "In Suffolk, they are in general bad
habitations; deficient in all contrivance for warmth, and
for convenience; the door very generally opening immediately

---

* Namely that of adhering to *local* circumstances; without in-
dulging in *general* remarks.—His words are—p. viii,—" any chapter,
section, dissertation, &c. that might be taken from the account of one
county, and with equal propriety inserted in another; or any observations that would come with peculiar propriety in a general treatise
on husbandry, are not properly a part of the return of a particular
district."

It frequently happens, however, that general matter aptly grows
out of local circumstances, as in the instance under notice;—and,
when it does, it might be wrong wholly to suppress it. It is the abuse
of the principle (as exercised by several of the Board's Reporters) and
not the proper use of it, that ought to be avoided.

diately from the external air into the keeping-room, and sometimes directly to the fire-side : the state of reparation bad, and the deficiency of gardens too general."—P. 12. " The general rent of cottages is from 40s. to 3l. with or without a small garden."

OCCUPIERS.—P. 5. "This district" (the sandy mara-time district of Suffolk) " I take to be one of the best cul-tivated in England ; not exempt from faults and deficien-cies, but having many features of unquestionably good management. It is also a most profitable one to farm in ; and there are few districts in the county, if any, abound-ing with wealthier farmers, nor any that contain a greater proportion of occupying proprietors, possessing from one hundred to three and four hundred pounds a year."

PLAN of MANAGEMENT of Farms.—P. 34. "The manage-ment of the arable land, in the four distinct soils, is essen-tially different, and merits a description as particular as can be given in the short compass of such a sketch as this.

" *Strong loam on a clay-marl bottom.*—Common exer-tions in common practice, diverge into such endless varia-tions, that to note the methods pursued by individuals, would fill a volume. * In a work of this nature, which must be considered but as a sketch of the subjects to be treated more particularly by those whose situation enables them locally to give the authority denied to others,† it is only practicable to seize the most prominent features, such as best discriminate the system pursued.‡

" In the strong soils of Suffolk, the course of crops, into whatever variations it may usually be thrown, includes summer fallow as the common preparation for the rotation of corn products."

P. 36. " *Rich loam and sand.*—On this soil the management

---

* And with which, it may be fairly said, this writer has filled many volumes.—The strong position here taken militates against, and powerfully tends to overthrow, and nullify, almost every chapter, section, and page of his Lincolnshire and Norfolk Reports.

† Is the Secretary of the Board a stranger in Suffolk ?—If *he* cannot produce the required authority. who can ?

‡ On REGISTERING the BEST PRACTICES of DISTRICTS.—*This* is the true groundwork of a provincial Report. The " system pur-sued," *in its best form*, being duly studied, clearly ascertained, and faithfully registered,—the Reporter may, or may not, mention such *varieties* of *practice*, followed by individuals, as he thinks may serve to throw additional light on the more GENERAL SYSTEM pursued:

ment is more uniform. The" (impracticable) "rotation,"
(improperly) " called the Norfolk husbandry, is very
generally introduced, which is making turnips the preparation for barley, and clover that for wheat, in the
course of,

1. Turnips,
2. Barley,
3. Clover,
4. Wheat;

which is certainly one of the best systems that ever was
invented, and, indeed, nearly unexceptionable."—See
abundant remarks on this topic, aforegoing.

P. 37.—" *Sand*.—On the sand districts, the management varies proportionably with the badness of the soil ;
but in one feature it is universal, that turnips are every
where the preparation, the basis for both corn and grass.
There is no sand so light that it will not yield, by means
of dung or fold, this crop."

For an ingenious rotation, on these sands, see *Buckweet*, ensuing.

For the general management of the " fens," or waterlands of Suffolk, see p. 289, aforegoing.

WORKPEOPLE.—P. 202. "The variations in the price
of labour in the county, are not considerable: it may be
stated generally (beer included) at 1s. 4d.* in winter,
1s. 6d. in summer, and 2s. 10d. in harvest. Call winter
twenty-nine weeks, harvest five, and summer eighteen ;
this will make the year's earnings 23l. 18s. A woman
earns sixpence, and the wages of men servants rise from
5l. to 10l."—In 1794.

Same P. "In my own vicinity, I remember it to have
risen in twenty to twenty-five years, from 1s. in winter,
to 1s. 4d. a day; and in harvest from 10s. to 12s. and of
late to 14s. a week. There are parts of the county, where
the rise has not been equally great."

WORKING ANIMALS.—P. 196. "The Suffolk breed of"
(cart) "horses, is no less celebrated than the cows. They
are found in most perfection, in the district of country
that

" * Labour by the day, in the parish of Hoxne, is only one shilling,
and beer, from the end of September till new layers are began to be
cut: from that time till the end of September, one shilling and four-
pence, and beer, except during the harvest : for the harvest month, if
the men are not taken into the family, they generally have half-a-
crown a day, and two bushels of malt.—*Note by a Correspondent of
the Board*."

that is upon the coast, extending to Woodbridge, Debenham, Eye, and Lowestoff The best of all were found
some years ago upon the *Sandlings*, south of Woodbridge
and Orford. Amongst the great farmers in that country,
there was, forty years ago, a considerable spirit of breeding, and of drawing team against team for large sums of
money. Mr. Mays, of Ramsholt-dock, was said to have
drawn fifteen horses for 1500 guineas. It is to be regretted,
that such a spirit of emulation was lost.—I remember seeing many of the old breed, which were very famous, and, in
some respects, an uglier horse could not be viewed;
sorrel-colour, very low in the fore-end, a large ill-shaped
head, with slouching heavy ears, a great carcass and short
legs, but short-backed, and more of the *punch* than the
Leicestershire breeders will allow *. These horses could
only walk and draw; they could trot no better than a cow.
But their power in drawing was very considerable. Of
late years, by aiming at coach-horses, the breed is much
changed to a handsomer, lighter, and more active horse.
It is yet an excellent breed; and if the comparison with
others, and especially the great black horse of the midland
counties, be fairly made, I have no doubt of their beating
them in useful draft, that of the cart and the plough. But
the fair comparison is this : let a given sum be invested in
the purchase of each breed ; and then, by means of which,
will a thousand ton of earth be moved to a given distance
by the smallest quantity of hay and oats? It is the oats
and hay that are to be compared, not the number or size of
the cattle. The present price of these horses is high ;
good geldings, of five or six years old, selling at thirty to
forty guineas. A spirited and attentive breeder, upon
a farm of 1000 or 1500 acres of various soils, that would
admit two or three stallions, and thirty or forty capital
mares, might, by breeding in and in, with close attention
to the improvements wanted, advance this breed to a very
high perfection, and render it a national object: but then,
query, whether the same expence and attention would not
produce a breed of cattle that would, by training, supersede the use of horses ? Of all the branches of live stock,
perhaps nothing is in such an imperfect state as working
oxen ;

" * Clean legs and well formed shoulders, are criterions of the true
Suffolk horse, points which entitle them to be good movers; and such
they are in general, if used in chaises, and not too long habituated to
draw only.—*Note by J. C.*"

oxen *; in every thing that concerns them, we are really
in the infancy of agriculture."

I am ever most happy when I can cordially agree with
this or, indeed, any other writer whose work I am estimating. In censure I have no delight; saving that of
doing my duty.

P. 198 (by "A. Collet, Esq.") "In the east district, in
winter, horses are never permitted to remain in the stable
at night, but about eight o'clock are turned out into a
yard, well littered with straw, and have plenty of good
sweet oat or barley straw to eat; but never clover or hay.
By this treatment, a horse is never swelled in his legs, or
seldom has any ailment about him. Horses in this country, are as good as any in England, and are kept in as fine
condition. A horse turned out every night, will hold his
work several years longer than one confined in the stable."

IMPLEMENTS.—*Plows.* P. 26. "The Norfolk wheel
plough, and the little light swing plough of Suffolk, are
the common implements."

MANURE.—P. 165. "Under this head the Suffolk
husbandry furnishes some information in the several articles of

"1. Marl, chalk and clay.

"2. Crag, or shell marl.

"3. Town manures.

"4. Farm-yard composts.

"*Claying.*—A term in Suffolk which includes marling;
and indeed the earth carried under this term, is very generally a clay marl; though a pure, or nearly a pure clay,
is preferred for very loose sands.

"The extent to which this improvement has been carried, in both the sand districts, is very considerable, there
being few farmers of any note, on very light land, that
have not carried large quantities. An excellent cultivator
near Bury, though not on a very large farm, has carried
140,000 loads. The operation of this manure, acting both
chemically and mechanically, is so obvious on very light
soils,

" * I have used for a year past, and continue to use, a pair of oxen
to a plough, harnessed exactly the same as horses, driven with reins,
and the same man drives and ploughs, as done with a pair of Suffolk
horses. I work the pair of oxen but one journey, taking another pair
in the afternoon: by practice, they will walk very fast, and in this
way I can plough from an acre to an acre and a half per day. As
they do nothing but ploughing, and are not used upon the road, they
are not shod.—*Note by a Correspondent of the Board.*"

soils, that it wants no explanation. But when the *clay* is
not of a good sort, that is, when there is really none, or
scarcely any clay in it, but is an imperfect, and even a
hard chalk, there are great doubts how far it answers, and,
in many cases, has certainly been spread to little or no
profit. The quantity usual is from 60 to 80, and sometimes an 100 loads an acre, the load containing about 32
bushels. Many experienced farmers prefer carrying 40 or
50 loads only, and repeating it after the first course. The
land receives more immediate benefit, and double the
number of acres may be clayed in the first years of the
lease, without any additional expence. The men are paid
from 27s. to 30s. per 120, for filling and spreading, earning 10s. or 11s. a week; and the expence of teams is
about as much more. When this manuring is done, therefore, on very poor land, the expence is equal to the
value of the fee-simple of the estate. The duration, and
indeed the whole effect, depends much on the course of
crops pursued. If the plough is too freely used, and corn
sown too often, it answers badly, and the effect is soon
lost; but, with good management, it lasts 20 years. Where
the management is good, and the clay well adapted to the
land, the profit is very great. In many cases, a course of
fallow and rye, or *light* oats, is converted to fine barley,
clover, and wheat, and the produce of the soil multiplied
twenty-fold; but, on the contrary, the cases in which the
return has been inadequate, are not a few. And I believe
it will be found, that on soils that will yield sainfoin, it is
more profitable to cultivate that grass, than to clay the
land for corn."

Crag.—P. 5 (section "Soil"). "The crag is a singular
body of cockle and other shells, found in great masses in
various parts of the country, from Dunwich quite to the
river Orwell, and even across it in Wolverston Park, &c.
I have seen pits of it from which great quantities have
been taken, to the depth of fifteen and twenty feet, for
improving the heaths. It is both red and white, but generally red, and the shells so broken as to resemble sand.
On lands long in tillage the use is discontinued, as it is
found to make the sands *blow* more."

P. 174. "In a part of the maritime sand district called
the Sandlings, which are south of Woodbridge, Orford, and
Saxmundham, they formerly made a very great improvement, by spreading shell marl on the black ling heaths,
with which all that tract was once covered. But as the
marl, called there crag, is all dry powdered shells, like
running,

running sand, without any principle of adhesion, the effect was good only once; for, after cultivating those heaths, on trying the crag a second time, it was found to do little or no good; and, in some instances, even to make the sand *blow* the more. It seems, therefore, to have acted in this respect like lime, which has been frequently found to have great effect on the first application, upon lands long in a state of nature; but on repetition, that effect has been found to be lost."

Town Manure.—P. 175. " In the neighbourhood of all the towns in this County, the farmers have for thirty years past been very assiduous in purchasing all sorts of manures; so that the price has been gradually rising to 5s. or 6s. a waggon load, for even the inferior sorts: at five miles distance, a load of dung is estimated to cost, by the time it is on the land, from 12s. to 15s.; an expence so enormous, as to leave it a question whether it answers. In the neighbourhood of Bury, farmers neglect soot, which is carried to others at Isleham, Burwell, &c. at a more considerable expence, eight-pence and nine-pence a bushel, besides many miles of carriage.

" In Sampford hundred, the soil a rich sandy loam, they buy large quantities at Manningtree, which come from London, and for which they give 10s. for a five-horse load of three tons at the quay, and which cost 20s. when on the land; all spread for turnips."

Farmyard Manure.—P. 175. " The methods of this county are those general in the kingdom, and extremely deficient. The dung and refuse straw is turned over in the spring, and thrown into heaps, where it lies some time to dry; or carted on to hedge-rows upon earth turned up to receive it, often remaining exposed to the sun and wind before it is covered up with earth, gaining nothing by the mixture; whereas, had the earth been carted into the yards in autumn, as a foundation for the dunghill, it would in the course of the winter be well saturated with urine, and in the spring be ready to cover the dung immediately in turning."

Application of Manure.—P. 176. " Upon this subject a question in practice arises in Suffolk, whether the dung and composts of various kinds should be spread for turnips, or upon clover lays and fallows for wheat? I have attentively remarked the practice in various parts of the County, and it appears, that in the best cultivated districts, manure is applied for turnips."

TILLAGE.—*Plowing.*—P. 32. " In every part of the County

County this is done with a pair of horses, conducted with reins by the ploughman ; and the quantity of land usually turned in a day, is an acre upon stiff soils, and from one and a quarter to one and a half on sands.

" The ploughmen are remarkable for straight furrows ; and also for drawing them by the eye to any object, usually a stick whitened by peeling, either for water cuts, or for new laying out broad ridges, called here *steatches;* and a favourite amusement is ploughing such furrows, as candidates for a hat, or pair of breeches, given by ale-house-keepers, or subscribed among themselves, as a prize for the straightest furrow. The skill of many of them in this work is remarkable."

Ridges.—P. 33. " The form of laying arable lands upon dry soils, is, on the flat, with finishing furrows; alternate gathering and splitting ; but on wet lands, the three foot Essex ridge of two *bouts* is most common *. In some districts, six, eight, and ten feet *steatches,* a little arched, are used."

Fallowing.—P. 33. " There is no question at all of the merit of fallowing, when compared with bad courses of crops. If the husbandry is not correct in this respect, the fallowist will certainly be a much better farmer than his neighbours : but there are courses which will clean the foulest land as well as any summer fallow, by means of plants, which admit all the tillage of a summer fallow."

This position,—if meant to be extended to all sorts of lands, I do not (speaking from experience on an extended scale, on almost every soil, and in every climature this island affords) hesitate to affirm is ill-founded †.

SEMINATION.

" * It may be worth noticing, that on many of the poorest and driest sands, rye is sown on four furrow ridges, which, to persons accustomed to a wet soil, appears absurd ; but it is done in order to lay a greater depth of mould (if such it may be called) together, for the corn to strike root in. The poorer the land, the more necessary is this mode thought to be.—*Note by T. L.*"

† Of course, what follows the above extract appears, to me, mere " theory "—not " practice,"—and the close of the paragraph,—as wild, uncultured words.—" Cabbages are not planted before June or July : winter tares admit three months tillage, if tillage is wanted. Beans well cultivated will preserve land clean, which has been cleaned by cabbages. And, in any case, two successive hoeing crops are effective in giving positive cleanness These observations are not theory, they are practice ; and it is high time that mankind should be well persuaded that the right quantity of cattle and sheep cannot be kept on a farm, if the fallows of the old system are not made to contribute to their support."

FURTHER

SEMINATION.—For the progress of *Dibbling* in Suffolk, see the ensuing head, *Wheat.*

RAISING Arable Crops.—*Vermin.*—P. 290. " On this subject, Mr. P. Edge, of Ipswich, thus expresses himself: —' An unnecessary consumption of corn is at all times to be carefully avoided. I will therefore take the liberty of informing the Board of Agriculture, that a most alarming quantity of corn is destroyed by game preserved in woods and plantations, in various parts of this kingdom. It is not possible for me to make any calculation as to the quantity destroyed; but I will beg leave to mention, that in a field of eleven acres of wheat within three miles of this town, the occupier, from the goodness of the land, from the excellent state of its cultivation, and from the health and vigour of the plant, had a right to expect from eight to ten coombs an acre. His neighbours, men of great respectability, were of the same opinion. Unfortunately for the farmer, the field joined a wood full of hares and pheasants, preserved and fed by the gamekeepers; and such was the havock made by the game, that the produce of the field was only fifteen coombs.

" ' In this single instance, no less than seventy coombs of wheat were lost to the tenant, as well as to the public. What therefore must be the astonishing quantity of corn destroyed throughout the kingdom by game that is preserved?' "

WHEAT.—*Succession* and *Tillage.*—P. 42. " Wheat in this County is usually sown on summer fallow, or on clover land; in the former case, after three or four ploughings; in the latter, upon one. Fallows are generally thrown into the three foot or two *bout* ridge the last earth but one, which is reversed in the sowing earth."

Time of *Sowing* Wheat.—P. 45. " October and November are the months in which this crop is sown in Suffolk:

experiments

FURTHER on the ADVANTAGES of FALLOWING.

A surplus advantage, over and above every other, which attends a WHOLE-YEAR'S FALLOW, and which has seldom been brought to account,—is that of its not consuming, like FALLOW CROPS,—any portion of the limited supply of farm-yard manure; and, consequently, throwing additional strength into the rest of the farm;—and this while it prepares the ground to bear a succession of ample crops, to encrease the supply, in future.

Cropping foul, out-of-tilth lands is the degenerate practice of indigent slovens. who live from hand to mouth, and drag on farming, from year to year; as if every year should be (as it ought) their last.

For other ADVANTAGES of FALLOWING, see p. 342, aforegoing.

experiments have been made in the County, which shew
that September is, if wet enough, a better time; but very
few farmers are so early."

Quantity of *Seed* of Wheat.—P. 45. "Two bushels an
acre, are the common allowance of seed; some will sow a
peck more, and if late in the season, even to three bushels;
and some will, on good land, trust to seven pecks; but
even in dibbling, that quantity is oftentimes put in."

Dibbling Wheat.—P. 47. "This practice, which there
is every reason to denominate excellent, is well established
in the county, and increases every year. In the maritime
sand district, many thousand acres are thus put in. One
farmer near Dunwich, the year before last, dibbled 258
acres, and this year above 250, that is, his whole crop; and
many others apply the same method also for their whole
crop."

Drilling Wheat.—P. 48. "Drilling is practised with
great intelligence and success, by individuals, in several
parts of the County; but no where has the least tendency
to become the common practice. In some districts it declines: and while dibbling spreads rapidly, this practice
moves with difficulty."

Harvesting Wheat.—P. 52. "They are more careful
and attentive in many parts of the kingdom, in harvesting
all sorts of corn, than they are in Suffolk. The wheat
sheaves are generally made too large, which is a heavy evil
in a wet harvest. Very attentive husbandmen are apt to think
all too large that are made by tying two handfuls to form
a band, one length of straw not very short, being esteemed
sufficient. In forming the *shocks*, or stooks, also, they use
no precautions against rain, merely setting ten or a dozen
together, without capping or other attention, a method that
is found in other Counties very useful.

" *Threshing.*—I do not know of any threshing-mill in
the County, which is rather surprizing, for one abounding
so greatly in corn.

" *Produce.*—The crops of wheat vary considerably: from
one quarter and a half on the poor sand, when substituted
for rye, and at that small produce answering much better,
to three and a half on the rich and strong loams. Upon
the finest soils in the County, specified elsewhere, four,
and even five quarters are not uncommon. Probably the
general average of the whole may be estimated at twenty-
two bushels per acre, on a medium of seven years.

" In the answers I have been favoured with to my circular

cular queries, there are a few minutes that merit being
noted.

" At Bardwell, Mr. Davenport remarks, that five combs
is an indifferent crop.

" At Brome, Mr. Negus mentions the produce to be five
combs.

" At Hopton, by Mr. Stone's account, four combs. At
Barningham, five."

RYE.—P. 57. "This grain has gradually given way to
the culture of wheat, by means of those improvements
which in the last fifty years have taken place in so many
parts of the kingdom. It is now found only on poor sands,
and from several observations I have made on the crops of
both on the same soil, I am much inclined to think that
wheat will generally pay better."

P. 57. " *Preparation.*—Fallow is the general preparation: by some a whole year; by others a bastard fallow.

" *Seed.*—Six pecks an acre, the usual quantity.

" *Time of Sowing.*—The end of September and beginning of October the common time.

" *Produce.*—Good crops of this grain are rare in the
sands of Suffolk; on better soils, three quarters an acre are
sometimes gained; but the common produce does not exceed two."

BARLEY.—*Succession* and *Tillage.*—P. 54. " Soils too
heavy for turnips, are in many places summer fallowed for
barley; and if fallows are applied, this is certainly one of
the best applications, in which case the grain is sowed
one spring earth."

P. 54. *Sort.*—The common barley, *hordeum vulgare,*
is the only sort I have known cultivated in Suffolk.

" *Quantity of Seed.*—On very light sandy lands in the
western district, so small a quantity as two bushels, and
two and a half, are sown; but the common practice on all
soils in general, is to sow from three to four bushels.

" *Time of Sowing.*—April is the season most common;
but varying with many circumstances from the beginning
of March to the beginning of May. I have known farmers wait by reason of drought, to the last week in May,
and even the first in June, and yet get large crops.

" *Harvest.*—Barley is every where in Suffolk mown, and
left loose: the neater method of binding in sheaves, is not
practised."

P. 55. " *Produce.*—The produce of barley varies
greatly; from two quarters to six. I am inclined to
                                                    think

think the average, so difficult in all cases to calculate, may be estimated at three quarters and an half.

"*Products, noted by Correspondents.*—At Bardwell, Mr. Davenport observes the average produce to be seven combs. At Brome, M. Negus notes eight combs as the average. At Hopton, Mr. Stone calculates it at three quarters."

BEANS.—P. 58. "It is difficult to cultivate rich moist soils to full advantage, without the assistance of this plant, which has two qualities of singular importance; first, that of extracting very little from the fertility of the land," &c. &c.

This, I humbly conceive, requires to be *proved.*—If true, why recommend the practice of *invigorating* the *land*, for beans? Yet, in the same page with the above, we find the following paragraph.—"In Kent, they find that no plant pays better for dung, but it is uncommon in Suffolk to afford them any; yet dunging fallows for wheat is found in all parts of the county, and is a most barbarous practice. Where this husbandry is pursued, there could be no improvement more obvious than giving the dung to beans, and then taking the wheat." *

Dibbling Beans.—P. 59. "Beans have been dibbled a row on every flag; by others, on every other flag. I have found it more advantageous to plant in clusters four or five beans in every hole, and eight or nine inches from hole to hole, which admits much better hoeing than when more thickly set. Dibbling is the best and most effective method of cultivating beans."

P. 60. *Produce* of Beans.—"Beans are every where an uncertain crop,† consequently the average produce difficult to estimate: in Kent, they probably exceed four quarters; but in Suffolk I should not estimate them at more than three, yet five or six are not uncommon.

"*Application of the Crop.*—The quantity given to horses is

---

* On the FOOD of VEGETABLES.—I may not have a more apt opportunity, than this, of exposing the silly notion, entertained by etherial agriculturists, that "broad leaved plants" receive their nourishment wholely, or principally, from the ATMOSPHERE; while "narrow leaved plants" are obliged to search for their's in the SOIL. —Yet it is pretty generally known, to terrestrial cultivators, and is tolerably well ascertained, in this volume, that *pease* and *clover* are among the most transitory of arable crops: not by reason of their *exhausting* the *air*, but the *soil*, of their favorite pabulum.

† Yet this writer is every where recommending them.

is not very considerable ; and the consumption by hogs, or ground for fatting cattle, is still less."

Buckweet.—P. 61. "Buckwheat is, in this county, on the very poorest sands, more common than in many other parts of England ; and is, for such soils, a very valuable crop.

"*Preparation.*—I never knew manure bestowed for this crop ; but the time of sowing admits so much tillage, that any land may be perfectly cleaned for it.

"*Seed.*—One bushel an acre is the common quantity.

"*Time of Sowing.*—The end of June the usual time ; but the whole of that month is proper ; and it is sometimes sown the first week of July.

"*Harvest.*—Mown, and gathered loose.

"*Produce.*—Crops vary, from four to eight sacks ; five probably the average.

"*Application of the Crop.*—It is found good for feeding and fattening hogs and poultry ; and some farmers have given it to their horses with success.

"*Ploughing in for Manure.*—This is not a common practice ; but one gentleman has with great skill applied a peculiar husbandry to it, which deserves reciting. The Rev. Mr. Moseley, of Drinkston, has the merit of planing and executing a system of tare husbandry which deserves considerable attention. The following is his own account of it."

The Reporter's *extravagant* observations, on Mr. Moseley's long account, will be quite sufficient for insertion, here.

P. 68. "I may call for the attention of farmers anxious to become acquainted with real improvements in agriculture, to this account of Mr. Moseley's system ; which is one of the best imagined arrangements that has been discovered. One ploughing puts in the winter tares ; that earth is given in autumn, and consequently opens the soil to the influence of frosts ; as the spring advances, and the sun becomes powerful enough to exhale the humidity, and with it the nutritious particles of the land, the crop advances and screens it from the action of his beams. (!) Whatever weeds are in the soil, vegetate with the young tares, and are either strangled by their luxuriance, or cut off with them before they can seed. A crop is gained at a very moderate expence, which is usually worth from 40s. to 3l. an acre ; oftentimes much more. But this crop is cleared so early from the land, that it would remain exposed to the sun through the most burning part of the summer

summer for three months,* as that ingenious gentleman rightly observes; if left so, there would be a call for three ploughings to do mischief, except in the point of killing some weeds. (!) To give one earth immediately, and harrow in buck wheat, spares that expence, and covers the earth when it most wants to be so protected. But a great deal more is done; for according to this comparison, a coat of manure is gained at absolutely no expence; and the year is carried through from Michaelmas to Michaelmas, and three crops put in on only three ploughings, viz. the tares, the buck wheat, and the wheat. It is not easy to invent a system more complete. Let me go further, and remark, that Mr. Moseley in this husbandry is original: many have sown tares; and many have ploughed in buck wheat; and most have given a year to each; but it is the combination of the two that forms the merit, and is a plan not before registered; and therefore, we are to pronounce (as far as the advancement of the art is concerned), not yet practised.

" When we see the universal eagerness and anxiety expressed by the experimental philosophers of the present age, to secure to themselves priority of discovery (an anxiety fair and honourable, as speaking a noble emulation in the best paths of fame), ought we not to do justice to those who in a less brilliant, but more useful walk, invent new combinations of old practices that have the merit, because the advantages of novelty."

Such a paucity of tillage may not be injuriously felt, the first year. But it requires not the gift of prophecy to foretell, that, sooner or later, very soon I conceive, it would, if pursued, bring the cultivator to a " stand-still."

Nevertheless, there are cases in which the ingenious practice thus lavishly recommended,—in effect as a general plan of management,—may, in particular cases, be adopted with profit.—It entitles the inventor of it to great credit.

HEMP.—The North of Suffolk (and the adjoining border of Norfolk) being the only remaining part of the kingdom, in which hemp is, at present, cultivated in quantity (the district of Bridport and the adjacent parts of Somersetshire, only I believe, excepted),—I will the more readily extract, from the publication before me, whatever may appear to be useful, or interesting in its *culture*.

The

* Possibly, the very best thing that could befall it.

The particulars of *manufacture* are less an object of attention, in my present undertaking.

P. 119. " The district of country in which this article of cultivation is chiefly found, extends from Eye to Beccles, spreading to the breadth of about ten miles, which oblong of country may be considered as its head-quarters.

" It is in the hands of both farmers and cottagers; but it is very rare to see more than five or six acres in the occupation of any one man. With cottagers, the more common method is, to sow it every year on the same land: there is a piece at Hoxne, which has been under this crop for seventy successive years. The soil preferred, is, what is called in the district, *mixed land,* that is, sandy loam, moist and putrid, (?) but without being stiff or tenacious; in one word, the best land the country contains; and does well, as may be supposed, on old meadow, and low bottoms near rivers. They manure for it with great attention; so that it may be taken as a maxim, that hemp is not often sown without this preparation: of dung and moulds, twenty-five three-horse loads per acre; of dung alone, sixteen loads. This is done directly after wheat sowing is finished.

" The tillage consists in three earths, with harrowing sufficient to make the soil perfectly fine; and it is laid flat, with as few furrows as possible.

" Time of sowing, from the middle to the end of April; but will bear being sown all May. It is often found, that the early sown yields hemp of the best quality.

" Quantity of seed, eleven pecks per acre, at the price of one shilling to two shillings a peck, generally from sixteen to eighteen-pence. Much is brought from Downham, and the fens; the seeded hemp is not so good by eighteen-pence or two shillings the stone.

" No weeding is ever given to it, the hemp destroying every other plant.

" It is pulled thirteen or fourteen weeks after sowing; the wetter the season the longer it stands; and it bears a dry year better than a wet one; make no distinction in pulling, between the male and female; or femble and seed hemp, as denominated in some places. In the Cambridgeshire fens they are frequently separated, which may arise from their hemp being coarser, and the stalk larger. The price of pulling is one shilling a peck of the seed sown, or eleven shillings an acre, and beer; but if it comes in harvest, the expence is higher. It is tied up in small bundles called *baits.*

" It

" It is always water-*retted**; clay pits preferred to any
running water, and cleaned out once in seven or eight
years. An acre of three small waggon loads are laid in
one *bed*. They will water five times in the same hole;
but it is thought by some too much. If necessary to wait,
they pull as the hole is ready, not chusing to leave it on
the land after pulled.

" It is generally four days in the water, if the weather is
warm, if not, five; but they examine and judge by feeling
it. The expence is twelve to fifteen shillings an acre.

" The grassing requires about five weeks; and if there
are showers, constantly turned thrice a week; if not,
twice a week. This is always on grass land or layers. It
is done by women; the expence ten shillings an acre. It
is then tied up in large bundles of eight or ten *baits*, and
carted home to a barn or house to break directly.

" Breaking is done by the stone, at one shilling. There
are many people in the district who do it, and earn fifteen or sixteen-pence a day, and beer. The offal is called
hemp *sheaves*, makes good fuel, and sells at two-pence a
stone.

" It is then marketable, and sold by sample at Dis, Har-
ling, Bungay, &c. price 5s. 6d. to 8s. a stone; generally
7s. 6d. In 1795, 10s."

P. 124. " The common method is to sow turnips on the
land immediately after the hemp is cleared: this is for
producing, among the little occupiers, some food for a
cow and the family. With good management, one ploughing and one hoeing will carry them to the value of 30s,
But an evil arising from the practice is, that the land
must for the next crop, be mucked in the spring, when
carting does more damage. When corn is sown after the
hemp, it is wheat; and these are the best crops in the
country, as nothing is esteemed to clean land like this
plant.

" * Generally; but in a circle of about six miles round Thilnetham,
the greater part is never put into the water at all, but is dew-retted,
which is done by laying it on pasture ground, for from three to six
weeks, according to the season, and turned five or six times. This
process costs about one shilling per stone per acre, including pulling,
spreading, turning, and getting up; and the hemp at market is not
worth so much by two shillings per stone, as that which hath been
water-retted, and therefore probably the custom of dew-retting is
only followed to any considerable degree where there are not pits
sufficient to water-ret what grows in a district.—*Note by a Correspondent of the Board.*"

plant. After the wheat, barley or oats, and this great also.

"Finding the profit so great, I demanded why the culture did not increase rapidly? I was answered, that its coming in the midst of harvest was embarrassing, and that the attention it demanded in every stage of its progress was great; being liable to be spoiled if the utmost care was not perpetual.

"It is considered, and with great justice, throughout the district, to be of infinite consequence to the country; and especially to the poor, who are entirely supported by it, and are now earning six-pence a day by spinning, with more ease than three-pence is gained on the other side the county by wool.

"The culture has increased considerably in the last ten years."

The Reporter proceeds to insert a communication of some length, from a "manufacturer at Stowmarket," principally relating to heckling, spinning, weaving; and prices, for these operations. The subjoined passage may be useful to the hemp *grower.*—P. 125. "Hemp may be grown, with success, on the same land, many years, by manuring annually. The quantity of seed usually sown, is from nine to twelve pecks per acre; varying with the strength of the soil, and the custom of the country. In those places where the finest and best hemps are grown, twelve pecks is a common quantity.

"The soil and season make a very material difference in the produce and quality. An acre will produce from 25 to 60 stone; an average crop may be estimated about 36 or 38.

"Hemp, when left for seed, is seldom water-retted, from the additional trouble and expence; but I am of opinion, it would be better if so done. It is generally stacked and covered during the winter, and is spread upon meadow-land in January or February. If the season suits, (particularly if covered with snow) it will come to a good colour, and make strong coarse cloths. It is much inferior to hemp pulled in proper time, and water-retted.

"The custom of many places is to dew-ret their hemp; that is, to spread it on meadow-land as soon as pulled, and turn it frequently; but this is a very bad method of retting it; the bark will not come off completely—it therefore requires more violent means of bleaching the yarn, and consequently diminishes the strength. It is likewise much sooner injured in rainy seasons than hemp water-retted."

The

The " Rev. Mr. Mills of Bury," also, contributes a paper on this subject.—The following extract may have its use.—P. 133. " Hemp delights in a black rich mould, the richer and stronger it is, the better. It has sometimes been sown upon the breaking-up an old lay, and where there has been sufficient depth, with success. Let the land be well worked and manured with 30 loads per acre, about a fortnight before seed time, which is from the beginning to the end of April; if sown earlier, as the plants are almost as tender as French-beans, the frosts would greatly injure, if not totally destroy them; the sooner (the season permitting) it is sown, the better, though it has been sometimes deferred to the 15th of May. Three bushels and an half of good bright seed are sufficient for an acre, which should be gently and lightly harrowed in— the birds must be kept off the land till the plants appear; the time of pulling is about the beginning of August, or, more properly speaking, thirteen weeks from the time of sowing: the leaves turning yellow and the stalks white, are signs of its maturity; the male and female hemp are pulled together: indeed when the crop is thick, it is impossible to separate them."

POTATOES.—P. 117. " This root has not been cultivated in Suffolk till within a few years."

CARROTS.—This is another crop, for whose culture we are to look up to Suffolk;—where its cultivation, *in the field*, has been longer established, probably, than in any other district in the kingdom; principally, it would seem, for the *London market*.—The refuse only (unless by some individuals of late years) being consumed on the farms of the growers.

P. 103. " The culture of carrots in the *Sandlings*, or district within the line formed by Woodbridge, Saxmundham, and Orford, but extending to Leiston, is one of the most interesting objects to be met with in the agriculture of Britain. It appears from Norden's Surveyors Dialogue, that carrots were commonly cultivated in this district two hundred years ago, which is a remarkable fact, and shews how extremely local such practices long remain, and what ages are necessary thoroughly to spread them. *

For

---

* On the ORIGIN of ESTABLISHED PRACTICES.—The particular nature of the land, and the ready conveyance of the produce, by water, to the London market, may serve to account for the locality of the practice, in this instance:—joint circumstances, those, which probably

For many years, (generally till about six or seven past)
the principal object in the cultivation, was sending the
carrots to London market by sea: but other parts of the
kingdom having rivalled them in this supply, they have
of late years been cultivated chiefly for feeding horses;*
and thus they now ascertain, by the common husbandry
of a large district, that it will answer well to raise carrots
for the mere object of the teams.

" Not to enter very minutely into the cultivation, I
shall note here, that the most approved method is, to
leave a barley stubble (which followed turnips) through
the winter, and about Lady-day, to plough it by a double
furrow as deep as may be, and to harrow in 5 *lb.* of seed
per acre. About Whitsuntide they hoe for the first time,
thrice in all, at the expence of 18s. an acre†. The produce on good land, of 10s. to 15s. an acre, 400 to 500
bushels, but sometimes 800 are gained; on poorer soils,
less; even to 200 bushels. They are left in the field
during winter, and taken up as wanted; by which means,
in severe winters, they suffer by the roots rotting, unless
well covered by snow. In feeding, they give about eighty
bushels a week to six horses, with plenty of chaff, but no
corn; and, thus fed, they eat very little hay. Some
farmers, as the carrots are not so good to Christmas as in
the spring, give forty bushels, and four of oats, a week, in
the fore part of the winter; but in the spring eighty, and
no corn. By long experience they find, that horses are
never in such condition as on carrots, and will, on such
food, go through all the work of the season better than on
any other in common use; fed only with corn and hay,
even with a great allowance, they would not be in near
such order. If oats and carrots are given at the same
time, they leave the oats and eat the carrots; but for
horses that are rode fast, they are not equally proper.
They begin to use them before Christmas, and continue
it sometimes till Whitsuntide, those used in the latter
                                                        part

probably do not occur, with equal advantages, in any other extensive
district in the kingdom.
    This is but one instance, of many, in which ESTABLISHED PRAC-
TICES have grown out of given circumstances of soil, substrata, and
situation.—Cultivated, as natural, plants, sooner or later, find out
their favorite places of habitation.

    * This does not clearly appear, in the evidence adduced.

    " † Near Bury, they never cost less than 25s. and sometimes 30s.
per acre, for three hoeings."

part of the season being taken up and housed, **to have the land clear for sowing barley.**

" There is scarcely an article of cultivation in any county of England, that more demands attention than this of carrots in Suffolk, for it is applicable to *all sands*, (! *) and dry friable sandy loams, † of which immense tracts are found all over the kingdom, but this application of them unknown. The subject is so important, that I think it deserving the further attention of here adding the notes I took in a journey, the chief object of which was to ascertain the value and other circumstances of the crop."

Here, we find the Reporter descending from the character of a resident practitioner to that of an enquiring tourist. Having, however, only one object principally in view, his minutes are more intelligible and fuller of information, than those we have formerly had to examine. I will select such items as I think will serve to throw additional light on the subject under view :—more especially such as will tend to moderate the tourist's overweaning partiality for the carrot culture ;—valuable as it undoubtedly is, in certain situations, and to a certain extent.

P. 107. " The first place *we* came to in this excursion, was Sutton, on the farm of Mr. Gerrard, where we received the following information : that they ploughed for them but once, which was a double furrow as deep as possible ; but Mr. Gerrard put them in on one very deep furrow, the plough drawn by three stout horses."

P. 108. " Advanced next to Shottisham, where I viewed Mrs. Curtis's field of carrots, of eight acres, very fine. Sowed five pounds an acre on a double furrow ; hoed thrice at 18s. The product guessed at six or seven loads; the average ten (each 40 bushels). More than half the crop is saleable. Last year many rotted on the ground ; for their practice is to take them up as wanted, except having a store for their own use before hand, in case of frost. In feeding, they give six horses a load a week, and a coomb of corn ; this, in the fore part of the winter, when they

---

* Even (is it here meant) to the three or four inch deep sands of Norfolk ; tho resting on an iron " pan ! ! "

† No matter (shall it be said) as to their depth ; or the specific qualities of the substrata on which they lie?—On many rich, sound, deep, old grass lands, carrots might be grown in quantity ; were it proper to cultivate them, there.

they do not reckon them so good as they are in the spring; then two loads a week, and no corn."

P. 109. " Proceeded to Ramsholt, where, on repeating our inquiries concerning carrots, we found that they sow five pounds of seed, at 1s. a pound, upon a double furrow fourteen inches deep, worth 7s. an acre; hoe thrice at 15s. to 21s. an acre. Take up at 14d. to 16d. a load, topping included. Mr. Weeden, on eighteen acres last year, had eight loads an acre nett for London, and two loads for himself; which crop is an average one. I viewed his field this year, it is nineteen acres, a regular and fine crop, without a weed to be seen."

P. 110. " Proceeded next to Alderton, where we found that Mr. Abblet had eight acres of carrots; but last year twenty. He thought that six horses should not have more than one load a week; one bushel per horse a day a proper allowance; but they keep the horses so fed in such health, that he thinks the saving of hay is not considerable.(?) The food he should prefer would be both oats and carrots, one peck of oats to a bushel of roots. If he was forced to buy horse-food, he would prefer carrots at 15s. to oats at 10s. Culture and produce as before described.

" Called next on Mr. Wimper, a gentleman-farmer of the same place, very sensible and intelligent, who obligingly informed us, that he generally gives oats to his horses as well as carrots; not because they would not do upon the roots and chaff, but because he has usually a greater stock of horses, &c. than breadth of carrots, and therefore he limits the use of them. If forced to buy his horse-food, he would prefer refuse carrots at 12s. to oats at 9s. Fortunately I put to this gentleman a question which I had before omitted: would you cultivate carrots if there was no sale for them? To which he replied, that he would undoubtedly have a few; as many as his consumption demanded; not only for his horses, but for his weanling calves, to whom he gave as many as they would eat; and also for pigs, and sows with pigs, in which application they are particularly useful."

P. 112. " The culture of carrots was, some years ago, more common about Orford than at present, supposed to be owing to the great improvements in the sands near the Woodbridge river, which have rivalled them in the supply of the London market.

" About Leiston are many carrots: few farmers of any consideration but have ten or twelve acres every year; they

they have, however, a bad custom of continuing them on the same field for four or five years. The carrot culture improves the soil so much, (!*) that two years are the most they should be continued, by which means the larger track receives the benefit, I have no doubt, from the situation of their consuming all themselves.

" Passed over some poor land, commons, and uninteresting husbandry, till we came to Wantesden; where, on making farther inquiries, we found that Mr. Curteen, of the Hall, has four acres of CARROTS FOR HIS OWN CONSUMPTION ONLY, giving them to his horses. Mr. Simpson was, for many years, on the same farm, and constantly in the same practice; always had a crop for his horses, and neither he nor Mr. Curteen ever sold a load to London. Here then we have found this clear fact: the intelligence was from a labourer that worked with Mr. Curteen; it was soon after confirmed by a neighbouring farmer, who said there were some others in the practice as well as Mr. Curteen."

Thus, in making the grand tour of the carrot lands of Suffolk, the tourist finds *one instance,* in which a cultivator had " four acres of carrots for his own consumption, only :"—a fact so extraordinary as to be deemed worthy of SMALL CAPITALS in which to record it.—And even this happened in the practice of a *hall* farmer.

Finally, the Reporter enters upon an elaborate discussion of the precise quantity of carrots which horses ought to be allowed;—as if all kinds of horses, of all ages, at all seasons, and on all sorts of work, required exactly the same quantity and quality of food.—A man should look into his stable, from time to time, not into his closet, to ascertain this point.

The following hint, however, may be useful to the *practical* farmer.—P. 116. " One conclusion very naturally arises from this part of the intelligence, that the crop, or a considerable part of it, ought to be taken up in autumn, and packed in a barn ; in which they would much sooner lose their juiciness, and acquire that more withered state, in which they are found to yield the best nourishment."

GENERAL

---

* Double plowing may " improve the soil." But carrying off ten loads of produce, so nutritious as that of carrots, surely cannot.

GENERAL REMARKS on the CARROT CULTURE of SUFFOLK. From what I have gathered, in the Report before me, and from the impressions I received, in the carrot district of that County, it appears evident to me, that the prevalence of their culture, there (as I have intimated) has grown, fortuitously, out of the nature of the lands, and their situation, in regard to the metropolitan market, for that species of farm produce.

The LAND, which I particularly examined, was, in general appearance, uniform in soil, subsoil, base, and substructure, to the depth of twenty or thirty feet (as observed in a sand pit of that depth)—whether in regard to matter, texture, or color. The adjacent fields of corn showed the fertility of the soil, and the circumstance of double-plowing for carrots, and sowing the seed on that one plowing, sufficiently prove the fertile quality of the substratum; while the absorbency of the base affords the dryness and warmth in which the carrot delights.—Wherever rich sandy lands will bear to be double plowed, fourteen inches deep, and enjoy, beneath that depth, a dry warm fertile base, there carrots may be grown to a size, and in quantity, that will bring profit to the cultivator;— provided a good market be situated within his reach.

In regard to SITUATION, the "Sandlings" of Suffolk are not only nearly surrounded with navigable waters, but are deeply insected by inlets and estuaries; by whose aid their bulky products are readily conveyed to the largest and best market in the kingdom.

On the "Improvement!" otherwise, the EXHAUSTION of the SOIL, by the carrot crop, it is to be remarked, that, in the carrot district of Suffolk, or in any other rich deep sandy land, carrots, like sainfoin on calcareous lands, may feed principally in the substratum.—In a field of nearly twenty acres, which I examined while it was under the operation of hoing, the workmen were using "seven inch hoes"—hoes that measured six inches and a half in length; —setting out the plants, a foot apart.—In land like that above described, and under management such as this, the main roots would of course strike, downward, beneath the surface soil, and their feeding fibers much deeper into the substratum;—out of which, it is more than probable, the carrots of the Sandlings of Suffolk draw a principal part of their nourishment.—Hence, the exhaustion of the cultivated soil—the "corn mould"—by carrots thus raised, may

may be much *less*, than by crops which feed more superficially *.

Touching the NUTRITIVE QUALITY of carrots, as HORSE FOOD, it appears to be at present pretty well understood, throughout the kingdom, that they are wholesome provinder;—that they promote a cleanness of habit, and a sleekness of skin; and that they are, of course, eligible food for horses that are moderately, or lightly, worked:—but that they are, by no means adequate as a substitute for oats or other grains, for horses in full work.—For gentlemen and others who keep horses, in the country, without having constant work for them,—there are numberless situations in which a sufficient supply of carrots might, through the help of subdraining and deep culture, be raised, with advantage, for that purpose.

And were it to become fashionable for livery stable keepers (as it well might) to give carrots, to the underworked steeds of their sabbatical and other customers who seldom ride,—CARROT GARDENS might, in the neighbourhood of great towns, become an object of profit.

But there would be little risk, I think, in asserting, that, viewing the kingdom at large,—equally with an eye to *lands* and *markets*, there is not one acre in ten thousand, of its aggregate number, on which carrots could, *at present*, be cultivated, with strict propriety,—agreeably to the long-established, and *(there)* profitable practice of the Sandlings of Suffolk.

TURNEPS.—P. 75. The culture of this plant, may justly be esteemed the greatest improvement in English husbandry that has been established in the present century. In Suffolk, it has changed the face of the poorer soils, and rendered them more productive to the landlord, the tenant, and the public, than any other system of management, perhaps, that could be devised. The culture has been accurately described by a considerable and practical Suffolk

---

* On the EXHAUSTION of LANDS, by CROPS.—Altho it may be true that crops exhaust lands in proportion to the nutriment they afford, it does not follow that the *soil* is uniformly, or necessarily, exhausted, in that proportion.

Hence arises a valuable principle of management, on lands whose *substrata* are of a *fertile nature*;—namely, that of employing deep-rooting plants to draw up the nutriment which they are capable of supplying; and reserving, as much as may be, the strength of the surface soil, the " corn mold," for more superficially feeding crops.

folk farmer, in *The Annals of Agriculture*, from which I shall extract the material heads."

In these extracts, I perceive very little that is particularly novel or excellent, to be entitled to a place, here. The subjoined passages may serve as hints to practitioners.

Manuring for turneps.—P. 77. " In respect to the length of dung, it should neither be long nor quite rotten; the best condition is, when it is in such a state that the labourers say, it will neither spit nor fork."——" When the dung for turnips is rather long, and ploughed in with the seed-earth, the seed should only be rolled in."

Quantity of *seed* of turneps.—The following observations, on CHALKY SOILS, are new to me. They may be accurate. They will, at least, serve as a caution to cultivators of such soils.

P. 77. " The quantity of seed depends on the soil; upon a naturally good turnip sand a pint an acre, evenly delivered by a good hand, or sowing engine, will be enough; no soil demands so much seed as chalky land, when the chalk comes quite to the surface; upon such soil, a quarter of a peck an acre will seldom be too much; the reason of the difference is, that the fly is sure to attack the plants upon this soil much more voraciously and with greater certainty, than on any other."

There is much good sense in the subjoined remarks, on the *failures* incident to the turnep crop.—P. 79. " It is necessary to say something on the failures that turnip crops are liable to, which are the fly, the mildew, the black canker, and to rotting from frost. I calculate that the frost destroys half the crop once in six or seven years; the fly not only destroys some crops entirely, but even when a second or third sowing yields something, it is gained at the expence of one or two ploughings, harrowings, and seed, when no tillage is wanting for the land: this may, on an average, be calculated to amount to the loss of a whole crop once in five or six years; the mildew is rather connected with the rot, and the black canker has not yet been so common with us, as to demand a particular calculation.

" I would, for the above reasons, notwithstanding all the praise that is due to this most useful root, recommend to all sheep masters, especially those with breeding flocks, not to trust singly to them. I have found very great advantage from having certain breadths of cole-seed, rye, and winter tares, sown early on the first stubbles that were

cleared

cleared the preceding autumn ; indeed, supposing no failures, it is absolutely necessary to have some provision for the couples, by the time the lambs begin to feed, as it will put them on a great deal faster than the best turnips that can be given."

Clearing Turnep Grounds, in the spring.—The following practice (for such it would seem) is beautifully simplex. The thought is admirable ; and the effect has *probability* in its favor. It is well entitled to a *trial,* in many cases.

P. 80. "On this subject, the Rev. Mr. Orbell Ray, of Tostoc, thus expresses himself :—'Your address, requesting information of the measures pursued for preserving turnips, and relieving the land from the exhausting effects of their very rapid vegetation, during the spring, determined me to send you the following account of my treatment of this root, the advantages of which I have experienced for many years, and which, with a few variations, is, I believe, the general practice of the Suffolk farmers. About the middle of February, I began to draw my turneps, cutting off the tap-root at the same time, and carried them to a pasture field, adjoining to my farm-yard, where they were unloaded, and labourers employed to take the roots, one by one, and set them upon the grass, in as upright and close a manner as possible. I pursued this method through the month of March, until I had collected above an hundred loads; always availing myself of dry windy weather, when the tops are less brittle, and the roots in the cleanest state. The expence varies with the distance of carriage; the setting up, about three halfpence per load of forty bushels. The growth of the top is not much interrupted by the loss of the tap-root, and is an ample compensation for the waste of the bulb.'"

If the tap roots could be preserved, the bulbs would be less liable to decay. The longer they can be conveniently left, no doubt the better.—The middle of February would seem to be too early, for this business. The frosts are, then, frequently severe.—But, query, may not the closeness of their position, in a living state, accumulate a degree of vital warmth that may tend to resist the effects of frosts ?

RAPE.—"Cole-seed."—See *Waterlands,* p. 290, aforegoing.

CABBAGES.—P. 94. "The culture of cabbages, is another article which adds not inconsiderably to the agricultural merit of Suffolk."

P. 97.

P. 97. "The heavy part of Suffolk is the only district in England, that, to my knowledge, has the culture of cabbages established among common farmers, and is in that respect curious."

The Reporter claims the merit of having been instrumental in establishing this practice. He ingenuously remarks, however,—P. 98. "They" (quere, the common farmers?) " do not have recourse to either turnips or cabbages as a necessary article in any course of crops, but merely in subservience to the dairy. On the contrary, they are very generally of opinion, that the husbandry with any other view is disadvantageous. The wetness of their land is such, that carting off these crops poaches the soil to an extreme, so that the barley which succeeds them is damaged considerably."

Much is said about the *exhaustion* of cabbages, compared with that of turneps. But, if the following opinions and assertions be well founded, little argument can be required to decide the point.

P. 98. "The point, that they exhaust more than turnips, seemed upon the whole to be well ascertained; but some circumstances, even in this respect, deserve attention.

" Several were inclined to attribute this fact to the common practice of cutting off the cabbages, and leaving the shanks and roots in the ground, which throw out sprouts, and *draw* the land when the effect of the crop ought entirely to have ceased. The remark is sensible, and some effect must certainly flow from the neglect of not extracting them root and all. It seemed to be a general opinion, that barley after turnips was better by two coombs an acre than after cabbages ; but it was admitted as generally, that the cabbages were superior to the turnips in quantity and value of food, by more than the amount of two coombs of barley. The opinion most common is, that one acre of cabbages is equal to an acre and a half of turnips : several farmers assured me, that it was equal to two of turnips. Mr. Garneys, of Kenton, that an acre of his cabbages has been better than any two of turnips he ever grew."

It is always dangerous to lay down general rules ; there being none (according to the proverb) without exceptions. I will, therefore, only say, that, as far as my observations have, hitherto, gone,—crops exhaust in proportion to the animal nutriment they are capable of affording, when favorably, and judiciously harvested.

It

It therefore appears, to me, that what immediately follows the above extract, as well as the extract itself, is vague, or not wholely well founded. " And farther, that altho his" (Mr. Garney's) "barley after turnips has had the longest straw, yet he thinks the quantity of corn little superior, and the sample of it not equal. I met with several whose cabbages were done, who thought turnips superior as a preparation for barley; but who wished very earnestly they had planted more cabbages.—Mr. Dove, of Euston-Hall, thought that barley after a summer fallow without dung, would give more, by three coombs an acre, than cabbage or turnip land would, though dunged for that crop. John Fairweather has had part of a field turnips and part cabbages, equally dunged for, and the barley as good after one as the other."—And the subjoined " Note, by J. P. Denham," inserted, not in the section " Cabbages," but in that of " Cattle,"—powerfully militates against the accuracy of the latter statement :—in as much as the practice of a country is frequently (not always) better evidence than the opinion of an individual.

N. P. 182. " The practice of growing cabbages in this neighbourhood, about ten years since, amongst the dairy farmers, was almost general; and some were grown by graziers : the food was much approved of ; but the damage done to the succeeding crops was looked upon as very great. This seems confirmed by there not being one acre growing within six miles this year."

Thus, so far from the practice being permanently established, in Mr. Denham's neighbourhood, at least (we are not informed in what part of Suffolk it lies, nor what is the nature of his or any one's soil!)—it had, at the time of reporting, declined, and passed away.

For an evidence of cabbages being a favorite food of store hogs, see the head, *Swine*, ensuing.

CULTIVATED HERBAGE.—Under the head " laying down to grass," no notice is taken of the " *Suffolk grass*"—POA *annua*—which has long been *understood* to be an ordinary seminal ingredient, in converting arable lands to permanent herbage.

Clover.—P. 83. " It has been cultivated in Suffolk largely beyond the memory of the oldest man ; and is, in every branch of its management, perfectly well understood by good farmers."

P. 84. " For *Seed.*—Great quantities are seeded in Suffolk, it being a very favourite, because sometimes a very
profitable

profitable crop. But there are farmers that have been injured by repeating it too often.

"*Failure of Clover.*—By repeating clover too often, as
every fourth or fifth year, the lands in this county have become tired of it. Though the plant rises well, and has a
good appearance in autumn, after the spring corn is removed, yet it dies in the winter; and there is nothing
more mischievous to the soil than half a plant of clover,
as weeds are sure to supply its place."

Yet unaccountable, as it really is, this very writer is
never ceasingly recommending, the "course of turnips,
barley, clover, wheat." And what is almost equally extraordinary, he inserts the request of a correspondent to
be informed of a substitute for clover;—and this is his
reply.—P. 85. "Chicory" *(Cichory—*CICHORIUM) "is
this great desideratum, (!) and it will answer on all soils. It
may be managed, in every respect, like clover."—But this
happened some years ago.

SAINFOIN.—P. 86. "This noble plant, the most profitable of all others on the soils it affects, is much cultivated
in Suffolk. In the sandy districts, especially the western,
it is every where found, though not in the quantity that
ought to be sown of it. The culture, however, has increased of late years."

Judging from what is said of the soil and subsoil of the
heathland district (see p. 409, aforegoing) there are few
passages of land, in the kingdom, (as I have already intimated,) on which sainfoin ought to be so assiduously cultivated, as on those *superficially barren* grounds.

HOPS.—P. 88. "At Stowmarket and its vicinity, there
are about 200 acres of hops, which deserve mention, as
an article which is not generally spread through the kingdom."—"Eighteen or twenty acres are" (have been)
"grubbed up and turned to meadow within a few years,
owing to bad times. The soil they plant on, is a black
loose moor, on a gravelly bottom, very wet and boggy,
lying on a dead level with the little river that runs by the
town; the more boggy and loose it is, the better the hops
thrive, especially if the gravel be within three feet; the
neighbouring grounds rise in such a manner as to shelter
them very well. Before planting, these morassy bottoms
were coarse meadow, worth about 20 s. an acre, and some
much less.

" In preparing for hops, they form them into beds sixteen feet wide, by digging trenches about three feet wide,
and two feet or two feet and an half deep, the earth that
comes

comes out being spread upon the beds, and .he whole dug and levelled."

Watering Hop Grounds.—P. 90. " Mr. Rout has raised a bank against the river about three feet high, to lessen the force of floods; but does not wish to keep them entirely out; as he finds, that if the water comes in gently, and does not wash the earth away, it is rather beneficial. And he is clear, that if he was to let the river into his drains to a certain height, in very dry weather, it would be of service to the crop."—This is new, I believe, and is interesting to written agriculture.

GRASS LANDS.—P. 138. " The management of meadows and upland pastures, in this county, in general, can scarcely be worse. Upon the same farms, where almost every effort is made upon the arable, the grass is nearly, or quite neglected. A little draining is sometimes, though rarely, bestowed. Manuring them is almost unknown in the hands of tenants; and as to mole and ant hills, bushes, and other rubbish, immense tracts of what is called grass, are over-run with them. Rolling is seldom performed. Things wear rather a better aspect upon farms occupied by the owners; but, speaking generally, I allude principally to tenants. As to lands in the hands of gentlemen, they are managed, in many cases, in a much superior stile, but not always."

In this, as in other particulars of management, the established practice of Suffolk much resembles that of Norfolk.

CATTLE.—*Breed.*—P. 179. " The breed is universally *polled* *, that is, without horns; the size small; few rise, when fattened, to above 50 stone, (14 lb.) The points admitted are, a clean throat, with little dewlap; a snake head; clean thin legs, and short; a springing rib, and large carcass; a flat loin, the hip bones to lie square and even; the tail to rise high from the rump. This is the description of some considerable dairy-men. But if I was to describe the points of certain individuals, which were very famous for their quantity of milk, it would vary in several points; and these would be such as are applicable

---

" * The breed is in general polled; but a certain proportion of the calves would have horns if reared: the inconvenience of horned cattle among horses, and the damage they do to fences, are an inducement to the farmers to sell all the calves as veal to the butchers, or to the sucklers, which would have horns, and to keep for stock only the polled ones. The horns are to be felt at a very early age."

cable to great numbers : a clean throat, with little dewlap ; a thin clean snake head ; thin legs ; a very large carcass ; rib tolerably springing from the centre of the back, but with a heavy belly ; back-bone ridged ; chine thin and hollow ; loin narrow ; udder large, loose, and creased when empty ; milk-veins remarkably large, and rising in knotted puffs to the eye. This is so general, that I scarcely ever saw amongst them a famous milker that did not possess this point. A general habit of leanness, hip-bones high and ill-covered, and scarcely any part of the carcass so formed and covered as to please an eye that is accustomed to fat beasts of the finer breeds. But something of a contradiction to this, in appearance, is, that many of these beasts fatten remarkably well, the flesh of a fine quality ; and in that state will *feel* well enough to satisfy the touch of skilful butchers. The best milkers I have known, have been either red, brindle, or yellowish cream-coloured." *

Breeding Cattle.—P. 183. "The greatest fault to be found with their management, is the carelessness with which they breed. There is no such thing in the country as a bull more than three years old ; two years the common age. The consequence of this is inevitable, that, before the merit can be known of the stock gotten, the bull is no more."

Management of Store Cattle.—P. 102 (section "Cabbages"). " In the consumption of these crops" (cabbages and turnips) " the farmers of this district are in one instance exceedingly reprehensible.—There is no idea of confining cows to a farm-yard. They are universally open

---

* SUFFOLK CATTLE.—The *history* of this variety of English cattle, which were, not many years ago, peculiar to Suffolk, but which have of later years, been over-running Norfolk (see n. p. 395, aforegoing)—I have no where met with ;—not even in conjecture.

In the want of horns, and somewhat in frame, and a few or them in colour, the Suffolk breed bear some resemblance to the hornless varieties that are seen in the southwest quarter of Scotland. But their more prevailing color is that of the Alderney or French cattle. They differ much, however, from these, in regard to quantity and quality of milk. That of the Alderney is generally rich ; but is seldom abundant. Whereas the Suffolk cows afford large quantities, in proportion to their size ; but it is mostly, I believe, of an inferior quality.

On trying the qualities of milks, from different breeds of cows, with a LACTOMETER (at WOBURN in 1795) that from the Suffolk breed was found to be much inferior to that from the long-horned variety ; being similar, (I unfortunately write from recollection) to that from the short-horned breed.

open to two, three, or more pastures, so that the cattle have the barn-door at pleasure, and range over the fields almost where they please. The cabbages and turnips are scattered about on lands so wet, that the cattle at every step are up to the fetlock, and they walk regularly backwards and forwards to the farm-yards, poaching in such a manner, that if the soil was not very fertile, it would never recover, but harden with the summer sun into knobs of steril mortar."

This home charge against the Suffolk husbandry, however, is somewhat contradicted by the following entry, in the section " Cattle."—After speaking of the practice of feeding milk cows with cabbages, the Reporter says— P. 183. " Another circumstance in the management of their cows deserving notice, is, that of tying them up in the fields, without house, or shed, or roof, to cover them. With rails and stakes they form a rough manger; and the cows are tied to posts about three feet from each; at their heads is a screen of faggots. Litter is regularly given, and the dung piled up in a wall behind. They find this better than letting them range at will, for cows before calving; and that the shelter of the hedge and dung, and the warmth of their bodies, are enough without any cover."—This is, in truth, a most singular circumstance, in the winter management of cows.

Fatting Cattle.—P. 188. " In those parts of the county where the sheep and cows do not consume the turnips, the common practice is, to buy black cattle at fairs, from north country drovers, for that purpose. Some are Irish, and some Welch; but the greater part are Scotch, of various breeds; Galloways, Fifes, and Highlanders. The system in which they are grazed, is of two kinds: some farmers buy in autumn, and give a winter's straw, fattening them in summer; this takes place where live stock is wanting to consume the straw. The other method is practised when the common stock of the farm is sufficient for the straw; then to purchase in autumn, and put to rouen for seven or eight weeks, and from that to turnips, to which hay is added; and a few farmers have finished on oil cake, and other articles of food. The late Mr. Mure, of Saxham, stall-fed on a very large scale, upon cabbages and potatoes."

In the concluding lines of the paragraph from which the last extract is taken, and which closes the section Cattle, is sported the following ' dangerous doctrine.'— P. 189. " This is a branch of the farmer's business, in which

which *general* details are nearly useless; it is only by the recital of particular experiments, that any accurate conclusions can be drawn."

Rather let it be said—it is only from "GENERAL DETAILS," faithfully given, that any thing resembling sound conclusions, in practical husbandry—can be safely drawn :—certainly not from crude, uncircumstantially stated and uncorroborated "experiments." *

DAIRY.—The Dairy *District* of Suffolk.—P. 179. "The country, which is more peculiarly, but not exclusively, the seat of the dairies, is marked out by the parishes of Codenham, Ashbocking, Otley, Charlsfield, Letheringham, Hatcheston, Parham, Framlingham, Cransford, Bruisyard, Badingham, Sibton, Heveningham, Cookly, Linstead, Metfield, Wethersdale, Fressingfield, Wingfield, Hoxne, Brome, Thrandeston, Geslingham, Tenningham, Westrop, Wyverston, Gipping, Stonham, Cretting ; and again to Codenham, with all the places within, being a tract of country of 20 miles by 12. The limits cannot be exact, for this breed of cows spreads over the whole county ; but this space must be more peculiarly considered as their head-quarters."—This is well given valuable report.

Butter is the main *object* of the Suffolk dairy.

The *number* of *cows* kept for supplying the London market, with that article, may be estimated from the number of firkins supposed to be sent up; namely 40,000, (see *Markets*, p. 417, aforegoing).—If we reckon on three firkins as the par produce of a cow, the number of cows may be set down at thirteen or fourteen thousand.

Proportion of *Cows* to *Acres.*—P. 181. "The common calculation is, that a cow in milk eats in summer two acres of grass ; and that on an average of twenty miles by twelve,

---

* ON PROMOTING AGRICULTURAL SCIENCE.—First, let us have the BEST PRACTICE of a country, by which men of EXPERIENCE get money ; and whereby the community are clothed and fed, to the BEST ADVANTAGE.—Then will the public be ready to receive, and capable to judge of, any "*experiments*," that may be made with a view toward the IMPROVEMENT of such best practice.

Let us not only have a "general" and full view of the FOUNDATION, but also of the SUPERSTRUCTURE, IN ITS BEST FORM, before we bestow a moment's attention on its IMPROVEMENT.—FOR HOW ARE WE TO PROCEED IN THE WORK OF IMPROVEMENT, UNTIL WE HAVE EXAMINED THE EXISTING STRUCTURE,—ASCERTAINED ITS SEVERAL BEARINGS, AND DEPENDENCIES,—AND THOROUGHLY UNDERSTAND ALL ITS EXCELLENCIES AND DEFECTS?

twelve, there is one cow to every five acres of the whole country."

The *quantity* of *Milk*, given by the Suffolk cows, has ever been spoken of as extraordinarily large.—The subjoined extract corroborates that idea.—P. 180. " The quantity of milk given is very considerable indeed. There is hardly a dairy of any consideration in the district, that does not contain cows which give, in the height of the season, that is, in the beginning of June, eight gallons of milk in the day; and six are common among many for a large part of the season. For two or three months a whole dairy will give, for all that give milk at all, five gallons a day on an average, if the season is not unfavourable, which, *for cows of this size*, is very considerable."

Produce of *Cows.*—P. 181. " When the quantity of milk in any breed is very great, that of butter is rarely equal. It is thus in Suffolk; the quantity of milk is more extraordinary than that of the butter. The average of all the dairies of the district may be estimated at three firkins; and three-fourths of a wey of " (skim) " cheese per cow, clear to the factor's hands, after supplying the consumption of the family. The hogs are very generally laid at a guinea per cow, and a calf, at a fortnight old, half-a-guinea.

	£.	s.	d.
" Three firkins, at 38s. average price of last seven years,	5	14	0
Three-fourths wey, at 36s.	1	7	0
Hogs,	1	1	0
Calf,	0	10	6
	£. 8	12	6

" About 2s. or 3s. may be deducted from this, on account of the calves reared to keep up the stock; and if something more is struck off on account of a few ill-managed dairies, that do not properly come into the account, it may reduce it to eight guineas. Instances are numerous, that raise it higher."

Beside the Reporter's own account of the Suffolk dairy, a communication, by Mrs. CHEVALLIER of Aspal, is inserted in this Report.

It does not come within my general plan, to insert lengthened communications, entire; as I rarely find them uniformly valuable.—But Mrs. Chevallier's Letter is so full of intelligence, and so pleasingly written, that I am
induced

induced to transcribe the whole of it, in the order in which
it stands in the original.

P. 184. "In the visit we had lately the pleasure of receiving from you, your inquiries concerning cows, and the
management of our dairies, were, I believe, much more
numerous than very easily to be satisfied. Your request
that I would make up the deficiency, by sending you such
particulars as have occurred to me, was dictated, I am
afraid, rather by your partiality than your judgment; for
I assure you, there is nothing in my own management peculiar, nor does it exceed that of any well-conducted
dairy in this country. And I request you will observe,
that my only inducement for throwing a word of the subject on paper, is your opinion that there are circumstances
common here which are not so in other Counties; but
which may be useful if better known: should this not be
the case, remember that you are more answerable for this
letter than myself."

Breed of *Cows* (by Mrs. C.)—"In the conversation I
heard on your purchasing cows, I observed that you
inquired after large and handsome ones; but I have
often known little cows not at all remarkable for
beauty, give more milk than the greatest; for instance,
at present, the smallest cow we have, a cream coloured
polled one, gives more milk than any of the rest, though
some are almost double the size. This cow last summer, for some time in the height of the season, gave four
gallons of milk at a meal twice a day; three gallons for
the rest of the summer, and has given more than two gallons within two months of calving. This vast quantity of
milk is not uncommon in this country."

Proving the *Quality* of *Milk* (by Mrs. C.)—"I recollect
an observation you made, on the product in money of
cows being nearer a par through the kingdom than the
quantity of milk; and it may be said, that the milk of
cows which gives so much, is not so rich as when the quantity is less. Mr. Chevallier having some horned cows,
partly from Mr. Toosey's breed, and originally from Mr.
Bakewell, which do not give so much milk as our Suffolk
breed, I tried an experiment lately for comparing the quality of the milk. Three quarts from a Suffolk polled cow,
and the same quantity from a horned one of Mr. Toosey's
breed, were set in separate bowls; stood thirty-six hours,
and then skimmed; the Suffolk milk gave two and one-
third ounces more cream than the horned one; it was put
into two clean quart bottles and churned: the quantity of
butter exactly one-fourth more from the cream of the
                                                        polled

polled than from that of the horned cow. Then added to each bowl of milk an equal quantity of hot water, and after twelve hours skimmed them a second time; when the milk of the horned cow yielded four ounces more cream than that of the polled. As in the first experiment the superiority of butter was more than that in cream, we may conclude from this trial, that the quality of the milk was very nearly equal. I repeated the experiment to try the weight of an equal quantity of the cream of each: the milk stood thirty-six hours; the quantity was about one-sixth more from the polled than from the horned cow; the weight of the same measure of each, equal. I do not offer these experiments as decisive; nor by any means sufficient to draw conclusions from; but they seem to deserve attention for varying and repeating them with more care and accuracy, that if any material difference is found, it may be known. All I can conclude at present is, that the milk of the polled cows appears to be as rich as that of the horned ones; but the quantity they give in summer is greater; and that will be the proper season for repeating these trials.

"By similar experiments it would be easy to ascertain whether the milk of cows that are generally in good order or fat, is not superior in quality to that of others of the same polled breed, that are poor and lean."

This is a charming thought,—which conveys, to my mind, new and interesting ideas. And I value it the more, as it aptly emanates from that of a sensible, enlightened mistress of a dairy; whose experiments and observations, on the subject in view, are truly scientific.

It is well understood that lean cows, when first turned out to grass in the spring, give less *quantities* of milk, than those which go out in good condition;—but it never occurred to me, until I met with Mrs. Chevallier's valuable suggestion,—that the *qualities* of milk, drawn from animals, in different states of body, might vary. And, yet, analogy might well have led to such a suggestion. I allude to the feces of animals. Indeed, reason might have suggested, that the muscles, in a lean exhausted state, must necessarily absorb a greater portion of oleaginous particles, from the aliment taken in, than those which are already saturated, or approximating to the state of saturation.

If it is a fact, in the natural history of cows, that the richness of their milks vary with the condition they are in, it follows of course, that in making comparative experiments,

riments, on the milks of different breeds, or individuals, that circumstance should have due consideration.—See note p. 458, aforegoing.

Produce of *Cows* (by Mrs. C.)—" Certain it is, that the product of our polled breed is very great. In the year 1784, I made from five cows to the amount of 42*l*. besides the milk and cream consumed by a family of fourteen in number; nor was that a more productive year than common, for I have done it more than once: and I am informed that 7*l*. per cow is very common in this country, large dairies through, on an average.

" The following is the product of one with which I am well acquainted:

					£.	s.	d.
3 Firkins of butter, at 32s.	-		-		4	16	0
1 Wey of cheese,		-		-	1	12	0
Hogs,	-		-		1	0	0
Calf,	-	-		-	0	10	6
Per Cow,	-	-	-	-	£. 7	18	6

" And I may here observe to you, that a farmer at Badlingham, who has forty-eight cows, and has neither wife nor housekeeper, hired a dairy-maid at 9d. per firkin of butter and wey of cheese; and her wages came to 6*l*. 19*s*. 5*d*. the number must therefore have been 186, or very near four per cow."

Management of *Cows* (by Mrs. C.)—" In order to secure such products, several circumstances must unite: no cows are to be kept that do not milk well; they must be fed plentifully; and well kept in winter, when cabbages are found essentially useful; but this is a point which I leave to Mr. Chevallier; he can give you better information on it."

Management of the *Butter Dairy* (by Mrs. C.)—" Extreme cleanliness in the dairy is an article on which more depends than is usually conceived; not in quality only, but even in quantity of produce.

" I have found it a very good way to add, in winter, hot water to milk directly as it comes from the cow; it makes it yield the cream better. The trays in which it is set should also be scalded with hot water, or else warmed by the fire, before the milk is set in them. All trays should be of deal, about three inches and a half deep; they are preferable to lead, which not only blisters when hot water is poured into them, but are said to be unwholesome.

About

About twelve square yards of tray will do for twenty cows, with some spare bowls. And the churn for such a dairy should contain about fifty gallons, beer measure. The copper should hold an hundred gallons. Chaffing dishes of charcoal are kept in dairies in frost, but the cream does not rise so well. The best dairy-maids never put the butter in layers in the firkin; but leave the surface every day rough and broken, in order to unite better with that of the succeeding churning: from three and a half to four pints of salt commonly used to a firkin of butter; but two with good management are better. The milk after the first skimming is left twelve hours more in the farm-house, to make a second butter, which the poor buy at four-pence per pound. Another advantage for them is, skim-milk being constantly sold at three pints for a halfpenny. A dairy-maid commonly milks seven or eight cows in an hour; but Mr. Sad, of Little Stonham, had a maid who milked for a wager, thirty cows in three hours, and was followed to see that she milked clean. In your calculations, you must not charge the dairy with all the expence of the dairy-maids; for they spin usually four-pence a day (or to the full amount of their wages) either by hemp for the family use, or wool, the business of the dairy being over by nine or ten o'clock; and in all the calculations of produce in this country, the sale to the butter-factor is meant, which is exclusive of the family consumption. Hence the labour of the dairy is reduced exceedingly."

Rearing Calves (by Mrs. C.)—"In relation to weaning calves, my method, which has proved very successful, is to take them from the cow at a fortnight old, and to give them water-gruel and hay, by which means they are weaned at a very small expence, and with little skimmed milk.

"If not carefully attended to in the winter following, they are subject to the garget; by which distemper I have known eight lost out of nine. I believe it is nearly the same as the rheumatism in the human body; lying wet, or having only very wet land to be on, will certainly give it: I know no cure; but being kept perfectly dry, is an almost sure prevention."

SHEEP.—*Breed.*—P. 189. "The Norfolk breed of sheep spread over almost every part of the county; and as the most famous flocks are about Bury (much more celebrated than any in Norfolk), it has been observed, that they ought rather to be called the Suffolk breed."

My

My readers being aware of the marked prejudice of the Reporter, against this breed of sheep (see p. 397, aforegoing * ,—it would be a waste of time to follow *him*, farther, into the subject of breed.—I will, therefore, only transcribe the remarks of an *annotator*, on this particular; —and I will do it the rather, as they agree with my own ideas explained aforegoing, p. 400 ;—*before I had read the note here subjoined.*

N. P. 191. " It is not in my power to controvert what is here advanced by the author. I cannot, however, forbear remarking, that each County seems to have a breed of sheep peculiar to the soil. And were there as much pains taken to remedy the defects in our own breed, as there is in crossing the breeds, and in introducing those of other counties, I conceive that the Norfolk breed would be inferior to none. One method of remedying these defects, would be to alter the mode of chusing the lambs for stock. Instead of the largest, which are now universally preferred, we should chuse those which are shortest in the leg, and have the broadest loin and shoulder. This would contribute very considerably to improve the shape complained of, and make them more productive in the fleece. —*Note by J. R.*"

Breeding Sheep.—P. 193. " The rams are turned into the flock about a fortnight after Michaelmas, sometimes later: and in doing this, ten or twelve will be let in promiscuously among 600 ewes, without the least attention or idea of separating the sixty best ewes to put to the best ram, in order that some part of the flock might be improving : on the contrary, the worst ewes may, in the common method, have the best ram ; and the best ewes the worst ram. With such conduct, a farmer has good luck, if his flock is not in a state of degradation."

Nevertheless, it is the breed in this state of degradation, which the writer delights to revile!—His home *charge* against them (but without any *proof*) is that of their being *great eaters.*—But has not the same charge been brought (and dinned in our ears) against the Leicestershire, and the Lincolnshire breeds, in a similar state of degradation ? Yet, what extravagant praises have been bestowed on those breeds, in a state of improvement.

SWINE.—*Breeds.*—P. 199. " Of the hogs of Suffolk I shall

---

* Yet, here, we find him ' proud of the honor' of claiming them, as the " famous" and " celebrated " breed of *Suffolk !*

shall only observe, that the short white breed of the cow district has very great merit: well made, thick short noses, small bone, and light offals; but not quite so prolific as some worse made breeds."

From what I have incidentally seen of the Suffolk breed, they appear to be of a very superior quality :—a highly improved variety, it would seem, of the ancient white breed of the kingdom.

Food of *Store Swine.*—In a communication by "Mr. W. Green of Bradfield,"—we find the subjoined notice.— P. 95 (section "Cabbages"). "Hogs prefer them exceedingly to turnips ; of this I have a striking instance the present season; for having a field part under turnips and part cabbages, my sows, &c. have at various times this winter got into the field, and I do not think they have begun ten turnips in the whole field, but constantly got to the cabbages."

RABBITS.—This writer appearing,—from his remarks, in the Report now under Review, as well as in those of Lincolnshire and Norfolk,—to have little, if any, practical knowledge of rabbit warrens, and much ill-founded prejudice against them, *his* strictures concerning them cannot be entitled to especial attention.

An *annotator*, on this Report would seem to have more accurate ideas on the subject.—N. P. 200. " The calculation in Lincolnshire is, that an acre of warren should produce twenty rabbits annually. The carcass is estimated to defray the rent and expences, and the skins are considered as clear profit. If this calculation be generally true, there is no mode of occupying such land as is usually appropriated to warrens, that can compare with it, in point of profit to the occupier.—*Note by a Correspondent of the Board.*"

POULTRY.—P. 200. " The County is exceedingly well supplied, and especially with turkeys, for which it is almost as famous as Norfolk."

For calculations on the EXPENSE and PROFIT of FARMING, see p. 422, aforegoing.

NORTHEAST ESSEX.

A PRINCIPAL object, in my journey through the EASTERN DEPARTMENT, was to endeavour to ascertain its most natural and agricultural boundary, toward the south and southwest.—The result of my examinations has been already noticed. See note p. 2, aforegoing.

The part of Essex which I include in this department, whether it be considered in a natural, or in an agricultural, point of view, might, without great impropriety, have been considered as a portion of SUFFOLK, and passed over, without especial notice.—But as there have been *three*, in reality *four*, REPORTS, sent in, to the Board, concerning ESSEX, it will be right to look into them, and to extract the useful information, which they may contain, and which particularly relates to this part of the County.

The "original Report" is by Messrs. GRIGGS; the "second original," (in the 4to form with broad margins not reprinted) by Mr. VANCOUVER; the third, (never printed) by the late Mr. HOWLET; the last, by the SECRETARY of the BOARD;—who has incorporated much of Mr. Howlet's, (it would seem) and some of Mr. Vancouver's remarks, with his own:—thus forming a voluminous work.

" GENERAL

"GENERAL VIEW

OF THE

AGRICULTURE

OF THE

COUNTY OF ESSEX,

WITH OBSERVATIONS ON THE MEANS OF ITS IMPROVEMENT.

BY

Messrs. GRIGGS,

OF HILL HOUSE, NEAR KELVEDON, IN ESSEX.

1794."

THIS is one of the smallest, if not the very least, of the ORIGINAL REPORTS. Its contents are comprized in twenty pages.

Concerning the QUALIFICATIONS of Messrs. Griggs, little or nothing arises, in a perusal of their Report.—"Hill House" appears, in the map of the County, to be situated in the quarter of Essex which I include in the department now under view.

They speak exclusively, of that part of Essex, in the following manner.

P. 11. "Towards the middle of Essex, and the northern part bordering upon Suffolk, the SOIL varies considerably; some being light, with chalky clay or gravelly sand, at a foot, or a foot and a half below the surface; other parts are moist and binding, affording a quick vegetation, and requiring constant attention in the summer months to prevent it exhausting itself by a spontaneous produce; the plough is seen to occupy the larger part of this district, as little more meadow or old pasture grounds are found, than will supply hay and feed for the horses on the farms, and feed for a few cows, kept for the purpose of suckling, and dry cattle and sheep, which are principally bought in one year.

year, and sold out the next. Here, every common sort of
grain, pulse, and artificial grass is found, with some well
managed and productive hop grounds, which from the
vast expence of cultivating, and uncertain produce, are
kept in the hands of the most opulent landholders, to
whom they are upon the whole lucrative."

In POLITICAL ECONOMY, the most interesting matter,
contained in this sketch, relates to the *manufactures* of
Essex (which are, or were, carried on, in the part of the
County under consideration); and the exorbitant *poor*
rates, which have arisen from their decline.

P. 11. "Very extensive woolen manufactories of bays,
says, &c. are carried on at Colchester, and the towns in
this part of the County, in times of peace, and occasion a
great increase of population, and of course consumption
of the products of the land; but when one considers the
heavy and almost unsupportable burden, of innumerable
poor falling upon the land, the instant a proclamation for
war is heard, and see the rates rise to *three-fourths of the*
rent, and sometimes even exceeding it *, it seems to strike
at the very root of a farmer's industry, and to act almost
as a prohibition to all hopes of success, whilst the opulent
manufacturer, who alone has grown rich by the labour of
the pauper, now seems, from custom, released from dis-
bursing any part of his gains, to support the instruments
of his wealth, when trade declines, and they are compelled
to apply to their parish for relief."

On ESTATE AGENCY, are the following brief remarks.—
P. 22. "The houses upon the Essex farms are good and
conveniently constructed, and the stables, barns, cow-
houses, and other buildings, more numerous than in most
other counties. These, after being put into repair by the
landlord, at the commencement of the lease, are generally
to be kept so at the tenant's expence, at least as far as
workmanship goes; this clause, with others to prevent
meadows and old pastures from being broken up; *to oblige*
the tenant to fallow every second or third year †, to prohibit
the growth of hemp, flax, wood, and such exhausting crops
from

* In 1810, these distressing effects remain, without abatement !—
A caution, this, to shortsighted "improvers" who wish to introduce
manufactures upon their estates.
How irrational are the Poor Laws of this land !

† This relates to the southerly and western quarters of the County
where the lands are strong and cool, rather than to the Suffolk side
of it.

from being sown; to forbid the disposal of any of the
hay, straw, or manure arising on the farm, are generally
inserted in all leases, though particular covenants are
entered into in almost every grant, according to the
particular circumstances of the case."

Respecting AGRICULTURE, proper (excepting what is
first above extracted) I perceive nothing that is entitled
to transcription.

The subjoined particulars, however, relating to an extraordinary practice (for such it appears to be, from this
as well as the other Reports of the County) in FIELD
GARDENING, are well deserving of a place, here.

P. 18. " *Coriander, Teazel, and Carraway*. As Essex
is rather singular in the production of a kind of treble
crop, consisting of coriander, teazel, and carraway, a particular mention of it may be acceptable to the public.
The seeds of these several plants are sown together, very
early in the spring, upon a strong old ley, once ploughed;
and generally yield very considerable returns: the usual
mode is, for a substantial farmer to take in a sort of part-
ner, in this species of husbandry, who is in an inferior situation, and will give up his time to the hoeing and managing of it: the agreement is, that the farmer supplies the
land, ploughs it, and pays all parish and other usual
charges incident to land; and the labourer sows it, keeps
it clean by frequent hoeings, cuts, threshes, and makes it
ready for market; and then the produce is equally divided:
this connection lasts three years, and sometimes longer.

" In the first, the several seeds come up; and, when of
sufficient growth, are set out with a hoe; and the coriander, which is an annual, is ripe before harvest, and produces a return of from ten to fourteen hundred weight an
acre: in the second year the teazel, most of which will
run now, yields a load, or six score staffs, of fifty heads
each staff; and the carraway from three to six hundred
weight of seed: the third year the teazel declines, and the
carraway is in perfection, and will yield an equal bulk
with the coriander; and most of the teazel that did not
run last season, will produce heads this, and afford a fourth
or fifth part of the crop it did the preceding season; by
which time the several plants are in general exhausted,
though a fourth and even fifth year of carraway, has been
known to succeed.

" The coriander, or *col*, as some call it, and carraway, are
to be treated with great care when ripe, otherwise the
largest and best part of the seed will be lost; to prevent
which,

which, women and children are employed to cut it, plant by plant, as soon as it is ripe, and put it immediately into cloths, prepared to receive it; and in them it is carried to the middle, or some other convenient part of the field, and threshed upon a sail cloth, spread for the purpose, upon which men stand to receive it; who, with a few strokes of the flail get the seed clean out of the straw, and are ready for another little load in a few minutes. The use of these seeds is too well known to need a word upon that subject.

" The teazel is also cut by women; who are instructed to leave the weak and rotten heads, and select only the strong and healthy ones; the others, being of no use, would spoil the sample, and the credit of the grower ; at the same time these heads are cut with a stalk, of six or eight inches in length, and bound up in small bunches, or gleans, of five and twenty heads each ; the like number of which bunches, or gleans, constitute half a staff; which, after a few days sun, to harden and dry them, are tied together upon a stick, or staff, of two feet and a half long ; and, in this form, carried to market.

" The head of the teazel is of a conical form, two or three inches in length, and one, or one and an half, in diameter, at the bottom, or largest end, armed on every part with small, strong points, turned a little downwards ; and are bought by the woolen manufacturers; who fix them upon frames, calculated to cover a cylinder, which is made to turn round, and slightly catch their says, bays, &c. which another part of the weaver's machine draws against them; by which means the knap is raised to almost any length the manufacturer wishes. Sometimes, where the farmer prefers a certainty, he will let his land, for three, four, or five pounds an acre per annum, for three years, ploughing and paying as before, rather than risk the hazards of blights, strong winds, when the seeds are ripe, or a decay of the woolen trade ; any of which, greatly lessen the profits of this speculation. After the carraway is worn out, the farmer resumes his land, and has nothing to do, but plough and sow, for a good crop of wheat the following year, which is seldom known to disappoint him, after the land has been thus treated."

" GENERAL

"GENERAL VIEW

OF THE

AGRICULTURE

IN THE

COUNTY OF ESSEX;

WITH OBSERVATIONS ON THE MEANS OF ITS IMPROVEMENT.

BY

CHARLES VANCOUVER.

FEBRUARY 1795."

MR. VANCOUVER'S QUALIFICATIONS have been already noticed, in p. 224, aforegoing.

His MODE of SURVEY, in ESSEX, as in Cambridgeshire, was that of a TOURIST. But his examinations would seem to have been prosecuted by somewhat different methods, in the two Counties.—In Cambridgeshire, each village in the County was examined (some few excepted) and the remarks on each reported, separately:—whereas, in Essex, the several parishes were thrown into districts, and a separate tour made through each district. Hence

The PLAN of the REPORT, in this case differs, in some sort, from that of Cambridgeshire;—in which the whole of the parishes, examined, were brought into one table, at the end of the parochial journal (see p. 243): whereas, in the Essex Report, a separate table is given, at the end of each district:—tho it may contain but a few parishes.

By this mode of proceeding, the journal part of the Report, under consideration, notwithstanding the great number of parishes, mentioned in it, is brought within a comparatively small compass. But the simplicity and clearness, observable in the Cambridgeshire journal, are in vain looked for, in that of Essex; and every idea of a doomsday book vanishes.

Of the *fourteen districts*, into which Mr. V. has divided the County, only the five first (with part of the sixth, and

a smaller

a smaller part of the twelfth) come within the outline of the EASTERN DEPARTMENT.

District I.*—P. 9. "Temperate mixed soil, lying upon a gravel; a sand, a blue and white chalky clay, a brown tender clay, or brick earth; and a tough strong clay, or tile earth."

District II.—P. 37. "Light mixed soil, upon a gravel, a sand, and a brown tender loam."

District III.—P. 42. "Temperate mixed soil, upon a gravelly loam, a sandy, or a fine gravel; a brown clay, or brick earth; and a red clay or tile earth."

District IV.—P. 47. "(Mersea Island)—Temperate mixed soil."

District V.—P. 49. "Strong heavy mixed soil upon a brown clay, or brick earth, a gravelly loam, and a tough red clay or tile earth."

District VI.—P. 52. "Temperate mixed soil upon a gravel, a sand, a brown tender clay, and some strong clay, or tile earth."

These may, without severity, be deemed loose, if not vague, definitions. The epithets "temperate"—"tender" —"gentle" &c.—applied to soils (and unexplained) are not only intechnical, but unmeaning.—Beside, in viewing a country or district, with regard to agriculture, it is not the *soil*, but the LAND, which is to be attended to. Land is composed of three parts;—the SOIL, the SUBSOIL, and the BASE on which they rest. The nature of land, and its fitness for particular purposes in AGRICULTURE, depend more essentially on the *substrata*, than on the *surface soil*. —The same soil, for instance, which, resting on an *absorbent* base, is proper for the culture of TURNEPS and BARLEY, would, if incumbent on a *repellent* subsoil, be best suited to the production of WHEAT and BEANS:—that is to say, would become land of an *opposite* quality, in the eye of an experienced cultivator;—not only in regard to ARABLE crops, but to LIVESTOCK;—the one being best adapted to SHEEP, the other to CATTLE. Yet we see, above, lands thus opposite in their natures, for agricultural purposes, included in almost every one of Mr. V's districts.

But the propriety and advantages of resolving a *country* into *really* natural and agricultural districts, having been perceived in the PROTOTYPE of the BOARD'S REPORTS,—it would

---

* A small part of this properly belongs to the MIDLAND DEPARTMENT.

would seem to have become a standing order, to instruct the Surveyors of *Counties*, to divide *them* into districts—" natural ones, if you can ;—if not, divide them into districts :"—and Mr. Vancouver has done his best.—ESSEX admits but of few natural and agricultural divisions.

Not having the same motive, toward making copious extracts, from the journal, in this as in the former case (in which I was anxious to register every scrap I could collect, concerning the fens and marshes of Cambridgeshire)—I will only digest such items of information, therein contained, as are suitably adapted to the intention of the present volume.

Should I, in doing this, have good occasion to censure any particular I may meet with, I shall be better authorized to exercise that most irksome part of my duty to the agricultural public,—in the present, than in the former case; in which I could only admire the quantity of useful materials collected in so short a space of time. But, in Essex, the Reporter appears (from the subjoined extract) to have taken sufficient time to have collected, and duly arranged, matter, for a more *regular work*.—Indeed, this may fairly be considered, what it really is, a *second*, rather than an *"original"* Report. The apology made at the close of " part the second," is I conceive insufficient to obviate these remarks.

After enumerating a long list—a very long and respectable list—of "Gentlemen, who, not only in the most handsome and liberal manner, afforded and procured for him all the assistance, and information in their power, but many of them received and treated him with much attention, politeness and hospitality,"—the Reporter continues—P. 188. " Nor can he take his leave of the above gentlemen, or those from whom he derived similar assistance, and by whom he was equally well received in Cambridgeshire, without expressing much concern, for that pressure of circumstances which prevented his more full and complete investigation of the subjects of the respective surveys. In the loose manner in which he has consequently been obliged to execute these inquiries and to hasten them out of hand, they have cost him for unavoidable expences only, more than two hundred guineas, over and above the one hundred and twenty-five pounds the Board of Agriculture has allowed for his indemnification of all the expences he has been put to, together with the sixteen months labour, he has so unremittingly bestowed upon the business."—Admitting that the time, here noted,

was

was expended in the two surveys, and that four months were spent on the Cambridgeshire Report, a period of twelve months remained for that which is now under review.

It would be a sort of forgetfulness of my own labors, were I not to say, here,—seeing the fairness of the opportunity,—what sums of money, and years of exertion, must have been expended by one who has "bestowed" full half a life time, on such pursuits,—without *any* "allowance for his indemnification:"—regretting, however, at the same time, that a man of so much activity of person and mind, as the author of the works under notice, evidently possessed at the time of performing them,—should not have been more amply remunerated, for his time and labor.

NATURAL ECONOMY.

Waters.—See *Grass Lands*, Water for Stock, ensuing.

Soils.—Definitions of the soils of each of Mr. Vancouver's districts are seen, aforegoing.—But the impropriety of determining agricultural districts, by surface soils, alone, has been there likewise shown; even tho an entire district were covered with a uniformity of any specified soil: which rarely is the case, to any considerable extent.—It is not the nature of the soil, separately,—but of the component parts of land, aggregately,—considered, which gives character to a country, viewed in an agricultural light.

What renders this method of dividing the County of Essex, into agricultural districts, altogether unfit, is the want of uniformity, even in the surface soils.—In following the Reporter through the several parishes of each district, we are continually finding a heterogeniety of soils;—not only in every district; but, frequently, in individual parishes.—And such will ever be found to be the case, in a VALE-LAND COUNTRY;—such as NORTHEAST ESSEX truly is. —The following short extracts will warrant these observations.—Numberless others might be adduced.

P. 12 (District I.) "The soil in general in the parish of Birdbrook, is extremely various; but the most striking difference

difference is found along the course of the river Stour, where, from a quarter to half a mile in width, a well stapled gravelly loam prevails. South and rising towards Whitley, the land becomes heavier, and forms upon the highest levels, a close cold earth, upon a chalky clay, below which clay at irregular depths, are found veins of pure blue clay, and some gravel. Thence southerly, and descending towards the principal branch of the river Colne, a more gentle soil is discoverable upon a brown clay."

P. 16 (the same.) "Crossing the valley, and ascending from Lammarsh, to Alphanstone, the land changes to a heavy cold thin soil, upon a red clay, or tile earth; a brown clay, or brick earth; a blue and white chalky clay; and in some places, a gravel. The stiff heavy cling soil, generally prevails through this parish, and often requires seven or eight ploughings, before it is brought into a proper state to receive the seed of wheat, barley, or even of black oats."

P. 28 (the same.) "The higher parts of the parishes of Pebmarsh and Colne Engane may be described, a brown tender loam upon a brick earth, the greater part of which has been much benefited by hollow draining. The sides of the hills are much inconvenienced by springs; though the lighter lands that are properly drained, afford excellent turnips. A very different soil prevails through the parishes of White and Wakes Colne, being that of a strong compact close clay, extremely retentive of water, and lying upon a tough red clay or tile earth."

P. 30 (the same.) "Rayne, Black and White Notley, and Falkbourn: through these parishes the land is very much intermixed and broken, the higher parts consisting of clay, and the hollows and sides of the hills of gravel and moor."

P. 47 (District IV.) "The island is divided into the two parishes of East and West Mersea, the higher parts of which, consist of a dark coloured friable mould, upon a sandy and a gravelly loam; and a deep hazel coloured strong earth, upon a brown tender clay or brick earth. The first of these soils is advantageously employed in the culture of turnips, barley, and clover, the last in that of beans and wheat."

It is true that some parts of Essex,—as are some parts of every vale-land district,—are better suited to the turnep husbandry, and others more adapted to the bean culture, than the generality of its lands. But, in Essex, it is pretty evident,

evident, those dissonant parts are not easily separable. For, in the "maps of its soils,"—given by two of its Reporters, Mr. Vancouver and the Secretary of the Board,—there is scarcely any resemblance of outline, in their several districts;—excepting in what might be termed the DISTRICT of COLCHESTER ; and, even this is by no means, uniformly, a "light" or a "turnep, loam" passage ; as it is represented to be. Viewing the two maps of the County at large, nothing resembling a sameness of outline is observable :—and "who shall decide when doctors disagree?"

These remarks are intended to show the great attention that is required, in separating *with due effect*, an extent of country into AGRICULTURAL DISTRICTS; and to gain a fair opportunity of suggesting that such a measure ought not to be *attempted*, where nature and experience will not warrant it.

Number of pages 214.

A map of the County.

No other engraving.

POLITICAL ECONOMY.

APPROPRIATION.—P. 35. (In Dist. I.) "There are two hundred acres of waste *forest land*,"—and "one hundred and forty acres of *common*."

P. 41. (In Dist. II.) "There are 2829 acres of *common*."

P. 46. (In Dist. III.) "There are 170 acres of thicks or forest,"—and "265 acres of *common*."

P. 51. (In Dist. V.) "There are sixty acres of *common*."

P. 62. (In Dist. VI.; only part of which comes within the eastern department) "there are 3770 acres of waste *common;* including Tiptree Heath."

In *common fields,* Essex, it is probable, never abounded. Its lands have, from what I have had opportunities of observing, mostly been inclosed from the forest state.—In the northwest quarter of it, however, bordering on the chalk lands of Cambridgeshire, and Suffolk, some open field townships are, even to this time (1810) observable ; and some have been recently inclosed. But, in passing
through

through NORTHEAST ESSEX, not the least appearance, nor any trace, of the *feudal system* of *aration* was observed.

PROVISIONS.—P. 36. "Beef and mutton $4\frac{1}{2}d.$ per lb.—veal and fresh pork $5\frac{1}{2}d.$ per lb.—pickled pork $7\frac{3}{4}d.$ per lb.—butter $10\frac{1}{2}d.$ per lb.—cheese $6d.$ per lb.—flour $23\frac{1}{4}d.$ per peck—potatoes $13\frac{1}{4}d.$ per bushel."

MANUFACTURES.—P. 28. (District I. parish of Halsted)—" The manufacture of baize, says, and lately of blankets, in this town, has had a disadvantageous effect upon the agriculture of the parish, by increasing the burthen of poor's rates upon the farmer; and which is alledged to be in no wise compensated by any convenience which the parishioners exclusively draw from the manufactory, by the assistance of labourers in hay-time and harvest, as the surrounding parishes equally participate in the advantage of procuring hands in the busy seasons, and are not contributory to the rates."

P. 37. (District II. Dedham)—" By the failure of the baize manufacture, which flourished in this parish some. years ago, the expensive burden of the poor has been considerably increased."

I will here mention, as a matter of *hearsay*, that, in travelling through Essex, I was incidentally informed, that, in the parish of Coggelshall, recently a " florishing," now a *wretched* place,—the poor's rate was " $43s.$ in the pound;"—and that, at Bocking, reduced to the same lamentable state, the *lands* of the parish were paying " $5s.\ 6d.$ a quarter," or $22s.$ a year, in maintainance of paupers that have been *deserted* by *manufactures*. What a lesson, if nearly true, to men of landed property!

POOR RATE.—In District I, p. 36, the poor tax was, in 1795, $4s.\ 4\frac{1}{2}d.$, on the rack rent.—In District II, p. 41, $4s.\ 2\frac{1}{2}d.$—In District III, p. 46, $3s.\ 2\frac{1}{2}d.$—In District IV—(Mersea Island) p. 48. " The failure of the oyster trade, which before the present war, was carried on to a very considerable extent, has subjected the principal occupiers of the island to an increased burthen in the poor's rates of from $2s.$ to $4s.$ in the pound."—In District V. p. 51, $2s.\ 10d.$

TITHE.—P. 35. (District I.) " The present composition for the great and small tythes, is three shillings and nine-pence farthing,"—"per acre."—In District II. p. 41, $3s.\ 3\frac{1}{4}d.$—In District III, p. 46, $3s.\ 5\frac{1}{4}d.$—In District V. p. 51, $3s.\ 11d.$

RURAL ECONOMY.

TENANTED ESTATES.

Draining Estates.—Of the Essex practice of draining with *bushes* and *straw ropes*, I find no notice, in this Report, within the districts now in view; excepting the following.—P. 28. (District I.) "Much of this land" (see p. 474, aforegoing) "has been hollow drained at a pole apart, costing about a guinea per acre, but with so little effect, as in a great measure to discourage that important practice. The means at present pursued to relieve the land of its surface water, is to use the land-fall plough, (?) and to water furrow; and though these operations are performed in the best possible manner, the land is still left saturated with water, and is much later in the seed time and harvest than the adjacent parishes."

Rent.—It is difficult for any stranger to come at the truth, in regard to existing rents; and even if obtained with strict accuracy, no practical use could arise from it; unless the precise *quality* of the *soil*, and the *influential circumstances* of *situation*, were minutely detailed.—As data in political arithmetic, the *true rental values* of the lands of the kingdom (rather than the rent which *happens* to be *paid)* might have their use.

In this Reporter's tables, at the ends of the five journals, now under examination, the rent of "arable and grass taken together," is from 14*s.* to 15*s.* an acre.—The average, or par, rent of the five districts, in 1795, may be set down (on the Reporter's authority) at 14*s.* 6*d.*

WOODLANDS.

Woods.—*Draining.*—P. 22. "A considerable improvement has been made by the same gentleman" (at Finchingfield) "by forming walking paths through the wet woodlands: foot drains, or those one spit wide and deep are there cut parallel to each other, and at the distance of
from

from eighteen inches to two foot apart; between these drains the sods that are raised are laid; thus raising a path-way above the general level of the wood, and at the same time forming drains which effectually relieve the wood of its superabundant water : hence a more durable undergrowth is encouraged, and as oak timber is always found to flourish better in woods moderately moist, than those that are wet, there is reason to believe that a due attention to this point, in the wet heavy woodland counties, would prove highly beneficial, and much promote the growth and durability of oak and other valuable timber."

TIMBER.—The subjoined notice, respecting the alder, is worthy of preservation.—P. 12. " In Baythorne Hall garden, by the side of the river Stour, a clump of alders justly excite notice and admiration. The largest of these trees (and they run tolerably even) at five feet from the ground, is seven feet four inches in circumference, and is in height from thirty to thirty-five feet of clear timber."

AGRICULTURE.

PLAN of MANAGEMENT.—P. 45. " The husbandry most generally practised in this district " (the third) " is to make a thorough summer fallow for oats or barley, and to sow about one half of the spring corn land with clover, dunged when young, and succeeded by wheat upon the clover ley. The oat and barley etches which are not filled with clover, being previously dunged in the winter, are sown early in the spring with beans, drilled or broadcast, kept well hoed through the summer, and succeeded by wheat. The wheat stubbles are haulmed immediately after harvest, and a part of them are sown with tares, which are either fed completely off, or only partly fed, and then left to stand for a crop; the land is then fallowed for spring corn and the same course repeated."

Summer fallowing, for spring corn and ley herbage, is a most valuable process, which I have long practised, and recommended to others (see MINUTES of AGRICULTURE, in 1775) for cleaning *foul lands in general;* and especially those that are too retentive of moisture, to admit of the turnip

turnip husbandry.—I was not aware, however, until I read Mr. V's Report, that it had become, in 1795, the established practice of a district. Again,

P. 50. " The course of husbandry through this district," (the fifth) " is to make a thorough summer and winter fallow for oats or barley, with a small proportion of which is sown clover, dunged when young, and after lying one year, the ley is sown with wheat upon once ploughing. The wheat etches are often dunged in the winter, and drilled with beans in the spring following, two rows upon a four furrow ridge, kept well hoed during summer, the bean etche well cleaned in the autumn, and sown again with wheat : a small portion of these etches are occasionally sown with tares, which are fed off, or left to stand for a crop, and in either case the land is fallowed again in course for spring corn. The black grass (?) through this district is extremely troublesome, and without winter fallowing, it is alledged to be utterly impossible to keep it within such bounds as would admit any reasonable chance for a crop of wheat."

WORKPEOPLE.—I insert the following extraordinary instance of practice (if such it continues to be) as a new *variety* of the *harvest process.* In a country where hands are scarce, an increase of *dispatch* may, on a certainty be gained, by such a measure ; but whether with strict propriety of *execution*, may well be doubted.

P 11. " The harvestmen are not boarded by the farmers here, as in most other places, but in lieu thereof, they each receive four bushels of malt and two lbs. of hops, from which about forty gallons of strong nourishing drink is usually drawn : They also receive one shilling each on hiring, and five shillings per acre, for cutting and inning the whole crop ; apportioning about thirteen acres to each man. The carts, horses, and drivers, are provided by the farmers ; and when the weather proves favourable, and the corn a fair standing crop, a man will cut, and in, sixteen acres of winter and summer corn in the course of a month ; as was the case in the year 1793 ; previous to which time, and when the harvestmen were boarded by the farmers in the usual manner, twelve acres per man were rarely known to be harvested in the same time, from the same land."

P. 36. " Stated price of daily labour in the winter 7s. 6d., in the summer 9s. per week. Threshing wheat 28½d. per quarter; barley 16¼d. per quarter; oats 14½d. per quarter; peas 27d. per quarter ; beans 14d. per quarter.

ter. Head man's wages, with board and lodging, 8 *l.* 10*s.* per annum; boy's wages, with the same, 40*s.* per annum; women's wages, with board, washing, and lodging, 4*l.* per annum; girl's, with the same, 45*s.* per annum."

MANURES.—In passing through the middle of North Essex, nothing engaged my attention, more, than the abundance of arable crops, and the small proportion of herbage; and this in a country where extraneous manures appeared to be unobtainable.—I was not aware, that, not only *rubbish chalk* of the quarries on the Thames, but "*London muck*," is brought, by water, up the estuaries of Essex, to the eastern and southern parts of the county; and that, in the western and northern parts, *marls,* of different species, would seem to abound;—as the subjoined extracts will show.

P. 17. (District I.) "East, and south of the town of Castle Hedingham, the soil of which forms a light coloured loam of a fair staple, a brown clay, has been much improved by hollow draining, and by the application of white chalky clay, at the expence and in the proportion following per acre:

	£.	s.	d.
Four score loads of clay, filling and spreading, at 5*s.* per score	1	0	0
Allowance for beer upon ditto	0	3	4
Five horses, four days work, at 2*s.* 6*d.* per horse per day	2	10	0
Wear and tear of two tumbrells, four days, at 6*d.* each per day	0	4	0
Driver, four days work, including beer, at 1*s.* 6*d.* per day	0	6	0
	£.4	3	4

P. 30. (same Dist.) "In the last mentioned parish" (Kelvedon) "the soil is found chiefly to consist of a light friable loam, upon a tender brown clay, containing in a north-west and south-easterly direction, a vein of rich marley clay: This has been applied with an equally good effect, as well upon the wet heavy, as on the more dry and lighter lands."

P. 32. (same Dist.) "The beneficial effects of this last substance, * as a manure when applied on the light lands, at

* Namely "chalky clay," or clay marl; but, quere, of what specific quality?

at the rate of sixty loads (forty bushels each) and at an
expence of four pounds per acre, is supposed, in this
neighbourhood, to last twenty years."

P. 38. (District H.) "In this neighbourhood" (the
eastern extremity of the County) "the usual mode of
manuring per acre, is to mix one waggon load of London
muck, with about five times the quantity of fresh soil collected from the road and hedge greens. The cost of the
London muck at the wharf, is fifteen shillings per waggon
load."

P. 49. (District V.) "Beginning at Abberton, where
the land lying south of the church, and hanging towards
Langenhoe and Peldon, consists of a strong heavy soil
upon a tile earth, which has been chalked with very good
effect in the proportion, and at the expence following per
acre:

	£.	s.	d.
Eight waggon loads of chalk, first cost 10s. 6d.			
per load at the wharf, or landing-place -	4	4	0
Carting and spreading at 7s. per load - -	2	15	0
	£.6	19	0

The effect of which, as a manure is thought to operate for
fifteen or twenty years, during which time, and for a considerable period after, the land will remain more tractable
and easier managed."

P. 53. (District VI.) "The marshes which were formerly under grass, are now very generally under the
plough. Chalk has answered a very valuable purpose
upon those lands, particularly when applied in sufficient
quantities (i. e. eight waggon loads per acre) and left to
melt and moulder upon the surface for three or four years
before it is ploughed in, it will then intermix and incor-
porate very minutely with the soil, and is esteemed by far
the best mode of first bringing into action, and afterwards
by good husbandry, of preserving the enriching qualities
of these lands."

SEMINATION.—*Varieties.* The subjoined is an interesting fact, in the vegetable economy; and is creditable to
the observation, and research, of the "gentleman" who
established it. His name might well have been mentioned. For altho nothing practically useful may result
from it, it is from attentions of this sort, that valuable dis-
coveries are made.

P. 25. "A few years ago, as a gentleman in this parish" (Great Bardfield) "was walking through his wheat
fields,

fields, when the corn was in full blossom, he was struck with the variety of hues, or colours, which the blossoms assumed: at first he conceived it might be owing to the different stages of forwardness in the blossom; but on particular examination, and more mature reflection, concluded, that they were certain signs of a specific difference in the quality of the wheat; impressed with this idea, he selected the ears of several different hues, and particularly marked eleven distinct numbers; noting very minutely, their characteristic qualities and appearances in the field: these he gathered and kept separate when ripe, and planted them apart from each other in his garden: the same characteristic difference was observed to continue upon the several numbers when growing in the garden, as was observed in the field the preceding summer."

P. 50. "The *quantity* of seed used in this district" (the fifth) "(through the heavier part of number seven, and the whole of number ten, is much the same, and) may be stated thus, viz. wheat from eleven to twelve pecks—barley from fifteen to sixteen pecks—oats from seventeen to nineteen pecks—tick and horse beans, when drilled, two furrows upon a three-foot ridge twelve pecks, the same drilled every furrow sixteen pecks, and clover sixteen pounds to the acre."

PRODUCE of GRAIN CROPS.—By Mr. Vancouver's tables, at the ends of the districts, now under notice, the average produce stands thus.

	Wheat.	Barley.	Oats.	Beans.
District I.	22.3	34.2	33.0	21.0
II.	21.3	30.2	35.0	25.0
III.	24.0	33.2	38.1	27.1
IV.	28.0	40.0	40.0	32.0
V.	25.1	32.1	38.3	32.0
Average	24.1	34.1	37.0	27.2

CORIANDER, &c.—P. 54. "The culture of coriander has been much attended to in this neighbourhood,* and is thus managed: old ley ground is ploughed in the beginning of March, and after the surface is completely pulverized, the seed is sown fourteen pounds to the acre; thrice hoeing and setting out the plants four inches square, will cost one guinea per acre. Average produce 10 cwt. per acre, 12s. per cwt. This is considered to be a very good preparation after once ploughing for wheat, and as the land is generally ploughed in two-yard ridges, or
sketches

* District the sixth; north of Malden.

sketches of eight furrows wide, a row of beans is generally planted with the coriander on each side of the open furrows between the sketches, and are usually harvested at the same time.

" When carraway is sown with the coriander, from the care and attention necessarily bestowed in distinguishing the plants, the hoeing seldom costs less than one guinea and a half per acre; but the carraway is not regularly set out for a crop till after the coriander is harvested, at which time a very expensive hoeing becomes indispensably necessary.

" Teazel is sometimes cultivated in the same field, the seed being sown with the coriander and carraway ; but as neither the carraway or teazel come completely and regularly the second year, both crops are usually allowed to stand for the third summer: this is esteemed good management for old coarse pasture grounds."

WELD.—The following mode of culture, by *transplanting*, is new to me.—P. 10. (District I.) " Weld is occasionally cultivated for the manufacture of checque and fustian ; its culture is simply that of transplanting from the seed beds at Midsummer ; stands all winter, and is the summer following, when in full bloom, cut, dried, and laid up for use. The soil it favours most, is a stiff strong loam, moderately moist, but not wet." (?)

HOPS.—P. 17. (District I, parish, Castle Headingham) " On the west, the parish is bounded by the river Colne ; along whose course is a considerable tract of meadow and rich hopland."

P. 19. (Maplestead.) " The vallies are chiefly occupied in the culture of hops, which is well understood and practised to advantage, although the grounds are not so productive as they are generally found to be, in the marsh of Castle Hedingham."

CULTIVATED HERBAGE.—*Clover.*—P. 15. (District I, Bulmer.) " Upon the heavy lands in this neighbourhood, clover is sometimes sown with barley, but the frequent failure of the plant in the spring following, prevents the culture of that valuable grass from being more general."

P. 31. (District I, the Notleys, &c.) " Clover has been so generally sown in this neighbourhood, that the land has in a great degree become tired of it; and tares now sown as its substitute, seem to encourage a well grounded expectation that the soil in a few years will again admit the culture of that valuable *grass.* The principal observation respecting the clover sick lands is, that although at the

the time of harvest, and during winter there appears to be
a very sufficient plant, yet in the spring it is always found
to fail, particularly on the tops of the ridges."—This observation is not new; but is, I believe, every where, just.

GRASS LANDS.—Perennial herbage would seem to be
confined to the water-formed lands of rivered vallies;
and the marshes which margin the estuaries and the sea
coast.

Concerning the former, I find nothing that requires particular notice, here.

Regarding the *marsh lands*, that are already *reclaimed*,
we have the two following items of information.

Water for pasturing Stock.—P. 44. "The embanked
marshes in this quarter, are greatly inconvenienced through
the want of good water in summer; and although in the
higher parts of the country there are some springs, yet
their water is so bad (though beautiful to the eye) that in
a short time after it has been drawn from the well, it becomes extremely offensive, and is rendered totally unfit
for domestic use. Tanks or reservoirs of rain water, seem
the only succedaneum for relief; but this important convenience is rarely to be met with."

Clearing from *Anthills.*—P. 54. "A considerable improvement has been lately made in the rough marshes
here, by removing the ants hills; the operation is performed by chopping round the hills with a heavy adze or
grubbing hoe, the cutting edge of which is circular, and
ten and a half inches wide; the depth of the blade, including its neck to the eye (or where the handle is fastened)
is eight and a half inches; from half a dozen to half a score
strokes will belt the largest hill, and loosen it from its
seat, which is always left lower than the adjoining surface
of the marsh, to receive and hold the rain water, by means
of which, the ants are more completely destroyed. Boys
follow the grubber, and carry the ants hills into the rills,
and low places in the marsh, and thus a considerable increase of surface is obtained, that in the course of a year
becomes profitable by getting coated with grass, and at
an expence which seldom exceeds 15s. per acre."

Many of those reclaimed marsh lands, it would seem,
have been broken up.—See the head, *Manure*, p. 484,
aforegoing.

Beside those reclaimed, or embanked marshes, Mr. Vancouver mentions the following extents of "salt marshes,"
or *unreclaimed marsh lands*, which occupy the margins of
the districts whose outskirts are layed by salt water;—
namely,

namely, of Dist. II. 530 acres,—of Dist. III. 1700,—
of Dist. IV. 1000,—and of Dist. V. 1370;—in all 4,600
acres;—which might, in Mr. V's opinion, "be advantageously embanked from the sea." (p. 51.)

CATTLE.—The only passage which I find that comes
within the limits of my present view of Essex, is the subjoined; which I insert to show that lands, in process of
time, are taken possession of by the products best suited
to their natures, or specific qualities; and remain in their
possession, so long as ordinary circumstances continue.
But that, by the altered demand of a market; by a change
of manners; or through the influence of fashion, either
fortuitously induced, or unduly enforced;—the natural
stream of production is capable of being cut off.

P. 97. (District XII.) "From Stambourn westerly to
Steeple Bumpsted, the soil varies from a gravelly to a thin
cold loam upon a chalky clay.

"This neighbourhood was very famous formerly for the
manufacturing of cheese, but of late years the dairy business has generally given place to the suckling of calves for
the London market, and for which purpose, a preference
is decidedly given to the North Wales Cows."

Thin cold loam, on clay, is the species of land from
which cheeses of the first quality are made, throughout the
dairy department (see the WESTERN DEPARTMENT).—The
reason why the occupiers of the neighbourhood above
named, departed from the track of their ancestors is not
mentioned. It may have been that the demand for veal,
in the London markets, of late years, has rendered "suckling" more profitable than the cheese dairy; or that the
farmers' wives and daughters of Steeple Bumpstead are
no longer the notable pains-taking laborious race which
established the fame of the North-Essex cheeses; or that
the fashion of calf-fatting, which has long been established,
in the neighbourhood of the metropolis, may have, at
length, reached the more distant parts of Essex.—Cheeses
can now be made, and conveyed, to market, by water carriage, with full profit, from a distance too great for the
production of veal, for the London market.

It is at least interesting to trace the rise and fall of
ESTABLISHED PRACTICES in HUSBANDRY; in like manner, as
it is to mark those of ESTABLISHED GOVERNMENTS, of COUN-
TRIES. True history, in either case, may have its use.—
There is, indeed, more affinity between those establishments, than may, at first sight, appear. In almost every
instance,

instance, either of them may be safely *improved*.—
But, in very few can they be entirely *altered*,—without
risk.

SHEEP.—The following is the only information which
I find in the North-Essex part of this Report, that
is of sufficient importance to be entitled to transcription.

P. 20 (Dist. I. Finchingfield).—"The Norfolk and
Cambridgeshire sheep, with a cross of the West Country
and Hertford are generally preferred; and as a great diversity of opinion prevails, respecting the superiority of
the Norfolk and Southdown, it has led to the following
experiment by a very accurate and well informed gentleman at Finchinfield. At Horringer fair, in Suffolk, in
September 1791, a lot of ewe lambs was bought in at six
pound ten shillings per score. At Lewes fair, Sussex, in
the October following, a lot of Southdown ewe lambs was
bought in at thirteen pound per score. These sheep were
depastured together, and in every respect received the
same treatment until the 25th of September, 1793; a
single sheep, which was adjudged to be the level of each
lot, was then taken out, and after both had fasted twenty-
six hours, were weighed alive, the Southdown weighing
ninety-six pounds, and the Norfolk ninety-five pounds;
they were then slain, and the following resulted from the
experiment.

SOUTHDOWN.			NORFOLK.
lbs.			lbs.
52½ carcase	-	-	53½
8½ skin	-	-	7 and horns
1½ legs cut off at the usual knee joints			1½
4¾ call	-	-	3
4 blood	-	-	5
7½ head and pluck	-	-	7½
2¼ gut fat	-	-	2¼
12¼ entrails and their contents	-		14
2 lost by killing supposed to be urine			1¼

lbs. 96   lbs. 95

In favour of the Southdown were
  2¼ lbs. of fat, 4¼d. per lb.   0 0 10
    1¾ lbs. of skin and wool 0 0 5
                          ———— 0 1 3

In

In favour of the Norfolk were
1 lb. of mutton   -   -   0   0   5
and first cost   0   6   6
——————   0   6   11

Total difference in favour of the Norfolk sheep   0   5   8

It is to be observed that neither of these ewes had had any young, but at the time of making the experiment, the Norfolk was more than half gone with lamb, and the Southdown had but just taken the ram."

NORTHEAST

NORTHEAST ESSEX,

The SECRETARY of the BOARD.

1807.

AGAIN, we find the Secretary of the Board, in the character of an ENQUIRING TOURIST :—but not merely such.—He was once, for a short time, a RESIDENT in the County *. He, moreover, appears to have been a frequent VISITOR therein. And he has of course been a frequent TRAVELLER through it,—between Suffolk and the metropolis.

Hence, we may reasonably expect, in this instance, more accurate information than can possibly be obtained, in a mere tour of fortuitous enquiry, at some particular season of the year. And we are not disappointed in such reasonable expectation. Next to the Report of Suffolk, that of Essex is the most creditable to the Secretary of the Board ; as a Reporter of rural practices.

The following is an extract from the author's own account of this work,—in an "Introduction" prefixed to it.

"The County of Essex was originally surveyed by Messrs. GREGGS. Mr. VANCOUVER was next employed to form a new Report of it, and his work was nearly as voluminous as the present one. (!) Their two Reports were afterwards put into the hands of the Rev. Mr. HOWLETT, to form a new one on the modern arrangement recommended by the Board. He made very large additions; but the Committee to whom that work was referred, having declined to direct the printing, a new Survey was ordered : this undertaking fell, unsought for, into my hands. Had any other person offered, I should most willingly have relinquished it, knowing well the amount of the labour, exertion,

* See the art. *Soils,* ensuing.

tion, and expense *, that are requisite, in making a journey of above 1000 miles in the vicinity of the capital, to examine a county containing a million of acres."

The author,—or rather should we not say, the compiler (seeing the different sources from which the materials of these volumes have been collected),—proceeds to expatiate on the proper business of Report, and "the difficulty of producing a good one." Something, it is true, is said concerning that matter; but nothing, to my mind, is satisfactorily made out †.

With the mass of materials collected, by the SECRETARY himself, he has incorporated copious extracts from Mr. VANCOUVER's Report; and taken still more largely from Mr. HOWLETT's manuscript:—also a few passages from the original Report, by Messrs. GRIGGS:—thus filling two octavo volumes, to the extent of 850 pages ‡.

These volumes are rendered the more bulky, by the number of PLATES which they contain;—namely fifty eight!—the Reporter having, previously to entering on his tour, engaged a draughtsman—" to travel the County, without any salary for his time, on being paid a very moderate price for such drawings, as he should be required to make." (p. 126.) This circumstance may serve to account for the number.

A MAP of "the soil of Essex" is prefixed to the work.

NATURAL ECONOMY.

EXTENT.—Vol. I. P. †. "Mr. Neele, map-engraver to the Board, from measuring the new map of the Board of Ordnance, makes it" (the whole County) " about 942,720 acres.

---

* We are not informed whether the Secretary of the Board prosecuted his several "Surveys" in the Eastern Department, at his own (as Secretary) or at the Board's expense.

† Nevertheless, some remarks on the Secretary's sentiments concerning that subject, will appear in a note, under the head *Plan* of *Management*, ensuing.

‡ A defect in the *editorship* of these volumes is the cause of irksomeness to the reader; who frequently has to pry into several pages, perhaps, before he can know whose remarks he is about to peruse; owing to the name of the writer being placed at the *end*, instead of at the *beginning* of the extract.

acres. The table annexed to the returns of poor-rates, in consequence of the act of the 43d of the King, makes it 976,000 acres."

Northeast Essex (within the outline drawn aforegoing, n. p. 2,) may be estimated at about one third of the County; or nearly 500 square miles.

WATERS.—The Reporter, not finding matter enough, in the ample sources of *modern information*, above enumerated, has had recourse to *obsolete learning*, to swell out his volumes; and has, accordingly, inserted in them a long extract from *Derham's Physico-theology*, to show "that springs have their origin from the sea, and not from rains and vapours."—Had this truly *preposterous* error been brought forward to expose its absurdity, one might have excused the obtrusion. But, from the manner in which the extract is placed in the *Report*, one is led to conceive that the extractor, himself, really believed in it!—But as well might any other man believe that *rivers* "have their origin from the *sea*, and not from rains and vapours:" or, in other words, that they run upward toward the mountains, not downward to the sea.

The only plausible excuse, for inserting it, is that DERHAM resided in Essex.

For a *natural* THEORY of SPRINGS,—see TREATISE on LANDED PROPERTY.

SOILS.—On this subject, we find the *Reporter* more in character;—treading firmer ground;—with nature, reason, and common sense by his side.—His account of the soils of Essex, as far as I am able to judge, is, in a great degree, satisfactory. It is written as if it were intended to *instruct;*—not merely to *amuse.*—Having seen occasion to censure Mr. Vancouver's account of them, he may thereupon have been urged to an assiduous research into their real characters.

The Secretary opens his section, "Soil," in the following manner.—Vol. I. P. 4. "With regard to soil, every species of loam, as Messrs. GRIGGS have justly observed, from the most stubborn to the mildest, is to be found; nor is the county without a portion of light gravelly land, or a good share of meadow and marsh ground, the major part of which, with management adapted to its different qualities, is very productive.

"Mr. VANCOUVER has, under this head, divided the county into fourteen districts, marking each with his characteristic distinctions of soil.

"I have

" I have a very high opinion of his practical knowledge, but as I do not think he has been explicit enough in his distinctions, I find it necessary also to form an arrangement from my own observations in the county.

" I divide it into eight districts.

" I. The crop and fallow district of strong loam, including the roodings.

" II. The maritime district of fertile loam.

" III. IV. & V. Three districts of strong loam, not peculiar in management.

" VI. The turnip land district.

" VII. The chalk district.

" VIII. The district of miscellaneous loams."

Those eight " districts," or *divisions*, are outlined, numbered *and* coloured, on the map above mentioned.— The portion of this map which comes within the boundary of the EASTERN DEPARTMENT, comprizes the following of those " districts," or parts of " districts," or *divisions*: namely,—the whole, or the principal part of Number III. About one-fourth of No. VIII. (which covers nearly one-half of the County, passing through its center; and reaching from its northern border, to its southwestern, extremity) the whole of No. VI. About half of No. II. And the whole of No. IV. These parts and parcels I will notice, geographically, as they stand, here.

No. III. (denominated in the explanation of the map, " Clay ") is situated on the borders of Cambridgeshire and Suffolk; extending from Haverhill, on the north, to below Finchingfield, on the south; and between Saffron Walden, on the west, and Castle Headingham, on the east.—The Secretary's account of this division is as follows.

V. I. P. 21. " I viewed this from Wethersfield to Hempstead, from the Hedinghams to Haverhill, from Clare to Belchamp Walter, from Yeldham to Toppesfield; and on a former occasion I crossed it in different lines, as from Clare to Finchingfield, and from Baythorn-end to Walden, by Samford; and I once resided six months in this district. The general feature of the whole is that of a strong, wet, poaching, sandy loam on a whitish clay marl bottom. A great deal of it letts for 20*s.* per acre, but the worst at not more than 12s. The exceptions or variations are not numerous: we must deduct a certain breadth along every stream, or brook, in the district (and indeed in the whole county), for bottoms of meadow, many of them

them on a gravel; also slopes, to those meadows of greater or less extent, which are sound land, and a proportion dry enough for turnips; but the moment you rise up the hill to the more level tract, there all is wet loam and clay *. These wet spaces have been all hollow-drained more than once, and it continues to be the staple improvement of the country. Some of the land is so stiff, that the drains (to use the expression of Mr. EATON, at Yeldham) draw more from the top than the bottom, which, however, must be the case, if the bottom is very stiff. Part of Yeldham is on a blue clay; and in Toppesfield there is not an acre of turnip land.

" The soil at Hempstead, and the adjoining parishes, is a very wet, stiff, and tenacious clay on a strong marly clay; some of it so poor and wet, that it letts only at 12s. an acre, and much dearer than any of the better lands at double the rent.

" Yeldham has both dry and wet land; the line by the turnpike-road and brook, very good: not one-tenth of the parish, however, will do for turnips.

" Stambourn, heavy.

" Tilbury, Birdbrook (of which not one-fourth turnip land,) Ashen, Ridgwell, Ovington, and Belchamp St. Paul, on a clay bottom, and not so good as Yeldham.

" Helion, and Steeple Bumpsted, have much good dairy land.

" Sturmer, good, but on a clay bottom.

" Pebmarsh has no turnip land.

" Lamarsh has a good share of turnips, and some very fine land.

" Twinstead and Alphanstone good, but on a clay bottom.

" At Little Samford, the meadows are good; but there is no turnip land, though I have seen one field sown in 300 acres."

No. VIII. (" various Loams "). The portion of this division, which comes within North Essex, reaches from the border of Suffolk, about Clare, to near Malden, on the south: and from Braintree, on the west, to Aldham and the Teys, on the east.

V. I. P. 27. " Having thus," says the Reporter, " struck off the three strong land districts, that of the Roodings,

* This, I have pleasure in saying, is written, I conceive, in the best style of Report. It well describes *a vale-land passage of country.*

Roodings, the maritime district of rich loam, the turnip loam, and the chalk, there remains the larger part of the county, which is so intermixed with a variety of loams, that no separation can with propriety be made. The variety of soils in this space is great. At Foxhearth, Leiston, and Borely, there is much sand; at Lamarsh, some very rich sandy loam; also a fine white sandy loam at Bulmer, and Belchamp Walter. At the Hedinghams and Halsted, rich vales under hops; at Markshall, &c. strong clays; at Wickham Bishop, sound sandy loams."

V. I. P. 241 (section "Course of Crops"!) "I was told by many persons, that the soils of the county of Essex were so intermixed, that no map could be given of them, and the titles annexed to Mr. VANCOUVER'S districts were cited as a proof that he could scarcely avoid running together in every one of his divisions, soils directly the reverse of each other; but after viewing the county in its principal features, there appeared to be some clear discriminations: after these were made, however, there remained a large portion of the county, in which the mixture of soil and management were so nearly what the general opinion had represented the whole, that I was obliged to leave it in one mass of miscellaneous soils, in which they are all found, and under every kind of management."

Further remarks, relating to this division, within Northeast Essex.—V. I. P. 27. "Finer land is very rarely to be seen, than a vein of loamy sand found at Borely, Belchamp, Bulmer, and Gestingthorpe. It is in the state of fallow, after rain, nearly white; and this in proportion to the quantity of sand in it. I found a farm (Brickwall) at Bulmer of this soil, but not so white as some; the land so good, apparently, and of so high a reputation, that I brought away a specimen of it. These sands are exceedingly fertile; four or five quarters of wheat, six or seven of barley, seven or eight of oats, and four or five of pease, are not uncommon crops on them. There is a strong principle of adhesion in them, though so sandy to the touch; for if placed in the wet, they become hard clods. In all this country, whatever land does not want draining, is excellent.

"About Ballingdon, Middleton, &c. the general features of the vicinity of the river Stour, the slopes that hang to the meadows are a fine, sound, friable, sandy loam; the hills are strong and harsh, and near a stiff clay,

clay, but with variations. The Suffolk side of the river presents nearly the same features, with the exception that the range of slope from Melford to Sudbury is superior, and is, indeed, a tract of some of the finest and deepest loam in that county.

" About Little Maplestead, they have light loams on gravel, and good strong loam, two feet deep, on a whitish clay marl bottom; some of this wants draining. The texture of the loam is excellent; it varies in tenacity.

"Great Maplestead resembles Little Maplestead; about half the parish may admit turnips, and the other half too heavy. It is a hilly country, and the vales and slopes good land; the tops of the hills heavy, but with variations.

"From Sibble Hedingham to Wethersfield, is, in general, strong loam on a clay marl bottom, all drained, but too wet for turnips : a large portion summer-fallowed, and laid up on the two-bout ridge for barley or wheat.

" Around Spains-hall, Mr. RUGGLES possesses 1000 acres within a hedge: the soil of two sorts; one dry, sound, gravelly, or sandy loam ; the other, strong loam ; both on clay marl, but the former 18 to 24 inches deep; so that the permeable space below the plough is sufficiently deep to render drains unnecessary; but where the loam is more tenacious, and nearer the clay, there draining is necessary, and turnips improper. The dry land runs to white clover, and makes fine pasture and upland meadow. The whole is, on an average, worth from 20s. to 25s. per acre; some 30s.

" From Braintree to Coggeshall, strong loam on clay : many fallows on the two-bout ridge for barley and wheat. At Markshall, very stiff and tenacious, and, in many fields, shallow, on an ill-looking yellow clay bottom ; but seeing very fine crops of wheat on it, I examined the thin surface, and remarked, that with all its tenacity, it was of a good texture for so strong a soil.

" About Coggeshall, in the vale, a very fine, rich, putrid (?) loam, eighteen inches deep, on clay; worth 40s. to 60s. an acre for common crops. Mr. HANBURY's farm there, and much of the higher lands in the vicinity, a strong, stiff, wet loam on a whitish clay marl ; but he thinks, not so heavy a soil as in the Roodings.

" Little Tey, heavy; Feering, heavy, but very good; Bradwell, a kindly soil ; Cressing, heavy, but good.

" The vales, and part of the slopes, at Kelvedon, are a
good

good sandy loam; but the flatter parts, and general face, is strong loam on clay, and all summer-fallowed.

"The soil around Felix-hall has the varieties of this part of Essex, but may, in general, be considered as a strong heavy loam on a whitish clay marl: there are some fields which will admit turnips, but very few with propriety; and summer-fallowing the characteristic feature. The surface, nine or ten inches deep; and drains well by hollow cuts: the same features, in this respect, continue to Witham.

" Birch, Great and Little, various; some dry, some strong: a mixed loam on a whitish clay marl; also a dry loam proper for turnips The parish being valued for the rates, the dry turnip land was estimated higher than the heavy land; yet the latter, if on a brown clay bottom, gives greater crops; but not, if on a whitish clay marl bottom.

" Messing, lighter than Birch."

No. VI. (" Turnep Loam "). This is the Colchester district, or division. It is bounded on the north by Suffolk; the town of Colchester being situated toward its center.—V. I. P. 25. " Colchester is situated in the midst of a district of dry, sandy, and gravelly loam, which is perfectly well adapted to the turnip culture; it extends east and west from Stanway to the Bromleys, and north and south from Mistley to Fingringhoe. The additional tract added in the map, extending towards Bures, partakes in a good measure, of the same soil, but with more variations from a mixture of heavier fields. Part of Copdock, Stanway, and Lexden, is a sand, and a loamy sand on a gravel bottom; much of it light, and much also so deep above the gravel, as to be very excellent land, and, in wet seasons, yields great crops. Pretty considerable tracts near Colchester are in the occupation of gardeners, who, beside supplying the town and barracks with vegetables, raise considerable quantities of garden seeds for the country, and the supply of London.

" About Beerchurch," (Donyland) " &c. a dry, sound, sandy, or gravelly loam; all, or nearly all, good turnip land, and for feeding off; but most productive in wet seasons, and some apt to burn in dry ones, from the shallowness of the surface soil, or the sharpness of the under stratum. Of this description is a level of sound dry land, with some variations, to the south and west of the town.

" Most of the land from Colchester to Maningtree, is nearly the same light loamy sand, or sandy loam on
gravel

gravel, which is found at Ardleigh: much of Lawford so."

No. II. ("fertile Loam"). The part of this division, which is comprized within the limits of the Eastern Department, lies between the last-mentioned division and the sea. The "district" (!) at large, is a narrow ragged margin, winding along the sea coast, the estuaries, and the Thames, to the extent of eighty miles or more (reaching from one corner of the County to its opposite extreme); yet not, in many parts, more than one, two, or three miles in width. The part of this pretty green fringe which is attached to North Essex, reaches from the mouth of the estuary of the Stour, at Harwich, to the head of the estuary of the Blackwater, near Malden; and includes the island of Mersea.—The following are the Reporter's observations on these parts.

V. I. P. 9. " At Bradfield, near Maningtree, I entered a soil which had not occurred before during the course of the journey; a very rich loam, which, apparently and to the touch, should not be called either a sandy or a clayey loam; perhaps an *impalpable* one would not be an improper term. It nearly resembles the fine loams of Flanders. The dry surface is a very light pale stone colour, tending to white, and in many fields almost white. It is tenacious or friable, according to weather; the clods are found sometimes as hard as those of pure clay, but fall by rain to powder, after well roasting in the sun. The quantity of sand, or rather probably the size of the particles, gives the variation of being pitchy, and adhering to the mould-board of the plough, rather more than the quality of the under stratum, which is very generally a strong loam, tending to that species of clay which in some cases moulders into small particles, and in others shivers, by the action of the atmosphere, into dies, and angular bits; the colour dark brown. Some of the stiffer bottoms assume the appearance of tile clay, and has a yellow hue. Some of these very rich loams are, from a gravelly tendency of the subsoil, or from the depth and more sandy quality of the surface mould, dry enough for turnips: a few dry enough to feed off with sheep; but the much larger extent in several parishes, consists of a loam too heavy and too retentive of moisture for that root; so that in much the greater part, a *summer fallow* is given once in four or five years. Mr. HARDY, of Bradfield, shewed me many fields of these soils at that place, and also at Wicks; the latter stronger, more retentive, and wetter, than those of Bradfield

Bradfield, yielding greater crops of corn, but worked with more difficulty and expense, than the lands at Bradfield, sticking to the ploughs like pitch. The farming traveller will find these .soils deserving much attention; for they are not to be seen in whole counties, and, I suspect, no where at a distance from the sea. There is much resemblance with the fine loams of East Norfolk, but are more stiff. and difficult to manage.

" Wrabness parish has more sand. Ramsey is more generally heavy. Wicks has some turnip land, but more that is heavier than Bradfield. Dovercourt much fine turnip land; but in all of them the good loams are of this pale and impalpable character.

" Bradfield to Tendring, heavy; but a level of 200 acres about Tendring, chiefly turnip land.

" Beaumont generally strong, but has some turnip land.

" To Ramsey and Harwich very good turnip loams; but some heavy that are excellent, of the quality above described.

V. I. P. 11. " The same fine impalpable loams are at Little Oakley, where the Rev. Mr. SCOTT showed me the variations of soil; some of the high lands strong, but much lighter, and turnip land; the slopes light, and finishing in the marsh, where the arable is very heavy and strong, but rich. All the stronger loams here are of so tenacious a quality, that, when moist, they stick to the plough like pitch; so that cast plough-irons, they assert, cannot be used.

" The same land is found at Beaumont, and with nearly the same variations; this township was named to me as one of, if not the best in the whole hundred of Tendring.

" At Kirby, I remarked a browner hue in the soil of some of the fallows, inclining a shade or two to red; but many of them are still of the same pale and excellent loam which has travelled with me from Mistley.

"This loam occurs also at Great Holland, with the general variation of some admitting turnips, and some being too heavy for that root. Mr. COTES agreed with me, in its resemblance to the best land of Fleg hundred, in Norfolk, and remarked that, like Fleg, it is pale and deep, and works wet or dry. A fourth of the parish is mixed, and dry enough for turnips; but the strong land is in higher estimation.

" Great

" Great Clackton has more light and poorer land than in the parishes yet noted, and some wet ; but it possesses a good deal of the fine strong loam. In Little Clackton much strong land. At St. Ossyth's are the same soils ; but more light for turnips than of the impalpable loams.

" Tollesbury, strong but rich loam. Toleshunt Darcey, some heavy, but good ; the rest good free mixed loam. Goldhanger, dry and very good turnip loam. Beckingham, good, and not strong. Ousy Island, in Blackwater, a fine spot of 200 acres, rich turnip loam.

" By far the most interesting tract of land near Maldon, is the dead level space which extends from about Langford, along the coast, to Goldhanger church, and is of various breadths. Much the greater part is arable, there being only here and there a pasture of convenience. I accompanied Mr. LEE to his farm at Goldhanger, and found that the soil improved as I advanced for about five miles. His fields close to the sea wall are of an excellent quality ; a deep, putrid, dry, sound, friable, red and black earth, for two feet deep, on a bottom of gravel, which forms the subsoil of the whole level. The crops equal to the appearance of the land, which is of admirable fertility : it does much better for barley than wheat, having had ten quarters an acre of the former on it, but seven common. Of oats, eight or ten constantly. I saw immense crops of beans on it. It extends to the sea wall. I brought specimens for chymical examination.

" Some spots, however, of a loose frothy sand, are bad, and crops of every kind failing, either eaten by the wireworm, or root-fallen. These should be squared for a different management, and would be much safer if trodden well after sowing, even in wet weather ; they could not be too much kneaded. A coat of clay, were it to be had, would much improve them."

V. I. P. 13. " The soil of Mersea Island is all good ; in general a sandy loam, very rich and fertile. It has no wet strong clay, nor any striking tendency to it, except a narrow slope falling from the general level of the surface, down to the narrow tract of the north marshes. Here there is some strong land ; but land-draining is rarely necessary, except on spots, and for carrying off springs. In a similar manner the southern part of the island is generally light land, dry, sound, and very excellent turnip soil ; and the centre of the isle from E. to W. contains the best land, which they call a *mixed soil*. Much of this part is as fine land as any one can wish to farm ; a sandy loam,

not

not gritty, nor impalpable, of a dark hazel brown colour; friable, yet moist; never burns; wants no drains; not dry enough, however, to eat off turnips, as the lower stratum is a yellow adhesive loam. The dry turnip loams are very sandy, and the grains of sand large and gritty; this also is very fine and profitable land. The rent of the whole island may be 20s. or 21s. per acre; but rising rapidly, the late bargains having been made at 25s. 30s. and even 40s."

In looking over the map, before I had read the above remarks, I had conceived the green edging, marked II, to be the *marshes* or waterformed lands of Essex; and had, in my mind, given the Reporter some credit for thus ingeniously stringing them together; so as to enable one to compare, with the least trouble, the Waterlands of Essex, with those of Lincolnshire, Cambridge, &c. But instead thereof, those of Essex are *confused* with the *natural aboriginal lands* of the County,—in the same " district" of *soil!*

No. VI. (" Clay."—A small plot, situated in the line, between Colchester and Malden).—V. I. P. 23. "The second strong land district is that small space including Wigborough, Peldon, &c.

" One-third of Layer de la Haye is light turnip land, and two-thirds too strong to feed off that crop on the land. The heavy land here is a shallow surface on a very strong loam bottom, but Mr. BUXTON thinks, not *clay*. It is exceedingly wet: he has tried land draining at half a rod asunder, and no benefit whatever resulted from it. Tiles might be made of the loam. It is evident enough that this soil is, to every purpose of farming discrimination, clay.

" At Abberton, I found a strong brown clay, tenacious, but good. At Langenhoe, what I saw was generally strong and heavy.

" At Great Wigborough a new soil occurred: the farmers call it strong loam, and so it is; but the strength, heaviness, and tenacity are such, that it has all the qualities of the stiffest clay. It will not bear barley; turnips are out of the question. It is of a rich brown colour, and falls by the action of the atmosphere, into dies and angular bits; but does not, like weaker soils, crumble into powder: a very decisive characteristic whereby to discriminate these soils. It is nearly the same to the depth of six or seven feet. There are no springs in it; so that the farmers suffer a very great inconvenience in sending
(sometimes

(sometimes several miles) for water. Hollow-drains, for surface water, are absolutely useless ; they will not *draw* for a single yard. The expense of working such a soil, is, of course, great; but the crops are great also. They throw the fallows on to the four-furrowed ridge for winter.

" At Peldon, some very strong land.

" Layer Marney, and Layer Breton, strong."

FOSSILS.—V. I. P. 11. " At Harwich examined the strata of the cliff. The conversion of the clay ooze into that hard stone of which Framlingham and Orford castles are built, is curious. It is found here quite soft like clay, and in all the progressive stages, till it becomes stone. There are masses of it, which are at one end ooze, and at the other stone.   There is also a stratum of concreted shells, which breaking down from the cliff, are found in lumps below ; some of them mixed with pyrites, of which imperfect ore, pieces are found scattered.   I brought away specimens of these soils, stones, &c. and have since found that a given weight of the ooze stone contains a vastly greater proportion of air (gas) than the ooze itself, being as 115 to 15."

It would not be ingenuous were I not to express the satisfaction I have experienced, in perusing, and abstracting, the Secretary's account of the soils and substrata of Essex. The matter and the manner equally show, that, when this voluminous author allows himself time to *examine* and *think*, he not only can *write*, but convey to his readers valuable information.

POLITICAL ECONOMY.

APPROPRIATION.—Neither in the chaper " Enclosing," in the first volume, nor in that entitled " Wastes," in the second, have I found any thing which claims notice, here, relative to the state of Appropriation, in Northeast Essex.

The following is the Reporter's general remark, on this subject, respecting the County at large.—V. I. P. 164.

" Essex

" Essex has for ages been an enclosed country, so that there was no field here for the great parliamentary exertions which have been made in so many other counties; few applications have been made, till very lately, and these are not yet in a state to afford any information that is material."

PROVISIONS —V. II. P. 376. " In June 1767 I found the prices at Hedingham, Braintree, &c. to be as follow butter $6\frac{1}{2}d$. per lb.; such cheese as the poor ate $3\frac{1}{4}d$. per lb.; mutton $4\frac{1}{4}d$. per lb.; beef $4d$. per lb.; veal $4\frac{1}{4}d$. per lb.; candles $7\frac{1}{4}d$. per lb.; coals $1l$. $13s$. per chaldron.

" In 1794, Mr. VANCOUVER in the same district found : butter $10\frac{1}{2}d$. per lb.; cheese $6d$. per lb.; mutton $4\frac{1}{2}d$. per lb.; beef $4\frac{1}{2}d$. per lb.; veal $5\frac{1}{2}d$. per lb.

" In 1805, I again found at the same places the prices to be : butter $13d$. per lb.; cheese $8d$. per lb.; mutton $7\frac{1}{4}d$. per lb.; beef $8d$. per lb.; veal $9\frac{1}{2}d$. per lb.; candles $11\frac{1}{4}d$. per lb.; coals $3l$. per chaldron. Rise per cent. on these articles in eleven years; in butter $23\frac{2}{4}$, in cheese 33, in mutton 72, in beef 77, in veal 72."

FUEL.—V. II. P. 381 (by Mr. Howlett). " Forty years ago our farmers burnt very little else but wood; at present a large proportion of them burn a considerable quantity of coal; and this quantity is every year increasing. Gentlemen and tradesmen have always burnt both; but coal is every where gaining ground upon wood; and in a few years, not improbably a great part of our labourers must have recourse to the same substitute."

MANUFACTURES.—V. II. P. 390 (by Mr. Howlett). " The woollen manufacture for time immemorial has taken the lead in this county; but from its long continued dwindling condition, it is uncertain whether it will many years remain so.

" Our manufacture of sacks for the use of our farmers, from their increasing cultivation, seems gradually advancing. I know not that that of hop-bags is any where very flourishing amongst us: this manufacture, from the deficiency of our crops in the years 1799 and 1800, was astonishingly diminished, but is now, January 1802, reviving."

Same page (by On?). " Baize wool in the neighbourhood of Bocking, which varies as to length, pliancy, and softness, according to the sort into which it is to be wove, is delivered out to the spinner, who always cards it too, to be returned in nearly an equal weight of yarn.

V. II.

V. II. P. 392. (by the Reporter.) "At Coggeshall, some baize are still made ; and the straw-plat fabric has got in, by which large earnings are made. This is also well established at Bocking and Braintree, where some shops take to the amount of 60*l.* or 70*l.* per week ; and at Hedingham one man has bought to the amount of 1500*l.* in a year.

" At Colchester, in the manufacture of baize for Spain, are employed about 150 or 160 men, who earn about 14*s.* per week each ; about the same number of women and children, who earn from 4*s.* to 7*s.* per week. Before the breaking out of the war with Spain, nearly five times the above number were employed ; and it is probable at least that number will be employed on the return of peace.

" *Weekly Manufacture of Baize in Colchester,* 1794.

IN PEACE.

In the time of peace immediately preceding the present war, - - - - - - - -	400
Exported, or used at home, - - - - - -	400
Hands employed in Colchester and the adjacent country, - - - - - - - - -	20,000

IN WAR.

In the time of war, January 1794, - - - -	160
Exported, or used at home, - - - - - -	40
Hands employed in Colchester and the adjacent country, - - - - - - - - -	8000"

FISHERIES.—V. II. P. 387. (by the Reporter.) " In the Blackwater river, &c. is a considerable oyster fishery, and West Mersea one of the principal stations of the dredgers: above 30 boats belong to the island, and are almost always at work. Vessels come from Kent to purchase the oysters ; and they sell some to Wivenhoe, where the Colchester beds are. They are sold by the tub of two bushels; generally from 4*s.* to 6*s.* a tub ; at present 6*s.* A dredging boat is from 14 to 30 or 40 tons burthen; all are decked, and built at Wivenhoe, Brightlingsea, &c. &c. The price 10*l.* a ton for the hull of the vessel only ; and fitting out one of 20 tons will demand 150*l.* There are from two to four men to each vessel, who are paid by shares ; and the master has a share for the vessel. In the spring they go to the coast of Hants and Dorset, dredging there : last week Mr. Buxton counted 130 vessels at work within sight of Mersea. This fishery is an object of considerable importance to the country, from the earnings being great : when the men die, their families come to the parish greatly increased by the number of apprentices they have taken. Can any thing be so preposterous as a police of the poor, which permits the benefit of commerce and manufactures to load the land with rates at 8s. in the pound !"

POOR RATES.—The County of Essex is a proper field in which to observe the mischiefs, not only of MANUFACTURES, but even of FISHERIES,—*under the existing laws,*—to the permanent interests of the country. And as the now blighted manufactures of Essex were *forced,* by an inordinate commerce, to the bloated state which brought on their decay, in the part of the county which is now in view,— I will here insert an extract from the Secretary's long list of notices on the " Poor Rates," in Essex.

V. I. P. 87. " Belchamp Walter, 5s. in the pound; have been 12s. and 13s. ; were once only 2s. 6d.

" Little Maplestead, 1804, 11s. in the pound; 25 years ago, 2s.

" Hastead, now 12s. to 14s.; were once 28s.

" Castle Hedingham, 10s.; but on nominal rent.

" Bocking, 5s. a quarter : lowered by many having left the parish, and by the straw-platting being introduced from Gosfield.

" Hempstead, 7s. at four-fifths of the rent.

" Gosfield, 3s. 6d. in the pound, real rent; greatly in the straw-plat.

" Coggeshall, 16s. in the pound, at three-fourths rent.

" Kelvedon, 6s. 6d. or 7s. on real rent.

" Beerchurch, 5s. to 7s. 6d. on two-thirds, or three-fourths rent.

" At Witham, about 7s. to 8s. on an average: not on real rent, but near it.

" At Hatfield Peverel, average 5s. in the pound.

" At Sandon, 4s. on real rent.

" At Purley, 6s. to 8s.

" At Colchester, poor only, without including other rates, from 8s. to 20s.; probably, on an average, 10s. on the real rent.

" At Ardleigh, 6s. in the pound on the real rent.

" At Bradfield, 3s. 6d. on the real rent.

" At Little Oakley, all parish rates, 3s. 6d. in the pound, real rent.

" At Beaumont, 5s. on three-fourths real rent.

" At Great Holland, 6s. in the pound on half rent, or 15s.; *new* rents *estimated* at 30s.; this is 3s.

" At

" At Great Clackton, 6s. on the rack.

" At St. Osyth's, 5s.

" At Layer de la Haye, 3s. in the pound, rack.

" East Mersea, low; West Mersea, high; 7s. in the pound on six-tenths, being rated at 12s.; arising from the population and earnings of the oyster-dredgers, which like manufactures, so often cause high rates by the very means which ought to extinguish them.

" At Great Wigborough, rated at 12s. an acre rent; it is 8s. or 9s. in the pound.

" At Birch, 5s. rack-rent.

" At Kelvedon, 6s. on three-fourths rent.

" At Bocking, 20s. in the pound on four-fifths rent; other rates make it 20s. on real rent. Mr. Saville has paid, on rather more than 500 acres, 800l. in poor-rates, for four quarters, within two years." *

TITHE.—V. I. P. 80. " General average of 56 notes, 4s. 9d. per acre, great and small."

		s.	d.
V. I. P. 86. " Composition per acre, 1805,	-	4	9
———————————— 1794,	-	3	5½
Raised in 11 years,	- -	1	3½'"

EMBANKMENT.—V. II. P. 253. (by the Reporter.) "The whole coast of Essex to the ocean and the Thames, is embanked: I saw no exceptions but at Harwich, South End, and Purfleet; and these not extensive. These embankments are most of them old, with several new ones of saltings, contiguous to older intakes proportionably to the degree in which the sea retires; but on the south coast of Tendring hundred no new acquisitions are thus made; and they have apprehensions that the sea has a strong disposition at present to resume some of its former grants."

MARKETS.—V. II. P. 386. (Reporter.) " The town of Colchester was always a populous place, and therefore a good market for all the neighbouring country: the decline of the manufactory lessened its powers in this respect: but

* MANUFACTURES.—If effects, mischievous as these, are capable of being brought on by a *woolen* manufacture, what may not be expected from the failure of the *cotton trade*,—when *silks* have recovered their sway, in courts and fashionable companies throughout Europe! —The information here adduced will serve to show,—what needed no *proof*,—that even the WOOLEN MANUFACTURE,—when madly goaded on to *excess*,—can become a grievous curse in a country.

but having since become the station of a numerous body
of troops, with extensive barracks built, it has fully, and
even more than regained its former importance in this
respect."

Here, we *see*, and the writer of the above extract would
seem to *feel*, the ADVANTAGES of WAR!!!—What a "flourishing" country is this! How prolific in "resources"!

RURAL ECONOMY.

TENANTED ESTATES.

ESTATES.—*Proprietors.*—V. I. P. 39. (by Mr. Howlett.)
"If by estates, are meant possessions in landed property,
they are, in this county, in point of size and extent, almost
infinitely various : from one, five, and ten pounds a year,
to ten, and even twenty, thousand ; and, although there
may be a few considerable and extensive estates in the
hands of the nobility, or of some very wealthy private individuals, yet, perhaps, there never was a greater proportion of small and moderate-sized farms, the property of
mere farmers, who retain them in their own immediate
occupation, than at present. Such has been the flourishing state of agriculture for twenty or thirty years past, that
scarcely an estate is sold, if divided into lots of forty or
fifty to two or three hundred a year, but is purchased by
farmers, who can certainly afford to give for them more
than almost any other persons, as they turn them to the
highest advantage by their own cultivation ; and hence
arises a fair prospect of landed property gradually returning to a situation of similar possession to what it was a
hundred, or a hundred and fifty years ago, when our inferior gentry resided upon their estates in the country, and,
by their generous hospitality, diffused comfort and cheer-
fulness around them. Nor let us envy or grudge the
farmers this prosperity : by their laborious and spirited
exertions, they highly deserve it. Nor, indeed, after all
their toils, are their acquisitions of wealth comparable to
those in other situations and departments of society."

Tenures.—V. I. P. 41. (by the same.) "The tenures
of the landed proprietors are in almost all the diversities
of

of freehold, leasehold, and copyhold; but what are the number of estates holden by these several species of tenure, or what their proportion to each other, either in number, value, or extent, I am totally unable to say. I conjecture, however, that freehold estates are by much the most numerous, extensive, and valuable. Next to these are the copyhold, there being few parishes in any part of the county, especially in the quarter of Dunmow,* in which there are not one, two, three, or more manors; to the lords of which, annual quit-rents are paid, besides fines, or heriots, upon deaths, purchases, or other events or contingencies; some certain and fixed, others variable and arbitrary. Our leasehold estates are, I suppose, by much the fewest, and least extensive. We have also many estates in mortmain, belonging to Guy's and Christ's Hospitals, and other corporate bodies."

DRAINING ESTATES.—Much have we long heard, concerning the "bush-draining" of Essex; and the subjoined description of it having been drawn up, by an improver of note, in the part of Essex now under research for information, I think it right to insert it, here, at length.

V. II. P. 169. "ESSEX UNDER-DRAINING, BY L. MAJENDIE, ESQ.—" 1. The course of the drains being determined upon (on which the greatest judgment and attention are requisite) they are drawn out by a plough with four, and often six horses, a suitable depth; the small, or land-ditch spade, is then used, with which the drains are formed, in depth twelve inches, which, added to that first obtained by the plough, is generally quite sufficient.

" 2. The drains, when spitted, are filled with spray wood covered with straw, and the earth is shovelled, which completes the operation. Some farmers, to decrease expense, use haulm instead of straw, and some exclude the wood altogether, using only straw, or haulm, pressed hard with a spade into the drains; but this last is a very inferior practice. The best and most usual way is, to fill with good spray wood, which is covered with wheaten straw twisted or spun into long bands or ropes, with a simple instrument now in possession: these ropes are expeditiously made, and when duly pressed into the drains, give them a firmness and durability superior to those where the straw or haulm is loosely put in.

" 3. The usual distance between the drains in Essex is one

* Mr. Howlett's parochial residence.

one rod, but in very stubborn soils, especially in those where the under stratum is a stiff blue clay, I have found it adviseable to make the drains at half a rod apart; the increased expence is amply repaid by the superior dryness of the land.

" 4. It is found by experience, that the drains are best when narrow; the small, or land-ditch spade, should there be made gradually tapering from the shoulder to the bottom, and which should not be more than one inch at the most in width. The expense in wood and straw are also by this means diminished.

" 5. The fewer outlets from the main or receiving drains into the ditches of the fields, the better; these should also be frequently visited and kept open, or the drains in the field will blow. These general outlets, without such attention, are frequently stopped up by the treading of cattle or other accidents.

" 6. It is advisable to fill up the drains with wood, &c. *daily*, as they are dug, to prevent the sides in dry weather from crumbling, and falling to the bottom of the drains. When stones occur in digging the drains, they should be taken out by the pick-axe, or broken with an iron crow, or they will stop the current of the water.

" 7. It frequently happens in digging the drains, that the spit of earth arising from the small spade, besides being of a different quality from the upper stratum, is of a nature highly calcareous; in this case it is usual, and reckoned good management, not to fill up with it, but to spread it thinly and evenly over the adjacent surface as a manure, using instead of it for filling up, some of the upper stratum.

" 8. The spray wood should be of a sufficient age; thus wood felled at eighteen years growth, is found greatly more durable in land-ditching than that of twelve or fourteen years growth.

" 9. It is particularly desirable that the farmer should fill up the drains by his own servants, on whom he can rely, and not to let this part of the operation to the ditcher. Much injury has arisen from the neglect of this necessary precaution. The drains have either been improperly filled up, or perhaps only with earth; it has been frequently discovered, that the drains, after being dug, have, in the absence of the employer, been filled up with earth, and the wood taken away in the night.

" The labour of digging these drains has been attended with the following expense to me, viz.

Digging

Digging the drains with the small or land-ditch spade, per score rods, -	20d. to 24d.
Digging the main drains, which require one full spit before the small spade is used, per score rods, - - - -	3s. to 3s. 6d.

" In this manner the under-draining one acre (the drains at one rod apart) has, including wood, straw, and all other incidental charges, amounted to an expense of from forty to forty-five shillings.

" The advantages of this practice are fully known and acknowledged in Essex; the greatest exertions are made in it, and the operation is, I believe, in few counties better or more durably executed."

Mr. HOWLETT takes the above extract as his text; and fills many a page with learned annotations upon it. The text, however, is sufficiently adequate to my purpose; which is that of recording the outlines of a practice, which, in the kingdom at large, has long been considered as obsolete.

Nevertheless, in loose ground, and where stones cannot be had at a moderate expense, the Essex method may, no doubt, be sometimes practised with advantage. But, surely, the practice of "turf," or *sod draining*, as established, many years ago, in the MIDLAND COUNTIES (and whose origin and method I have there described) is, in most cases, preferable.

TENANCY.—V. I, P. 98. (by the Reporter.) "I am afraid that leases are going rapidly out of fashion in this county; and I cannot but lament it, as a sure sign that the great exertions, which have long been such a credit to Essex agriculture, will gradually wear away on the estates where this pernicious system shall take place."

The Reporter, in continuation, comes forward, *in proper person*, (notwithstanding the resolution taken, in his "introduction," to keep himself cautiously behind the scenes) and delivers his sentiments concerning the "*necessity*" of long leases.

But, about the time when the Secretary wrote the work under review, a delightful controversy was brewing up, about whether *no leases*, or *twentyone-years' leases*, ought to be universally adopted;—without either party considering that they might be " both in the wrong;" or that a more rational and practical mean lies between the two extremes:—a species of tenancy, which, while the nominal value of the " circulating medium" quivers in awful poise, ought to be stedfastly eyed, both by proprietors and

tenants,

tenants, who are desirous to tread the safest line of conduct.— Let *gamesters* go to it *.

See the head, *Tenancy*, in the tables of contents, prefixed to this and the two former volumes of the Review,
for other remarks on this important topic.

RENT.—V. I. P. 72. (by the Reporter.)

	Square Miles.	Acres.	Per Acre.	Total Rent.
" District No. I.	156	99,840	16s. 0d.	£79,872
II.	255	163,200	25 0	204,000
III. IV. and V.	222	142,080	16 8	118,400
VI.	114	72,960	21 0	76,608
VII.	45	28,800	15 0	21,600
VIII.	681	435,840	20 0	435,840
		942,720		£.936,320

The rent of the whole may therefore be called 20s. per
acre."

In 1795, Mr. Vancouver laid the average rent of the
County, at 14s. 6d.,—the Secretary of the Board, in 1807,
at 20s. Hence, admitting those statements as sufficient
data, the rise of rent has been 5s. 6d. an acre, or near
forty percent. on the former rent, in twelve years.

WOODLANDS.

Woods.—On the west side of Essex, an extent of
woodland appears. And in the northeast quarter, even on
the " turnip loams," round Colchester, some scattered old
woods are observable:—a circumstantial evidence of the
coolness of some of its lands.

PLANTATIONS.—I make the subjoined extract, to gain an
opportunity of saying, that, in crossing the fens, or "moor
lands," of the eastern department, I saw several instances
of *ash* plantations florishing on the black moory fen lands.
—And that I formerly observed the same tree thrive with
singular

---

* The above remarks were written, in August or September 1810;
before the public mind was roused by more recent occurrences. Yet,
under that state of uncertainty, we have heard of meetings, if not
resolutions entered into, for granting twentyone years' leases!! !

singular luxuriance, on the "moory grounds" of NOR-FOLK :—See Min. 38.

V. II. P. 148. (by the Reporter.)   "Mr. Saville, of Bocking, planted five acres of moory land, fourteen years ago with ash, and they have thriven so greatly, as to promise to be the most profitable crop on his whole farm."

AGRICULTURE.

Farms.—V. I. P. 58. (by the Reporter.)   "Viewing the county in general, the *size* of farms is very moderate ; in all the interior of the county, four, or five hundred acres are a large farm ; and the number of much smaller ones very great ; from one hundred acres to three hundred a pretty general size, of the better sort ; but many smaller in most districts ; probably the average of the whole county would not rise to 200 ; perhaps not to 150."

Farm Fences.—The following is a good description of the Essex hedges.—V. I. P. 179. (by Mr. Howlett.) "Our Essex fences generally consist of hedge-rows, of various kinds of wood—hazel, maple, ash, oak, elm, black thorn, white thorn, bramble-bushes, with timber and pollard trees interspersed and growing in them at different distances."

V. I. P. 191. (by the Reporter.)   "Mr. Ruggles has applied the sweet briar as a fence, with much success; the growth is rapid, and scarcely any failures.

"I never saw the elm applied as a hedge plant, till I came to Layer de la Haye; there and all the way to and in Mersea Island, I found them common."

Homesteads.—Granaries.—V. I. P. 46. (by the Reporter.) "Mr. Rogers, of Ardleigh, has built a new granary over a cart-lodge, which has one convenience which merits noting.   It is in two divisions: first, a small room with some bins; here he can dispose of any small parcels of horse or hog corn, to which a servant may in his absence have recourse, without being entrusted with the key of the larger heaps.

"Mr. Hanbury, at Coggeshall, in his granary has two stories of corn bins, one directly above another; and a hole

hole in the floor of the upper one, for skreening the corn into the lower one."

Farm Cottages.—V. I. P. 49. (by the Reporter.) "At Gosfield, the Marquis of Buckingham has built fourteen new cottages, to every one of which a garden of a quarter of an acre is assigned; and it proves of very great consequence to the comfort of the inhabitants. They pay a moderate rent, and so regularly, that the landlord loses nothing."

OCCUPIERS.—V. I. P. 66. (by the Reporter.) "I cannot let this subject pass" (Farms) "without adding my testimony to the very respectable character of the Essex farmers: there will in all professions and bodies of men, be here and there found one of a narrow and prejudiced mind; but the readiness with which by far the greater number of those I applied to, resolved my inquiries, and in the whole county, meeting with but two flat refusals, is an extraordinary proof that these men are enlightened, and that their ideas have taken a much larger range than would have been found some twenty or thirty years ago."

For particular remarks on the character of the Essex *Yeomanry,* see *Estates,* p. 508.

On the requisite *capital* of occupiers, I insert the following memoranda, by the Reporter;—tho they do not wholely come within the limits of my present view of Essex.—V. I. P. 103. "Mr. Sewell, of Maplestead, remarked, that many years ago, farms might be well stocked at the rate of 5*l.* an acre: now it demanded 7*l.*

"At Beerchurch, near Colchester, for dry turnip land, 6*l.* to 7*l.* per acre.

"At Bradfield, Mr. Hardy is decidedly of opinion, that a farm of their land cannot be stocked under 10*l.* per acre; and that draining and chalking demands 15*l.* more.

"Mr. Blythe, of Kirby, certainly 10*l.* per acre. At Waltham, and Little Leighs, some farms 10*l.* per acre.

"Mr. Lee, of Maldon, is of opinion, after having stocked five or six farms, that 10*l.* per acre is necessary in Dengey hundred, if any improvement is to be effected: if not, 7*l.* 10*s*

"Mr. Wakefield has stocked, &c. at the rate of 12*l.* per acre." See p. 420, aforegoing.

PLAN of MANAGEMENT of Farms.—V. I. P. 205. (by the Reporter) "Wherever I have travelled, whether on the continent or in these islands, husbandry generally flourishes in proportion to the accuracy of the course of crops; nor

nor is it any where easy to correct errors in this point by extraordinary exertions in any other.

" The county of Essex, viewed with an eye only to this object, has considerable merit ; and even her errors of an excess of fallowing in some instances, flow from correct ideas, though misapplied : she every where aims at keeping the soil clean, by the interposition of a fallow or a fallow crop between every two of white corn ; this is universally the general principle. Cases to the contrary occur, but they are exceptions, and to be assigned to individual management, not a general rule."

V. I. P. 219. (by the Reporter.) "At Walton," (Div. No. II) "I was assured more than once on this journey, that beans and wheat were continued in succession 36 years, and the husbandry being changed for some years, the farmer complained that he had not been paid by it so well as his father was by that incessant cropping."

V. I. P. 229. (Div. III. by the Reporter.) "There is not any circumstance in the soil, or management, peculiar to this district, that makes it remarkably interesting ; such parts as are of a heavy wet soil, comprising much the greater portion of it, are under an improved system of crops, far removed from that of crop and fallow, or the more ancient husbandry of two crops and a fallow ; the parts that admit turnips are cultivated accordingly."

V. I. P. 246. (Div. VIII, by the same.) "Mr. Saville, at Bocking, has for two or three years past, sown white clover and ray-grass, in one field each year, with cole-seed for feeding by sheep, having twelve acres this year, which I viewed with much pleasure : a good crop of cole, and a beautiful plant of those grasses amongst it, even where thickest and highest ; this grass he means to feed or mow three, four, or five years, according to circumstances, and then breaking it up, expects to get good corn. He will not be disappointed ; but the success with ray demands close feeding, and no mowing."

This is the only instance that has struck me, in going through the Secretary's fiftyfour pages of *changes* on " the course of crops,"—which evinces a tendency toward MIXED HUSBANDRY, or an ALTERNACY of ARABLE CROPS and TEMPORARY HERBAGE. See p. 137, aforegoing.

V. I. P. 248. (as above.) "On the strong loams on a clay bottom at Kelvedon, Rivenhall, &c. Mr. Western thinks summer-fallow essentially necessary : if it occurs but seldom, it may be consistent with the best husbandry. He shewed me one of his fields, part of which was under cabbages,

cabbages, part turnips, both dunged for; and part summer-
fallow, ridged up for barley without dung ; and remarked,
that the barley would be a quarter per acre better after
the fallow than after the turnip or cabbage. This may
be ; for a turnip should never be seen on such land. As
to cabbages, he has, in an adjoining field, eight, probably
nine, quarters an acre of potatoe oats after that crop,
which rather tends to a refutation of his doctrine."

Here, we see the Reporter coming forward in the character of a *critic*, rather than as a modest *amanuensis* (as
he represents himself) " to Essex farmers in general, and
individuals in particular*."

V. I. P. 252. (as above.) "The account given me by
the Earl of St. Vincent, of his course of crops, had strong
sense in it. *I cultivate wheat, barley, oats, beans, tares for
soiling, cole for feeding, clover, potatoes, turnips, and Swedish turnips ; and I intend cabbages next spring: and my
rule of arrangement is so to dispose the succession, that no
two crops of white corn come together ; for the rest, the
crops are put in as the season, and other circumstances, demand.*"

This

---

* REPORTS to the BOARD of AGRICULTURE.—In his introduction, p. vij, the Secretary of the Board speaks out, regarding *his idea*
of the proper matter and business of a Report. His words are these.
—" In drawing up this general view of it, I have followed the same
rule by which I acted on former occasions—to let the reader have the
authority, not only of Essex farmers in general, but of the individuals
in particular. I take it for granted that he does not want my ideas,
or my proposals. He has accordingly only Essex authority ; I offer
myself rarely to his notice, and never without warning him :"(?)—and,
here, I think it right to join issue with him.

It does not, *I conceive*, come within the province of a public Reporter, to collect and send in to the Board, *private opinions*, perhaps
cautiously given, and strung together in crude, uncircumstantiated
memoranda (under the plausible name of " authorities") ; but a com-
prehensible, intelligible, and well digested account of the *established
practices in the best cultivated parts of a County or District ;*—of the
practices followed by the first class of occupiers, in those parts ;—by
the men whom amateurs, and novitiate agriculturists,—whether
gentlemen, clergy, or others,—look up to, and court, for information.

Why go about to catch the prompt assertions, and unfledged opinions of the *pupils*, while the PROFESSORS, and the THEATRES of
their PRACTICE, are at hand?—In *these* are to be found the fit subjects of study, for an agricultural Reporter.

" Farmers in general " (in Essex or any other County) have not a
collective voice. All, therefore, that can be got at, by QUESTION-
ASKING, must be from " individuals in particular."

This not only gainsays, in some measure, what is advanced, with apparent consideration, and unbounded latitude, at the opening of the Reporter's section, now under view; namely, that " husbandry generally flourishes in proportion to the accuracy of the course of crops;"—but might be said to set aside all the volumes of matter he has collected on this subject. For Lord St. Vincent's was *no course*, " *at all*."—Yet the Reporter says, it " had strong good sense in it."—How inconsiderate to insert, in the same section, sentiments so contradictory.—No wonder that practical men should complain of being weary with reading books on agriculture.

WORKING ANIMALS.—V. I. P. 194. (by the Reporter.) " Scarcely any common farmers use oxen ; there are such cases, but they are very few: some gentlemen have them."

V. II. P. 349. (by the Reporter.)   "The Suffolk breed of horses are the favourites in Essex ; and several persons have made considerable exertions in procuring good mares and stallions."

IMPLEMENTS.—On this subject, we find, in the volumes under review, thirty nine pages of letter-press ; and thirty seven engravings!—This extraordinary circumstance is accounted for in the subjoined extract.—V. I. P. 126. " A material deficiency in most of the Reports, and in my own as well as in those of the other gentlemen who undertook the surveys, was the want of plates to represent the various tools met with in the respective counties. To execute drawings of these is impracticable, without skill in that art, or being accompanied by an artist for the purpose. Fortunately, I met with one who engaged to travel the county, without any salary for his time, on being paid a very moderate price for such drawings as he should be required to make: this advantage has enabled me to detail the implements of Essex in a much more satisfactory manner than it would have been possible to effect without the occurrence of such a circumstance."

Engravings of implements I have long been convinced, in my own experience, are little better than waste paper. In the case under view, they are a heavy incumbrance on the volume they swell out.—Judging from those representations there are very few of the icons from which they have been taken (and apparently in a masterly manner) that are fit for a better purpose, than to boil the pot.

MANURES.—I have already given my readers a general idea of the manures of Essex (p. 483, aforegoing) ; and, in the

the fifty pages found on the subject, in the volumes now before me, I perceive nothing to be added to that account: —Nothing I mean which relates, peculiarly, to the practice of Northeast Essex.

TILLAGE.—*Plowmanship.*—V. I. P. 194. (by the Reporter.) " Ploughing is in general extremely well performed in Essex, which abounds with skilful and accurate ploughmen. I have walked over forty acres of wheat fresh put in, eyeing the land carefully, and not discovering a single false furrow; no variations in breadth of stitch or of furrow; no depressions, nor any variation in the curvature of the stitch. They do not plough so deep as in Kent, nor so flat as in Norfolk, nor is it their wish so to do."

Something is collected on the " *depth of plowing :*" p. 196. But, unless in two instances, neither the depth or the specific quality of the soil, nor the nature of the substratum, is given!—Strange, that a veteran writer should spend his own and his reader's time so unprofitably."

Fallowing.—V. I. P. 195. (by the Reporter.) "Mr. Polley, the experienced bailiff of Mr. Fenn, at Middleton-hall, remarked, that nothing was worse management than to make fallows for barley, the common Essex practice, and not to plough them sufficiently : they cannot be too much stirred in summer for that crop; they ought never to have fewer than seven or eight ploughings, though the expense be 6s. 6d. or 7s. an acre, for each clean earth. The land is hilly."

V. I. P. 201. (by the same.) "This subject will demand attention under various other heads, especially that of courses of crops; but I should in general observe, that on all but sound dry turnip soils, it is universal in Essex : in one large district, to the extreme of crop and fallow; half the arable being under a dead summer fallow. In others, a fourth, fifth, or sixth."

Contract Work.—V. I. P. 200. (by the same.) "Dr. Asplin, at Little Wakering, used to contract with one labourer for all the tillage of his farm, at 2s. an acre for ploughing, 6d. for harrowing, and 2d. for rolling. More work was done, always five roods ploughed; but he left it off on account of shallowness and wide furrows."

SEMINATION.—V. II. P. 73. (by the Reporter.) "There is a scattering of this mode of culture throughout the county, but no district in it where the practice is established as it is on the sands of Norfolk, and on the clays

of

of Suffolk; nor is the increase of it rapid in any part of Essex."

May we, here, say, in parody of a prophane adage— "the nearer the drillmaker's shop, the farther from drilling?"

RAISING CROPS.—*Weeds* of arable Crops.—The following account of ALOPECURUS AGRESTIS—the "black grass" of Essex—only shows—not "that certain weeds are apt to be so predominant on certain lands, as to influence very materially the husbandry applied to them" (as the Reporter observes);—but that the occupiers of the lands in view are, or have been, unpardonable slovens.

V. II. P. 82. "This plant is the curse of the fine pale impalpable loams of Bradfield Wicks, Ramsey, and the Oakleys, &c." (Div. II.) "Those loams class high among the finest soils to be met with in the kingdom; but this weed abounds to such a degree; the seeds in perfect concealment and torpid through a dry summer-fallow, but vegetating in such profusion when autumnal rains come, that the fallows which a stranger would consider as beautifully clean, become speedily to the eye a very meadow; so that nothing is even a partial cure but a ploughing after such rains come."

By eighteen-months fallows, *duly executed,* and *persevered in,* any farm may be freed from this and every other troublesome weed.

Vermin of arable Crops.—Wire Worm.—This mischievous reptile would seem to be equally troublesome on the northern, as on the southern, banks of the Thames.— See my SOUTHERN COUNTIES for remarks on it.

In Essex, as in Kent, TRAMPLING appears to be the best preservative against its ravages. In Essex, not only *sheep,* but *cattle* and *horses* are used, with that intention:—of course, on soils, and in seasons, that will properly admit of such a practice.—Even the *human foot,* it would seem, is there, employed for that purpose.—V. II. P. 93. "They are sometimes troubled with this worm in Mersea, and it is an inducement with Mr. Bennet Hawes for dibbling wheat, as the treading is some security against it, and he uses this also as an argument for feeding clover."

WHEAT.—The Secretary of the Board has appropriated sixtyseven pages to this imperial crop:—reporting, *in detail,* many of the processes and operations that are incident to its culture.—I perceive, however, very few particulars that are well suited to my present design.—Most of the sub-sections are either filled with miscellaneous memoranda

memoranda, made perhaps in every quarter or division of the County, and often of so contradictory a tendency, as to balance each other:—or with extracts from . Mr. HOWLETT (many of them of great length, but few of them of much consideration) and Mr. VANCOUVER.

The few following particulars I have selected, as being proper for insertion, here.

Tillage for Wheat.—V. I. P. 260. " Mr. KEMP, of Hedingham, has scarified pea and bean stubbles, and drilled wheat without any ploughing, and never had better crops."

V. I. P. 261. " Mr. NEWMAN, of Hornchurch, last year put in wheat on a bean stubble without any plough-ing, and the success was great ; the crop far better than the land in common management was adapted to pro-duce. He drills all his corn."

Further notice of this *great modern discovery* will be found in the next section, *Barley.*

Semination of Wheat.—DIBBLING.—V. I. P. 262 (by the Reporter). " A very excellent practice of Mr. HARDY's, at Bradfield, well deserves noting : in sowing clover lands broad-cast, the outside furrows of the stitch are apt to lose much of their seed ; he therefore dibbles a row on each of the finishing furrows."

This is an admirable minutia of management.—The in-terfurrows of dibbled wheat have a beautifully striking ap-pearance.—The stems of the corn rise upright as walls, on either side of them. No straggling undergrowth is seen ; free open spaces appearing between the beds.

V. I. P. 271 (by the same). " Mr. SAVILLE, at Bocking, introduced this husbandry ; he had some weavers in-structed in it, who learning it readily, and earning good wages, his farm labourers applied for the same employ-ment, which was readily complied with. The poverty occasioned by the decline of the manufacture, was his in-ducement ; and the same motive has kept him in the practice, notwithstanding the evil of careless droppers. He has thus put in as far as 130 acres in one year : in-deed he dibbles his whole crop ; last year above 80 acres ; and pays 10s. an acre for it. The practice has spread much."

V. I. P. 272 (Mr. Western). " Relative to the mis-chief of dibbling wheat in wet lands, I am quite confirmed in ; and from experience, to my cost. I am of opinion it will never answer in wet tenacious soils ; the dibble forms such a pan for the water, that the seed perishes, and it is

almost

almost impossible to fill these holes in such soils, though harrowed ever so often ; these objections however, by no means apply to light loose soils, where it may answer extremely well, and is certainly carried to great perfection in some parts of Suffolk *."

These remarks require further qualification. If a tenacious soil be plowed *(for this purpose)* too deep beneath the roots of the herbage that occupies its surface (neither the existing state of the soil nor the depth of plowing, in this case, is given) and the operation of dibbling be performed, not only in a wet, but in a late, season, the evil effect, mentioned, must almost necessarily take place. — But, if the seed be lodged among what were the lower fibrils of the roots of leyground, as it ever ought, in lands of that description, each fibril will become a conductor to carry down superfluous moisture; and, of course, will prevent the bad effect complained of.

A new *Distemper* of Wheat.—V. I. P. 302 (by the Reporter). " At Mr. AMBROSE'S, at Copdock, I became acquainted with a distemper in wheat which I had never before heard of; and which I afterwards inquired concerning, even in the neighbourhood, but found it unknown. The ears affected are perceived at once by their colour, a dirty brown mixed with green, as if part was ripe, with some chests quite green : they feel nearly, but not quite, like blighted or abortive ears, which are brown, while the ears in general of the crop are of a bright red or white : when rubbed in the hand, as if to get the grain, no wheat is found, but apparently the small grains of a flattened indented globular form, and of a darkish purple, greenish, or dark hue. It has not the smallest resemblance, in appearance or scent, to smutty grains or bladders, and is certainly a distinct distemper. In many of these purpled ears are found some grains of good wheat. In order to discover if all the ears from the same root were affected, which Mr. AMBROSE had not before examined, we made the experiment in many instances, and found all similar from every root. It appears to me very singular that no account (to my recollection) should have been given of such a strange malady, and so distinct from all others. Smutty ears were found in the same field, under all the common circumstances of that distemper. In Kent this distemper is called *cockle-eared*."

This

This malady has been known in the northeast part of Yorkshire, some four or five years. It was first detected in a delicate thinskinned variety, called " eggshell white."

This year, 1810, the wheats of the vale of Pickering have nearly escaped that disease. The season of filling and ripening was remarkably fine ; the grain plump and the straw bright. Scarcely any " meldew;" and but very little " new slain."—The same in 1811.

Barley.—*Succession.*—V. I. P. 327 (by the Reporter). " Upon strong lands this is a fallow; and upon dry land, turnips. This is the uniform management of the country. Beans, pease, and tares, are sometimes preparatory to it ; but no where the standard management. For one acre of wheat put in on a fallow, there are fifty of barley and oats; and I must remark, that this is a very capital feature of merit. *It was not thus formerly, for wheat on fallows were general;* but the enlightened cultivators of Essex have completely convinced themselves that wheat on fallows was *barbarous* management—their own expression in more instances than one."

This principle of management of strong lands is precisely what I have been inculcating, and practising in various parts of the island, during thirty or more years :— a principle of practice which arose, and reached maturity, in the course of my earliest experience,—in the Southern Department.—Facts relating to its rise, progress, and adoption, may be seen in the Minutes of Agriculture,— first published in 1778,—by referring to the numbers 136, 154, 188, 272, 338, 343, and 350;—where the reader will find the inconveniencies of fallowing retentive soils for *wheat,* and the advantages of thoroughly cleansing such soils, for *spring corn* and *ley herbage.*

The radical, more essential, and most valuable attendant of this principle is, that, in fallowing for WHEAT, the soil is fouled again, by the *first crop.*—Whereas, by putting it into a high state of cleanness and tillage, for SPRING CORN, whether oats or barley (for the principle is applicable to every species of land)—and LEY HERBAGE,— a *succession* of *crops* may become the reward of the fallow.

Some time after the publication of the Minutes above referred to, a GERMAN, who came to this country, under the orders and patronage of the late King of Prussia, to study English agriculture, was pleased to say—I had taught his countrymen to manage their strong retentive lands.

lands. And I am willing to believe, that I may have been instrumental in effecting the radical change that has taken place, in the arable management of the County of Essex; where it appears, by the above extract, to be a modern practice.

Tillage for Barley.—V. I. P. 328 (by the Reporter). " The tillage given to the fallows for barley in this country much exceeds that which is generally bestowed. The grand modern discovery of Suffolk, the banishment of spring-ploughing, is creeping into Essex, and will gradually extend itself."

How long " this grand discovery of Suffolk" has been made, we are not told. That it had not, there, entered into *practice*, nor even been admitted into *fashion*, in 1796, is evidenced, in the Suffolk Report.

In 1791, I met with an instance of *wheat* being sown after turnips *without plowing*, and published that circumstance, in 1798, in the RURAL ECONOMY of the SOUTHERN COUNTIES; in which the particulars concerning that incident, and the remarks I made thereon, stand thus:— V. II. P. 187. " This instance occurred in the practice of one of the principal farmers of the district " (of Petworth).—" Part of a piece of turnep ground was plowed and sowed in the usual way. The rest was only harrowed or " dragged,"—the seed sown, and covered with fine harrows. The consequence, as related, was a fine crop, and free from smut; while the part plowed was not only an inferior crop, but was smutty.

" This loosely reported incident, however, only suggests the idea, that *light* and *absorbent* soils, which are *already in a state of cleanness and tilth*, may be injured by a seed plowing; especially in a dry season."

It has long been an established practice on the light thinsoiled lands of the chalk hills of the Southern Department, to put in the wheat crop, after what is called a " drag," or a " drag plow;" an implement which resembles the " tormentor " of Devonshire, and the " shuffler "—" scuffler "—(or whatever other slang name it may go by) of other districts.—But, in that case—under that practice—for such it is—only *one crop* is asked for; —the wheat being succeeded by a barley or a turnep fallow.—See my SOUTHERN COUNTIES, vol. ii. p. 322.

In the WEST of ENGLAND (VOL. I. p. 287, Ed. 1805) the " tormentor" is seen to do good service, in preparing partially sod-burnt ley ground, to be sown with turneps, on one *turning;* as well as in loosening the surface of
turnep

turnep ground that had been cleared late in the spring, to be sown with barley on one plowing.

And there may be circumstances of soils and seasons, under which *scratching*, alone, may be used in preference to *plowing*.

But let not the inexperienced practitioner, on hearing of "the grand discovery of Suffolk, the banishment of spring ploughing" (!!) believe thàt, in all seasons, on all soils, and in whatever state they may be, he can pursue, with profit, the SCRATCHING SYSTEM:—not even with the "scuffler," the "tormentor," the "cultivator,"! the "scarifier," the "eradicator," the "extirpator," and all the other instruments of torture belonging to "modern husbandry;"—by which, not only fallowing but PLOWING, it would seem, is about to be "exploded."—See p. 340, aforegoing.

It is not, as has been said, any *one* crop, in a course, that ought to be kept especially in view; but a *succession* of crops—the *entire course*—which calls for the attention of the cultivator. If any one crop requires to be sacrificed, or risked, for the good of the whole, it is the *first*, *after a fallow*.—By a fallow, duly performed, he may and ought to *secure* a succession of four, five, six, or seven crops (according to the nature of his land); and let him not, by adopting a "new fangled" *cheap* method of putting in one of them, even *risk* the productiveness of the rest.

If the soil has not been sufficiently prepared, by the previous fallow, it ought not only to be plowed, again and again, in the spring; but the tillage, should it still be found wanting, is required to be continued into the summer months; and the seeds of herbage to be sown, alone:—thus foregoing, the first crop, altogether.

To talk of "the banishment of spring ploughing," without stating the nature of the land, its state as to tillage, or the progress or character of the given season of sowing,—may lead to much error; but cannot tend to the promotion of useful science; or induce cultivators of experience to throw aside the plow, altogether, in performing the important operation of seminating barley or oats, as the first crop of a course. For both of them are involved in this "discovery."

I have thought it right to say thus much, by way of caution to the young practitioner;—lest "banishing spring ploughing" should turn out to be, not only, literally, but figuratively, a superficial scheme.

Far

Far be it from me, however to wish, much less to expect, that the "spirited agriculturists" of Suffolk should
abate, by reason of these remarks, one tittle of their exertions toward LESSENING THE LABOR OF TILLAGE, AND, AT THE
SAME TIME, ENABLING THE SOIL TO PRODUCE, IN UNINTER-
RUPTED CONTINUANCE, THE GREATEST PROFIT TO THE OCCU-
PIER, THE PROPRIETOR, AND THE COMMUNITY.

Whenever this great discovery shall have stood the test
of experience, and be found preferable to the established
practices of Norfolk and the kingdom at large,—THROUGH-
OUT A FULL COURSE, or SUCCESSION OF COURSES,—I shall be
happy to recommend it, unqualified, to inexperienced
practitioners. At present I have thought it right to advise them not to follow, too implicitly, what may happen
to prove delusive as a PRACTICE;—how eligible soever it
may, in some cases be, as an EXPEDIENT;—especially in a
dry season.

In the ample matter of this Report, I find nothing to
add to the preceding extracts, relative either to ARABLE
CROPS or to LIVESTOCK, that calls for *especial* attention in
this place. The following notices, respecting hops, and
decoys, almost *distinctly* belong to the EASTERN DEPART-
MENT.

HOPS.—V. II. P. 31 (by Mr. Howlet). "The plantation of hops in this county is confined to comparatively a
few parishes, the principal of these are the following : the
two Hedinghams, Castle and Sible, the two Maplesteads,
Halstead, the Colnes, Chelmsford and Moulsham, Shalford,
Wethersfield, Finchingfield, and Great Bardfield. They
were formerly much more widely extended; but whether
the total numbers of acres was greater than at present, I
am unable to say. They are probably now confined to
the soils most congenial to their nature, and which, from
repeated trials and long experience, have been found
most effectually to answer. They were early introduced
into this neighbourhood, and numerous grounds were
planted with them in the parishes of Stibbing, Lindsell,
Thaxtead, Broxtead, Dunmow, &c. but now there are
very few remaining, certainly not twenty acres in the
whole, and I believe not even ten."

Thus it appears that, in regard to hops, as well as to
cattle, sheep, soils, and other distinguishments, Northeast
Essex, naturally and agriculturally unites with the County
of Suffolk.

DECOYS.—V. II. P. 361 (by the Reporter). "One of
the best, if not the most considerable decoy in the county,

13

is in Mersea Island, and rented with a small farm of about sixty acres, by Mr. BUXTON, of Layer de la Haye. He was so obliging as to accompany me from thence into Mersea, and to shew me his decoy. Not having before viewed a decoy in the *taking* season, I had not remarked the precaution of each person taking a piece of lighted turf stuck on a table fork in his hand to approach the decoy; as the wild ducks, it is said, would smell the person without this caution, and immediately quit the pond. I found the expenses of this decoy considerable : two men attend it, who are paid above 100*l.* a year; repairs, nets, rent, &c. amount in all to about 300*l.* a year. Ducks are sometimes so low as 14*s.* a dozen.

" The contrivance for taking dun birds was new to me. At the decoy for them near Ipswich, there are a series of very high poles, to which the nets are attached, for taking them in their flight; and these poles are permanent. At this Mersea decoy, to which this bird resorts in large quantities as well as ducks, the net poles are suspended when not at work.

" Mr. LEE has a decoy at Goldhanger, in which he took at one haul one waggon load and two cart loads of dun birds; but the disturbance made, frightened such as escaped so much, that he took no more that season."

These volumes will require farther attention, in reviewing the Reports to the Board, from the MIDLAND and SOUTHERN DEPARTMENTS.

THE END.

Mr. MARSHALL's other WORKS on RURAL ECONOMY.

1.

In two Volumes, Octavo, price 15s. in Boards,

MINUTES and EXPERIMENTS on AGRICULTURE; containing his own Practice in the Southern Counties; and moreover conveying to practical Men in general, an accurate Method of acquiring Agricultural Knowledge, scientifically, from the Results of their Experience.

2.

In twelve Volumes, Octavo, price 4l. in Boards,

The established Practices of the higher Orders of Professional Men, in the six Agricultural Departments of England:

The Practice of the Northern Department being shown, in the RURAL ECONOMY of YORKSHIRE; price 12s.

That of the Western Department, in the RURAL ECONOMY of GLOCESTERSHIRE; price 12s.

That of the Central Department, in the RURAL ECONOMY of the MIDLAND COUNTIES; price 14s.

That of the Eastern Department, in the RURAL ECONOMY of NORFOLK; price 12s.

That of the Southern Department, in the RURAL ECONOMY of the SOUTHERN COUNTIES; price 15s.

That of the South-western Department, in the RURAL ECONOMY of the WEST of ENGLAND; price 15s.

3.

In two Volumes, Octavo, price 16s. in Boards,

A general Work on PLANTING and RURAL ORNAMENT; with the Management of WOODLANDS and HEDGEROW TIMBER.

4.

In one Volume, Quarto, price 2l. 2s. in Boards,

An elementary and practical TREATISE on the LANDED PROPERTY of ENGLAND: comprising the Purchase, the Improvement, and the executive Management of Landed Estates; and moreover containing what relates to the general Concerns of PROPRIETORS, and to such Subjects of Political Economy, as are intimately connected with the LANDED INTEREST.

5.

In one Volume, Octavo, price 10s. 6d. in Boards,

A general Work on the MANAGEMENT of LANDED ESTATES; being an ABSTRACT of the above Treatise; for the Use of professional Men: including whatever relates to the BUSINESS of ESTATE AGENCY; whether it be employed in the Purchase, the Improvement, or the executive Management of Estates.

Also,

In one Volume, Octavo, price 12s. in boards,

A REVIEW

OF THE

REPORTS to the BOARD of AGRICULTURE,

FROM

The NORTHERN DEPARTMENT *of England*;

COMPRIZING,

NORTHUMBERLAND,	WESTMORELAND,
DURHAM,	LANCASHIRE,
CUMBERLAND,	YORKSHIRE,

and the

MOUNTAINOUS PARTS OF DERBYSHIRE.

With an INTRODUCTION; showing—1. The ORIGIN and PROGRESS of the BOARD of AGRICULTURE. 2. The PLAN and EXECUTION of the REPORTS. 3. The requisite QUALIFICATIONS of a REPORTER. 4. The PLAN of the REVIEW; and the Advantages of proceeding by DEPARTMENTS:—together with the OUTLINES of the six AGRICULTURAL DEPARTMENTS into which ENGLAND naturally separates.

Also,

In one Volume, Octavo, price 12s. in boards,

A REVIEW

OF THE

REPORTS to the BOARD of AGRICULTURE,

FROM

The WESTERN DEPARTMENT *of England*;

COMPRIZING,

CHESHIRE,	WORCESTERSHIRE,
FLINTSHIRE,	GLOCESTERSHIRE,
SHROPSHIRE,	NORTH WILTSHIRE, AND
HEREFORDSHIRE,	NORTH SOMERSETSHIRE.

INDEX.

From the Office of
THOMAS WILSON and SON,
High Ousegate, York.